Readings in
Physiological
Psychology

Readings in Physiological Psychology

The bodily basis of behavior

EDITED BY

Thomas K. Landauer

Assistant Professor of Psychology
Stanford University

McGraw-Hill Book Company

New York   St. Louis   San Francisco
Toronto   London   Sydney

Readings in Physiological Psychology:
The bodily basis of behavior

1 2 3 4 5 6 7 8 9 0 MP 7 3 2 1 0 6 9 8 7 6

Preface

The main purpose of this book, like any "readings" book, is to make primary source material conveniently available so that students of the subject can get a firsthand look at the raw materials from which lectures and textbook generalizations are constructed. The hope is that exposure to such material will give the topic more meaning for the student, that by seeing the facts in full detail he will also see the conclusions as more real, more interesting, and more exciting. Even better, by reading the sources in the original the student may become skeptical of the conclusions drawn from them. In any event, reading a selection of relevant research reports provides the student with an additional way of learning the material and thus, if only by increasing redundancy, increases his opportunity for learning and understanding.

In selecting articles for a book of this kind, there are clearly numerous and not altogether concordant criteria. The coverage should make some stab at representing the needs of many instructors and many students with differing interests. On the other hand, there is much to be said for inclusion of a series of papers on the same topic. Through such a series a student can glimpse the excitement of the development of a finding, and can appreciate the complexities and difficulties which arise in the lack of correspondence between one finding and the next. Of course, then, there are always such criteria as readability, length, and suitable style. Primary research reports are not always written with students in mind; they are sometimes too long or depend on prior knowledge to an extent that makes them incomprehensible to any but the initiated.

The selections in this book are a compromise among all these criteria. There is some attempt to represent most of the traditional topics within physiological psychology. There are several topics in which a series of related papers are presented, some related by advancing knowledge and some related by controversy. An attempt has been made to pick papers that are pedagogically possible. On the other hand, only a few topics have been omitted because all relevant materials were judged to be too difficult. Some quite difficult papers are included.

If there is a unifying thread in the articles, it is an attempt to convey excitement. For this reason, there is an emphasis on articles that are new and on reports of "breakthroughs," even to the inclusion of some rather controversial materials which may have been discredited by the time the book is published. (There are, however, footnotes to warn the student from time to time.) There is a much larger number of papers devoted to learning and memory than to any other topic because, at least in the editor's view, this is where excitement is currently most feverish.

The book is primarily designed to accompany a textbook which sets forth the necessary basic science—neuroanatomy, neurophysiology, endocrinology, genetics, sensory physiology, etc.—and gives a broad synthesis of the field. Some topics, such as the anatomy of the autonomic nervous system, are omitted entirely on the grounds that they are better covered in such a standard text where the results of many experiments can be synthesized.

Nonetheless, the book should be able to be used on its own. The selections provide a reasonable overview of modern physiological psychology and might in some instances be used alone or in conjunction with a basic text in neurology rather than as an accompaniment to a text in physiological psychology as such.

The complete reference for each article is given in the footnote on its first page. The footnote acknowledges the permission of the author or authors and the original publisher or copyright holder to reprint the article here. However, much more than formal acknowledgment is called for. The authors and publishers were exceedingly cooperative in providing both permissions and materials, and their helpfulness is gratefully appreciated. I would also like to thank Norma Johnson for invaluable editorial assistance.

THOMAS K. LANDAUER

Contents

Learning and Memory: Theory and Speculation   473

Development   503

Psychosomatics and Psychopathology   541

Introduction

In physiological psychology, we are in a decade in which promising advances have already been made, significant new discoveries are frequent, and the air is filled with optimism and excitement. The questions in physiological psychology are hoary. Man has long asked how his intricate and delicate behavior can be produced by the mechanisms of his corporeal body. The answers, though hard sought after and long, have been slow in coming. Recently, however, powerful new techniques of investigation and powerful new understandings of the nature of living things have been developed in a variety of sciences which open up whole new ways of investigating the biological basis of behavior. We are just beginning to reap the rewards of the application of these powerful tools.

Clearly the central questions of physiological psychology—the quest for understanding of how the body produces the mind—are among the grandest, most challenging intellectual problems ever posed. Of the handful of really fundamental questions which have troubled scientific man since his beginnings—the nature of the universe, matter, life—most are by now well on the way to solution. The question of man's nature, posed as the question of the mechanisms (that is, the biological mechanisms) of behavior, remains. A good case can be made for it as the single greatest outstanding challenge to science.

Within the last twenty years, giant steps have been taken in three areas of science and technology which are of the greatest relevance to the study of physiological psychology. The first of these, of course, has been in psychology. A large amount of empirical knowledge of a phenomenal or descriptive kind has accumulated surrounding the way in which animals and men behave. Such knowledge is obviously a prerequisite of studying the mechanics by which behavior is produced. More important, psychologists have developed standard and reliable methods for observing behavior and changes therein. The second area of relevant advance has been in the technological field of information processing. The development of computers has had facilitating effects on physiological psychology in two distinct ways. In the first place, computers are now being applied directly to the analysis of information obtained from the nervous system, an aid the value of which can be appreciated by anyone who has considered the hopeless complexity of the squiggles obtained from an electrical recording of the activity of the brain. In the second place, the construction and programming of artificial "brains" have yielded a number of insights into the general logic and possible principles of operation of all brains, artificial or natural. The third relevant advance has come in the astounding progress of molecular biology. Where twenty years ago we were almost totally in the dark as to how cells manufactured new components, we are now well on the way to understanding such phenomena in useful detail. Since all life processes, including behavior, depend in the final analysis on intracellular biochemical events, an understanding of these cannot help but be of tremendous value in our task.

Added to these great general advances in sister sciences, has been a huge array of technological improvements and inventions which make the task of exploring the nervous system and its functions more feasible. A list of examples, by no means complete, would include the electron microscope, nonpolarizable and exceedingly tiny recording electrodes, a variety of powerful new micro-techniques for chemical analysis, radioactive tracer methods and materials, the availability of a wide assortment of drugs, hormones and enzymes with nervous system affect, and automated data-collecting devices for behavioral experiments. Perhaps even more important to the present rapid progress and promise is the fact that significant advances have already begun to pile up in the field of physiological psychology itself. Most areas of knowledge grow exponentially. The first part of their growth is slow, but once a start is made there is a snowballing effect. It is perhaps not too optimistic to say that the snowball, in physiological psychology, has begun to roll. Some of the evidence on which this hopeful view is based is to be found in the research reports reproduced in the following pages.

Readings in
Physiological
Psychology

Neurophysiology

SUPPRESSION OF AUDITORY NERVE ACTIVITY BY STIMULATION OF EFFERENT FIBERS TO COCHLEA

Robert Galambos

WALTER REED ARMY MEDICAL CENTER

Editor's Note   In this reading, Galambos shows that the nervous system can damp its own input at points quite far out in the periphery. The existence of feedback loops in which control is exercised by the altering of incoming sensory signals had previously been known for postural reflexes involving efferent impulses from muscle spindles, and has since been observed in other ways (for instance in the visual system by Spinelli, Pribram, and Weingarten, **Experimental Neurology,** *1965,* **12,** *303–319). Demonstration of these feedback relations in the nervous system not only makes the "wiring" look somewhat more complicated—and thus plausible—than the simple spinal reflex arcs of Sherrington, but also provides the possibility of rather simple and discoverable bases for many of the otherwise mysterious higher functions of attention, etc. If the animal can shut off input from his ears, for instance, it is clear that he has a way of "not paying attention" to what he is hearing. In fact, reading 14 by Hernández-Peón, Scherrer, and Jouvet reports a similar efferent damping as the result of an environmental stimulus in a situation demanding attention from the animal.*

Source   Reprinted from the **Journal of Neurophysiology,** *1956,* **19,** *424–437, with permission of the author and the American Physiological Society.*

The observation that prompts this communication is illustrated in Fig. 1 which shows electrophysiological responses obtained from the round window membrane of the cochlea of a cat. In the upper row (click alone) the electrical events that customarily follow click stimulation are to be seen. The major deflections recordable under these conditions are labelled according to a current convention on the trace labelled C. M is the aural microphonic response, derived in all likelihood from the hair cells in the cochlea; N_I and N_{II} are considered to be the signs of neural events. Since N_I is the first, or earliest, neural event known to occur in the auditory system, it has generally been agreed that N_I is the sign of the discharge of the afferent fibers of the auditory nerve (1). A change in its magnitude is ordinarily taken to mean that a corresponding change has occurred in the amount of excitation produced by the sound stimulation.

In the second row of Fig. 1, clicks identical to those in the first row were presented; while these were delivered to the ear, however, electrical shocks were being applied to the floor of the medulla. As can be seen, the effect of these shocks is to produce partial or complete suppression of both N_I and N_{II}, with little or no change in the magnitude of M. This change is reversible, for when the shocks were discontinued, the normal click response returned. As will be developed below, this observation means that nerve impulses aroused in the medulla by the electrical stimulation pass out to the cochlea where, through a physiological interaction, they suppress the expected auditory nerve inflow.

METHOD

A total of 51 cats was used in this study. Most were anesthetized with Dial-urethane (75 mg./kg.); Nembutal (60 mg./kg.), ether-curare, and ether-decerebrate preparations, when tried, yielded similar results. Operative procedures began with tracheal cannulation followed by reflection of the muscles of the head and neck to permit bilateral isolation of the external auditory meatus and a clear view of both bullas. Each meatus was then cut across and a brass tube to which an earphone was attached inserted into it. These tubes, when adjusted, both held the head fixed as do the earplugs of a Horsley-Clarke apparatus, and permitted a clear sound path from earphone to eardrum. Each bulla was then opened so as to expose the round window, upon which a silver wire was placed. The occipital bone over the cerebellum was then removed and sufficient cerebellum suctioned out to reveal the floor of the fourth ventricle upon which the shock electrodes, controlled by a manipulator graduated in 1 mm. steps, were placed.

The animals were located in a "soundproof" room during the measurements. Clicks were generated by 0.075 msec. square waves transduced by Permoflux (PDR-10) earphones. Shocks to the medulla were generated by 0.1 msec. square waves isolated from ground through a Grass stimulus isolation unit and presented to the preparation through a pair of bare silver wires, or a concentric electrode made from a #13 hypodermic needle, or a pair of #34 stainless steel wires that passed down the bore of #20 tubing insulated except at their tips. This last array, the so-called bipolar concentric pair, proved especially useful in the localization studies; at the tip the electrodes are separated by 0.3 mm. and the current flowing between them evidently provides a reasonable approximation of point-stimulation. The strength of the shocks cited in this paper is simply the voltage-dial readings of the Grass Model 4A stimulator used; the voltage values that produced suppression when delivered through bare silver wire were approximately one-tenth those required when the bipolar concentric was employed.

For differential recording of the round window response one active lead was located at the round window, and the other at a nearby cochlear, bulla, neck muscle or skin location. Tektronix Model 122 amplifiers, a 4-channel Electronic Tube Corporation oscilloscope, and a Grass Model C4A camera were employed for recording. The measurements of N_I given in the graphs in this paper are approximate averages of 10 or more responses measured directly upon the tube face in mm.; comparison of the values so derived with actual measurements from photographs have, in the cases where this was done, established the validity of the simpler procedure.

In the control experiments hereinafter described a Zeiss operating microscope made possible direct observations of the middle ear that would otherwise have been exceedingly difficult or impossible. The mechanical records of Fig. 7 were made with a movable plate vacuum tube (Type 5734) and a conventional DC circuit. For curarization, Flaxedil (Gallamine Triethiodide, Lederle), 2 mg./kg. was used; in many of these experiments the femoral blood pressure was recorded concomitantly.

RESULTS

Variables that influence suppression of N_I

1. STRENGTH OF CLICK   In Fig. 1 the click applied in the traces labelled A was near the threshold for a response from the ear. In B the click strength was 10 db, and in C, 20 db above this value. The data show that, for constant shock values, the auditory nerve response is more likely to be abolished when the click is weak. Figure 2A presents graphically a more complete study of this point from another cat; at a given shock strength (*e.g.*, 10 V.) N_I for a weak click (15 db) may be completely obliterated, while that for a strong one (35 db) is reduced by only 40 per cent.

2. FREQUENCY AND INTENSITY OF SHOCK   Figure 3A shows a series of traces taken as the frequency of the applied shock was increased. Square wave stimuli of 0.1 msec. were used throughout, and when these occurred at rates less than about 30/sec. little suppression of N_I could be seen. Rates around 100 (± 20)/sec. proved optimal, a point repeatedly estab-

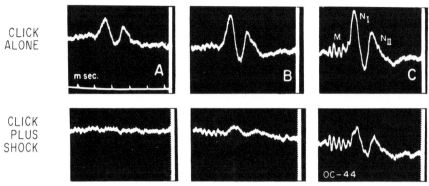

CLICK
ALONE

CLICK
PLUS
SHOCK

TENSOR AND STAPEDIUS CUT; CURARIZED;
STAPES DISARTICULATED

FIGURE 1 *Suppression of auditory nerve response by shocks to medulla. Upper row: Auditory nerve activity (N_I and N_{II} in C) evoked by weak (A), and progressively stronger (B, C), clicks is abolished or reduced (lower row) when 100/sec. shocks are applied to medulla, hair cell response (M in C) being unaffected.*

lished in preparations both with and without functioning intra-aural muscles. Figure 3B illustrates how, at a given shock frequency (65/sec.), an increase in suppression of N_I follows a rise in intensity of the applied stimuli. Shock strengths greater than the maximum shown in Fig. 4 (0.8 V.), yielded no increased suppression in that experiment. Fig. 2 may now be re-examined as a summary of the details of the interactions among the three parameters discussed thus far—click strength, shock strength and shock frequency. The neural consequences of a given click are more readily suppressed when the intensity or the frequency of the medullary shocks rises. Clicks may, however, be so strong that even under optimal shock conditions the N_I response is not entirely suppressed (*e.g.*, Fig. 2A, 25 and 35 db contours). Thus the suppression under consideration behaves as if it were indeed the result of neural processes obeying well-known general principles.

Examination of the development and decay of the suppression provides further evidence that we are dealing here with a valid physiological effect. Figure 4 [Omitted in reprinting. (ed.)] is taken from one of several preparations in which the test click was introduced at fixed intervals after shocking of the medulla began. The shocks were usually presented at 100/sec. The apparatus was arranged so that a click was triggered by any desired shock; it was thus possible to test for the presence of N_I suppression at 10 msec. intervals, or at any desired multiple thereof. The preparations all show that N_I is entirely normal until 2 to 4 shocks (20–40 msec.) have been applied. N_I is regularly reduced to about 75 per cent of its control value after 5 to 6 (50–60 msec.). Thereafter N_I drops at an approximately constant rate until 25 to 35 shocks (0.25–0.35 sec.) have been presented, by which time the suppression is as complete as it ever will be.

Recovery of N_I from suppression follows approximately the same time course. Within 50 msec. after the last shock of a train lasting some seconds, N_I has begun to return toward its control size. Within 0.5 sec. N_I is frequently at or around its control value except in cases where the medulla has been shocked for many seconds or minutes. Full recovery of N_I is almost invariably observed at 2 sec. after the shock train ceases. While numerous features of this recovery cycle still require study, the data at hand argue strongly for a neural explanation for the development and decay of the suppression.

3. LOCATION OF SHOCKING ELECTRODES   To produce the suppression under discussion the stimulating electrodes must lie near the midline on the floor of the medulla approximately 1 cm. ±2 mm. rostral to the obex. Shocks presented here through closely spaced electrodes (#34 wires within #20 hypodermic needle tubing) produce approximately equal suppression bilaterally, and this will be more or less complete depending upon the exact location of the electrodes. Lateral or rostro-caudal movements of more than 2 or 3 mm. and penetrations of more than 2 mm. make shocks of any intensity ineffective. The experiments thus define the necessary location for the shocking electrodes as a block of tissue some $4 \times 4 \times 2$ mm. thick. A transverse section at the center of this region (*i.e.*, about 1 cm. rostral to the obex) is shown in Fig. 5, [Fig. 5, a photomicrograph of the region referred to, has been omitted in reprinting. (Ed.)] which comes from a

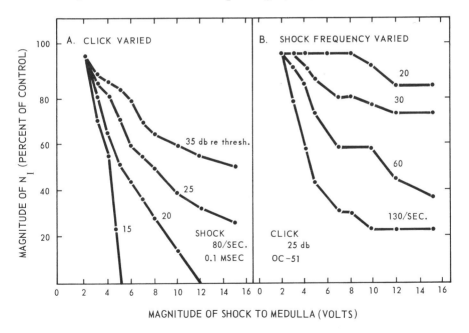

FIGURE 2   *Parametric study of suppression of N_I. A: Weak shocks suppress N completely when click is weak (15 and 20 db contours), but strong shocks are only partially effective for stronger clicks. B: Higher shock frequencies (60 and 130/sec. contours) are more effective in decreasing N_I magnitude than are lower ones (20 and 30/sec.).*

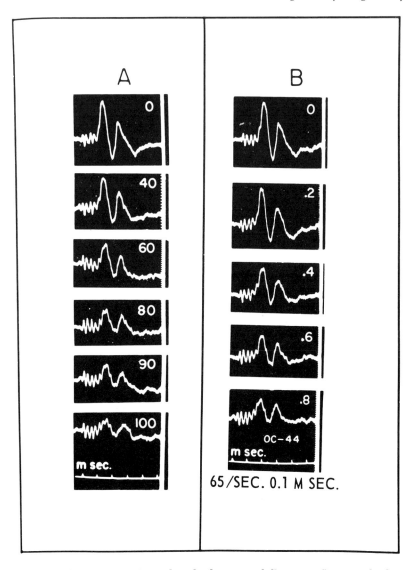

A   B

0   0
40   .2
60   .4
80   .6
90   .8
100   OC-44
m sec.   m sec.

65/SEC. 0.1 M SEC.

FIGURE 3 *Suppression of N_1 by shocks to medulla. A: Effect of shock frequency. The higher the shock rates, indicated in upper right of each trace, the greater the suppression; 100/sec. is the optimum. B: Effect of shock strength. At fixed frequency (65/sec.) the higher the shock voltage, indicated in right corner, the greater the suppression.*

cat studied in particular detail to establish the "best" location for the shocking electrodes. This section passes directly through the decussation of the olivo-cochlear (efferent auditory) pathway described by Rasmussen (13). Originating from cells near the superior olive, the fibers in this pathway rise to the floor of the medulla, decussate, pass out the contralateral internal auditory meatus, form the vestibulo-cochlear anastomosis (bundle of Boettcher, Oort) and enter the spiral ganglion. They account for about 50 per cent of the internal spiral bundle of the cochlea, and are distributed to the entire length of that organ (14). Where they end is still controversial, some (see 2, p. 502 for discussion) contending they do so upon internal hair cells, while some (14) claim this has not been adequately demonstrated. Despite the unsolved anatomical questions, it is difficult to avoid concluding that impulses in these olivo-cochlear fibers, on arrival at the cochlea, are somehow required for the suppression under discussion.

If this pathway is cut peripheral to the site of its stimulation, the results provide further support for such a conclusion. Experiments of this type were attempted in seven animals, cuts being made bilaterally in two. Histological examination revealed that six of the nine attempts were successful; in every one of these cases the suppression of N_I noted immediately prior to placement of the lesion had disappeared at once when the bundle was cut. In three instances (two animals) the knife cut missed the olivo-cochlear bundle, came close to severing it, and caused extensive damage to nearby structures. Records taken after these "unsuccessful" cuts had shown unchanged suppression of N_I. Thus cutting the pathway abolishes the suppression, and failure in an attempt to do so does not.

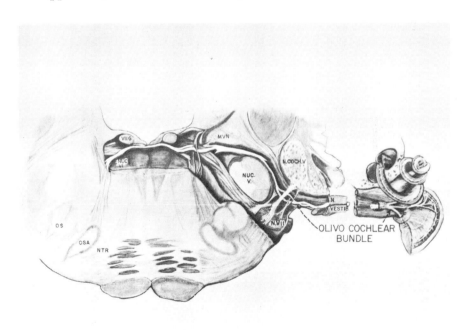

FIGURE 6   Origin, course and distribution of olivo-cochlear bundle. Originating in region of accessory olive (OSA) it crosses midline just beneath fourth ventricle, passes over fifth nerve nucleus (Nuc. V) and exists with eighth nerve complex. In cochlea it is distributed to the whole length of basilar membrane.

CONTROL STUDIES

Because of the implausible nature of the results just described, it has been found necessary to undertake somewhat more elaborate control experiments upon this preparation than is usually the case. Of these only the measurements upon intra-aural and other somatic muscles need be considered in detail.

As will be apparent at once, shocks applied to the region shown in Fig. 5 are likely to stimulate fibers other than those of the olivo-cochlear bundle. The nearness of the genua of the facial roots should cause most concern, for these motor fibers innervate, among other things, the stapedius muscle of the middle ear. After appropriate dissection under the microscope, this muscle and the region of its insertion into the stapes at the incudo-stapedial joint can be visualized. If devices for recording movements there are attached, single twitches will be recorded after single shocks are applied to the medulla (Fig. 7A). [Fig. 7 (A and B) has been omitted in reprinting. (Ed.)] As the shock frequency rises, the twitches fuse gradually into a tetanus. Fusion is essentially complete at frequencies around 20 or 30 shocks per sec., but slight ripples remain in the tension curve even at 60 or 70 per sec. These twitches are vigorous muscle movements that jerk the head of the stapes violently out of its normal relation to the lenticular process of the incus. The joint capsule is seriously deformed—momentarily with the twitch, and steadily during the tetanus—but at the end of the stimulation it resumes its normal aspect.

If a click is presented to the ear while the stapedius muscle is undergoing either shortening or lengthening—or, better, as the joint is undergoing dis- or re-articulation—suppression of N_I entirely similar to that seen in Fig. 1 will be recorded (Fig. 8). However, the suppression shown in Fig. 8 does not occur under the following conditions. (i) A stiff metal rod is placed against the stapes so as to prevent movement of the incudo-stapedial joint while permitting isometric contraction of the muscle. (ii) The muscle is in tetanus, i.e., the shock rate is 20/sec. or higher, in which case the joint capsule is maintained in a steady

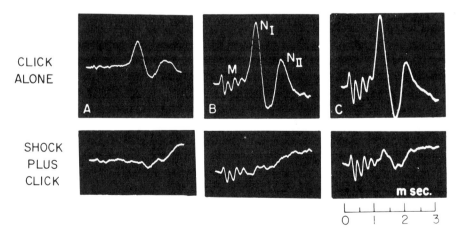

FIGURE 8 *Suppression of N_I by single shocks to medulla. N_I and N_{II} are abolished (second row) when shock precedes click by 8 msec. When stapedius muscle is cut, effect shown here disappears but no change is noted in phenomena of Fig. 1.*

but deformed state (Fig. 7A). (iii) The tendon attaching the stapedius muscle to the head of the stapes is cut, an operation that permits muscle shortening but prevents displacement at the incudo-stapedial joint. (iv) The incudo-stapedial joint is abolished by dissecting the incus away without apparent damage to the stapes and stapedius muscle, both of which move vigorously when the medulla is stimulated. (v) The animal is curarized, a procedure that stops all muscle activity and consequently prevents motion of the incudo-stapedial joint. These observations have in common a single mechanical phenomenon, namely, that the rate of change of distortion in the joint capsule connecting the incus and stapes is zero or approaches zero.

It seems clear, then, that movement of the stapes relative to the incus due to stapedius muscle contraction is the underlying reason for the N_I suppression recorded at low shock rates and shown in Fig. 8. It is thought likely that the explanation for this suppression is noise produced as the articulating surfaces of these two bones slide back and forth upon one another. Such a noise, if present, would be expected to operate like any other noise upon the nueral component of the click response. White noise, hisses and similar sounds have long been known to "mask" N_I, and there is no reason to believe that noises generated within a joint would fail to do so. In any event, the control experiments yield this the most likely explanation for the phenomenon of suppression encountered with stapedius contraction. To eliminate this undesirable activity our critical measurements were made under Flaxedil with direct visualization of the paralyzed stapedius, and frequently the stapedius tendon was cut in addition. Such precautions should be routinely taken even though they can ordinarily be shown to have little influence upon results obtained with shock rates around 100/sec. As for the tensor tympani muscle, it can also be made to contract if strong shocks are applied to the medulla, but such contractions never suppress N_I, and cutting its tendon is without important consequences (see Fig. 1).

Some of the most revealing control experiments have been those in which the response of each ear was recorded with a common sweep upon separate channels of the oscilloscope. The various manipulations were performed on one side, with the other serving as the control. An example of one such is shown in Fig. 9, which represents both the paradigm of the experiments reported herein, and a summary of the most important results obtained. In each portion of that figure the response from both ears is shown, the right being displayed above the left. In A, a control record, one can see the (small) microphonic and prominent N_I responses to clicks 15 db (right ear) and 25 db (left ear) above threshold. B shows the obliteration of N_I that accompanies stimulation of the floor of the medulla with shocks at 100/sec. at the point where the olivo-cochlear bundle decussates. The location of these electrodes and the strength of the applied shock were unchanged throughout. Immediately after B was recorded, a cut designed to sever the left outgoing olivo-cochlear bundle was made with an iridectomy knife, freehand, under microscopic control. Figure 10, [Omitted in reprinting. (Ed.)] a photomicrograph of one section from this animal, shows the lesion to sever the olivo-cochlear bundle at this level; the sections ahead of and behind the one reproduced show the whole of the bundle to be cut with minimal other damage. The effect of this operation can be seen in C, in which the stimulus conditions present about 2 minutes earlier in B are repeated. N_I suppression is still complete on the right, but it does not occur on the left. Thus cutting the olivo-cochlear bundle along with the structures

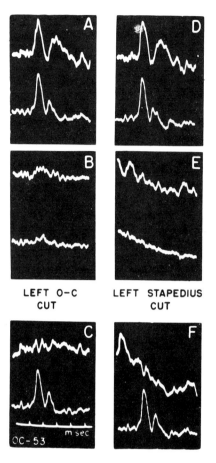

LEFT O-C CUT   **LEFT STAPEDIUS CUT**

FIGURE 9 *Suppression of auditory nerve response by olivo-cochlear and stapedius mechanisms. A: Control auditory nerve responses to click to each ear, right above left. B: Suppression of both left and right responses with shocks at 100/sec. delivered to medulla at decussation of olivo-cochlear bundle, as in Fig. 1. C: Following cut of left olivo-cochlear bundle, suppression shown in B occurs only on right. D: Another control response showing that lesion made between B and C has not interfered with auditory nerve response from either ear. E: Single shocks to medulla 13 msec. prior to click suppress eighth response bilaterally as in Fig. 8. F: Following cutting of tendon of left stapedius muscle the suppression shown in E is seen only on right.*

very closely adjacent to it is shown to prevent N_1 suppression on the cut side only; the effect is permanent and irreversible.

The records of D, E, and F continue the experiment. D is a control, like A, which demonstrates that the lesion in the medulla has not influenced the response of either ear to its click. E, like B, shows complete suppression of N_1 bilaterally, but this time through the action of the stapedius muscle, as discussed above and shown in Fig. 8. The medullary shock in E and F occurred 13 msec. prior to the click; the click triggered the sweep. The left stapedius muscle was observed under the microscope to twitch briskly with each shock to the medulla. Its tendon was then cut across. The muscle continued contracting to each shock, but, as shown in F, these contractions no longer produced N_1 suppression on the operated side.

This experiment makes a clear distinction between the two ways by which N_1 suppression can be caused by shocks to the medulla. The first, like that of Fig. 1, occurs only with high frequency shocks (above about 50/sec.), and it disappears when the olivo-cochlear pathway is interrupted (with unavoidable minimal damage to nearby structures). An exactly similar suppression, as shown in Fig. 8, occurs with shocks at low frequencies (here, 1/sec.); it is uninfluenced by cutting the olivo-cochlear bundle but disappears when the stapedius muscle is prevented from acting upon the bone to which it is attached. If both the olivo-cochlear bundle and the stapedius tendon have been severed it is impossible to suppress N_I by any shocks applied in the midline. It might parenthetically be added here that if one moves the shocking electrodes toward the cut side, placing them so that there is reason to believe they will excite the peripheral cut end of the olivo-cochlear bundle, then shocks at frequencies around 100/sec. once more produce suppression of N_I.

DISCUSSION

The first point to be settled with respect to these experiments is whether they do indeed depend upon function in the olivo-cochlear pathway. Two main alternate possibilities exist. Can it be, first of all, that the shocking current spreads toward the cochlea where it acts directly, through anti-dromic effects, or in some other way upon the neurons that produce N_I? Such an explanation is highly unlikely, for the following reasons. (i) The necessary and sufficient shock-electrode location is restricted to a locus measuring as little as 2×2 mm. in the midline between the facial colliculi (Fig. 5). Electrode placements much closer to the cochlea, including ones directly upon the dorsal cochlear nucleus, fail to suppress N_I. (ii) The small knife-cut that severs the olivo-cochlear bundle can hardly be expected to interfere with shock-spread in any important way, yet it abolishes the suppression (Fig. 10). A similar knife-cut that does not sever the bundle has no effect upon the suppression. (iii) If shock-spread were the responsible agent, its consequences might be expected to coincide in time with the shocks. This is not the case. No suppression is seen until a number of shocks have been delivered and the effects of the shocks can be traced for tens of msec. after the last of them (Fig. 4).

A second set of questions revolves around whether it is excitation of olivo-cochlear efferents, as opposed to some other fiber tract (e.g., the facial), that is responsible for the suppression. The evidence implicating the olivo-cochlear bundle in the suppression observed with 100/sec. shocks may be summarized here. First, the effect is seen when these shocks are applied where they can reasonably be expected to activate the bundle, namely, at the decussation (Fig. 5) or peripheral to where the bundle has been cut. Second, cutting the bundle with minimal damage to adjacent structures causes immediate, irreversible disappearance of the suppression, and on the cut side only (Fig. 9C). In such a preparation, however, lively normal activity in structures innervated by the facial nerve continues (Fig. 9E). Finally, middle ear contents and striated muscle activity can be entirely eliminated from consideration since the effect is observed in their absence (Fig. 1).

What is excited to produce N_I suppression must therefore be something other than the facial nerve that (a) is available for stimulation in the medulla at the locus of the decussation of the olivo-cochlear bundle, (b) is destroyed when the bundle is cut, and (c) can be activated by shocks intended to stimulate peripheral cut ends of that bundle. If the relevant fibers are not actually those of the olivo-cochlear bundle itself, they must pass along with it over a substantial portion of its course and terminate within the cochlea. The question of how these olivo-cochlear neurons might achieve the observed results is not easy to answer. It will be recalled that suppression begins 20–30 msec. after the first shock in the train, and the effectiveness of the train increases up to a limit reached at around 300 msec. (Fig. 4). Furthermore, the dissipation of the capacity to suppress as measured by events following the last shock in the train has a similar time course. What "summates" and "dissipates" over a period of 0.3–0.5 sec.? How do impulses arriving in the cochlea manage to throttle off the afferent neuron discharge? Rasmussen (14) describes a plexus formed by the efferents at the margin of the osseous spiral lamina around the afferent fibers as these pass from their endings upon the hair cells toward their cell bodies. It is possible but unlikely that the efferent fibers prevent conduction in the afferent fibers at this point. The possibility that the efferents pass directly to the hair cells and there create conditions unfavorable for the arousal of auditory nerve impulses must also be entertained. Unfortunately it is not clear, anatomically, whether and how the efferents end upon the internal hair cells, and no available report traces them in any substantial numbers to the external hair cells. Since it is generally supposed that weak stimuli activate these external hair cells, and it being recalled that the suppression described here occurs best with weak and very weak clicks, considerable difficulties oppose the hypothesis that the efferents achieve their results by direct action on the hair cell, or at the hair cell-auditory nerve junction. It would therefore appear that all questions of the details of the mechanism by which the suppression is accomplished must still be left open.

The observations reported here demonstrate that the neural inflow aroused at a sense organ can be suppressed by impulses aroused in the brain that pass out to that sense organ. The idea that such mechanisms might operate in the nervous system is not new. Thus when Toennies (17), in 1939, found a reduction in sensory inflow from the limbs of a cat if a prior reflex discharge through that nerve had been aroused by spinal cord stimulation, he proposed, as one possible explanation, "a special system of centrifugally conducting dorsal root fibers capable, when active, of conditioning sensory endings" (p. 524). Yet neurophysiologists have only recently begun assembling substantial data in support of such mechanisms. For example, the series of observations apparently originating with Leksell (12), expanded by Kuffler and Hunt (11), and treated in detail by Granit (4) upon the fine motor fibers that pass from the spinal cord to the muscle spindles demonstrate the principle unequivocally. Among the invertebrates, Kuffler and Eyzaguirre (10) have shown for a stretch receptor in the crayfish that stimulation of its efferent fiber prevents the appearance of expected afferent impulses, and Hartline et al. (7) have described for the photoreceptor of *Limulus* certain efferent suppressor fibers from distant parts of the receptor. Prior to this work, Leksell suggested that such efferent mechanisms might operate for both the ear and eye (12, p. 74), a point also made by Herrick (8), among others.

To this evidence that the energy-exchange at the receptor is not the sole arbiter of what enters the central nervous system from a sense organ can be added numerous recent studies indicating that the sensory message, once entered, undergoes substantial further modification in the central sensory nuclei (3, 5, 6, 9). The simple conception of the sensory pathway as one that delivers receptor events, unchanged, to the cortex is certainly no longer tenable. The evidence is accumulating for its extensive modification at every level from the receptor upward by events originating within the nervous system itself.

A few statements relating these observations specifically to the auditory system and hearing may be in order in conclusion. The efferent olivo-cochlear pathway seems clearly to represent the final link in a chain of neurons that pass from the auditory cortex to the cochlea. Certain components of this descending auditory system have been known for a long time (see 2, p. 502 for summary), and Rasmussen, in his examination of these tracts, has recently established experimentally that axons originating in the dorsal nucleus of the lateral lemniscus and the nucleus of the inferior colliculus terminate in the region of the cells that give rise to the olivo-cochlear pathway (15, 16). The existence of such recurrent systems strongly suggests that the output of a given auditory nucleus is the result of influences arriving from both more central and more peripheral nuclei. The experiments reported here suggest inhibition to be the function of one component of the recurrent system, and the description of what it and others do is almost certainly related to how and what we hear.

SUMMARY

1. Experiments are described in which the auditory nerve discharge to a click stimulus of weak or moderate strength is reduced or abolished by concomitant electrical stimulation of the floor of the medulla.

2. The shock stimulation, to be effective, must be applied to the medulla at the site of the decussation of the olivo-cochlear pathway, a collection of fibers that originate in the superior olivary region and terminate near or on the hair cells in the contralateral cochlea.

3. The phenomenon persists after removal of the bones and muscles of the middle ear and in the completely curarized preparation; it disappears when the olivo-cochlear bundle is severed peripheral to the site of stimulation.

4. It is concluded that the olivo-cochlear bundle, when functioning, suppresses the expected inflow of auditory nerve activity to normal acoustic stimuli.

ACKNOWLEDGMENT

It is a pleasure here to thank Mr. Allen Rupert and Drs. Grant L. Rasmussen, Patrick D. Wall, Jerzy E. Rose and Walle J. H. Nauta for their technical and intellectual contributions to these experiments.

REFERENCES

1 Davis, H., Tasaki, I., and Goldstein, R. The peripheral origin of activity, with reference to the ear. *Cold Spr. Harb. Symp. quant. Biol.*, 1952, **17**: 143–154.
2 Galambos, R. Neural mechanisms of audition. *Physiol. Rev.*, 1954, **34**: 497–528.
3 Galambos, R., Sheatz, G., and Vernier, V. G. Electrophysiological correlates of a conditioned response in cats. *Science*, 1956, **123**: 376–377.
4 Granit, R. *Receptors and sensory perception.* New Haven, Yale Univ. Press, 1955. xii, 369 pp.
5 Granit, R. Centrifugal and antidromic effects on ganglion cells of retina. *J. Neurophysiol.*, 1955, **18**: 388–411.
6 Hagbarth, K.-E. and Kerr, D. I. B. Central influences on spinal afferent conduction. *J. Neurophysiol.*, 1954, **17**: 295–307.
7 Hartline, H. K., Wagner, H. G., and Tomita, T. Mutual inhibition among the receptors of the eye of Limulus. *Abstr. XX int. physiol. Congr.*, 1953, p. 441.
8 Herrick, C. J. *The brain of the tiger salamander (Ambystoma tigrinum).* Chicago, Univ. of Chicago Press, 1948, viii, 409 pp.
9 Kerr, D. I. B. and Hagbarth, K.-E. An investigation of olfactory centrifugal fiber system. *J. Neurophysiol.*, 1955, **18**: 362–374.
10 Kuffler, S. W. and Eyzaguirre, C. Synaptic inhibition in an isolated nerve cell. *J. gen. Physiol.* 1955, **39**: 155–184.
11 Kuffler, S. W. and Hunt, C. C. Small-nerve fibers in mammalian ventral roots. *Proc. Soc. exp. Biol., N. Y.*, 1949, **71**: 256–257.
12 Leksell, L. The action potential and excitatory effects of the small ventral root fibres to skeletal muscle. *Acta physiol. scand.*, 1945, **10**: suppl. 31, 84 pp.
13 Rasmussen, G. L. The olivary peduncle and other fiber projections of the superior olivary complex. *J. comp. Neurol.*, 1946, **84**: 141–220.
14 Rasmussen, G. L. Further observations of the efferent cochlear bundle. *J. comp. Neurol.*, 1953, **99**: 61–74.
15 Rasmussen, G. L. Recurrent or "feed-back" connections of the auditory system of the cat. *Anat. Rec.* 1953, **115**: 361.
16 Rasmussen, G. L. Recurrent or "feed-back" connections of the auditory system of the cat. *Amer. J. Physiol.*, 1955, **183**: 653.
17 Toennies, J. F. Conditioning of afferent impulses by reflex discharges over the dorsal roots. *J. Neurophysiol.*, 1939, **2**: 515–525.

Genetics and
Maturation

STUDIES IN EXPERIMENTAL BEHAVIOR GENETICS: I. THE HERITABILITY OF PHOTOTAXIS IN A POPULATION OF *DROSOPHILA MELANOGASTER*

Jerry Hirsch

COLUMBIA UNIVERSITY

James C. Boudreau

UNIVERSITY OF CALIFORNIA, BERKELEY

*

Editor's Note   *Heritability refers to the proportion of the variation in an observed trait (phenotype) which is due to genetic factors. While it is not feasible to get a single completely accurate number to represent heritability of any given trait—for one reason because the amount of variation due to environment depends on just how extreme the variations in the environment are—it is possible to get a rough approximation. Hirsch and Boudreau do this for a behavioral trait in the fruitfly. This is neither the first nor the last demonstration of heritability of a behavioral trait; many instances have been observed in animals, including man. However, as the authors comment, the method used here is much more practical than those used earlier and indicates the feasibility of detailed genetic analysis of some kinds of behavior. The eventual hope in this work will be to find single genetic loci associated with behavioral characteristics. It is even conceivable that once such loci have been established further analysis to elucidate the biochemical basis of the behavior involved may follow.*

Source   *Reprinted from the* Journal of Comparative and Physiological Psychology, *1958,* **51,** *647–651, with permission of the authors and the American Psychological Association.*

It has frequently been observed that individual differences (IDs) in behavior can be inherited; e.g., Tryon (11) has reported on the inheritance of maze-learning ability, and Kallmann and Baroff (5) on the inheritance of behavior pathologies. The present paper extends the study of the inheritance of IDs in behavior to a part of the phylogenetic series at which experimental behavior genetic (BG) analysis is feasible, viz., the genus *Drosophila*. The behavior chosen for BG analysis is the reaction to light, phototaxis—an apparently innate or unconditioned response. Taxes have the advantage of representing relatively constant S-R relationships: the repeated presentation of a single stimulus value appears to elicit, depending on the method of measurement, either a characteristic response or a characteristic probability of response. Both the characteristics of the response and the probability of the response have been shown to vary as a function of two parameters, the value of the stimulus presented and the strain of organisms stimulated (1, 8).

Brown and Hall have measured strain differences in phototaxis. The immediate purpose of the present study is to measure IDs in, and to estimate the heritability of, phototaxis within a single strain. (Roughly, "heritability," h^2, refers to that portion of the total variance due to additive genetic causes [6, p. 111].) This is one of several studies of *Drosophila* behavior in which an experimental attack is being made on the long unresolved question of whether abilities are under the control of one general factor (9) or many specific factors (10).

At present three *Drosophila* behaviors are under study: phototaxis, geotaxis (3), and eating rate (2).

METHOD

EXPERIMENTAL DESIGN

Individual differences in phototaxis were measured in a Y maze by the method of mass screening (4). The measurements consisted of ten mass-screening trials, which in the foundation population had the reliability, $r_{tt} = 0.673$ (4, Formula 6).

Selection pressure was applied, and a system of assortative mating was used, i.e., the highest-scoring animals within the high strain and the lowest-scoring animals within the low strain were bred together, respectively.

[1] This work was initiated during the senior author's tenure as a National Science Foundation postdoctoral fellow at the University of California, Berkeley, and completed under Grant No. G-3846 from the National Science Foundation.
[2] The authors gratefully acknowledge their indebtedness to Curt Stern and Th. Dobzhansky for generously supplying many useful facilities.

BEHAVIORAL ANALYSIS

Apparatus. Individual differences in the approach to light were studied in the Y maze shown in Figure 1. The maze consisted of three 5-in. lengths of acrylic tubing, *f, e, d,* having ½-in. inside diameter. These tubes were attached to a Y joint, *a,* having ½-in. outside diameter and ⅜-in. inside diameter. Tubes *d* and *e,* which served as the starting path and the lighted arm of the Y, respectively, were attached to the center unit, *a,* by plastic sleeves, *b* and *c.* Both sleeves were fitted with sliding plastic "doors" 0.02-in. thick to prevent premature approach to the choice point and retracing after a choice.

All parts of the maze were painted black on the outside with the exception of the starting tube, *d,* and the lighted tube, *e.* To eliminate reflections, the cotton plunger in the starting tube was dyed black. The attrahent was light reflected from cotton at the end of Arm *e.* Although the same tube (Arm *e*) was always illuminated, the illuminated side was varied after each block of two trials (tests have shown that the tubes themselves do not act as stimuli). This was accomplished by rotating the entire front section of the maze 180° on the Y joint and shifting the light to the other side. A microscope light was placed at *h* and focused on the cotton at the end of *e.* The distance from the light source to the cotton was 6 in. The illumination at this distance is 100 ft-c., as measured by a Weston illumination meter, Model 756. Thus, the stimulating source of light was indirect. This was necessary because in preliminary studies using a direct source, i.e., a light shining through *e* to *d,* it was evident that secondary reflections were being set up in the starting arm, *d,* and that these constituted competing attrahents with the result that many flies never left the starting tube.

Procedure. The sexes were run separately on successive days. Each generation the males were run one day after hatching and the females two days after hatching. The role of heredity in determining IDs in behavior was assessed

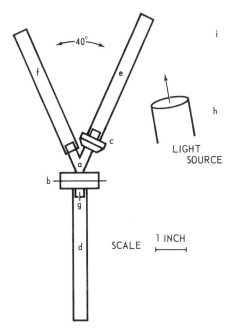

FIGURE 1 *Apparatus for measuring the reaction of Drosophila to light.*

by the response of the population to selection. Virgin females are necessary for selective breeding. Since *melanogaster* females remain virgin for only the first 7 to 8 hr. after hatching, the cultures were cleared of all flies the day before an experiment, and only those flies that hatched in the following 7 hr. were tested. Occasionally, to obtain larger samples, flies were collected over two consecutive 7-hr. periods. Hence, the maximum age difference among the animals never exceeded 14 hr.

The behavior experiment consisted of introducing a group of flies into the starting tube of the Y maze and inserting a plug of black cotton behind them to seal the tube. The cotton was immediately pushed forward to within 0.5-in. of the door to the choice point so that all flies would be in the vicinity of the choice point at the start of a trial.

A trial lasted 30 sec. Both doors were opened at the beginning of a trial, and 30 sec. later the door to the illuminated arm of the Y was closed. In this way, on each trial the flies that approached the light were separated from the others. That is, on Trial 1 the initial group of flies was separated into two pass-fail subgroups. On Trial 2 both the pass group and the fail group from Trial 1 were tested and were in turn subdivided into pass-fail subgroups. In the method of mass screening, the subgroups obtained on one trial are retested separately on the next trial and further subdivided. A complete account of the method is given elsewhere (4). In this experiment ten mass-screening trials were used; therefore, the distribution of final scores ranges from 0 through 10.

Dyes were added to the medium on which the flies were raised. Bismark brown was used for the low strain and Nile blue for the high strain (tests have shown that reversing the colors does not affect the behavior). The colors were ingested along with the food. Since the females of the high and low strains could be distinguished by the colors they had absorbed, they were run in the apparatus together. It was necessary, however, to run the males in separate groups, since they did not show the colors clearly.

GENETIC ANALYSIS

Subjects. The Ss were 3,424 fruit flies, *Drosophila melanogaster*, Formosa wild type. The initial sample of animals was obtained from regular stocks in the genetics laboratory of the zoology department of the University of California, Berkeley. The flies were raised on standard *Drosophila* medium (to which color had been added) in ½-pt. culture bottles at 25° C.

Mating System. Selection pressure of variable intensity was applied under a system of restricted assortative mating. Animals were mated on the basis of phenotypic merit without regard to family relationship. In the foundation population animals with similar extreme phototactic scores were mated. In all filial generations the same selection criteria were applied with the further restriction that matings were always within and never between the two strains established by selection from the foundation population. Thus, the high and low strains were reproductively isolated, and inbreeding undoubtedly increased down through the generations.

If a sufficient number of animals received extreme scores, i.e., 0 or 10, only members of these classes were chosen for breeding. If not, individuals in adjacent classes were also used for breeding. The intensity of selection pressure increased because the percentage of animals receiving extreme scores increased as selection progressed. Selection was carried on over 29 generations with the exception of Generations 10, 11, 12, and 13, when mass mating was permitted (within the separate strains) and no behavior tests were made.[3]

RESULTS

Male and female data have been combined except for Generations 7, 8, and 9, for which female data alone are presented. In these generations the males were given only enough test trials to identify the extreme scorers for breeding. Data are not available for Generations 10 through 13 or for Generation 16, when the apparatus broke.

Figure 2 presents the percentage of trials on which the light was approached by the high and low strains over 29 generations of selection. Clearly, there is an early response to selection, and despite fluctuations the expected values of the selected strains show progressive divergence from the foundation population value of 51.6% to asymptotic values of approximately 80.0% for the high strain and 15.0% for the low strain.

Figure 3 presents the distribution of phototactic scores for the foundation population and for filial Generations 1, 2, 7, and 29. Inspection of the figure reveals that selection effects marked changes in dispersion as well as in central tendency. The changes in dispersion are shown in Figure 4, where the ratio of the variance of each selected generation to that of the foundation population is plotted.

It has been predicted that the limits of selective breeding would depend upon the reliability of the ID measurements in the foundation population (4, p. 410), i.e., when the variance in the selected lines decreases to the size of the variance error of measurement in the foundation population, further selection should be ineffective, since at that point the method of observation is no longer discriminating among individuals. In the present study the foundation population measurements have a reliability

[3] As the medium on which to establish the basic principles of BG, *Drosophila* is thus an animal quite superior to the laboratory mammals such as mice, rats, or guinea pigs. Compare the present results, obtained in about a year, with the Tryon study (11), which required over 15 years.

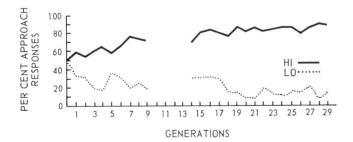

FIGURE 2 *Percentage of trials on which light was approached per generation.*

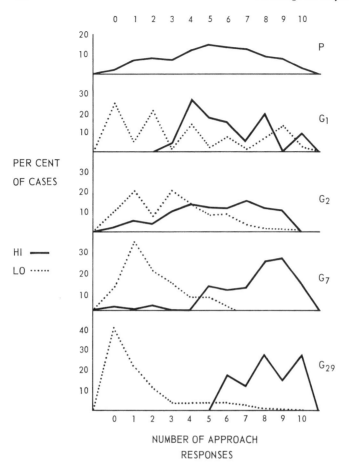

FIGURE 3   *Distribution of light-approach scores for Generations*
0, 1, 2, 7, and 29.

$r_{tt} = 0.673$, a variance $\sigma_0^2 = 6.38$, and a variance error of measurement
$\sigma_e^2 = \sigma_0^2 (1 - r_{tt}) = 6.38 (1 - 0.673) = 2.09$ (4, Formula 8). Hence the
ratio of the variance of the selected strains to that of the foundation population should approach the asymptote:

$$\frac{\sigma_e^2}{\sigma_0^2} = 2.09/6.38 = 0.327$$

In Figure 4 it can be seen that the variance ratio for the high photo
strain appears to be settling down near the line 0.327. The variance ratio
for the low strain, however, has not stabilized enough yet to determine
whether it is approaching the predicted asymptote.

Next, let us examine the extent to which IDs in phototaxis are genetically
determined. If it is assumed that the average of the variances of the two
selected strains over Generations 28 and 29 represents an upper limit to
the variability to be expected in an isogenic line, then we have available

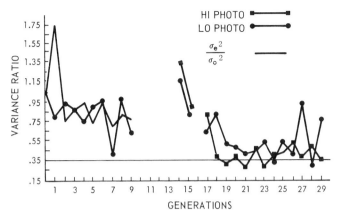

FIGURE 4 *The ratio of the variance of each selected generation to the variance of the foundation population, σ_i^2/σ_0^2, for the "high" and "low" phototactic strains. σ_e^2/σ_0^2 is the asymptote predicted from the relability of the foundation population scores (see text).*

a conservative estimate of the heritability, h^2, of phototaxis in the foundation population under the present experimental conditions.

All methods of estimating heritability rest on measuring how much more closely animals with similar genotypes resemble each other than less closely related animals do. . . . Variation within isogenic lines is wholly environmental. Comparing this with the variation in an otherwise similar random breeding population may give an estimate of heritability (7, p. 92).

For the high strain $\sigma_{28}^2 = 2.88$ and $\sigma_{29}^2 = 2.08$, for the low strain $\sigma_{28}^2 = 1.63$ and $\sigma_{29}^2 = 4.51$. The average of these four variances is $\overline{\sigma^2} = 2.77$. Hence: $h^2 = (\sigma_0^2 - \overline{\sigma^2})/\sigma_0^2 = (6.38 - 2.77)/6.38 = 0.566$, i.e., at least 57% of the phenotypic variance is genetic variance. This is a conservative estimate because the value of the reliability coefficient sets an upper limit to the values an estimate may take (as calculated, h^2 is 84% of the reliable phenotypic variance). Furthermore, h^2 contains only the additive portions of the genetic variance; it does not include variance due to dominance or to epistasis (i.e., dominance of nonallelic genes).

No estimate can be made of the heredity-environment interaction because only a single stimulus condition has been employed.

DISCUSSION

The aim of the present experiment has been both exploratory and descriptive. Its purpose has been to examine the possibility of studying IDs in behavior and their genetic bases in a species on which detailed genetic analysis can be performed.

The results which have been reported indicate that the study of *Drosophila* behavior is quite feasible, that IDs in performance can be measured in groups both reliably and efficiently by the method of mass screening, and that the ID's variance contains a large genetic component to which the techniques of experimental genetics may now be applied.

Since the present data have been obtained with a laboratory stock considered to be rather inbred[4] and therefore not very heterogeneous genetically, it is to be expected that a larger genetic variance would be found in a less inbred natural population. These findings have implications for psychological theory.

Theory testing in psychology is usually done on human Ss or on laboratory strains of animals which, it is reasonable to assume, are genetically much less alike than our *Drosophila*. (The Formosa stock has been maintained in the laboratory in small cultures for more than 20 years. Inbreeding has, therefore, had over 700 generations in which to exercise its homogenizing influence. Within the same period of time laboratory strains of rats would have completed about 70 generations. Furthermore, *Drosophila melanogaster* have only 4 independently assorting pairs of chromosomes whereas rats have 21 and human beings at least 23.) If large genetic differences do exist in the populations now being studied by psychologists, it should be of interest to determine in what ways stimulus control of behavior depends upon the genotype under stimulation.

SUMMARY

Behavior genetic analysis of the unconditioned response, phototaxis, has been carried through several steps: Individual differences in phototaxis have been measured reliably and efficiently in a *Drosophila* population by the method of mass screening. The genetic determination of individual differences in behavior has been demonstrated by the response to selection, and the heritability has been estimated to be more than one-half the phenotypic variance.

REFERENCES

1 Brown, F. A., & Hall, V. A. The directive influence of light upon *Drosophila melanogaster* Meig and some of its eye mutants. *J. exp. Zool.*, 1936, **74**, 205–220.
2 Durkin, R. D. Eating behavior of *Drosophila melanogaster*. Unpublished honors study, Psychol. Dept., Columbia Univer., 1957.
3 Hirsch, J. Behavior genetic studies of individual differences in *Drosophila melanogaster*. *Amer. Psychologist*, 1956, **11**, 450–451. (Abstract)
4 Hirsch, J., & Tryon, R. C. Mass screening and reliable individual measurement in the experimental behavior genetics of lower organisms. *Psychol. Bull.*, 1956, **53**, 402–410.

[4] Personal communication from Th. Dobzhansky.

5 Kallmann, F. J., & Baroff, G. S. Abnormal psychology. *Ann. Rev. Psychol.*, 1956, 6, 297–326.

6 Lerner, I. M. *Population genetics and animal improvement.* Cambridge: Cambridge Univer. Press, 1950.

7 Lush, J. L. *Animal breeding plans.* Ames, Iowa: Collegiate Press, 1945.

8 Scott, J. P. Effects of single genes on the behavior of *Drosophila. Amer. Naturalist,* 1943, 77, 184–190.

9 Spearman, C. *The abilities of man.* New York: Macmillan, 1927.

10 Tryon, R. C. A theory of psychological components—an alternative to 'mathematical factors.' *Psychol. Rev.,* 1935, 42, 425–454.

11 Tryon, R. C. Genetic differences in maze-learning ability in rats. In *Yearb. nat. Soc. Stud. Educ.,* 1940, 39(I), 111–119.

PREFERENTIAL SELECTION OF CENTRAL PATHWAYS BY REGENERATING OPTIC FIBERS

Domenica G. Attardi and R. W. Sperry

CALIFORNIA INSTITUTE OF TECHNOLOGY

Editor's Note   How do developing nerve fibers find their way to connect the central and peripheral organs which they serve? A prior question, however, is whether they actually do make specific point-to-point connection at all. Perhaps the connections in the nervous system are random and their function is imposed on them by activity. Such problems are clearly basic to understanding how the circuitry of the nervous system works. Here Attardi and Sperry show that for regeneration—a special case of developmental innervation in the goldfish —the fibers do find their way in an exquisitely accurate fashion to their appointed terminals.

Source   Reprinted from **Experimental Neurology,** *1963,* **7,** *46–64, with permission of the authors and Academic Press Inc.*

The time-course and general features of optic nerve regeneration in goldfish were followed in sections prepared at spaced intervals between 3 and 67 days after nerve section. Differential route and destination preferences of fibers from different parts of the retina were then tested by removing specific portions of the retina in combination with complete section of the optic nerve. With the dorsal half of the retina destroyed, surviving ventral fibers became segregated beyond the nerve scar and selectively entered the medial tract to connect with dorsal tectum. Conversely, when dorsal retina remained intact, the regenerating fibers filled selectively the lateral tract and the ventral tectum. Fibers from the posterior (temporal) hemiretina invaded the anterior portion of the tectum and did not extend into the posterior regions. Conversely, those from the anterior hemiretina bypassed the anterior zones to innervate the posterior tectum. Fibers from the center of the retina, after reaching the parallel layer within the tectum, bypassed the plexiform layer in the margin to connect only in the central zone. The plexiform layer in the marginal zones was innervated only when fibers were available from the peripheral retina. The results furnish direct microscopical evidence for the orderly selective termination of optic fibers in the brain centers. They also demonstrate a remarkable and unexpected (presumably chemotactic) selectivity in the tendency of different retinal fiber groups to choose and to follow specific central pathways en route to their synaptic destinations. The thesis that specific chemical affinities govern the formation and maintenance of neuronal associations is extended on the basis of the present results to include the patterning of central fiber pathways.

INTRODUCTION

Regeneration of the severed optic nerve in fishes and amphibians leads, under optimal conditions, to good recovery of visual function (21). The perception of color, directionality, movement and pattern as well as visual acuity have all been shown to be recovered at a high level approximating that of normal vision. Further, visual discrimination habits involving color, brightness and pattern, learned by fishes prior to section of the optic nerve are reinstated by the regeneration process and in cichlids, *Astronotus ocellatus;* these have been found to exhibit interocular transfer and to survive the combined ablation of forebrain plus cerebellum (1, 2).

The collected evidence including histological observations and mapping data obtained with localized tectal lesions (16–21) was taken to indicate that the regenerating fibers re-establish their central connections on an orderly plan that systematically reduplicates the original topographic projection of the retina on the tectum in accordance with the projection pattern

[1] This investigation was supported in part by the Frank P. Hixon Fund and by a PHS research grant (M3372) from the National Institute of Mental Health, Public Health Service. A brief presentation of the results was made at the 1960 Fall meetings of the American Physiological Society (3).

characteristic of the species. It has been suggested that the establishment of this topographic projection may be regulated by specific chemical affinities between matching loci in retinal and tectal fields respectively, the affinities being established by embryonic differentiation gradients that sweep over retina and tectum early in development, first, along the rostrocaudal axis and then the dorsoventral axis.

Extension of the experiments into early embryonic stages has brought more direct evidence for the presence of at least the two main retinal gradients and for the respective timing of their establishment (22, 23). Recent mapping of retinally evoked electrical potentials in the tectum of anurans following optic nerve regeneration by Gaze (4, 5) and by Lettvin, Maturana and associates (12, 13) has brought further support for the inference that the regenerating optic axons achieve selective reconnection with their original loci of termination.

A question long at issue in the foregoing is whether the experimental data including the electrophysiological maps might not be accounted for without assuming any orderly regeneration of central connections. It has been pointed out that certain coding-decoding schemes might in theory account for all the observed behavioral data without the assumption of anything more than a randomized reconnection (11). The available data could also be accounted for in terms of the resonance principle of Weiss (24), which was designed expressly to explain organized function within randomized networks, and in networks deranged by surgery and misregeneration.

Neither the lesion nor the electrical mapping studies have been decisive on this question, in part because of uncertainty as to whether the observed scotomata and the tectal potentials reflect presynaptic or postsynaptic effects. Postsynaptic activity could yield the orderly maps obtained after a purely haphazard regrowth if something caused the resultant synapses to be functionally effective only within the appropriate loci. This might be the case, for example, in the above resonance or coding schemes. The exact source of the tectal potentials is considered uncertain by Gaze (4–6), while Maturana and his colleagues (14) favored the terminal arborizations of the optic axons as the probable origin. In the latter case the possibility of random meandering and widespread arborization is not excluded. The electrical studies of Gaze (6) and Jacobsen (8) have suggested the possibility of a scheduled timing of fiber ingrowth and the presence of an early diffuse nonlocalized phase of regeneration that subsequently may or may not be transformed into a systematized topographic organization. They have also pointed out another complicating factor in the presence of a previously unrecognized projection of each retina to the ipsilateral as well as to the contralateral tectum (7). The overlapping ipsilateral projection is not in register with the main contralateral projection.

The following was undertaken in the hope that some of the above and other uncertainties about the regeneration process might be clarified. The experiments, started in 1958, were undertaken on the supposition that the sectioned optic fibers probably remain fortuitously scrambled in regeneration until they regain the plexiform layer of the tectum, an inference drawn from earlier results on the frog (21). It thus proved something of a surprise to find evidence of highly discriminative, presumably chemotactic, differences among the regenerating fiber groups enabling them to select and to follow preferentially their own original pathways en route to their specific terminal stations.

MATERIALS AND PROCEDURE

Most of the experiments were carried out on goldfish, *Carassia aurata*, about 5 to 9 cm in standard length. Selected aspects of the work as mentioned in context below were repeated in the cichlid, *Astronotus ocellatus*, in which the visual system is more highly developed. Results in the two species were essentially the same; the following text applies principally to the goldfish unless otherwise indicated.

NORMAL ANATOMY WITH REFERENCE TO THE REGENERATION PROBLEM   The main retinal projection to the optic tectum in the goldfish is diagrammed in Fig. 1. The optic nerves cross completely at the chiasm so that each eye connects to the contralateral optic lobe. Before entering the midbrain tectum the primary optic tract divides into two main bundles, the medial and lateral optic tracts. These course along the medial and lateral circum-

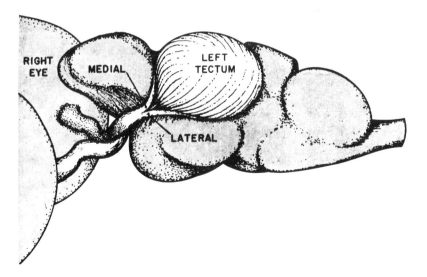

FIGURE 1   *Schematic drawing of goldfish optic system showing division of main optic tract into medial and lateral bundles and their relations with midbrain tectum.*

ference of the optic lobe, respectively, giving off fibers all along the periphery which they turn radially into the optic tectum where they run in a superficial parallel layer to reach their local synaptic zones.

The medial tract, as shown below, consists of fibers arising in the ventral part of the retina. The fibers spread fanlike into the dorsal portion of the tectum from its medial border. Conversely, the fibers of the lateral tract arise in the dorsal retina and spread from the ventral border of the lobe into its ventral and lateral areas.

Along the circumference of the tectum small bundles of fibers separate from the main medial and lateral tracts to enter the tectum where they then proceed in a relatively straight, roughly parallel course toward the center of the optic lobe. Fibers originating in the posterior (temporal) quadrants of the retina are destined for the anterior or rostral quadrants of the optic lobe and accordingly they leave the main tracts earlier, whereas those from the anterior (nasal) retina remain in the tracts until they reach the posterior regions of the tectum.

After the fibers have run their course in the superficial parallel layer of the tectum they exit from this layer by dipping centrally into an underlying plexiform layer. In accordance with the principle of topographic correspondence between retina and tectum, fibers arising from the outer periphery of the retina exit from parallel to plexiform layers abruptly after entering the tectum. Whereas those from more and more central points along a given retinal radius successively delay their entrance into the plexiform layer until reaching correspondingly more central zones of the tectum.

Thus the normal central course of the optic fibers is so laid out that, in effect each regenerating optic axon finds itself confronted by a kind of multiple Y-maze. In order to return to the tectum by its own original pathway, a given regenerating axon must first select correctly the medial or the lateral tract. After that comes a continuous series of decision points along the circumference of the tectum at each of which the fiber can either turn radially into the parallel layer of the tectum or continue to push ahead tangentially in the main tract. Upon entering the parallel layer of the tectum, each fiber again meets a series of choice points as it advances from periphery to center wherein it can either dip downward into the plexiform layer or continue to grow on farther centrally within the parallel layer.

Finally, after entering the plexiform layer the different types of retinal fibers must again select presumably the proper tectal units for appropriate patterns of synapsis, not only with reference to tectal topography and directionality in vision but also with respect to other dimensions of physiological specificity. For example, fibers for red, blue, green, and yellow, those for luminous flux, the "on," "on-off" and "off" fibers, and perhaps other specialized detector types (11–14), must each form its own characteristic pattern of tectal linkages after arrival at the correct locus of the tectal map. Within the plexiform layer it can be seen that the fibers begin to bifurcate and the branches get thinner than the parent fiber, lose their myelin, and no longer run parallel, but course erratically in all directions, eventually to synapse with tectal neurons.

EXPERIMENTAL PLAN   In a first group of thirty-nine goldfish one optic nerve was severed in order to study the time-course of optic fiber regeneration in sections prepared at spaced intervals varying between 3 and 67 days after nerve section. In cases with fully regenerated nerves, the fiber pattern within the nerve, tracts, and in the parallel and plexus layers of the tectum were compared with those of normal fish.

In a second group of seventy-four fishes, removal of a large sector of one retina was combined with section of the optic nerve of the same side in order to determine the course taken by the fibers regenerating from the remaining intact retinal areas, as follows:

(a) Ventral-dorsal series. The ventral (or, in other cases, the dorsal) half of one retina was removed and the optic nerve of the same side completely severed. As a control in some cases, the opposite nerve was sectioned as well.

(b) Anterior-posterior series. The anterior (or the posterior) half of one retina was removed and the optic nerve of the same or both sides completely severed.

(c) Central-peripheral series. A partial or complete peripheral ring of retina was removed and one or both optic nerves severed.

Many of the operated fish yielded little or no information owing to inadequate differentiation of the stain, poor placement or excessive extension of the retinal lesion, inadequate regeneration, poor plane of section, and other factors encountered in the early exploratory procedures. Further cases were prepared in each series until a convincing mass of evidence was obtained. The described results represent a composite impression drawn from the total but based largely on the several best cases in each series. In most cases the histology was checked at 17 to 25 days after nerve section, though a few were taken earlier and later for special purposes.

SURGICAL PROCEDURE   The surgery was performed out of water under a stereoscopic microscope. The fish were anesthetized in a 0.5% solution of tricaine methanesulphonate (MS 222 Sandoz Chemical Co.) in conditioned tap water. The anesthetized fish was wrapped in a wet cloth and placed in a plasticene mold to hold it in the desired position. Anesthesia was maintained during surgery by dropping a dilute solution of tricaine over the gills.

The nerve section was performed within the orbit. The approach was posterodorsal with the eyeball tilted anteroventrally. The nerve was severed fairly close to the eyeball at about one-fourth of its length to the chiasma. The nerve was cut and broken with finely pointed forceps leaving intact only a small strand of the outer dural sheath. This remnant of the outer sheath was left to hold the nerve stumps close together and to serve as a bridge for the regenerating fibers.

The retinal lesions were made in different ways. In the earlier cases the retina was approached through the pupil after cutting the cornea and lifting the lens. The area of retina to be removed was pinched and teased with fine forceps after which the fragments were delicately sucked away. The lens was then replaced and the shreds of the cornea rejoined.

In the majority of cases, the retina was approached by making a cut along more than a half of the border of the anterior face of the eyeball with fine scissors. The front part of the eyeball with the attached lens was then lifted and the whole retina clearly exposed. In a few of these the portion of retina to be removed was cut away together with the external layers of the eyeball. In most, however, an incision was made through only the retinal layer with the sharpened edge of a fine wire loop, thus separating the selected part of the retina from the adjacent portions without injury to the outer membranes. Care was taken to avoid damage to the peripapillar area. The isolated sector of retina was then removed with fine forceps. In practice this latter became the preferred method and most of the results described below were obtained with this technique.

HISTOLOGY   At sacrifice the retinal lesions were checked. Under deep anesthesia, the eyeball was opened and the retina examined in the living state with the stereomicroscope.[2] Afterward the cranium was opened and the whole head quickly immersed in abundant fixative (18 parts of 80% ethanol, 1 part acetic acid, 1 part formalin). A few hours later, the brain with the optic nerves and eyes attached was carefully dissected free and placed for 24 to 48 hours in fresh fixative. The fixed brains were then embedded in paraffin, serially sectioned at 15μ, and the sections stained with the Bodian protargol method.[*] In most cases, the normal fibers stained black with this method while the newly regenerated fibers acquired an intense pink or reddish hue. The contrast seemed to be enhanced by increasing the prescribed amount of protargol until the pH approached 8.8 and by reducing the amount of copper to about 0.25 gr.

OBSERVATIONS

TIME-COURSE AND GENERAL FEATURES OF OPTIC NERVE REGENERATION.   The speed of the regeneration process, as judged from the time required for recovery of visual function (14 to 18 days in *Carassius;* 25 to 35 days in *Astronotus*) was found to vary in relation to various factors such as the size and age of the fish, the season, and the degree of hemorrhage and displacement of the cut stumps. The following times indicate a rough summer-season average for goldfish 5 to 9 cm long.

At 3 to 4 days after nerve section, the whole distal segment of the optic nerve and the two bundles, medial and lateral, into which the optic nerve divides before entering the tectum, appear to be degenerated. Within the

[2] It is of incidental interest that extensive regeneration of the ablated retinal areas was found to be well underway in many cases. Further details of this retinal regeneration are left for another study.

[*] The student should notice the importance of this new staining method by which regenerated, as compared to original, fibers can be differentially visualized. (Ed.)

tectum, the two main bundles are completely degenerated up to the point at which the fibers spread into the parallel optic layer. Within the retinic layers of the tectum, however, signs of fiber degeneration are not yet noticeable at this time. It is known that the process of elimination of the retinic fibers of the cortex is a relatively slow one (10). In the proximal segment of the severed optic nerve also there were signs in many cases of some retrograde degeneration due perhaps to surgical trauma, such as stretching of the nerve and of the retinal artery which were difficult to avoid.

At 4 to 7 days after section, the optic fibers have started to regenerate and have become mixed and entangled in a dense and swollen neuromatous growth between the two nerve stumps. Here one cannot recognize any orderly pattern of regeneration, although the possibility that the fibers tend to segregate cannot be ruled out. As soon as the entangled regenerated fibers have reached the central stump of the severed nerve, they take again a grossly parallel alignment. Where the fibers emerge from the scar one can observe a progressive rearrangement; the fibers gather in groups becoming more and more conspicuous. In most cases, when the regenerated nerve reaches the point of separation into medial and lateral bundles the fibers destined for one or the other tract seem to have gathered in advance toward the corresponding lateral or medial side. Sometimes one sees small bundles of fibers transferring from one nerve sector to another just before the point of bifurcation.

At 10 to 12 days after nerve section the regenerated fibers start to reinnervate the optic lobe. Small groups of fibers exit from each bundle at different points along the circumference of the lobe and enter the tectum to course in the superficial parallel layer. This layer is markedly thicker in the proximity of the bundles, along the inner and ventral borders of the optic lobe, and becomes progressively thinner toward the central areas of the cortex. Already fibers may be seen leaving the parallel layer to enter the underlying plexiform layer particularly in the border regions.

At 14 to 18 days after nerve section, when visual function is being reinstated, the plexiform layer formed by the regenerated fibers is visible in all areas of the optic tectum. The layer as a whole is markedly thicker and the fiber bundles are more richly interwoven than in the normal tectum as can be seen in Fig. 2. [Omitted in reprinting. (Ed.)]. Also the distinction between parallel and plexiform layers is less clear.

The regenerated fibers were clearly distinguishable from the normal ones for several weeks after recovery of vision, not only by the reddish hue that they assumed with the modified Bodian stain, but also by their structure and their interrelationships. The normal optic fibers, which are myelinated in the nerve and in the parallel layer of the cortex and unmyelinated in the plexus layer, appear when stained by the above method, as black, well-individualized filaments. The regenerated fibers, on the other hand, which are not yet myelinated when vision returns, are packed together in the nerve in small bundles within which single fibers are not clearly distinguishable. In the optic layers of the cortex the bundles of regenerated fibers appear thicker, often ribbon-shaped, and not well individualized.

During the following weeks the regenerated fibers undergo a slow process of maturation toward the normal aspect. They become better individualized as the myelin sheath is forming, assuming then a filamentous, normal appearance. This process does not take place simultaneously in the whole fiber, but proceeds from the nerve cell in the retina toward the terminal arborization.

SELECTIVITY OF REGENERATION   Ventral-dorsal series. The first set of experiments was aimed at determining whether the fibers regenerating from the ventral or dorsal half of the retina would show any preference to enter the medial or, respectively, the lateral optic tract. The results for this series are schematically summarized in Fig. 3. When the dorsal half of the retina was removed and the optic nerve of the same side severed, the remaining fibers originating in the ventral half of the retina regenerated and were found to enter the medial bundle. The route of the lateral bundle was left empty with the exception of a few fibers that presumably originated mainly in the zone immediately adjacent to the papilla in the dorsal retina, which was intentionally left intact during the surgery. The retinic parallel and plexiform layers were restored in the dorsal tectum only. Conversely, when the ventral half of the retina was removed, nearly all of the regenerated fibers were found to enter the lateral bundle, and only the ventral half of the cortex was reinnervated.

In each case the one half of the tectum showed an abundant supply

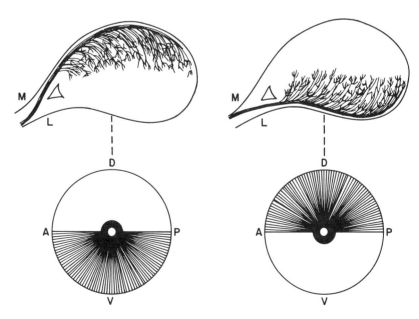

FIGURE 3   *Schematic representation of the regeneration fiber patterns obtained with nerve section and ablation of dorsal or ventral hemiretina, respectively.*

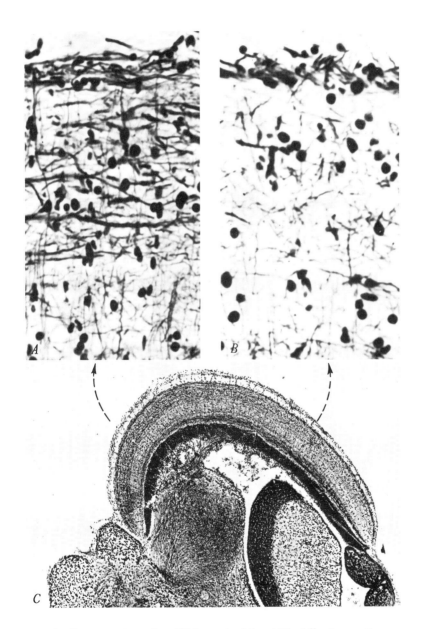

FIGURE 4 *Cross section of goldfish optic lobe (C) following optic nerve regeneration with ventral hemiretina ablated; details from the reinnervated ventral zone (A) and from the dorsal zone lacking regenerated fibers (B). The level of the parallel retinic layer is indicated at r. Bodian stain; A and B, 360 ×.*

of regenerated fibers both in the parallel and plexus layers, whereas the other half appeared generally void of regenerated fibers (Fig. 4). The border between the empty and reinnervated halves of the cortex was not abrupt but was fairly distinct, especially in *Astronotus*. More exact determinations along this line must be left for further study with different procedures.

In some cases the two types of retinal lesion were made in the same animal, i.e., a ventral removal was made in one eye and a dorsal removal in the other and both optic nerves sectioned. Under these conditions the double reverse effects were evident and easily compared in the same transverse sections.

Anterior-posterior series. The second set of experiments was designed to test for preference on the part of the regenerating fibers for the point of entrance into the tectum along its circumference. The results are schematically summarized in Fig. 5.

When the posterior half of the retina was removed and the nerve of the same side severed, the regenerating fibers arising from both ventral and dorsal quadrants of the anterior retina split into two groups, one of which entered the medial and the other the lateral bundle. Within both tracts the bulk of the fibers were found to remain in the bundle until they approached the posterior regions of the tectum. A few fibers were evident anteriorly in the parallel layer but they passed through without

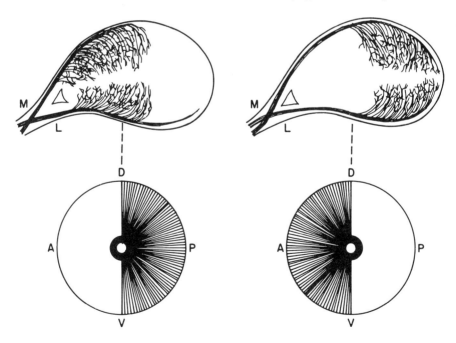

FIGURE 5 *Schematic representation of regeneration patterns obtained with removal of anterior (nasal) or posterior (temporal) hemiretina, respectively.*

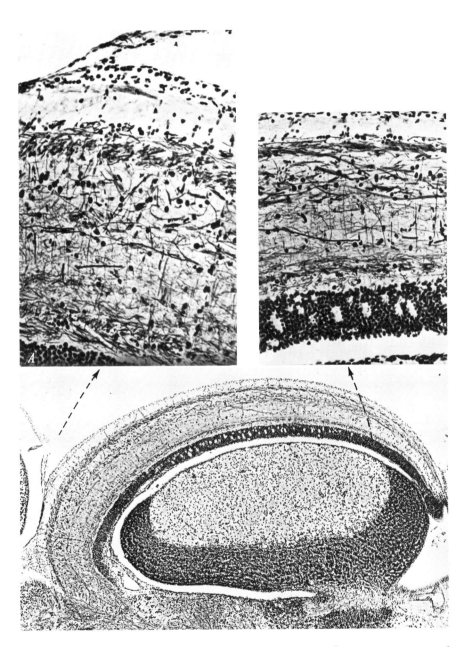

FIGURE 6 *Sagittal section of goldfish tectum (C) showing selective reinnervation of posterior zone following ablation of temporal hemiretina. Enlarged details from anterior (A) and posterior (B) sectors show plexiform layer to be absent in anterior region but richly developed posteriorly. Bodian stain. A and B, 170 ×.*

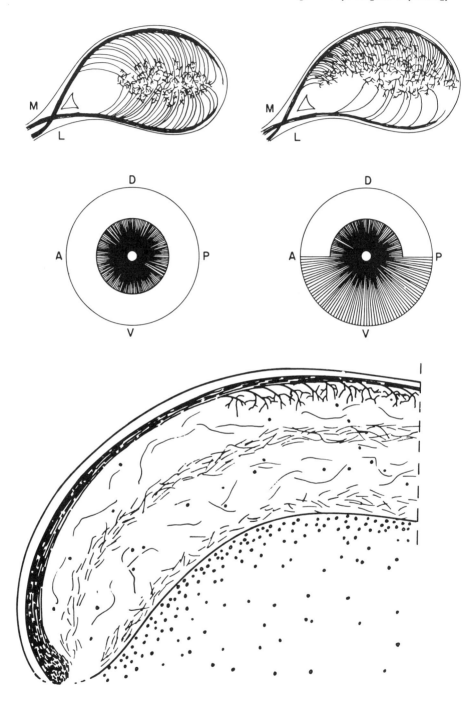

FIGURE 7 *Type of regeneration patterns obtained with removal of peripheral retina. Below: Enlarged detail of the result as viewed in a transverse section of tectum.*

FIGURE 8 *Cross section of ventral region of reinnervated right and left optic lobes. A, complete reinnervation with no retinal lesion; B, selective by-passing of plexiform layer in marginal zone (lower half of photo) after removal of dorsal periphery of retina. Bodian stain; 68 ×.*

entering the plexus layer. The plexiform layer was formed only in the posterior of the tectum (Fig. 6).

In the other fishes in which the anterior portion of the retina was excised and the nerve severed, the fibers similarly split into two groups, one of which entered the medial and the other the lateral tract. However, in these the fibers from both tracts entered and reinnervated the anterior regions of the tectum and did not extend back into the posterior regions in either the parallel or plexiform layers.

Radial series. The third set of experiments was designed to determine whether the regenerating fibers after their entry into the parallel layer of the cortex, would show any preference in entering the underlying plexiform layer. The results are schematically summarized in Fig. 7.

In this series the peripheral retina was first removed from just the dorsal half and the same or both optic nerves were severed. In these fishes the regenerating fibers coming from the intact ventral retina entered the medial bundle and reached their terminations throughout the dorsal part of the tectum. The fibers coming from the central peripapillar portion of the dorsal retina, on the other hand, after running through the lateral bundle, entered the parallel layer of the cortex but remained in this layer until they arrived at the central zone of the tectum. Thus the marginal part of the ventral tectum contained a parallel layer but the plexiform formation was absent (Fig. 8).

When a complete peripheral ring of retina was removed, leaving intact only the center of the retina, the regenerating fibers entered the tectum through both the medial and lateral bundles, but in neither case after entering the tectum did the fibers descend into the plexiform layer until they had reached the central zone. The entire margin of the optic lobe was thus by-passed by these fibers arising from the central retina.

DISCUSSION

The foregoing provides direct microscopical confirmation of earlier deductions that the regenerating optic axons reconnect selectively in matching loci of the tectal field to restore an orderly topographic projection of the retina upon the tectum. In addition the findings disclose for the first time an unexpectedly high degree of specificity in the choice of central pathways taken by the fibers en route to their terminal stations. The results would appear to dispell any remaining doubts that the growing optic fibers are destination-bound. They appear to be not only rather specifically destination-bound, but also definitely inclined to follow particular routes to their respective destinations.

It would seem most probable that the selective growth along specific central routes by the different fiber types is chemotactic in nature and is based on biochemical specificities, presumably similar to or identical with those we have inferred to be operative in the formation and maintenance of functional synapses. The same set of anteroposterior and dorsoventral gradients in retina and tectum needed to explain the topographic reconnection pattern would be sufficient to account also for the orderly tract and radiation formations observed.

In addition it would seem likely that the various extraneuronal elements in and immediately around the nerve routes, must also possess distinctive chemical properties. For example, the opposite walls of the main nerve trunk just before its bifurcation into medial and lateral tracts may differ sufficiently to favor an advance segregation of fibers into medial and lateral bundles. We may imagine any growing fiber tip to be continuously testing its surroundings as it advances, by extending and retracting a number of microfilaments along the surrounding cellular surfaces in all directions. Most of these scouting filaments are then withdrawn in favor of the one that finds the substrate most favorable and the extension of which also is most in accord with the intrinsic individual growth properties of the given fiber.

Our thesis that specific chemical affinities govern neuronal synapse (1–3, 15–21) may be extended on the basis of the present findings to include the patterning of central fiber pathways. Not only the details of synaptic association within terminal centers, but also the routes by which the fibers reach their synaptic zones would seem to be subject to regulation during growth by differential chemical affinities. This becomes essentially a chemotactic interpretation and takes us a long way from the prevailing doctrine of the 1920's, and 30's which held that nerve fiber outgrowth and termination is basically nonselective, with chemotropic and electrical factors seemingly ruled out in favor of mechanical contact guidance. The well-demonstrated importance of mechanical factors (25) is not to be minimized, but the present evidence suggests a reconsideration of some of the more ancient ideas of chemotaxis, chemotropism, neurotropism and of chemical selectivity in general in the guidance of nerve fiber growth and connection particularly within the central nervous system.

We found no indication in these fishes of an early nonselective phase of regeneration. Selectivity was already evident with respect to choice of medial and lateral tracts and the invasion of the tectum as early as 12 days after nerve section. The possibility of initial diffuse and excessive growth of fibers with subsequent elimination of the more devious and circuitous branches remains to be considered; however, with reference to the local terminal growth on microscopical dimensions within the plexiform layer.

REFERENCES

1 Arora, H. L. 1959. *Ann. Repts. Biol., Psychobiol. Sect., Caltech.* 1956–60.

2 Arora, H. L., and R. W. Sperry. 1958. Studies on color discrimination following optic nerve regeneration in cichlid fish, *Astronotus ocellatus. Anat. Record* **131:** 529.

3 Attardi, D. G., and R. W. Sperry. 1960. Central routes taken by regenerating optic fibers. *Physiologist* **3:** 12.

4 Gaze, R. M. 1958. The representation of the retina on the optic lobe of the frog. *Quart. J. Exptl. Physiol.* **43:** 209–214.

5 Gaze, R. M. 1959. Regeneration of the optic nerve in *Xenopus laevus. Quart. J. Exptl. Physiol.* **44:** 290–308.

6 Gaze, R. M. 1960. Regeneration of the optic nerve in Amphibia. *Intern. Rev. Neurobiol.* **2:** 1–40.

7 Gaze, R. M., and M. Jacobson. 1962. The projection of the binocular visual field on the optic tecta of the frog. *Quart. J. Exptl. Physiol.* **47:** 273–280.

8 Jacobson, M. 1961. Recovery of electrical activity in the optic tectum of the frog during early regeneration of the optic nerve. *Proc. Roy. Soc. Edinburgh,* **B28:** 131–137.

9 Koppanyi, T. 1955. Regeneration in the central nervous system of fishes, pp. 3–19. *In* "Regeneration in the Central Nervous System," Wm. F. Windle [ed.]. Thomas, Springfield, Illinois.

10 Leghissa, S. 1955. La struttura microscopica e la citoarchitettonica del tetto ottico dei pesci teleostei. *Z. Anat. Entwicklungsgeschichte* **118:** 427–463.

11 Lettvin, J. L., H. Maturana, W. H. Pitts, and W. S. McCulloch. 1959. How seen movement appears in the frog's optic nerve. *Federation Proc.* **18:** 90.

12 Lettvin, J. Y., H. R. Maturana, W. S. McCulloch, and W. H. Pitts. 1959. What the frog's eye tells the frog's brain. *Proc. Inst. Radio Engrs.* **47:** 1940–1951.

13 Maturana, H. R., J. Y. Lettvin, W. S. McCulloch, and W. H. Pitts. 1959. Evi-

dence that cut optic nerve fibers in a frog regenerate to their proper places in the tectum. *Science* **103**: 1409–1710.

14 Maturana, H. R., J. Y. Lettvin, W. S. McColloch, and W. H. Pitts. 1960. Anatomy and physiology of vision in the frog (*Rana pipiens*). *J. Gen. Physiol.* **43**: 129–175.

15 Sperry R. W. 1941. The effect of crossing nerves to antagonistic muscles in the hind limb of the rat. *J. Comp. Neurol.* **45**: 1–19.

16 Sperry, R. W. 1942. Re-establishment of visuomotor coordinations by optic nerve regeneration. *Anat. Record* **84**: 470.

17 Sperry, R. W. 1944. Optic nerve regeneration with return of vision in anurans. *J. Neurophysiol.* **7**: 57–69.

18. Sperry, R. W. 1945. Restoration of vision after crossing of optic nerves and after contralateral transplantation of eye. *J. Neurophysiol.* **8**: 15–28.

19 Sperry, R. W. 1948a. Orderly patterning of synaptic associations in regeneration of intracentral fiber tracts mediating visuomotor coordination. *Anat. Record* **102**: 63–75.

20 Sperry, R. W. 1948b. Patterning of central synapsis in regeneration of the optic nerve in teleosts. *Physiol. Zoöl.* **21**: 351–361.

21 Sperry, R. W. 1955. Functional regeneration in the optic system, pp. 66–76. *In* "Regeneration in the Central Nervous System," W. F. Windle [ed.]. Thomas, Springfield, Illinois.

22 Stone, L. S. 1960. Polarization of the retina and development of vision. *J. Exptl. Zoöl.* **145**: 85–95.

23 Szekely, G. 1954 Zur Ausbildung der lokalen funktionellen Spezifität der Retina. *Acta Biol. Acad. Sci. Hung.* **5**: 157–167.

24 Weiss, P. 1936. Selectivity controlling the central-peripheral relations in the nervous system. *Biol. Rev.* **11**: 494–531.

25 Weiss, P. 1960. Nervous system: Neurogenesis, pp. 346–401. *In* "Analysis of Development." B. H. Willier, P. A. Weiss, and V. Hamburger, eds. Saunders, Philadelphia.

Instinctive
Behavior

MATERNAL AND SEXUAL BEHAVIOR INDUCED BY INTRACRANIAL CHEMICAL STIMULATION

Alan E. Fisher

UNIVERSITY OF WISCONSIN

Source *Reprinted from Science, August 3, 1956, 124, 228–229, with permission of the author and the American Association for the Advancement of Science.*

A technique permitting chemical or electric stimulation, or both, of restricted brain areas in unanesthetized rats, and electroencephalographic (EEG) recording from these areas, has been developed and found to be of value (*1*).

Implants are prepared as follows. Two Tygon-insulated copper or silver wires (0.1 mm in diameter) are baked along the outside of No. 22 hypodermic tubing extending from 2 to 9 mm below the base of a plastic holder (*2*). The wires lead from contact points on the holder and terminate at opposite sides of the end of the shaft as a bipolar stimulating-and-recording electrode. The implant shaft is permanently inserted in the brain while the anesthetized rat is held in a stereotaxic instrument. Four holes in the base of the holder permit rigid attachment to the skull with jeweler's screws.

Two or more days later, rats are placed in 3- by 3- by 2.5-ft boxes for stimulation testing. A small clip connects the implant to light overhead leads from a 0- to 12-v, 60 cy/sec stimulator, or to an EEG machine. The clip also contains a No. 30 metal cannula that penetrates the implant shaft to the depth of the electrode tips or lower. Seven feet of PE 10 polyethylene tubing (0.024 in. in diameter) leads from the cannula to a microsyringe which can release a minimum of 0.0001 cm^3 of solution into the brain. All overhead leads are intertwined and spring-mounted, permitting repeated, controlled stimulation of a freely moving animal. Behavioral tests with a series of external stimulus objects are given before, during, and after chemical stimulation, and placebo solutions and nonhormonal neural excitants are used for control brain injections during initial tests or retests.

The technique is first being used to test whether there are "primary drive centers" under hormonal influence or control (*3*). Thus far, maternal and sexual behavior have been elicited from separate brain loci in a series of males during stimulation with sodium testosterone* sulfate in 0.09-percent saline, and, subject to verification, a mixture of a pure salt of estrone and a suspension of progesterone has induced heat behavior in two females (*4*). Maternal behavior elicited during chemical stimulation includes nest building and a persistent retrieving and grooming of litters of young. All aspects of mating behavior have been induced or accentuated. Attendant high-drive states are suggested by an exaggerated speed, compulsiveness, and frequency of all overt responses during positive test periods.

Although individual animals respond positively for up to 4 test days, duplication of effect from animal to animal has imposed difficult problems. Of 130 male operates tested with the testosterone salt, five have shown

* Note that testosterone is a hormone ordinarily involved in *male* sexual charactestics. (Ed.)

complete maternal response, 14 have shown nesting behavior only, and six have shown exaggerated sexual response. Histological data suggest that locus of immediate action is a critical factor, with slight variation in placement leading to incomplete, confounded, or diffuse drive states, or negative results. Initial findings tentatively implicate the medial preoptic area in maternal behavior and the lateral preoptic area in sexual behavior.

A variety of effects have been noted during testosterone stimulation at adjacent loci. Those seen in five or more cases include respiratory changes, diffuse hyperactivation, long-lasting exploratory-like behavior, repetitive localized muscular response, digging, leaping, and seizures.

The following list includes other significant points of departure from chemical- or electric-stimulation data reported in the literature. Since positive test responses completely transcend control behavioral data, two single cases of possible theoretical significance are also briefly described.

1. Elicited behavior, whether specific or diffuse, commonly continues without decrement for more than 90 minutes following chemical stimulation.

2. An entire hierarchy of related responses can be brought to the threshold of activation, with adequate stimulus objects insuring integrated behavior.

3. A segment of a response hierarchy may occur alone. Excessive nest-building is often seen, and one aspect of the nesting pattern, "pick up paper and push under body," continued rapidly for more than 1 hour in three cases.

4. Specific behavior has occurred in the absence of appropriate external stimuli. One male continuously "retrieved" his tail when stimulated with testosterone and then repeatedly retrieved a female in heat. When pups and paper were supplied, however, the male built a nest and retrieved and groomed the young, neglecting the objects to which he previously reacted.

5. In one case, maternal and sexual drives were activated simultaneously. The testosterone-treated male reacted to stimuli related to each drive and to a degree never shown in control tests. Double activation was most convincingly illustrated when a female (not in heat) and newborn rat pups were presented. The male attempted copulation twice while a pup he was retrieving to a nest was still in his mouth. Shaft placement was adjacent to both areas previously implicated in sexual and maternal response.

All effects have followed injection of minute amounts of solution, containing from 0.003 to 0.05 mg of the testosterone salt. In this connection, it must be emphasized that the possibility remains that causative factors other than hormonal properties may be operating. Thus far, however, control testing with neural excitants, physiological saline, and electric stimulation has failed to produce or perpetuate these complex behavior patterns.

Initial EEG data are promising. Records from six testosterone-treated "maternal" or "nesting" males have shown single spiking lawfully spaced in a normal record rather than the general spiking seen after picrotoxin or metrazol injection. Selective chemical action seems probable. Also, testosterone-induced spiking occurs before, not during, elicited overt behavior. Correlation of EEG changes with brain stimulation and with elicited response presents technical problems but could become a powerful tool.

The early data suggest other implications and further applications.

1. A neurophysiological definition of drive seems within reach. The role of hormones in eliciting behavior should be clarified as well as the organization of neural circuits that mediate or integrate primary drives. Present data favor a "neural center" theory, but control studies are needed.

2. Responses analogous to symptoms of mental dysfunction often occur during chemical stimulation. These include "obsessive-compulsive acts," tics, diffuse excitation, and states of hypo- and hypersensitivity to sensory stimuli. Further work may establish tie-ins between shifts in chemical balance in the central nervous system and certain forms of mental dysfunction.

3. Males having no adult contact with females, young, or paper have responded to chemical stimulation with integrated maternal behavior on the first trial. The data are pertinent to the problem of whether innate, centrally organized sensory-motor connections exist for complex response systems.

4. Testosterone has ostensibly elicited both sexual and maternal patterns. The findings may reflect multiple properties for the hormone. Limited progesterone-like activity has been proposed for the androgens by Selye, and progesterone has been linked to maternal response.

5. Chemical stimulation has elicited long-lasting, integrated behavior that was free of lapse or interference. The data strongly suggest selective chemical action within the central nervous system. Further work may demonstrate that differential sensitivity to specific physiological change by functionally organized areas of the nervous system is a basic principle of neural function.

In summary, integrated, long-lasting drive states have been induced by direct chemical stimulation of brain loci. Further work with techniques of this type could well lead to breakthroughs in the study of pharmaceutical action, brain organization and function, and the dynamics of behavior.

REFERENCES AND NOTES

1 I initiated the work as a public health postdoctoral fellow at McGill University with D. O. Hebb as sponsor. Work continues at the University of Wisconsin during the second fellowship year with H. F. Harlow as sponsor.

2 The Lucite holder is identical with that described by J. Olds and P. Milner, *J. Comp. Physiol. and Psychol.* **47**: 419 (1954).

3 For example, F. A. Beach, *Psychosomat. Med.* 4, 173 (1942).

4 Hormone salts supplied by Ayerst, McKenna and Harrison, Ltd., Montreal, Canada.

INDIVIDUAL DIFFERENCES IN THE RESPONSE OF MALE RATS TO ANDROGEN

Frank A. Beach and Harry Fowler

YALE UNIVERSITY

Source *Reprinted from the* **Journal of Comparative and Physiological Psychology,** *1959,* **52,** *50–52, with permission of the authors and the American Psychological Association.*

Beach and Holz-Tucker (1949) found that within specified limits the level of sexual performance in castrated male rats was a function of the amount of exogenous androgen supplied by daily injection. Grunt and Young (1952, 1953) later reported that castrated guinea pigs receiving the same amount of testosterone propionate displayed different intensities of "sexual drive." Individual differences in drive before castration tended to persist postoperatively despite the equating of hormone dosages. Grunt and Young suggested that differences in the sexual drive of intact guinea pigs involve some factor other than the level of testicular hormone.

The present study was conducted to compare the pre- and postcastrational sexual activity of male rats receiving equal amounts of androgen postoperatively.

METHOD

SUBJECTS

Subjects were 16 male rats 120 to 150 days old at the beginning of the experiment. They were selected on the basis of performance in preliminary tests in which they were required to mate with a female and achieve ejaculation. Subjects lived in individual cages in the experimental room in which the day-night cycle of illumination was artificially controlled. Drinking water and Purina chow were constantly available.

PROCEDURE

All tests were conducted during the dark phase of the light-dark cycle. The semi-circular observation cages were 20 in. wide, 12 in. deep, and 10 in. high and had glass fronts. Attached to each cage was a special compartment in which the stimulus female could be confined until the test began, and from which she could be automatically released by *E*.

Stimulus animals were female rats brought into estrus by hormone treatment. Three days before testing, 0.21 mg. of estradiol benzoate in 0.15 cc. of sesame oil were injected subcutaneously, and this treatment was repeated 24 hr. later. Approximately 6 hr. before testing 1.0 mg. of progesterone was injected. Only those females that came into full behavioral estrus were used in the mating tests.

Five minutes before the beginning of a test the experimental male was placed in the observation cage. The test started when the receptive female was introduced into the cage. The *E* recorded different measures of sexual performance on a constant-speed kymograph. After the test the kymographic record was

[1] This study was supported in part by a research grant (M-943) from the USPHS.

The hormone products used in this experiment (Progynon-B, Proluton, and Oretone) were generously supplied by Edward J. Henderson of Schering Corporation, Bloomfield, N.J.

analyzed to determine the frequency and duration of the various measures. Each test continued until the male allowed 30 min. to elapse without mounting the female. In previous studies (Beach & Jordan, 1956) this has been used as an operational definition of sexual exhaustion. Tests in which the male failed to mount the female within 30 min. after her introduction were terminated at the end of that time.

SCHEDULE OF TESTS, OPERATIONS, AND HORMONE TREATMENT

All males were given three preoperative sex tests at weekly intervals. A week's rest is sufficient to restore full potency (Beach & Jordan, 1956). The animals were castrated two to six days after the third test, and postoperative testing began ten days after castration. Three tests were given at the rate of one per week.

Beginning on the day of castration and continuing to the end of the experiment each male received daily intramuscular injections consisting of 100 μg of testosterone propionate in 0.20 cc. of sesame oil. Beach and Holz-Tucker (1949) found that this dosage was sufficient to maintain normal sexual performance in castrated male rats.

Although every animal received the same amount of androgen, the effective dosages were not equal because the mean body weight of different Ss ranged from 377 to 585 gm. As a result the dosage in terms of micrograms per gram of body weight varied from 0.171 to 0.265 for different individuals.

TREATMENT OF DATA

If individual differences in sexual behavior are due in part to factors other than testosterone level, then, in this experiment, differences in potency seen before castration might be expected to persist after operation. To investigate this possibility rank-order correlations between pre- and postoperative scores for each measure were calculated.

If the sexual behavior of castrates is affected by differences in the amount of androgen injected, then the present study could be expected to reveal a relationship between body weight and postoperative sexual performance, because body weight and effective dosage varied inversely. To test this prediction, the correlations between individual body weights and postoperative test scores were calculated by the rank-order method.

Correlations were performed on six measures. *Intromission latency:* time from the introduction of the female until the male first achieved intromission. Average values for three preoperative and three postoperative tests were used. *Ejaculation frequency:* sum of all ejaculations in each series of three tests. *Intromissions per ejaculation:* sum of intromissions in a three-test series divided by the sum of ejaculations in that series. *Mount-without-intromission frequency:* calculated in the same way as intromission frequency. *Intercopulatory interval:* time from the first intromission to ejaculation divided by the number of intromissions preceding that ejaculation. Every test involved a succession of ejaculations, and the average interval between intromissions preceding each ejaculation was calculated separately. The resulting means were then averaged for each test, and the three test means were averaged again. *Postejaculatory interval:* every ejaculation is followed by a period of sexual inactivity. The intervals following successive ejaculations grow progressively longer (Beach & Jordan, 1956). It is therefore not meaningful to average the intervals that occur in a given test. For this reason only the interval following the first ejaculation of each test was used to calculate a mean value for each series of three tests.

RESULTS AND DISCUSSION

The principal results are incorporated in Table 1. For all measures the correlations between pre- and postoperative behavior were positive and statistically significant. This suggests that individual differences in sexual behavior cannot be explained solely in terms of differences in androgen level. Other factors must be involved.

Correlations between body weight and postoperative behavior scores were statistically significant for three measures. The negative correlation between body weight and "Ejaculations" indicates a *positive* relation between effective hormone dosage and total number of ejaculations. The positive coefficients involving the intercopulatory interval and intromission latency point to the conclusion that higher androgen levels were associated with shorter delays between intromissions and more rapid initiation of mating after the female was introduced.

The third column in Table 1 relates to correlations between body weight and sexual performance before castration. None of the coefficients approaches statistical significance and this indicates that the correlations with body weight obtained after operation were not due solely to weight per se.

It seems clear that some of the individual differences shown by castrated

Table 1. Rank-order Correlations Between Average Measures[a]

	Correlations		
Measure	*Between Pre- and Post-operative Scores*	*Between Body Weight and Postoperative Scores*	*Between Body Weight and Preoperative Scores*
Ejaculations	$+.60**$	$-.82**$	$-.33$
Intromissions	$+.70**$	$-.38$	$-.17$
Mounts	$+.63**$	$+.37$	$+.31$
Intromission latency	$+.61**$	$+.48*$	$+.29$
Intercopulatory interval	$+.60**$	$+.80**$	$+.37$
Interval after first ejaculation	$+.75**$	$-.22$	$+.01$

[a] Application of a multiple-regression analysis to those data which fulfilled the underlying assumptions of this statistical technique yielded results comparable to those shown in this table.

* $p < .05$ (but $>.02$).

** $p < .01$.

males in this experiment were due in part to differences in the effective hormone dosages. This finding is in harmony with the earlier findings of Beach and Holz-Tucker (1949), although the results of their experiment were reported in terms of group averages. It is equally obvious that the relatively small differences in androgen level cannot account for all the variance between individual castrates. Some other factor or factors were involved. These unidentified factors were probably responsible for the positive correlations between behavior before and after castration.

It is tempting to assume that individual differences in the sexual behavior of normal males are due in part to differences in the output of testicular androgen, but present results are not adequate to support or refute such an assumption. The findings reported here do contradict the hypothesis that individual differences in the sexual activity of unoperated rats are explainable solely in terms of different concentrations of testosterone.

The identity of the nonhormonal determinants of sexual performance must be discovered by future experimentation. It has been suggested (Beach, 1948; Grunt & Young, 1953) that there may be individual differences in the sensitivity of various "target organs" or tissues which respond to androgen. Chai (1956) has shown that the responsiveness of the seminal vesicle to testosterone propionate varies markedly between different inbred strains of mice. It is at least a plausible assumption that comparable differences exist between individuals, and that they involve not only the sex accessories, but neural mechanisms for behavior as well.

SUMMARY

Sixteen male rats were observed in three sex tests before and three tests after castration. During the postoperative period every male received daily injections containing 100 μg. of testosterone propionate. Because the Ss had different body weights, the effective dosage in terms of micrograms of hormone per gram of body weight ranged from 0.171 to 0.265 for different individuals.

Rank-order correlations between pre- and postoperative scores for six measures of sexual behavior were calculated. All the coefficients were positive and statistically significant. Similar correlations were determined between body weight (which was inversely related to effective dosage) and postoperative test scores. Three measures yielded statistically significant coefficients, indicating that larger doses of androgen were associated with more rapid and potent sexual performance.

The positive correlations between behavior scores for pre- and postoperative tests is interpreted to mean that individual differences in sexual activity after operation were not due solely to differences in effective dosages of testosterone. Correlations between effective dosage and some of the measures in postoperative tests are taken to indicate that differences in testosterone level do produce differences in sexual behavior. It is concluded that both hormonal and nonhormonal factors contribute to the existence of individual differences in sexual activity.

REFERENCES

Beach, F. A. *Hormones and behavior.* New York and London: Paul B. Hoeber, 1948.

Beach, F. A., & Holz-Tucker, A. M. Effects of different concentrations of androgen upon sexual behavior in castrated male rats. *J. comp. physiol. Psychol.,* 1949, **42**, 433–453.

Beach, F. A., & Jordan, L. Sexual exhaustion and recovery in the male rat. *Quart. J. exp. Psychol.,* 1956, **8**: 121–133.

Chai, C. K. Comparison of two inbred strains of mice and their F_1 hybrids in response to androgen. *Anat. Rec.,* 1956, **126,** 269–282.

Grunt, J. A., & Young, W. C. Differential reactivity of individuals and the response of the male guinea pig to testosterone propionate. *Endocrinology,* 1952, **51** 237–248.

Grunt, J. A., & Young, W. C. Consistency of sexual behavior patterns in individual male guinea pigs following castration and androgen therapy. *J. comp. physiol. Psychol.,* 1953, **46**: 138–144.

Sensation and Perception

CURRENT STATUS OF
THEORIES OF HEARING

Georg v. Békésy

HARVARD UNIVERSITY

Source Reprinted from *Science*, May 4, 1956, *123*, 779–783, with permission of the author and the American Association for the Advancement of Science.

By the middle of the 19th century a large number of theories of hearing had been proposed (1). At that time the main problem was to determine which part of the inner ear is set in vibration by sound waves. Since very little was known of the anatomy of the inner ear, the possibilities for theorizing were almost limitless, and the confusion became so great that, it is said, some lecturers in physiology simply did not treat the topic of hearing at all. After 1863, however, when Helmholtz proposed his resonance theory of hearing, the topic could no longer be ignored.

Helmholtz' theory was successful because it was based on anatomic and physical facts. When the cochlea was laid open in earlier times by cracking the temporal bone or chiseling away the bony wall, a half-dry gelatinous mass was found. It was not even clear whether the cochlea was filled with fluid or not. In my opinion, it was P. F. T. Meckel who performed the first basic experiment in the physiology of hearing when, in 1777, he opened the cochlea of a cat under water. He found no air bubbles coming out of the cochlea, thus proving that it is filled with fluid.

After histologists had found that a fixative acid would hold the gelatinous mass in its natural position, the anatomy of the inner ear could be worked out in detail by Corti, Hensen, and others. With this increased knowledge of the anatomy of the inner ear, Helmholtz and Hensen were able to conclude that the sensation of hearing is determined by the vibrations of the basilar membrane, a conclusion that is still generally accepted.

The next problem was, How does the basilar membrane vibrate? Helmholtz thought that the tension of the basilar membrane is greater transversely than longitudinally. Since it was known that the width of the membrane changes continuously from one end of the cochlea to the other, he concluded that it should behave like a set of resonators whose tuning changes continuously from one end to the other. The pitch discrimination of the ear could thus be accounted for since every frequency would bring a different resonator into vibration. Helmholtz' theory of pitch discrimination was not generally accepted, and the question of how the basilar membrane vibrates became and continues to be an issue. The various answers proposed have been presented as theories of hearing.

In my opinion, the words *theory of hearing* as commonly used are misleading. We know very little about the functioning of the auditory nerve and even less about the auditory cortex, and most of the theories of hearing do not make any statements about their functioning. Theories of hearing are usually concerned only with answering the question, How does the ear discriminate pitch? Since we must know how the vibrations produced by a sound are distributed along the length of the basilar membrane before we can understand how pitch is discriminated, theories of hearing are basically theories concerning the vibration pattern of the basilar membrane and the sensory organs attached to it.

The problem under discussion is a purely mechanical one, and it may well seem, at least to the layman, that it can easily be solved by looking at the vibration patterns in the cochlea. Unfortunately, this direct approach proves difficult for without stroboscopic illumination and other special devices, we can observe almost no vibration in the nearly transparent gelatinous mass in the cochlea of a living organism.

Furthermore, the maximal physiological vibration amplitudes of the basilar membrane can be seen and measured only when they are magnified between 100 and 300 times. Although observations have been made with this magnification (2), it is important to find other methods of observing the vibration pattern of the basilar membrane. Since hearing is the common concern of many disciplines—physics, engineering, physiology, psychology, zoology, and even mathematics—it is understandable that a great variety of solutions have been proposed. Naturally, each investigator has thought primarily in terms of his own field, and it was forgotten, for example, that vibration patterns are really a physical problem and not a musical one.

VARIOUS VIBRATION PATTERNS OF THE BASILAR MEMBRANE

Reports of the various vibration patterns of the basilar membrane that have been proposed thus far are to be found in textbooks on the psychology of hearing (3). These reviews point up the differences between the various hypotheses, and some of them are very critical. Indeed, they are so critical that they give the impression that the psychology of hearing is nearing the end of its productive period and entering a phase of unconstructive criticism. I would like to show in this paper, therefore, how the various hearing theories are interrelated and how by manipulating two independent physical variables of the basilar membrane—absolute stiffness and coupling of adjacent parts—we can obtain a continuous series of vibration patterns, each group of which is in agreement with one of the four major theories of hearing. We may proceed continuously from curves predicted by the resonance theory to curves predicted by each of the other three theories in turn. It is thus shown that the various theories form one continuous series of vibration patterns.

A schematic cross-section of the ear is presented in Fig. 1. Sound enters the external meatus and sets the tympanic membrane in motion, and the vibrations are conducted through the ossicles to the fluid in the cochlea. The basilar membrane, which acts as a partition between the two channels, is set in motion by any movement of the ossicles. Since the fluid is incompressible, the fluid displacement produced by the stapes is equal to the deformation of the round window. The question is, then, How is the basilar membrane displaced and how does it move during a sinusoidal vibration of the ossicles?

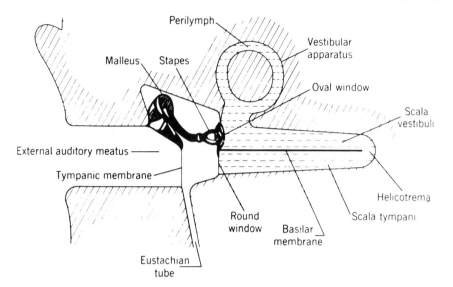

FIGURE 1   *Schematic cross-section of the human ear.*

Although the movement of a membrane depends on other factors as
well, we shall turn our attention first to the elastic properties of membranes.
Three elastic properties of the membrane in a cochlear model can be
varied: the absolute value of stiffness; the slope of stiffness along the length;
and the coupling between adjacent parts.

1. The absolute value of the stiffness of the membrane can be changed.
If the membrane is stiff, a pressure difference across the membrane causes
only a small displacement or deformation.

2. The stiffness of the membrane can be constant, or it can vary along
the whole length. The basilar membrane is stiffer near the stapes than
it is near the helicotrema; for man and most other vertebrates, the stiffness
near the stapes is about 100 times greater than it is at the other end.

3. The coupling between the adjacent parts of the membrane can be
varied. In a membrane made of thin elastic fibers stretched across a frame,
when there is no coupling between one strand and its adjacent strands,
each strand can vibrate freely. The strands can be coupled by a thin sheet
of rubber placed along the whole set. The coupling becomes larger as
the thickness of the rubber sheet is increased. A membrane can also be
made of a smooth sheet of rubber alone, without individual strands.

These three possibilities may be expressed mathematically by saying
that we have three independent variables for the elasticity of the
membrane.

There are two methods for investigating the effect of manipulating these
variables on the vibration pattern of a membrane. First, we can calculate
the vibrations. Unfortunately this is a time-consuming job. Or second, we
can construct a model of the cochlear membrane and vary its elastic properties. I have made models the size of the human cochlea and models

that were larger. The enlarged models were constructed in the same way that full-scale ships are constructed from small-scale models. As is well known, this kind of dimensional enlargement has proved quite successful.

Figures 2 and 3 show some of the effects that are obtained by varying the elastic properties of the membrane. Figure 2a shows a small section of the membrane model consisting of coupled strands acted on by a point force (needle tip). The absolute value of the elasticity of the different strands varies continuously from 100 to 1 from left to right along the membrane. Seen from the top, the deformation pattern is a group of elongated ellipses, the deformation spreading neither to the left nor to the right. The side view shows this limited lateral spread even better. This model simulates the system of almost freely vibrating elastic resonators that is postulated by the resonance theory of hearing. If we immerse this membrane in fluid, the vibration pattern seen in Fig. 3a is obtained for a steady tone.

With the same slope of elasticity and the same driving frequency, but with an increase in the absolute value of the membrane stiffness, a steady tone causes the whole membrane to vibrate in phase (all parts of the membrane reaching their maximal elongation simultaneously), in the manner of a telephone diaphragm, as shown in Fig. 3b. This is the pattern of vibration assumed by the telephone theory of hearing. The vibration pattern for the steady tone is independent of the coupling between adjacent parts of the membrane because the whole membrane vibrates in phase, with no force acting laterally. Because of the increase in stiffness, the same point force that was used before now produces a smaller deformation (Fig. 2b); if the rubber strands are replaced by a flat plastic sheet that is

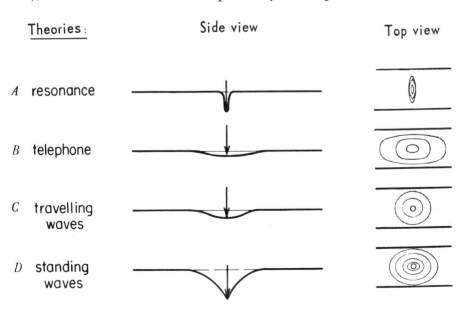

FIGURE 2   *Deformation patterns in membranes acted upon by a point force.*

theories:

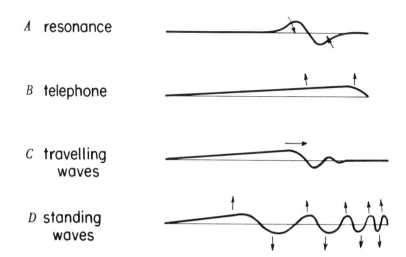

A resonance

B telephone

C travelling
    waves

D standing
    waves

FIGURE 3 *Vibration patterns in membranes for a continuous tone (with normal damping). The arrows indicate the direction of movement at a given instant.*

stretched and clamped along the two long sides to the frame of the model, the point force produces the same lateral spread.

We obtain substantiation of two other types of hearing theories simply by decreasing the thickness of the plastic sheet. As the thickness decreases, the maximal amplitude of the displacement becomes greater. When the thickness of the sheet is decreased slightly, the same steady tone produces a traveling wave moving away from the source (Figs. 2c and 3c). When a thinner sheet is used, the same point force pushes the partition out still farther; and the same steady tone produces traveling waves that get shorter and travel farther until some are reflected from the end of the membrane and standing waves result (Fig. 3d). The standing-wave theory was proposed by Ewald.

A change in the frequency of a steady tone moves the maximum of the vibrations along the basilar membrane, as the resonance theory assumes. An increase in the frequency moves the maximum of the vibrations toward the stapes. The resonance theory of hearing is a place theory in which pitch discrimination depends on locating the place along the membrane that is set in maximal vibration. According to the telephone theory, a change in frequency need not affect the displacement of the membrane, and pitch discrimination depends on some unknown function of the brain. The traveling-wave theory is also a place theory, since an increase in the frequency moves the maximum of the vibrations toward the stapes, and a decrease moves it toward the helicotrema. According to the standing-wave theory, an increase in frequency increases the number of nodes and decreases the distance between them. The brain uses this information to determine pitch.

As we can see from Fig. 3, four basically different vibration patterns can be obtained for a steady sinusoidal tone simply by manipulating two variables, the absolute stiffness of the membrane and the coupling between its adjacent parts. Since it is possible to go continuously from one pattern to another, an infinite number of intermediate patterns can be obtained; but all these belong to a single family of curves. Additional vibration patterns have been proposed, some of which I have tried to verify on models, but I have come to the conclusion that they are only drawings and have no physical existence. I believe that Fig. 3 shows all the principal patterns there are.

We have seen how, for a continuous tone, it is easy to substantiate each theory in turn simply by manipulating the elastic properties of the membrane. The differences among the theories depend wholly on the sizes of these variables. It is even more surprising, however, to find that for transients—for example, the onset of a steady tone—the differences between the resonance, traveling-wave, and standing-wave theories disappear completely, despite the emphasis that these differences have received. Traveling waves develop during the onset of vibrations in membranes whose vibration patterns are described by these three theories, as shown in Fig. 4. (The driving frequency is the same as it is in Fig. 3.) Only the telephone theory assumes that all parts of the membrane vibrate in phase, in complete conformity with the movements of the driving stapes.

theories:

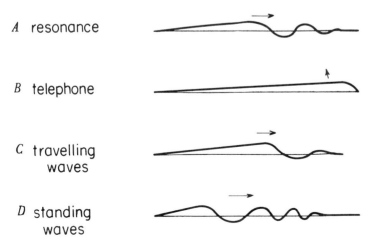

A resonance

B telephone

C travelling
waves

D standing
waves

FIGURE 4 *Vibration patterns in membranes for the transient state (with normal damping).*

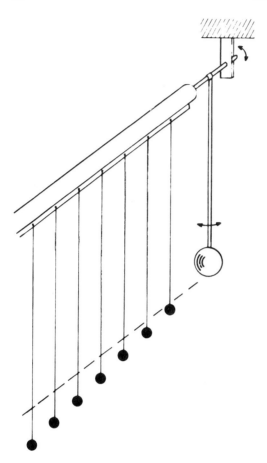

FIGURE 5 *Pendulum system set up to demonstrate*
occurrence of traveling waves in a system of free
resonators.

It is especially difficult to understand how in a system of free resonators
the onset of a continuous tone produces traveling waves. A simple experiment was set up to demonstrate the occurrence of traveling waves in a
system of free resonators (Fig. 5). A pendulum with a large mass
was clamped to a long, horizontal driving rod from which a series
of small pendulums was suspended. The lengths of the pendulums
increased continuously from one end of the system to the other, from
right to left in the figure. One pendulum in the middle of the series was
of the same length as the heavy driving pendulum. During continuous
oscillation of the driving pendulum, the resonant pendulum was set in
motion by small movements that were transmitted through the oscillating
supporting rod. A change in the period of the driving pendulum made
a different pendulum resonate—that is, the whole series was a system of
free resonators, each of which resonated at a different frequency. The
onset of the oscillations of the driving pendulum set in motion a large

section of the system, and a traveling wave was observed moving toward the longer pendulums, as can be seen in the sequence of film shown in Fig. 6. [Omitted in reprinting. (Ed.)].

To complete this survey of the various hearing theories, I should mention that at very low frequencies the movement of a vibrating system is independent of its mass; the displacement of the various parts of the membrane is determined solely by their elasticity. Since the slope of elasticity along the membrane is the same in all four models, the vibration patterns for low frequencies are similar, as shown schematically in Fig. 7. The largest excursions appear in the standing-wave model, which has the most yielding membrane.

Another factor that affects the movement of the basilar membrane is the damping provided by the fluid in the cochlea. In our models, when the viscosity is high, the differences between the various theories tend to disappear. When the fluid friction is extremely high, the movements of the membrane are determined solely by the frictional forces in the fluid, independent of the elasticity values of the membrane. Here again the vibration patterns are identical for all the theories, and even the displacements are equal (Fig. 8).

According to the foregoing discussion, the question of which hearing theory is valid reduces to the more easily answered question, What are the numerical values of the elasticity and coupling along the basilar membrane? In these experiments, when the tip of a needle was pressed perpendicularly on the surface of the basilar membrane of some lightly anesthetized vertebrates (guinea pig, mouse, cat, and pigeon), the resulting de-

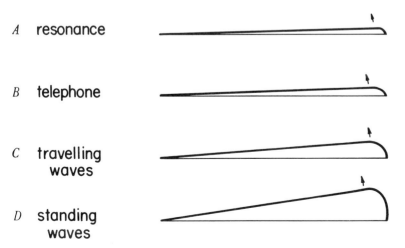

theories:

A   resonance

B   telephone

C   travelling
      waves

D   standing
      waves

FIGURE 7 Vibration patterns in membranes for continuous tones of very low frequency.

formation was almost circular; both the top and side views are identical to Fig. 2c. The shape of the deformation remained the same for many hours after the death of the animal. In preparations of the human cochlea and the cochlea of very large animals such as cattle and elephants, the same circular deformation is found. The shape of the deformation proves that the coupling between the adjacent parts of the basilar membrane is so large that it invalidates the resonance theory of hearing.

The side view of the deformation makes it clear that the stiffness of the basilar membrane is too great for standing waves to occur. The formation of standing waves along the basilar membrane is improbable also because standing waves with large amplitudes occur only at certain frequencies; if standing waves were to occur, the sensitivity of the ear would undergo large fluctuations during a continuous change in frequency. Figure 9 shows the type of audiogram we would obtain under these conditions.

It is clear, therefore, that the vibration of the basilar membrane cannot be accounted for by either the resonance theory or the standing-wave theory.

Observation of the basilar membrane in mammals substantiates the traveling-wave theory. Under stroboscopic illumination, a steady tone of 1000 cycles per second produces traveling waves similar to those pictured in Fig. 3c. When the frequency is lowered, the maximal amplitude moves toward the helicotrema (toward the right side of Fig. 3c), and the length of the membrane that is vibrating practically in phase is increased. The place of the maximum reaches that end of the membrane in the different animals at the following frequencies: mouse at 400 cycles per second,

theories:

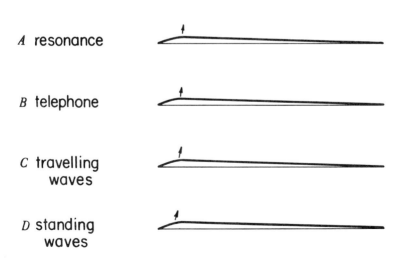

FIGURE 8 *Vibration patterns in membranes immersed in fluid with very high viscosity (for continuous tones).*

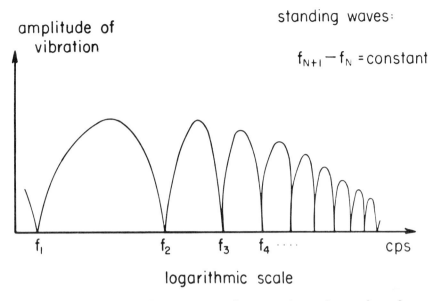

FIGURE 9 *Hypothetical audiogram for standing-wave theory showing large fluctuations which would occur during a continuous change in frequency.*

pigeon at 80, rat at 180, guinea pig at 200, man at 30, and elephant at 30. Below these frequencies the basilar membrane vibrates in phase, as postulated by the telephone theory (Fig. 3b).

Below the critical frequency, pitch discrimination depends entirely on the temporal sequence of the stimulation of the nerves. Above the critical frequency, there is a second factor, the shifting of the place of maximal stimulation along the basilar membrane. We must now ask, Is pitch discrimination improved by this shifting of the place of maximal stimulation as compared with the conditions under which it depends wholly on the temporal sequence of the vibrations? The problem is no longer mechanical, but one of how the nerves react to different vibration patterns on the basilar membrane.

MECHANICAL MODELS OF THE COCHLEA

In order to investigate this aspect of the problem, I built cochlear models in which the skin of the forearm was substituted for the nerve supply of the basilar membrane. Three mechanical models were made that stimulated the skin of the arm in accordance with the three vibration patterns in Fig. 3a, b, and c. No model with standing waves was built because change in frequency would produce a large change in amplitude, and consequently it would be very difficult to distinguish amplitude changes from frequency changes (which is not the case in the ear).

The mechanical model for the resonance theory is shown in Fig. 10,

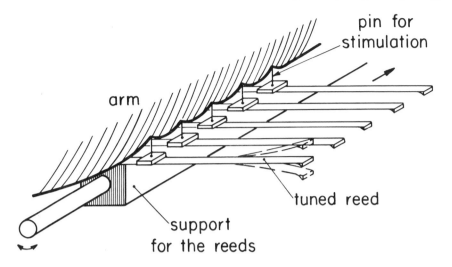

FIGURE 10   *Mechanical model for the resonance theory, with the skin of the arm*
substituted for the nerve supply of the basilar membrane. The reed system transforms
any change in frequency into an easily observable displacement of the stimulated
area on the skin.

for the telephone theory in Fig. 11, and for the traveling-wave theory
in Fig. 12.

The resonating model consisted of a series of tuned steel reeds attached
to a metal support that oscillated slightly around its longitudinal axis.
The length of the support was equal to the length of the forearm. Thirty-six
reeds, tuned in equal intervals over a range of two octaves, were distributed
along the whole length. A small pin on each reed, fastened close to the
support, touched the surface of the skin of the arm. The pins had rather
small points, so that the skin would not pick up too much energy from
the vibrating reeds; otherwise it would not have been possible to obtain
a sharp resonance of the reeds. When the arm is placed carefully along
the pins, so that the points just touch the skin, the reed system transforms
any change in frequency into an easily observable displacement of the
stimulated area on the skin.

The model for the telephone theory is a triangular metal frame made
of tubes (Fig. 11). The frame vibrates perpendicularly to the axis of the
edge in contact with the forearm. The rigidity of the frame insured that
all the stimulating parts touching the skin would vibrate in phase. From
time to time, phase constancy along the frame was verified by stroboscopic
illumination.

The model for the traveling waves was a section of a model of the
human cochlea, enlarged by dimensional analysis. The frequency range
was two octaves. The model was a plastic tube case around a brass tube
with a slit. The tube was filled with fluid. Figure 12 [Omitted in reprinting.
(Ed.)] shows the position of the arm on the vibrating membrane. A vibrating piston sets the fluid inside the tube in motion, and forces in the fluid

produce waves that travel from the hand to the elbow. The traveling waves thus produced are similar to those observed in preparations of human cochlea. The maximum amplitude of vibration is rather broad, and when it is observed under stroboscopic illumination, it moves along the membrane as the frequency is changed. Although the maximum is quite flat as it moves along the arm, the sensation of vibration is concentrated on a relatively short length (about 2 to 4 centimeters); hence, any frequency change is easily recognized by a shift in the stimulated area. Seemingly the nerve network in the skin inhibits all the sensation to either side of the maximum of the vibration amplitude, thereby producing a sharpening of the stimulated area.

If we compare the three models, we find that the difference limen for "pitch" discrimination below 40 cycles per second is the same because the skin is able to discriminate the roughness of the vibrations as such. But for higher frequencies, displacements of the sensation along the arm, produced either by the resonating model or the traveling-wave model, permit much more accurate frequency discrimination than the telephone theory model does.

The most surprising outcome of these experiments with models was that pitch discrimination did not deteriorate when the presentation time of the tone was very short. Even when the stimulus was only two cycles, the pitch discrimination for both the resonance model and the traveling-wave model was just as good as it was for a continuous tone of longer

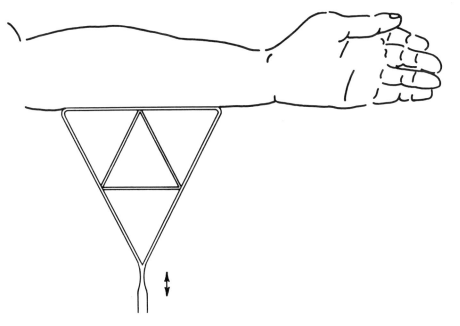

FIGURE 11 *Mechanical model for the telephone theory, with the skin of the arm substituted for the nerve supply of the basilar membrane. All parts of the triangular frame in contact with the arm vibrate in phase.*

duration. Closer examination showed that in both models the place of maximal amplitude was determined during the first two cycles of the onset of a tone. Figure 4 shows that for transients there is very little difference between vibration patterns of the resonance and traveling-wave theories. In both, waves travel over quite a long section of the vibrating system. The surprising fact is the inhibitory action of the nerve supply, which suppresses all sensation except on a small spot near the maximal amplitude of vibration. In the ear the situation seems to be the same because, there too, two cycles of a tone are enough to enable us to discriminate the pitch of the tone.

SUMMARY

In summing up the current status of the hearing theories, it may be said that each of the vibration patterns of the basilar membrane postulated by the four major theories of hearing can be obtained by varying two elastic properties of the membrane—namely, the coupling between adjacent parts and the absolute value of the elasticity. If these two variables are adjusted to their numerical values in the cochlea of a living animal or a fresh preparation of the human ear, traveling waves are observed along the membrane. These traveling waves have a flat maximum that shifts its location along the membrane with a change of frequency—the place of the maximum determining the pitch. An enlarged dimensional model of the cochlea in which the nerve supply of the sensory organs on the basilar membrane was replaced by the skin of the arm indicates that the inhibitory action in the nervous system can produce quite sharp local sensations, which shift their place with changes in the frequency of the vibrations.

REFERENCES AND NOTES

1 This article is based on a lecture given at the meeting of the American Otological Society in Chicago on 10 October 1955. The enlarged model of the cochlea was demonstrated at that meeting. Those present were able to try out the model for themselves and to observe the change in location of the stimulated area on the skin when the driving frequency of the model was changed. This article was prepared under contract N5ori-76 between Harvard University and the Office of Naval Research (project NR142201, report PNR-179).

2 Articles of mine that are concerned with measurement of the vibration pattern of the human cochlea have appeared in the main in *J. Acoust. Soc. Amer.* from 1947 to the present.

3 S. S. Stevens and H. Davis, *Hearing: Its Psychology and Physiology* (Wiley, New York, 1938); E. G. Wever, *Theory of Hearing* (Wiley, New York, 1949; O. F. Ranke, *Physiologie des Gehörs* (Springer, Berlin, 1953); E. G. Wever and M. Lawrence, *Physiological Acoustics* (Princeton Univ. Press, Princeton, N. J., 1954); and T. C. Ruch, "Audition and the auditory pathways," in Howell's *Textbook of Physiology*, J. F. Fulton, Ed. (Saunders, Philadelphia, ed. 17, 1955), pp. 399–423. For additional titles see S. S. Stevens, J. C. G. Loring, D. Cohen, *Bibliography on Hearing* (Harvard Univ. Press, Cambridge, Mass., 1955).

RECEPTIVE FIELDS, BINOCULAR INTERACTION AND FUNCTIONAL ARCHITECTURE IN THE CAT'S VISUAL CORTEX

D. H. Hubel and T. N. Wiesel

HARVARD MEDICAL SCHOOL

Editor's Note   *This is one of several papers in which Hubel and Wiesel have reported findings on the successive stages of processing and analysis of input to the eye as it passes from the retina to the geniculate and various parts of the cortex. They show here that the striate cortex analyzes input into patterns roughly corresponding to line segments of various orientations in the environmental stimulus, sometimes involving special sensitivity to motion of some kinds. In later papers they have gone on to show that "higher" cortical areas appear to contain detectors for more complex patterns, e.g., ones corresponding roughly to corners and angles.*

Source   *Reprinted from the* **Journal of Physiology,** *1962,* **160,** *106–154, with permission of the authors and the publisher.*

What chiefly distinguishes cerebral cortex from other parts of the central nervous system is the great diversity of its cell types and interconnexions. It would be astonishing if such a structure did not profoundly modify the response patterns of fibres coming into it. In the cat's visual cortex, the receptive field arrangements of single cells suggest that there is indeed a degree of complexity far exceeding anything yet seen at lower levels in the visual system.

In a previous paper we described receptive fields of single cortical cells, observing responses to spots of light shone on one or both retinas (Hubel & Wiesel, 1959).[*] In the present work this method is used to examine receptive fields of a more complex type (Part I) and to make additional observations on binocular interaction (Part II).

This approach is necessary in order to understand the behaviour of individual cells, but it fails to deal with the problem of the relationship of one cell to its neighbours. In the past, the technique of recording evoked slow waves has been used with great success in studies of functional anatomy. It was employed by Talbot & Marshall (1941) and by Thompson, Woolsey & Talbot (1950) for mapping out the visual cortex in the rabbit, cat, and monkey. Daniel & Whitteridge (1959) have recently extended this work in the primate. Most of our present knowledge of retinotopic projections, binocular overlap, and the second visual area is based on these investigations. Yet the method of evoked potentials is valuable mainly for detecting behaviour common to large populations of neighbouring cells; it cannot differentiate functionally between areas of cortex smaller than about 1 mm.[2] To overcome this difficulty a method has in recent years been developed for studying cells separately or in small groups during long micro-electrode penetrations through nervous tissue. Responses are correlated with cell location by reconstructing the electrode tracks from histological material. These techniques have been applied to the somatic sensory cortex of the cat and monkey in a remarkable series of studies by Mountcastle (1957) and Powell & Mountcastle (1959). Their results show that the approach is a powerful one, capable of revealing systems of organization not hinted at by the known morphology. In Part III of the present paper we use this method in studying the functional architec-

---

[*] The receptive field of a cell is found by determining what images projected onto a screen in front of the animal's eye—and thus also projected onto its retina—will cause that single cell to fire more rapidly. An "on-center" receptive field is possessed by a cell which fires when the animal is looking at a small spot of light surrounded by dark. An "off-center" field is possessed by a cell which fires when the animal is looking at a spot of darkness surrounded by light. Fibers coming from the retina in the optic nerve and cells in the lateral geniculate have been found to respond to "on" and "off" center fields in various parts of the overall visual field. (Ed.)

ture of the visual cortex. It helped us attempt to explain on anatomical grounds how cortical receptive fields are built up.

METHODS

Recordings were made from forty acutely prepared cats, anaesthetized with thiopental sodium, and maintained in light sleep with additional doses by observing the electrocorticogram. Animals were paralysed with succinylcholine to stabilize the eyes. Pupils were dilated with atropine. Details of stimulating and recording methods are given in previous papers (Hubel, 1959; Hubel & Wiesel, 1959, 1960). The animal faced a wide tangent screen at a distance of 1.5 m, and various patterns of white light were shone on the screen by a tungsten-filament projector. All recordings were made in the light-adapted state. Background illumination varied from -1.0 to $+1.0$ $\log_{10}$ cd/m^2. Stimuli were from 0.2 to 2.0 log. units brighter than the background. For each cell receptive fields were mapped out separately for the two eyes on sheets of paper, and these were kept as permanent records.

Points on the screen corresponding to the area centralis and the optic disk of the two eyes were determined by a projection method (Hubel & Wiesel, 1960). The position of each receptive field was measured with respect to these points. Because of the muscle relaxant the eyes usually diverged slightly, so that points corresponding to the two centres of gaze were not necessarily superimposed. In stimulating the two eyes simultaneously it was therefore often necessary to use two spots placed in corresponding parts of the two visual fields. Moreover, at times the two eyes were slightly rotated in an inward direction in the plane of their equators. This rotation was estimated by (1) photographing the cat before and during the experiment, and comparing the angles of inclination of the slit-shaped pupils, or (2) by noting the inclination to the horizontal of a line joining the area centralis with the optic disk, which in the normal position of the eye was estimated, by the first method, to average about 25°. The combined inward rotations of the two eyes seldom exceeded 10°. Since the receptive fields in this study were usually centrally rather than peripherally placed on the retina, the rotations did not lead to any appreciable linear displacement. Angular displacements of receptive fields occasionally required correction, as they led to an apparent difference in the orientation of the two receptive-field axes of a binocularly driven unit. The direction and magnitude of this difference were always consistent with the estimated inward rotation of the two eyes. Moreover, in a given experiment the difference was constant, even though the axis orientation varied from cell to cell.

The diagram of Text-fig. 1 shows the points of entry into the cortex of all 45 microelectrode penetrations. Most electrode tracks went no deeper than 3 or 4 mm, so that explorations were mainly limited to the apical segments of the lateral and post-lateral gyri (LG and PLG) and a few millimetres down along the adjoining medial and lateral folds. The extent of the territory covered is indicated roughly by Text-figs. 13–15. Although the lateral boundary of the striate cortex is not always sharply defined in Nissl-stained or myelin-stained material, most penetrations were well within the region generally accepted as "striate" (O'Leary, 1941). Most penetrations were made from the cortical region

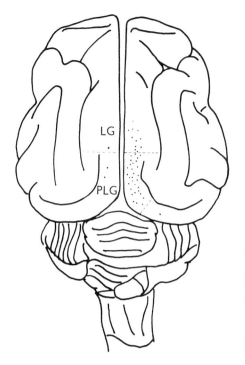

TEXT-FIGURE 1 *Diagram of dorsal aspect of cat's brain, to show entry points of 45 micro-electrode penetrations. The penetrations between the interrupted lines are those in which cells had their receptive fields in or near area centralis. LG, lateral gyrus; PLG, post-lateral gyrus. Scale, 1 cm.*

receiving projections from in or near the area centralis; this cortical region is shown in Text-fig. 1 as the area between the interrupted lines.

Tungsten micro-electrodes were advanced by a hydraulic micro-electrode positioner (Hubel, 1957, 1959). In searching for single cortical units the retina was continually stimulated with stationary and moving forms while the electrode was advanced. The unresolved background activity (see p. 129) served as a guide for determining the optimum stimulus. This procedure increased the number of cells observed in a penetration, since the sampling was not limited to spontaneously active units.

In each penetration electrolytic lesions were made at one or more points. When only one lesion was made, it was generally at the end of an electrode track. Brains were fixed in 10% formalin, embedded in celloidin, sectioned at 20 μ, and stained with cresyl violet. Lesions were 50–100 μ in diameter, which was small enough to indicate the position of the electrode tip to the nearest cortical layer. The positions of other units encountered in a cortical penetration were determined by calculating the distance back from the lesion along the track, using depth readings corresponding to the unit and the lesion. A correction was made for brain shrinkage, which was estimated by comparing the distance between two lesions, measured under the microscope, with the distance calculated from depths at which the two lesions were made. From brain to brain this shrinkage was not constant, so that it was not possible to apply an average correction for shrinkage to all brains. For tracks marked by only one lesion it was assumed that the first unit activity was recorded at the boundary of the first and second layers; any error resulting from this was probably small, since in a number of penetrations a lesion was made at the point where the first units were encountered, and these were in the lower first or the upper second layers, or else at the very boundary. The absence of cell-body records and unresolved background activity as the electrode passed through subcortical white matter (see Text-fig. 13 and Pl. 1) was also helpful in confirming the accuracy of the track reconstructions.

PART I

ORGANIZATION OF RECEPTIVE FIELDS IN CAT'S VISUAL CORTEX: PROPERTIES OF "SIMPLE" AND "COMPLEX" FIELDS

The receptive field of a cell in the visual system may be defined as the region of retina (or visual field) over which one can influence the firing of that cell. In the cat's retina one can distinguish two types of ganglion cells, those with "on"-centre receptive fields and those with "off"-centre fields (Kuffler, 1953). The lateral geniculate body also has cells of these two types; so far no others have been found (Hubel & Wiesel, 1961). In contrast, the visual cortex contains a large number of functionally different cell types; yet with the exception of afferent fibres from the lateral geniculate body we have found no units with concentric "on"-centre or "off"-centre fields.

When stimulated with stationary or moving patterns of light, cells in the visual cortex gave responses that could be interpreted in terms of the arrangements of excitatory and inhibitory regions in their receptive fields (Hubel & Wiesel, 1959). Not all cells behaved so simply, however; some responded in a complex manner which bore little obvious relationship to the receptive fields mapped with small spots. It has become increasingly apparent to us that cortical cells differ in the complexity of their receptive fields. The great majority of fields seem to fall naturally into two groups, which we have termed "simple" and "complex." Although the fields to be described represent the commonest subtypes of these groups, new varieties are continually appearing, and it is unlikely that the ones we have listed give anything like a complete picture of the striate cortex. We have therefore avoided a rigid system of classification, and have designated receptive fields by letters or numbers only for convenience in referring to the figures. We shall concentrate especially on features common to simple fields and on those common to complex fields, emphasizing differences between the two groups, and also between cortical fields and lateral geniculate fields.

RESULTS

Simple receptive fields

The receptive fields of 233 of the 303 cortical cells in the present series were classified as "simple." Like retinal ganglion and geniculate cells, corti-

cal cells with simple fields possessed distinct excitatory and inhibitory subdivisions. Illumination of part or all of an excitatory region increased the
maintained firing of the cell, whereas a light shone in the inhibitory region
suppressed the firing and evoked a discharge at "off." A large spot confined
to either area produced a greater change in rate of firing than a small
spot, indicating summation within either region. On the other hand, the
two types of region within a receptive field were mutually antagonistic.
This was most forcefully shown by the absence or near absence of a response to simultaneous illumination of both regions, for example, with
diffuse light. From the arrangement of excitatory and inhibitory regions
it was usually possible to predict in a qualitative way the responses to
any shape of stimulus, stationary or moving. Spots having the approximate
shape of one or other region were the most effective stationary stimuli;
smaller spots failed to take full advantage of summation within a region,
while larger ones were likely to invade opposing regions, so reducing the
response. To summarize: these fields were termed "simple" because like
retinal and geniculate fields (1) they were subdivided into distinct excitatory and inhibitory regions; (2) there was summation within the separate
excitatory and inhibitory parts; (3) there was antagonism between excitatory and inhibitory regions; and (4) it was possible to predict responses
to stationary or moving spots of various shapes from a map of the excitatory
and inhibitory areas.

While simple cortical receptive fields were similar to those of retinal
ganglion cells and geniculate cells in possessing excitatory and inhibitory
subdivisions, they differed profoundly in the spatial arrangements of these
regions. The receptive fields of all retinal ganglion and geniculate cells
had one or other of the concentric forms shown in Text-fig. 2A, B. (Excitatory areas are indicated by crosses, inhibitory areas by triangles.) In contrast, simple cortical fields all had a side-to-side arrangement of excitatory
and inhibitory areas with separation of the areas by parallel straight-line
boundaries rather than circular ones. There were several varieties of fields,
differing in the number of subdivisions and the relative area occupied
by each subdivision. The commonest arrangements are illustrated in Text-
fig. 2C–G: Table 1 gives the number of cells observed in each category.
The departure of these fields from circular symmetry introduces a new
variable, namely, the orientation of the boundaries separating the field
subdivisions. This orientation is a characteristic of each cortical cell, and
may be vertical, horizontal, or oblique. There was no indication that any
one orientation was more common than the others. We shall use the term
receptive-field axis to indicate a line through the centre of a field, parallel
to the boundaries separating excitatory and inhibitory regions. The *axis
orientation* will then refer to the orientation of these boundaries, either
on the retina or in the visual field. Axes are shown in Text-fig. 2 by continuous lines.

Two common types of fields, shown in Text-fig. 2C, D, each consisted
of a narrow elongated area, excitatory or inhibitory, flanked on either side

by two regions of the opposite type. In these fields the two flanking regions were symmetrical, i.e. they were about equal in area and the responses obtained from them were of about the same magnitude. In addition there were fields with long narrow centres (excitatory or inhibitory) and asymmetrical flanks. An example of an asymmetrical field with an inhibitory centre is shown in Text-fig. 2E. The most effective stationary stimulus for all of these cells was a long narrow rectangle ("slit") of light just large enough to cover the central region without invading either flank. For maximum centre response the orientation of the slit was critical; changing the orientation by more than 5–10° was usually enough to reduce a response greatly or even abolish it. Illuminating both flanks usually evoked a strong response. If a slit having the same size as the receptive-field centre was shone in either flanking area it evoked only a weak response, since it covered only part of one flank. Diffuse light was ineffective, or at most evoked only a very weak response, indicating that the excitatory and inhibitory parts of the receptive field were very nearly balanced.

In these fields the equivalent but opposite-type regions occupied retinal areas that were far from equal; the centre portion was small and concentrated whereas the flanks were widely dispersed. A similar inequality was found in fields of type *F*, Text-fig. 2, but here the excitatory flanks were elongated and concentrated, while the centre was relatively large and

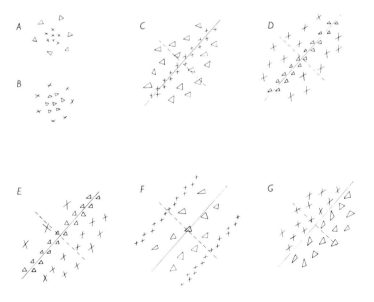

TEXT-FIGURE 2 *Common arrangements of lateral geniculate and cortical receptive fields. A. "On"-centre geniculate receptive field. B. "Off"-centre geniculate receptive field. C-G. Various arrangements of simple cortical receptive fields.* ×, *areas giving excitatory responses ("on" responses);* △, *areas giving inhibitory responses ("off" responses). Receptive-field axes are shown by continuous lines through field centres; in the figure these are all oblique, but each arrangement occurs in all orientations.*

diffuse. The optimum response was evoked by simultaneously illuminating the two flanks with two parallel slits (see Hubel & Wiesel, 1959, Fig. 9).

Some cells had fields in which only two regions were discernible, arranged side by side as in Text-fig. 2G. For these cells the most efficient stationary stimulus consisted of two areas of differing brightness placed so that the line separating them fell exactly over the boundary between the excitatory and inhibitory parts of the field. This type of stimulus was termed an "edge." An "on" or an "off" response was evoked depending on whether the bright part of the stimulus fell over the excitatory or the inhibitory region. A slight change in position or orientation of the line separating the light from the dark area was usually enough to reduce greatly the effectiveness of the stimulus.

Moving stimuli were very effective, probably because of the synergistic effects of leaving an inhibitory area and simultaneously entering an excitatory area (Hubel & Wiesel, 1959). The optimum stimulus could usually be predicted from the distribution of excitatory and inhibitory regions of the receptive field. With moving stimuli, just as with stationary, the orientation was critical. In contrast, a slit or edge moved across the circularly symmetric field of a geniculate cell gave (as one would expect) roughly the same response regardless of the stimulus orientation. The responses evoked when an optimally oriented slit crossed back and forth over a cortical receptive field were often roughly equal for the two directions of crossing. This was true of fields like those shown in Text-fig. 2C, D and F. For many cells, however, the responses to two diametrically opposite movements were different, and some only responded to one of the two movements. The inequalities could usually be accounted for by an asymmetry in flanking regions of the type shown in Text-fig. 2E, (see also Hubel & Wiesel, 1959, Fig. 7). In fields that had only two discernible regions arranged side by side (Text-fig. 2G), the difference in the responses to a moving slit or edge was especially pronounced.

Optimum rates of movement varied from one cell to another. On several occasions two cells were recorded together, one of which responded only to a slow-moving stimulus (1°/sec or lower) the other to a rapid one (10°/sec or more). For cells with fields of type F, Text-fig. 2, the time elapsing between the two discharges to a moving stimulus was a measure of the rate of movement (see Hubel & Wiesel, 1959, Fig. 5).

If responses to movement were predictable from arrangements of excitatory and inhibitory regions, the reverse was to some extent also true. The axis orientation of a field, for example, was given by the most effective orientation of a moving slit or edge. If an optimally oriented slit produced a brief discharge on crossing from one region to another, one could predict that the first region was inhibitory and the second excitatory. Brief responses to crossing a very confined region were characteristic of cells with simple cortical fields, whereas the complex cells to be described below gave sustained responses to movement over much wider areas.

Table 1. Simple Cortical Fields

	Text-fig.	No. of cells
(a) Narrow concentrated centres		
(i) Symmetrical flanks		
Excitatory centres	2C	23
Inhibitory centres	2D	17
(ii) Asymmetrical flanks		
Excitatory centres	—	28
Inhibitory centres	2E	10
(b) Large centres, concentrated flanks	2F	21
(c) One excitatory region and one inhibitory	2G	17
(d) Uncategorized	—	117
Total number of simple fields		233

Movement was used extensively as a stimulus in experiments in which the main object was to determine axis orientation and ocular dominance for a large number of cells in a single penetration, and when it was not practical, because of time limitations, to map out every field completely. Because movement was generally a very powerful stimulus, it was also used in studying cells that gave little or no response to stationary patterns. In all, 117 of the 233 simple cells were studied mainly by moving stimuli. In Table 1 these have been kept separate from the other groups since the distribution of their excitatory and inhibitory regions is not known with the same degree of certainty. It is also possible that with further study, some of these fields would have revealed complex properties.

Complex receptive fields

Intermixed with cells having simple fields, and present in most penetrations of the striate cortex, were cells with far more intricate and elaborate properties. The receptive fields of these cells were termed "complex." Unlike cells with simple fields, these responded to variously-shaped stationary or moving forms in a way that could not be predicted from maps made with small circular spots. Often such maps could not be made, since small round spots were either ineffective or evoked only mixed ("on-off") responses throughout the receptive field. When separate "on" and "off" regions could be discerned, the principles of summation and mutual antagonism, so helpful in interpreting simple fields, did not generally hold. Nevertheless, there were some important features common to the two types of cells. In the following examples, four types of complex fields will be illustrated. The numbers observed of each type are given in Table 2.

The cell of Text-fig. 3 failed to respond to round spots of light, whether small or large. By trial and error with many shapes of stimulus it was discovered that the cell's firing could be influenced by a horizontally oriented slit $1/8°$ wide and $3°$ long. Provided the slit was horizontal its exact positioning with the $3°$-diameter receptive field was not critical. When

Table 2. Complex Cortical Receptive Fields

	Text-fig.	No. of cells
(a) Activated by slit—non-uniform field	3	11
(b) Activated by slit—uniform field	4	39
(c) Activated by edge	5–6	14
(d) Activated by dark bar	7–8	6
Total number of complex fields		70

it was shone anywhere above the centre of the receptive field (the horizontal line of Text-fig. 3) an "off" response was obtained; "on" responses
were evoked throughout the lower half. In an intermediate position (Text-
fig. 3C) the cell responded at both "on" and "off." From experience with
simpler receptive fields one might have expected wider slits to give increasingly better responses owing to summation within the upper or lower part
of the field, and that illumination of either half by itself might be the
most effective stimulus of all. The result was just the opposite: responses
fell off rapidly as the stimulus was widened beyond about ⅛°, and large
rectangles covering the entire lower or upper halves of the receptive field
were quite ineffective (Text-fig. 3F, G). On the other hand, summation
could easily be demonstrated in a horizontal direction, since a slit ⅛°
wide but extending only across part of the field was less effective than
a longer one covering the entire width. One might also have expected
the orientation of the slit to be unimportant as long as the stimulus was
wholly confined to the region above the horizontal line or the region below.
On the contrary, the orientation was critical, since a tilt of even a few
degrees from the horizontal markedly reduced the response, even though
the slit did not cross the boundary separating the upper and lower halves
of the field.

In preferring a slit specific in width and orientation this cell resembled
certain cells with simple fields. When stimulated in the upper part of its
field it behaved in many respects like cells with "off"-centre fields of type
D, Text-fig. 2; in the lower part it responded like "on"-centre fields of
Text-fig. 2C. But for this cell the strict requirements for shape and orientation of the stimulus were in marked contrast to the relatively large leeway
of the stimulus in its ordinate position on the retina. Cells with simple
fields, on the other hand, showed very little latitude in the positioning
of an optimally oriented stimulus.

The upper part of this receptive field may be considered inhibitory and
the lower part excitatory, even though in either area summation only occurred in a horizontal direction. Such subdivisions were occasionally found
in complex fields, but more often the fields were uniform in this respect.
This was true for the other complex fields to be described in this section.

Responses of a second complex unit are shown in Text-fig. 4. In many
ways the receptive field of this cell was similar to the one just described.
A slit was the most potent stimulus, and the most effective width was

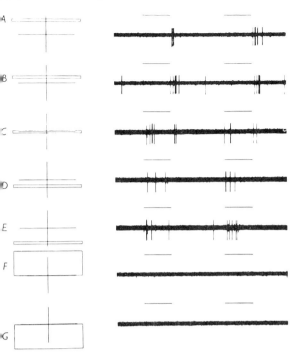

TEXT-FIGURE 3 *Responses of a cell with a complex receptive field to stimulation of the left (contralateral) eye. Receptive field located in area centralis. The diagrams to the left of each record indicate the position of a horizontal rectangular light stimulus with respect to the receptive field, marked by a cross. In each record the upper line indicates when the stimulus is on. A-E, stimulus $\frac{1}{8} \times 3°$, F-G, stimulus $1\frac{1}{2} \times 3°$ ($4°$ is equivalent to 1 mm on the cat retina). For background illumination and stimulus intensity see Methods. Cell was activated in the same way from right eye, but less vigorously (ocular-dominance group 2, see Part II). An electrolytic lesion made while recording from this cell was found near the border of layers 5 and 6, in the apical segment of the post-lateral gyrus. Positive deflexions upward; duration of each stimulus 1 sec.*

again $\frac{1}{8}°$. Once more the orientation was an important stimulus variable, since the slit was effective anywhere in the field as long as it was placed in a 10 o'clock–4 o'clock orientation (Text-fig. 4A–D). A change in orientation of more than 5–10° in either direction produced a marked reduction in the response (Text-fig. 4E–G). As usual, diffuse light had no influence on the firing. This cell responded especially well if the slit, oriented as in A–D, was moved steadily across the receptive field. Sustained discharges were evoked over the entire length of the field. The optimum rate of movement was about 1°/sec. If movement was interrupted the discharge stopped, and when it was resumed the firing recommenced. Continuous

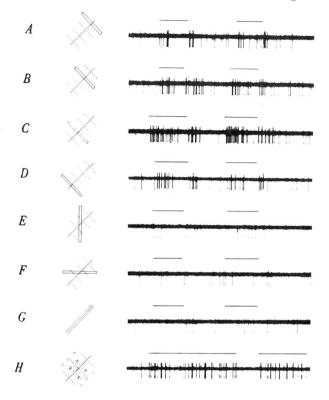

TEXT-FIGURE 4 *Responses of a cell with a complex field to stimulation of the left (contralateral) eye with a slit ⅛ × 2½°. Receptive field was in the area centralis and was about 2 × 3° in size. A-D, ⅛° wide slit oriented parallel to receptive-field axis. E-G, slit oriented at 45 and 90° to receptive-field axis. H, slit oriented as in A-D, is on throughout the record and is moved rapidly from side to side where indicated by upper beam. Responses from left eye slightly more marked than those from right (Group 3, see Part II). Time 1 sec.*

firing could be maintained indefinitely by small side-to-side movements of a stimulus within the receptive field (Text-fig. 4H). The pattern of firing was one characteristic of many complex cells, especially those responding well to moving stimuli. It consisted of a series of short high-frequency repetitive discharges each containing 5–10 spikes. The bursts occurred at irregular intervals, at frequencies up to about 20/sec. For this cell, movement of an optimally oriented slit was about equally effective in either of the two opposite directions. This was not true of all complex units, as will be seen in some of the examples given below.

Like the cell of Text-fig. 3 this cell may be thought of as having a counterpart in simple fields of the type shown in Text-fig. 2C–E. It shares with these simpler fields the attribute of responding well to properly oriented slit stimuli. Once more the distinction lies in the permissible variation in position of the optimally oriented stimulus. The variation is small (relative to the size of the receptive field) in the simple fields, large in the complex. Though resembling the cell of Text-fig. 3 in requiring a slit for a stimulus, this cell differed in that its responses to a properly oriented slit were mixed ("on-off") in type. This was not unusual for cells with complex fields. In contrast, cortical cells with simple fields, like retinal ganglion cells and lateral geniculate cells, responded to optimum restricted stimuli either with excitatory ("on") responses or inhibitory ("off") responses. When a stimulus covered opposing regions, the effects normally tended to cancel, though sometimes mixed discharges were obtained, the "on" and "off" components both being weak. For these simpler fields "on-off" responses were thus an indication that the stimulus was not optimum. Yet some cells with complex fields responded with mixed discharges even to the most effective stationary stimuli we could find. Among the stimuli tried were curved objects, dark stripes, and still more complicated patterns, as well as monochromatic spots and slits.

A third type of complex field is illustrated in Text-figs. 5 and 6. There were no responses to small circular spots or to slits, but an edge was

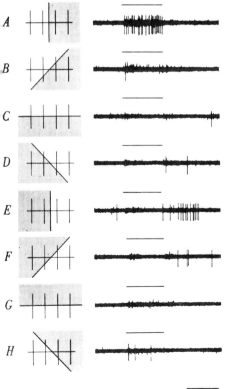

TEXT-FIGURE 5 *Responses of a cell with a large* (8 × 16°) *complex receptive field to an edge projected on the ipsilateral retina so as to cross the receptive field in various directions. (The screen is illuminated by a diffuse background light, at 0·0 log₁₀ cd/m² At the time of stimulus, shown by upper line of each record, half the screen, to one side of the variable boundary, is illuminated at 1·0 log₁₀ cd/m², while the other half is kept constant.) A, vertical edge with light area to left, darker area to right. B-H, various other orientations of edge. Position of receptive field 20° below and to the left of the area centralis. Responses from ipsilateral eye stronger than those from contralateral eye (group 5, see Part II). Time 1 sec.*

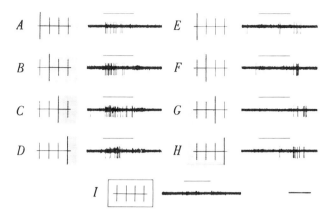

TEXT-FIGURE 6 *Same cell as in Text-fig. 5. A-H, responses to a vertical edge in various parts of the receptive field: A-D, brighter light to the left E-H, brighter light to the right; I, large rectangle, 10 × 20°, covering entire receptive field. Time, 1 sec.*

very effective if oriented vertically. Excitatory or inhibitory responses were produced depending on whether the brighter area was to the left or the right (Text-fig. 5A, E). So far, these are just the responses one would expect from a cell with a vertically oriented simple field of the type shown in Text-fig. 2G. In such a field the stimulus placement for optimum response is generally very critical. On the contrary, the complex unit responded to vertical edges over an unusually large region about 16° in length (Text-fig. 6). "On" responses were obtained with light to the left (A–D), and "off" responses with light to the right (E–H), regardless of the position of the line separating light from darkness. When the entire receptive field was illuminated diffusely (I) no response was evoked. As with all complex fields, we are unable to account for these responses by any simple spatial arrangement of excitatory and inhibitory regions.

Like the complex units already described, this cell was apparently more concerned with the orientation of a stimulus than with its exact position in the receptive field. It differed in responding well to edges but poorly or not at all to slits, whether narrow or wide. It is interesting in this connexion that exchanging an edge for its mirror equivalent reversed the response, i.e. replaced an excitatory response by an inhibitory and vice versa. The ineffectiveness of a slit might therefore be explained by supposing that the opposite effects of its two edges tended to cancel each other.

As shown in Text-fig. 6, the responses of the cell to a given vertical edge were consistent in type, being either "on" or "off" for all positions of the edge within the receptive field. In being uniform in its response-type it resembled the cell of Text-fig. 4. A few other cells of the same general category showed a similar preference for edges, but lacked this uniformity. Their receptive fields resembled the field of Text-fig. 3, in that a given

dge evoked responses of one type over half the field, and the opposite
ype over the other half. These fields were divided into two halves by
line parallel to the receptive-field axis: an edge oriented parallel to the
xis gave "on" responses throughout one of the halves and "off" responses
hrough the other. In either half, replacing the edge by its mirror image
eversed the response-type. Even cells, which were uniform in their re-
ponse-types, like those in Text-fig. 4–6, varied to some extent in the magni-
ude of their responses, depending on the position of the stimulus. More-
ver, as with most cortical cells, there was some variation in responses
ɔ identical stimuli.

A final example is given to illustrate the wide range of variation in
he organization of complex receptive fields. The cell of Text-figs. 7 and
, was not strongly influenced by any form projected upon the screen;
t gave only weak, unsustained "on" responses to a dark horizontal rectangle
ɪgainst a light background, and to other forms it was unresponsive. A
trong discharge was evoked, however, if a black rectangular object (for
ɪxample, a piece of black tape) was placed against the brightly illuminated

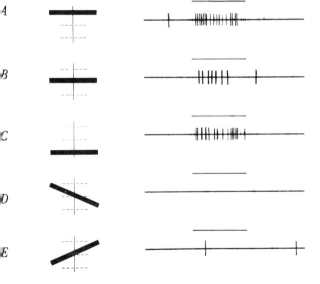

TEXT-FIGURE 7 *Cell activated only by left (contralateral) eye
over a field approximately 5 × 5°, situated 10° above and to
the left of the area centralis. The cell responded best to a
black horizontal rectangle, ⅓ × 6°, placed anywhere in the
receptive field (A-C). Tilting the stimulus rendered it
ineffective (D-E). The black bar was introduced against a
light background during periods of 1 sec, indicated by the
upper line in each record. Luminance of white background,
1·0 log₁₀ cd/m²; luminance of black part, 0·0 log₁₀ cd/m².
A lesion, made while recording from the cell, was found in
layer 2 of apical segment of post-lateral gyrus.*

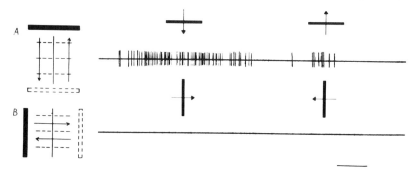

TEXT-FIGURE. 8 *Same cell as in Text-fig. 7. Movement of black rectangle ⅓ × 6°
back and forth across the receptive field: A, horizontally oriented (parallel to
receptive-field); B, vertically oriented. Time required to move across the field,
5 sec. Time, 1 sec.*

screen. The receptive field of the cell was about 5 × 5°, and the most effec
tive stimulus width was about ⅓°. Vigorous firing was obtained regardles,
of the position of the rectangle, as long as it was horizontal and within
the receptive field. If it was tipped more than 10° in either direction n
discharge was evoked (Text-fig. 7D, E). We have recorded several comple
fields which resembled this one in that they responded best to black rec
tangles against a bright background. Presumably it is important to hav
good contrast between the narrow black rectangle and the background
this is technically difficult with a projector because of scattered light.

Slow downward movement of the dark rectangle evoked a strong discharge throughout the entire 5° of the receptive field (Text-fig. 8A). I
the movement was halted the cell continued to fire, but less vigorously
Upward movement gave only weak, inconsistent responses, and left–right
movement (Text-fig. 8B) gave no responses. Discharges of highest
frequency were evoked by relatively slow rates of downward movement
(about 5–10 sec to cross the entire field); rapid movement in either direction gave only very weak responses.

Despite its unusual features this cell exhibited several properties typical
of complex units, particularly the lack of summation (except in a horizontal
sense), and the wide area over which the dark bar was effective. One
may think of the field as having a counterpart in simple fields of type
D, Text-fig. 2. In such fields a dark bar would evoke discharges, but only
if it fell within the inhibitory region. Moreover, downward movement of
the bar would also evoke brisker discharges than upward, provided the
upper flanking region were stronger than the lower one.

In describing simple fields it has already been noted that moving stimuli
were often more effective than stationary ones. This was also true of cells
with complex fields. Depending on the cell, slits, edges, or dark bars were
most effective. As with simple fields, orientation of a stimulus was always
critical, responses varied with rate of movement, and directional asymmetries of the type seen in Text-fig. 8 were common. Only once have we

seen activation of a cell for one direction of movement and suppression of maintained firing for the opposite direction. In their responses to movement, cells with complex fields differed from their simple counterparts chiefly in responding with sustained firing over substantial regions, usually the entire receptive field, instead of over a very narrow boundary separating excitatory and inhibitory regions.

Receptive-field dimensions*

Over-all field dimensions were measured for 119 cells. A cell was included only if its field was mapped completely, and if it was situated in the area of central vision. Fields varied greatly in size from one cell to the next, even for cells recorded in a single penetration (see Text-fig. 15). In Text-fig. 9 the distribution of cells according to field area is given separately for simple and complex fields. The histogram illustrates the variation in size, and shows that on the average complex fields were larger than simple ones.

Widths of the narrow subdivisions of simple fields (the centres of types C, D and E or the flanks of type F, Text-fig. 2) also varied greatly: the smallest were 10–15 minutes of arc, which is roughly the diameter of the smallest field centres we have found for geniculate cells. For some cells with complex fields the widths of the most effective slits or dark bars were also of this order, indicating that despite the greater overall field size these cells were able to convey detailed information. We wish to emphasize that in both geniculate and cortex the field dimensions tend to increase with distance from the area centralis, and that they differ even for a given location in the retina. It is consequently not possible to compare field sizes in the geniculate and cortex unless these variations are taken into account. This may explain the discrepancy between our results and the findings of Baumgartner (see Jung, 1960), that "field centres" in the cortex are one half the size of those in the lateral geniculate body.

Responsiveness of cortical cells

Simple and complex fields together account for all of the cells we have recorded in the visual cortex. We have not observed cells with concentric fields. Except for clearly injured cells (showing extreme spike deformation or prolonged high-frequency bursts of impulses) all units have responded to visual stimulation, though it has occasionally taken several hours to

* The overall field dimension of a cell refers to the area within which an appropriate stimulus image effected its firing. In more recent work, Hubel and Wiesel have shown that the ocular dominance observed here is present in infant cats. However, if a cat is raised with a blinder over one eye, a very large proportion of its cortical cells come under the dominance of the normally functioning eye. Thus while normal binocular interaction seems to be inherent, its alteration through function appears to be possible. (Ed.)

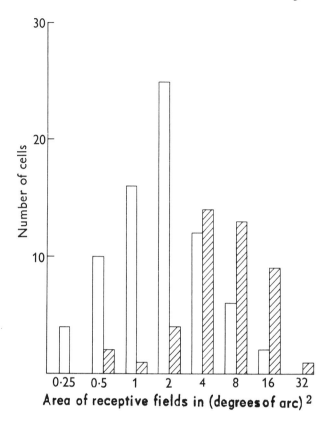

TEXT-FIGURE 9   *Distribution of 119 cells in the visual cortex with respect to the approximate area of their receptive fields. White columns indicate cells with simple receptive fields; shaded columns, cells with complex fields. Abscissa: area of receptive fields. Ordinate: number of cells.*

find the retinal region containing the receptive field and to work out the optimum stimuli. Some cells responded only to stimuli which were optimum in their retinal position and in their form, orientation and rate of movement. A few even required stimulation of both eyes before responses could be elicited (see Part II). But there is no indication from our studies that the striate cortex contains nerve cells that are unresponsive to visual stimuli.

Most of the cells of this series were observed for 1 or 2 hr, and some were studied for up to 9 hr. Over these periods of time there were no qualitative changes in the characteristics of receptive fields: their complexity, arrangements of excitatory and inhibitory areas, axis orientation and position all remained the same, as did the ocular dominance. With deepening anaesthesia a cell became less responsive, so that stimuli that had formerly been weak tended to become even weaker or ineffective, while those that had evoked brisk responses now evoked only weak ones. The last thing to disappear with very deep anaesthesia was usually the response to a moving form. As long as any responses remained the cell retained the same specific requirements as to stimulus form, orientation and rate of movement, suggesting that however the drug exerted its effects, it did not to any important extent functionally disrupt the specific visual connexions. A comparison of visual responses in the anaesthetized animal with those in the unanaesthetized, unrestrained preparation (Hubel, 1959) shows that the main differences lie in the frequency and firing patterns of the maintained activity and in the vigour of responses, rather than in the basic receptive-field organization. It should be emphasized, however, that even in light anaesthesia or in the attentive state diffuse light remains relatively ineffective; thus the balance between excitatory and inhibitory influences is apparently maintained in the waking state.

PART II

BINOCULAR INTERACTION AND OCULAR DOMINANCE

Recording from single cells at various levels in the visual system offers a direct means of determining the site of convergence of impulses from the two eyes. In the lateral geniculate body, the first point at which convergence is at all likely, binocularly influenced cells have been observed, but it would seem that these constitute at most a small minority of the total population of geniculate cells (Erulkar & Fillenz, 1958, 1960; Bishop, Burke & Davis, 1959; Grüsser & Sauer, 1960; Hubel & Wiesel, 1961). Silver-degeneration studies show that in each layer of the geniculate the terminals of fibres from a single eye are grouped together, with only minor overlap in the interlaminar regions (Silva, 1956; Hayhow, 1958). The anatomical and physiological findings are thus in good agreement.

It has long been recognized that the greater part of the cat's primary visual cortex receives projections from the two eyes. The anatomical evidence rests largely on the observation that cells in all three lateral geniculate layers degenerate following a localized lesion in the striate area (Minkowski, 1913). Physiological confirmation was obtained by Talbot & Marshall (1941) who stimulated the visual fields of the separate eyes with small spots of light, and mapped the evoked cortical slow waves. Still unsettled, however, was the question of whether individual cortical cells receive projections from both eyes, or whether the cortex contains a mixture of cells, some activated by one eye, some by the other. We have recently shown that many cells in the visual cortex can be influenced by both eyes (Hubel & Wiesel, 1959). The present section contains further observations on binocular interaction. We have been particularly interested in learning whether the eyes work in synergy or in opposition, how the relative influence of the two eyes varies from cell to cell, and whether, on the average, one eye exerts more influence than the other on the cells of a given hemisphere.

RESULTS

In agreement with previous findings (Hubel & Wiesel, 1959) the receptive fields of all binocularly influenced cortical cells occupied corresponding positions on the two retinas, and were strikingly similar in their organization. For simple fields the spatial arrangements of excitatory and inhibitory regions were the same; for complex fields the stimuli that excited or inhibited the cell through one eye had similar effects through the other. Axis orientations of the two receptive fields were the same. Indeed, the only differences ever seen between the two fields were related to eye dominance: identical stimuli to the two eyes did not necessarily evoke equally strong responses from a given cell. For some cells the responses were equal or almost so; for others one eye tended to dominate. Whenever the two retinas were stimulated in identical fashion in corresponding regions, their effects summed, i.e. they worked in synergy. On the other hand, if antagonistic regions in the two eyes were stimulated so that one eye had an excitatory effect and the other an inhibitory one, then the responses tended to cancel (Hubel & Wiesel, 1959, Fig. 10A).

Some units did not respond to stimulation of either eye alone but could

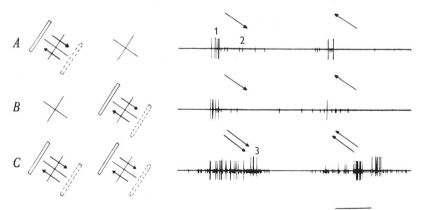

TEXT-FIGURE 10 *Examples of binocular synergy in a simultaneous recording of three cells (spikes of the three cells are labelled 1–3). Each of the cells had receptive fields in the two eyes; in each eye the three fields overlapped and were situated 2° below and to the left of the area centralis. The crosses to the left of each record indicate the positions of the receptive fields in the two eyes. The stimulus was ⅛ × 2° slit oriented obliquely and moved slowly across the receptive fields as shown; A, in the left eye; B, in the right eye; C, in the two eyes simultaneously. Since the responses in the two eyes were about equally strong, these two cells were classed in ocular-dominance group 4 (see Text-fig. 12). Time, 1 sec.*

be activated only by simultaneous stimulation of the two eyes. Text-figure 10 shows an example of this, and also illustrates ordinary binocular synergy. Two simultaneously recorded cells both responded best to transverse movement of a rectangle oriented in a 1 o'clock–7 o'clock direction (Text-fig. 10A, B). For one of the cells movement down and to the right was more effective than movement up and to the left. Responses from the individual eyes were roughly equal. On simultaneous stimulation of the two eyes both units responded much more vigorously. Now a third cell was also activated. The threshold of this third unit was apparently so high that, at least under these experimental conditions, stimulation of either eye alone failed to evoke any response.

A second example of synergy is seen in Text-fig. 11. The most effective stimulus was a vertically oriented rectangle moved across the receptive field from left to right. Here the use of both eyes not only enhanced the response already observed with a single eye, but brought into the open a tendency that was formerly unsuspected. Each eye mediated a weak response (Text-fig. 11A, B) which was greatly strengthened when both eyes were used in parallel (C). Now, in addition, the cell gave a weak response to leftward movement, indicating that this had an excitatory effect rather than an inhibitory one. Binocular synergy was often a useful means of bringing out additional information about a receptive field.

In our previous study of forty-five cortical cells (Hubel & Wiesel, 1959) there was clear evidence of convergence of influences from the two eyes in only one fifth of the cells. In the present series 84% of the cells fell into this category. The difference is undoubtedly related to the improved

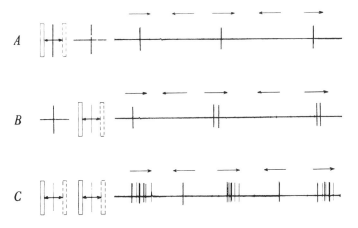

TEXT-FIGURE 11   *Movement of a ¼ × 2° slit back and forth horizontally across the receptive field of a binocularly influenced cell. A, left eye; B, right eye; C, both eyes. The cell clearly preferred left-to-right movement, but when both eyes were stimulated together it responded also to the reverse direction. Field diameter, 2°, situated 5° from the area centralis. Time, 1 sec.*

precision in technique of binocular stimulation. A field was first mapped in the dominant eye and the most effective type of stimulus determined. That stimulus was then applied in the corresponding region in the other eye. Finally, even if no response was obtained from the non-dominant eye, the two eyes were stimulated together in parallel to see if their effects were synergistic. With these methods, an influence was frequently observed from the non-dominant eye that might otherwise have been overlooked.

A comparison of the influence of the two eyes was made for 223 of the 303 cells in the present series. The remaining cells were either not sufficiently studied, or they belonged to the small group of cells which were only activated if both eyes were simultaneously stimulated. The fields of all cells were in or near the area centralis. The 223 cells were subdivided into seven groups, as follows:

Group	Ocular dominance
1	Exclusively contralateral
2*	Contralateral eye much more effective than ipsilateral eye
3	Contralateral eye slightly more effective than ipsilateral
4	No obvious difference in the effects exerted by the two eyes
5	Ipsilateral eye slightly more effective
6*	Ipsilateral eye much more effective
7	Exclusively ipsilateral

A histogram showing the distribution of cells among these seven groups is given in Text-fig. 12. Assignment of a unit to a particular group was to some extent arbitrary, but it is unlikely that many cells were misplaced by more than one group. Perhaps the most interesting feature of the histogram is its lack of symmetry: many more cells were dominated by the contralateral than by the ipsilateral eye (106 vs. 62). We conclude that in the part of the cat's striate cortex representing central vision the great majority of cells are influenced by both eyes, and that despite wide variation in relative ocular dominance from one cell to the next, the contralateral eye is, on the average, more influential. As the shaded portion of Text-fig. 12 shows, there is no indication that the distribution among the various dominance groups of cells having complex receptive fields differs from the distribution of the population as a whole.

A cortical bias in favour of the contralateral eye may perhaps be related to the preponderance of crossed over uncrossed fibres in the cat's optic tract (Polyak, 1957, p. 788). The numerical inequality between crossed and uncrossed tract fibres is generally thought to be related to an inequality in size of the nasal and temporal half-fields, since both inequalities are most marked in lower mammals with laterally placed eyes, and become progressively less important in higher mammals, primates and man. Thompson et al. (1950) showed that in the rabbit, for example, there is a substantial cortical region receiving projections from that part of the peripheral

---

* These groups include cells in which the non-dominant eye, ineffective by itself, could influence the response to stimulation of the dominant eye.

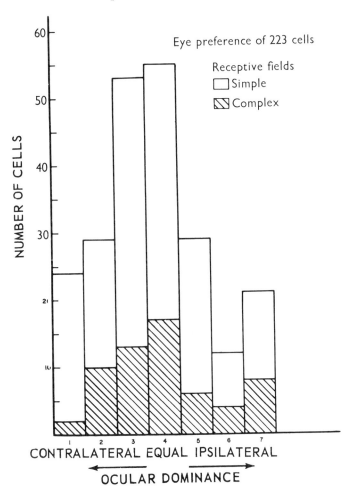

TEXT-FIGURE 12 *Distribution of 223 cells recorded from the visual cortex, according to ocular dominance. Histogram includes cells with simple fields and cells with complex fields. The shaded region shows the distribution of cells with complex receptive fields. Cells of group 1 were driven only by the contralateral eye; for cells of group 2 there was marked dominance of the contralateral eye; for group 3, slight dominance. For cells in group 4 there was no obvious difference between the two eyes. In group 5 the ipsilateral eye dominated slightly, in group 6, markedly; and in group 7 the cells were driven only by the ipsilateral eye.*

contralateral visual field which is not represented in the ipsilateral retina (the "Temporal Crescent"). Our results, concerned with more central portions of the visual fields, suggest that in the cat the difference in the number of crossed and uncrossed fibers in an optic tract is probably not accounted for entirely by fibers having their receptive fields in the temporal-field crescents.

PART III

FUNCTIONAL CYTOARCHITECTURE OF THE CAT'S VISUAL CORTEX

In the first two parts of this paper cells were studied individually, no attention being paid to their grouping within the cortex. We have shown that the number of functional cell types is very large, since cells may differ in several independent physiological characteristics, for example, in the retinal position of their receptive fields, their receptive-field organiza-tion, their axis orientation, and their ocular-dominance group. In this section we shall try to determine whether cells are scattered at random through the cortex with regard to these characteristics, or whether there is any tendency for one or more of the characteristics to be shared by neighbour-ing cells. The functional architecture of the cortex not only seems interest-ing for its own sake, but also helps to account for the various complex response patterns described in Part I.

RESULTS

Functional architecture of the cortex was studied by three methods. These had different merits and limitations, and were to some extent complementary.

1. CELLS RECORDED IN SEQUENCE The most useful and convenient proce-dure was to gather as much information as possible about each of a long succession of cells encountered in a micro-electrode penetration through the cortex, and to reconstruct the electrode track from serial histological sections. One could then determine how a physiological characteristic (such as receptive-field position, organization, axis orientation or ocular dom-inance) varied with cortical location. The success of this method in delineating regions of constant physiological characteristics depends on the possibility of examining a number of units as the electrode passes through each region. Regions may escape detection if they are so small that the electrode is able to resolve only one or two cells in each. The fewer the cells resolved, the larger the regions must be in order to be detected at all.

2. UNRESOLVED BACKGROUND ACTIVITY To some extent the spaces between isolated units were bridged by studying unresolved background activity audible over the monitor as a crackling noise, and assumed to originate largely from action potentials of a number of cells. It was concluded that cells, rather than fibres, gave rise to this activity, since it ceased abruptly when the electrode left the grey matter and entered subcortical white matter. Furthermore, diffuse light evoked no change in activity, compared to the marked increase caused by an optimally oriented slit. This suggested that terminal arborizations of afferent fibres contributed little to the back-

ground, since most geniculate cells respond actively to diffuse light (Hubel, 1960). In most penetrations unresolved background activity was present continuously as the electrode passed through layers 2–6 of the cortical grey matter.

Background activity had many uses. It indicated when the cells within range of the electrode tip had a common receptive-field axis orientation. Similarly, one could use it to tell whether the cells in the neighbourhood were driven exclusively by one eye (group 1 or group 7). When the background activity was influenced by both eyes, one could not distinguish between a mixture of cells belonging to the two monocular groups (1 and 7) and a population in which each cell was driven from both eyes. But even here one could at least assess the relative influence of the two eyes upon the group of cells in the immediate neighbourhood of the electrode.

3. MULTIPLE RECORDINGS   In the series of 303 cells, 78 were recorded in groups of two and 12 in groups of three. Records were not regarded as multiple unless the spikes of the different cells showed distinct differences in amplitude, and unless each unit fulfilled the criteria required of a single-unit record, namely that the amplitude and wave shape be relatively constant for a given electrode position.

In such multiple recordings one could be confident that the cells were close neighbours and that uniform stimulus conditions prevailed, since the cells could be stimulated and observed together. One thus avoided some of the difficulties in evaluating a succession of recordings made over a long period of time span, where absolute constancy of eye position, anaesthetic level, and preparation condition were sometimes hard to guarantee.

Regional variations of several physiological characteristics were examined by the three methods just outlined. Of particular interest for the present study were the receptive-field axis orientation, position of receptive fields on the retina, receptive-field organization, and relative ocular dominance. These will be described separately in the following paragraphs.

Orientation of receptive-field axis

The orientation of a receptive-field axis was determined in several ways. When the field was simple the borders between excitatory and inhibitory regions were sufficient to establish the axis directly. For both simple and complex fields the axis could always be determined from the orientation of the most effective stimulus. For most fields, when the slit or edge was placed at right angles to the optimum position there was no response. The receptive-field axis orientation was checked by varying the stimulus orientation from this null position in order to find the two orientations at which a response was only just elicited, and by bisecting the angle between them. By one or other of these procedures the receptive-field orientation could usually be determined to within 5 or 10°.

One of the first indications that the orientation of a receptive-field axis

was an important variable came from multiple recordings. Invariably the
axes of receptive fields mapped together had the same orientations. An
example of a 3-unit recording has already been given in Text-fig. 10. Cells
with common axis orientation were therefore not scattered at random
through the cortex, but tended to be grouped together. The size and shape
of the regions containing these cell groups were investigated by comparing
the fields of cells mapped in sequence. It was at once apparent that successively recorded cells also tended to have identical axis orientations and
that each penetration consisted of several sequences of cells, each sequence
having a common axis orientation. Any undifferentiated units in the background responded best to the stimulus orientation that was most effective
in activating the cell under study. After traversing a distance that varied
greatly from one penetration to the next, the electrode would enter an
area where there was no longer any single optimum orientation for driving
background activity. A very slight advance of the electrode would bring
it into a region where a new orientation was the most effective, and the
succeeding cells would all have receptive fields with that orientation. The
change in angle from one region to another was unpredictable; sometimes
it was barely detectable, at other times large (45–90°).

Text-figure 13 shows a camera lucida tracing of a frontal section through
the post-lateral gyrus. The electrode track entered normal to the surface,
passed through the apical segment in a direction parallel to the fibre bundles, then through the white matter beneath, and finally obliquely through
half the thickness of the mesial segment. A lesion was made at the termination of the penetration. A composite photomicrograph (Pl. 1) [Plate 1
(as well as plate 2) has been omitted in reprinting. (Ed.)] shows the
lesion and the first part of the electrode track. The units recorded in the
course of the penetration are indicated in Text-fig. 13 by the longer lines
crossing the track; the unresolved background activity by the shorter lines.
The orientations of the most effective stimuli are given by the directions
of the lines, a line perpendicular to the track signifying a vertical orientation. For the first part of the penetration, through the apical segment,
the field orientation was vertical for all cells as well as for the background
activity. Fibres were recorded from the white matter and from the grey
matter just beyond it. Three of these fibres were axons of cortical cell
having fields of various oblique orientations; four were afferent fibres from
the lateral geniculate body. In the mesial segment three short sequences
were encountered, each with a different common field orientation. These
sequences together occupied a distance smaller than the full thickness of
the apical segment.

In another experiment, illustrated in Text-fig. 14 and in Pl. 2 [Plate
2 has been omitted in reprinting. (Ed.)] two penetrations were made,
both in the apical segment of the post-lateral gyrus. The medial penetration
(at left in the figure) was at the outset almost normal to the cortex, but
deviated more and more from the direction of the deep fibre bundles.
In this penetration there were three different axis orientations, of which

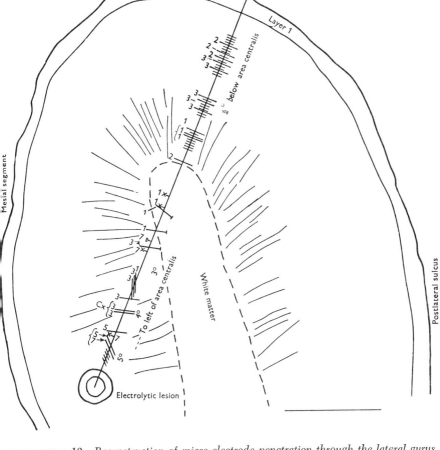

TEXT-FIGURE 13   *Reconstruction of micro-electrode penetration through the lateral gyrus (see also Pl. 1) [omitted in reprinting]. Electrode entered apical segment normal to the surface, and remained parallel to the deep fibre bundles (indicated by radial lines) until reaching white matter; in gray matter of mesial segment the electrode's course was oblique. Longer lines represent cortical cells. Axons of cortical cells are indicated by a cross-bar at right-hand end of line. Field-axis orientation is shown by the direction of each line; lines perpendicular to track represent vertical orientation. Brace-brackets show simultaneously recorded units. Complex receptive fields are indicated by "Cx." Afferent fibres from the lateral geniculate body indicated by x, for "on" centre; △, for "off" centre. Approximate positions of receptive fields on the retina are shown to the right of the penetration. Shorter lines show regions in which unresolved background activity was observed. Numbers to the left of the penetration refer to ocular-dominance group (see Part II). Scale 1 mm.*

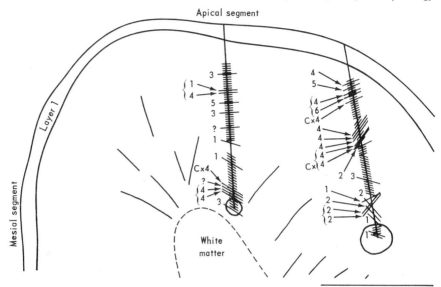

TEXT-FIGURE 14   *Reconstructions of two penetrations in apical segment of post-lateral gyrus, near its anterior end (just behind anterior interrupted line in Text-figure 1, see also Pl. 2) [omitted in reprinting]. Medial penetration is slightly oblique, lateral one is markedly so. All receptive fields were located within 1° of area centralis. Conventions as in Text-figure 13. Scale 1 mm.*

the first and third persisted through long sequences. In the lateral track there were nine orientations. From the beginning this track was more oblique, and it became increasingly so as it progressed.

As illustrated by the examples of Text-figs. 13 and 14, there was a marked tendency for shifts in orientation to increase in frequency as the angle between electrode and direction of fibre bundles (or apical dendrites) became greater. The extreme curvature of the lateral and post-lateral gyri in their apical segments made normal penetrations very difficult to obtain; nevertheless, four penetrations were normal or almost so. In none of these were there any shifts of axis orientation. On the other hand there were several shifts of field orientation in all oblique penetrations. As illustrated by Text-fig. 14, most penetrations that began nearly normal to the surface became more and more oblique with increasing depth. Here the distance traversed by the electrode without shifts in receptive-field orientation tended to become less and less as the penetration advanced.

It can be concluded that the striate cortex is divided into discrete regions within which the cells have a common receptive-field axis orientation. Some of the regions extend from the surface of the cortex to the white matter; it is difficult to be certain whether they all do. Some idea of their shapes may be obtained by measuring distances between shifts in receptive-field orientation. From these measurements it seems likely that the general shape is columnar, distorted no doubt by any curvature of the gyrus, which would tend to make the end at the surface broader than that at the white matter; deep in a sulcus the effect would be the reverse. The cross-sectional size and shape of the columns at the surface can be estimated only roughly. Most of our information concerns their width in the coronal plane, since it is in this plane that oblique penetrations were made. At the surface this width is probably of the order of 0.5 mm. We have very little information about the cross-sectional dimension in a direction parallel to the long axis of the gyrus. Preliminary mapping of the cortical surface suggests that the cross-sectional shape of the columns may be very irregular.

Position of receptive fields on the retina

GROSS TOPOGRAPHY   That there is a systematic representation of the retina on the striate cortex of the cat was established anatomically by Minkowski (1913) and with physiological methods by Talbot & Marshall (1941). Although in the present study no attempt has been made to map topographically all parts of the striate cortex, the few penetrations made in cortical areas representing peripheral parts of the retina confirm these findings. Cells recorded in front of the anterior interrupted lines of Text-fig. 1 had receptive fields in the superior retinas; those in the one penetration behind the posterior line had fields that were well below the horizontal meridian of the retina. (No recordings were made from cortical regions receiving projections from the deeply pigmented non-tapetal part of the inferior retinas.) In several penetrations extending far down the mesial (interhemispheric) segment of the lateral gyrus, receptive fields moved further and further out into the ipsilateral half of each retina as the electrode advanced (Text-fig. 13). In these penetrations the movement of fields into the retinal periphery occurred more and more rapidly as the electrode advanced. In three penetrations extending far down the lateral segment of the post-lateral gyrus (medial bank of the post-lateral sulcus) there was likewise a clear progressive shift of receptive-field positions as the electrode advanced. Here also the movement was along the horizontal meridian, again into the *ipsilateral* halves of both retinas. This therefore confirms the findings of Talbot & Marshall (1941) and Talbot (1942), that in each hemisphere there is a second laterally placed representation of the contralateral half-field of vision. The subject of Visual Area II will not be dealt with further in this paper.

Cells within the large cortical region lying between the interrupted lines of Text-fig. 1, and extending over on to the mesial segment and into the lateral sulcus for a distance of 2–3 mm, had their receptive fields in the area of central vision. By this we mean the area centralis, which is about 5° in diameter, and a region surrounding it by about 2–3°. The receptive fields of the great majority of cells were confined to the ipsilateral halves of the two retinas. Often a receptive field covering several degrees on the retina stopped short in the area centralis right at the vertical meridian.

Only rarely did a receptive field appear to spill over into the contralateral half-retina; when it did, it was only by 2–3°, a distance comparable to the possible error in determining the area centralis in some cats.

Because of the large cortical representation of the area centralis, one would expect only a very slow change in receptive-field position as the electrode advanced obliquely (Text-fig. 13). Indeed, in penetrations through the apex of the post-lateral gyrus and extending 1–2 mm down either bank there was usually no detectable progressive displacement of receptive fields. In penetrations made 1–3 mm apart, either along a parasagittal line or in the same coronal plane (Text-fig. 14) receptive fields again had almost identical retinal positions.

RETINAL REPRESENTATION OF NEIGHBOURING CELLS A question of some interest was to determine whether this detailed topographic representation of the retina held right down to the cellular level. From the results just described one might imagine that receptive fields of neighbouring cortical cells should have very nearly the same retinal position. In a sequence of cells recorded in a normal penetration through the cortex the receptive fields should be superimposed, and for oblique penetrations any detectable changes in field positions should be systematic. In the following paragraphs we shall consider the relative retinal positions of the receptive fields of neighbouring cells, especially cells within a column.

In all multiple recordings the receptive fields of cells observed simultaneously were situated in the same general region of the retina. As a rule the fields overlapped, but it was unusual for them to be precisely superimposed. For example, fields were often staggered along a line perpendicular to their axes. Similarly, the successive receptive fields observed during a long cortical penetration varied somewhat in position, often in an apparently random manner. Text-figure 15 illustrates a sequence of twelve cells recorded in the early part of a penetration through the cortex. One lesion was made while observing the first cell in the sequence and another at the end of the penetration; they are indicated in the drawing of cortex to the right of the figure. In the centre of the figure the position of each receptive field is shown relative to the area centralis (marked with a cross); each field was several degrees below and to the left of the area centralis. It will be seen that all fields in the sequence except the last had the same axis orientation; the first eleven cells therefore occupied the same column. All but the first three and the last (cell 12) were simple in arrangement. Cells 5 and 6 were recorded together, as were 8 and 9.

In the left-hand part of the figure the approximate boundaries of all these receptive fields are shown superimposed, in order to indicate the degree of overlap. From cell to cell there is no obvious systematic change in receptive-field position. The variation in position is about equal to the area occupied by the largest fields of the sequence. This variation is undoubtedly real, and not an artifact produced by eye movements occurring between recordings of successive cells. The stability of the eyes was

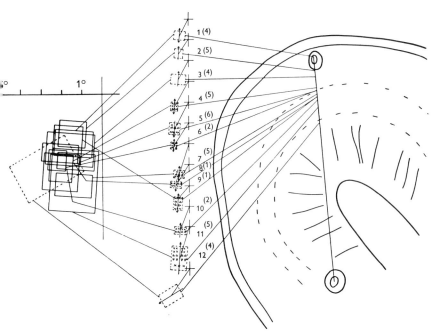

TEXT-FIGURE 15 *Reconstruction of part of an electrode track through apical and mesial segments of post-lateral gyrus near its anterior end. Two lesions were made, the first after recording from the first unit, the second at the end of the penetration. Only the first twelve cells are represented. Interrupted lines show boundaries of layer 4.*

In the center part of the figure the position of each receptive field, outlined with interrupted lines, is given with respect to the area centralis, shown by a cross. Cells are numbered in sequence 1–12. Numbers in parentheses refer to ocular-dominance group (see Part II). Units 5 and 6, 8 and 9 were observed simultaneously. The first three fields and the last were complex in organization; the remainder were simple. ×, areas giving excitation; Δ, areas giving inhibitory effects. Note that all receptive fields except the last have the same axis orientation (9.30–3.30 o'clock). The arrows show the preferred direction of movement of a slit oriented parallel to the receptive-field axis.

In the left part of the figure all of the receptive fields are superimposed, to indicate the overlap and variation in size. The vertical and horizontal lines represent meridia, crossing at the area centralis. Scale on horizontal meridan, 1° for each subdivision

checked while studying each cell, and any tendency to eye movements would have easily been detected by an apparent movement of the receptive field under observation. Furthermore, the field positions of simultaneously recorded cells 5 and 6, and also of cells 8 and 9, are clearly different; here the question of eye movements is not pertinent.

Text-figure 15 illustrates a consistent and somewhat surprising finding, that within a column defined by common field-axis orientation there was no apparent progression in field positions along the retina as the electrode advanced. This was so even though the electrode often crossed through the column obliquely, entering one side and leaving the other. If there was any detailed topographical representation within columns it was ob-

scured by the superimposed, apparently random staggering of field posi
tions. We conclude that at this microscopic level the retinotopic representa
tion no longer strictly holds.

Receptive-field organization

MULTIPLE RECORDINGS   The receptive fields of cells observed together in
multiple recordings were always of similar complexity, i.e. they were either
all simple or all complex in their organization. In about one third of the
multiple recordings the cells had the same detailed field organization; i
simple, they had similar distributions of excitatory and inhibitory areas
if complex, they required identical stimuli for their activation. As a rule
these fields did not have exactly the same retinal position, but were stag
gered as described above. In two thirds of the multiple recordings the
cells differed to varying degrees in their receptive field arrangements. Two
types of multiple recordings in which field arrangements differed seen
interesting enough to merit a separate description.

In several multiple recordings the receptive fields overlapped in such
a way that one or more excitatory or inhibitory portions were superimposed
Two examples are supplied by cell-pairs 5 and 6, and 8 and 9 of Text-fig
15. Their fields are redrawn in Text-fig. 16. The fields of cells 5 and 6
are drawn separately (Text-fig. 16A) but they actually overlapped so that
the reference lines are to be imagined as superimposed. Thus the "on"
centre of cell 6 fell directly over the upper "on" flank of 5 and the two
cells tended to fire together to suitably placed stimuli. A similar situation
existed for cells 8 and 9 (Text-fig. 16B). The field of 9 was placed so
that its "off" region and the lower, weaker "on" region were superimposed
on the two regions of 8. Again the two cells tended to fire together. Such
examples suggest that neighbouring cells may have some of their inputs
in common.

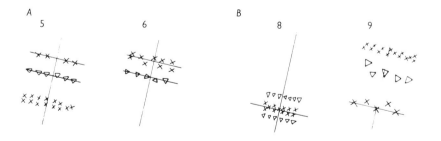

TEXT-FIGURE 16   *Detailed arrangements of the receptive fields of two pairs of
simultaneously recorded cells (nos. 5 and 6, and 8 and 9, of Text-figure 15).
The crosses of diagrams 5 and 6 are superimposed as are the double crosses of
8 and 9. Note that the upper excitatory region of 5 is superimposed upon the
excitatory region of 6; and that both regions of 8 are superimposed on the
inhibitory and lower excitatory regions of 9. Scale, 1°.*

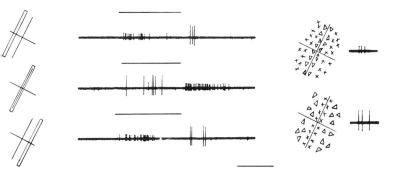

TEXT-FIGURE 17 *Records of two simultaneously observed cells which responded reciprocally to stationary stimuli. The two receptive fields are shown to the right, and are superimposed, though they are drawn separately. The cell corresponding to each field is indicated by the spikes to the right of the diagram. To the left of each record is shown the position of a slit, ¼ × 2½°, with respect to these fields.*

Both cells binocularly driven (dominance group 3); fields mapped in the left (contralateral) eye; position of fields 2° below and to the left of the area centralis. Time, 1 sec.

Cells responded reciprocally to a light stimulus in eight of the forty-three multiple recordings. An example of two cells responding reciprocally to stationary spots is shown in Text-fig. 17. In each eye the two receptive fields were almost superimposed. The fields consisted of elongated obliquely oriented central regions, inhibitory for one cell, excitatory for the other, flanked on either side by regions of the opposite type. Instead of firing together in response to an optimally oriented stationary slit, like the cells in Text-fig. 16, these cells gave opposite-type responses, one inhibitory and the other excitatory. Some cell pairs responded reciprocally to to-and-fro movements of a slit or edge. Examples have been given elsewhere (Hubel, 1958, Fig. 9; 1959, Text-fig. 6). The fields of these cell pairs usually differed only in the balance of the asymmetrical flanking regions.

RELATIONSHIP BETWEEN RECEPTIVE FIELD ORGANIZATION AND CORTICAL LAYERING In a typical penetration through the cortex many different field types were found, some simple and others complex. Even within a single column both simple and complex fields were seen. (In Text-fig. 13 and 14 complex fields are indicated by the symbol "Cx"; in Text-fig. 15, fields 1–3 were complex and 4–11 simple, all within a single column.) An attempt was made to learn whether there was any relationship between the different field types and the layers of the cortex. This was difficult for several reasons. In Nissl-stained sections the boundaries between layers of the cat's striate cortex are not nearly as clear as they are in the primate brain; frequently even the fourth layer, so characteristic of the striate cortex, is poorly de-marcated. Consequently, a layer could not always be identified with certainty even for a cell whose position was directly marked by a lesion.

For most cells the positions were arrived at indirectly, from depth readings and lesions made elsewhere in the penetrations: these determinations were subject to more errors than the direct ones. Moreover, few of the penetrations were made in a direction parallel to the layering, so that the distance an electrode travelled in passing through a layer was short, and the error in electrode position correspondingly more important.

The distribution of 179 cells among the different layers is given in the histograms of Text-fig. 18. All cells were recorded in penetrations in which at least one lesion was made; the shaded portions refer to cells which were individually marked with lesions. As shown in the separate histograms, simple-field cells as well as those with complex fields were widely distributed throughout the cortex. Cells with simple fields were most numerous in layers 3, 4, and 6. Especially interesting is the apparent rarity of complex fields in layer 4, where simple fields were so abundant. This is also illustrated in Text-fig. 15, which shows a sequence of eight cells recorded from layer 4, all of which had simple fields. These findings suggest that cells may to some extent be segregated according to field complexity, and the rarity with which simple and complex fields were mapped together is consistent with this possibility.

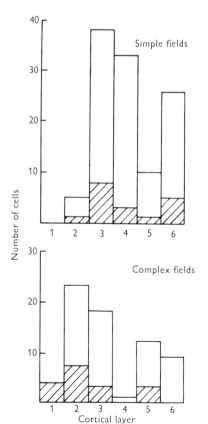

TEXT-FIGURE 18   *Distribution of 179 cells, 113 with simple fields, 66 with complex, among the different cortical layers. All cells were recorded in penetrations in which at least one electrolytic lesion was made and identified; the shaded areas refer to cells marked individually by lesions. Note especially the marked difference in the occurrence, in layer 4, between simple and complex fields.*

Ocular dominance

In thirty-four multiple recordings the eye-dominance group (see Part II) was determined for both or all three cells. In eleven of these recordings there was a clear difference in ocular dominance between cells. Similarly, in a single penetration two cells recorded in sequence frequently differed in eye dominance. Cells from several different eye-dominance categories appeared not only in single penetrations, but also in sequences in which all cells had a common axis orientation. Thus within a single column defined by a common axis orientation there were cells of different eye dominance. A sequence of cells within one column is formed by cells 1–11 of Text-fig. 15. Here eye dominance ranged from wholly contralateral (group 1) to strongly ipsilateral (group 6). The two simultaneously recorded cells 5 and 6 were dominated by opposite eyes.

While these results suggested that cells of different ocular dominance were present within single columns, there were nevertheless indications of some grouping. First, in twenty-three of the thirty-four multiple recordings, simultaneously observed cells fell into the same ocular-dominance group. Secondly, in many penetrations short sequences of cells having the same relative eye dominance were probably more common than would be expected from a random scattering. Several short sequences are shown in Text-fig. 13 and 14. When such sequences consisted of cells with extreme unilateral dominance (dominance groups 1, 2, 6, and 7) the undifferentiated background activity was usually also driven predominantly by one eye, suggesting that other neighbouring units had similar eye preference. If cells of common eye dominance are in fact regionally grouped, the groups would seem to be relatively small. The cells could be arranged in nests, or conceivably in very narrow columns or thin layers.

In summary, cells within a column defined by a common field-axis orientation do not necessarily all have the same ocular dominance; yet neither do cells seem to be scattered at random through the cortex with respect to this characteristic.

DISCUSSION

A scheme for the elaboration of simple and complex receptive fields

Comparison of responses of cells in the lateral geniculate body with responses from striate cortex brings out profound differences in the receptive-field organization of cells in the two structures. For cortical cells, specifically oriented lines and borders tend to replace circular spots as the optimum stimuli, movement becomes an important parameter of stimulation, diffuse light becomes virtually ineffective, and with adequate stimuli most cells can be driven from the two eyes. Since lateral geniculate cells

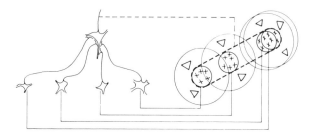

TEXT-FIGURE 19 *Possible scheme for explaining the or-*
ganization of simple receptive fields. A large number of
lateral geniculate cells, of which four are illustrated in
the upper right in the figure, have receptive fields with
"on" centres arranged along a straight line on the retina.
All of these project upon a single cortical cell, and the
synapses are supposed to be excitatory. The receptive
field of the cortical cell will then have an elongated
"on" centre indicated by the interrupted lines in the
receptive-field diagram to the left of the figure.

supply the main, and possibly the only, visual input to the striate cortex,
these differences must be the result of integrative mechanisms within the
striate cortex itself.

At present we have no direct evidence on how the cortex transforms
the incoming visual information. Ideally, one should determine the properties of a cortical cell, and then examine one by one the receptive fields
of all the afferents projecting upon that cell. In the lateral geniculate,
where one can, in effect, record simultaneously from a cell and one of
its afferents, a beginning has already been made in this direction (Hubel &
Wiesel, 1961). In a structure as complex as the cortex the techniques available would seem hopelessly inadequate for such an approach. Here we
must rely on less direct evidence to suggest possible mechanisms for explaining the transformations that we find.

The relative lack of complexity of simple cortical receptive fields suggests
that these represent the first or at least a very early stage in the modification
of geniculate signals. At any rate we have found no cells with receptive
fields intermediate in type between geniculate and simple cortical fields.
To account for the spatial arrangements of excitatory and inhibitory regions
of simple cortical fields we may imagine that upon each simple-type cell
there converge fibres of geniculate origin having "on" or "off" centres situated in the appropriate retinal regions. For example, a cortical cell with
a receptive field of the type shown in Text-fig. 2C might receive projections
from a group of lateral geniculate cells having "on" field centres distributed
throughout the long narrow central region designated in the figure by
crosses. Such a projection system is shown in the diagram of Text-fig.
19. A slit of light falling on this elongated central region would activate
all the geniculate cells, since for each cell the centre effect would strongly
outweigh the inhibition from the segments of field periphery falling within

the elongated region. This is the same as saying that a geniculate cell will respond to a slit with a width equal to the diameter of its field centre, a fact that we have repeatedly verified. The inhibitory flanks of the cortical field would be formed by the remaining outlying parts of the geniculate-field peripheries. These flanks might be reinforced and enlarged by appropriately placed "off"-centre geniculate cells. Such an increase in the potency of the flanks would appear necessary to explain the relative indifference of cortical cells to diffuse light.

The arrangement suggested by Text-fig. 19 would be consistent with our impression that widths of cortical receptive-field centres (or flanks, in a field such as that of Text-fig. 2F) are of the same order of magnitude as the diameters of geniculate receptive-field centres, at least for fields in or near the area centralis. Hence the fineness of discrimination implied by the small size of geniculate receptive-field centres is not necessarily lost at the cortical level, despite the relatively large total size of many cortical fields; rather, it is incorporated into the detailed substructure of the cortical fields.

In a similar way, the simple fields of Text-fig. 2D–G may be constructed by supposing that the afferent "on"- or "off"-centre geniculate cells have their field centres appropriately placed. For example, field-type G could be formed by having geniculate afferents with "off" centres situated in the region below and to the right of the boundary, and "on" centres above and to the left. An asymmetry of flanking regions, as in field E, would be produced if the two flanks were unequally reinforced by "on"-centre afferents.

The model of Text-fig. 19 is based on excitatory synapses. Here the suppression of firing on illuminating an inhibitory part of the receptive field is presumed to be the result of withdrawal of tonic excitation, i.e. the inhibition takes place at a lower level. That such mechanisms occur in the visual system is clear from studies of the lateral geniculate body, where an "off"-centre cell is suppressed on illuminating its field centre because of suppression of firing in its main excitatory afferent (Hubel & Wiesel, 1961). In the proposed scheme one should, however, consider the possibility of direct inhibitory connexions. In Text-fig. 19 we may replace any of the excitatory endings by inhibitory ones, provided we replace the corresponding geniculate cells by ones of opposite type ("on"-centre instead of "off"-centre, and conversely). Up to the present the two mechanisms have not been distinguished, but there is no reason to think that both do not occur.

The properties of complex fields are not easily accounted for by supposing that these cells receive afferents directly from the lateral geniculate body. Rather, the correspondence between simple and complex fields noted in Part I suggests that cells with complex fields are of higher order, having cells with simple fields as their afferents. These simple fields would all have identical axis orientation, but would differ from one another in their exact retinal positions. An example of such a scheme is given in Text-fig. 20. The hypothetical cell illustrated has a complex field like that of Text-figs. 5 and 6. One may imagine that it receives afferents from a set of simple cortical cells with fields of type G, Text-fig. 2, all with vertical axis orientation, and staggered along a horizontal line· An edge of light would activate one or more of these simple cells wherever it fell within the complex field, and this would tend to excite the higher-order cell.

Similar schemes may be proposed to explain the behaviour of other complex units. One need only use the corresponding simple fields as building blocks, staggering them over an appropriately wide region. A cell with the properties shown in Text-fig. 3 would require two types of horizontally oriented simple fields, having "off" centres above the horizontal line, and "on" centres below it. A slit of the same width as these centre regions would strongly activate only those cells whose long narrow centres it cov-ered. It is true that at the same time a number of other cells would have small parts of their peripheral fields stimulated, but we may perhaps assume that these opposing effects would be relatively weak. For orienta-tions other than horizontal a slit would have little or no effect on the simple cells, and would therefore not activate the complex one. Small spots should give only feeble "on" responses regardless of where they were shone in the field. Enlarging the spots would not produce summation of the responses unless the enlargement were in a horizontal direction; anything else would result in invasion of opposing parts of the antecedent fields, and cancellation of the responses from the corresponding cells. The model would therefore seem to account for many of the observed properties of complex fields.

Proposals such as those of Text-figs. 19 and 20 are obviously tentative and should not be interpreted literally. It does, at least, seem probable that simple receptive fields represent an early stage in cortical integration, and the complex ones a later stage. Regardless of the details of the process, it is also likely that a complex field is built up from simpler ones with common axis orientations.

At first sight it would seem necessary to imagine a highly intricate tangle of interconnexions in order to link cells with common axis orientations while keeping those with different orientations functionally separated. But if we turn to the results of Part III on functional cytoarchitecture we see at once that gathered together in discrete columns are the very cells we require to be interconnected in our scheme. The cells of each aggregate have common axis orientations and the staggering in the positions of the simple fields is roughly what is required to account for the size of most of the complex fields (cf. Text-fig. 9). That these cells are interconnected is more-over very likely on histological grounds: indeed, the particular richness of radial connexions in the cortex fits well with the columnar shape of the regions.

The otherwise puzzling aggregation of cells with common axis orientation now takes on new meaning. We may tentatively look upon each column

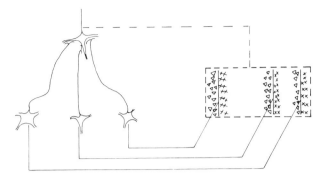

TEXT-FIGURE 20 *Possible scheme for explaining the organization of complex receptive fields. A number of cells with simple fields, of which three are shown schematically, are imagined to project to a single cortical cell of higher order. Each projecting neurone has a receptive field arranged as shown to the left: an excitatory region to the left and an inhibitory region to the right of a vertical straight-line boundary. The boundaries of the fields are staggered within an area outlined by the interrupted lines. Any vertical-edge stimulus falling across this rectangle, regardless of its position, will excite some simple-field cells, leading to excitation of the higher-order cell.*

as a functional unit of cortex, within which simple fields are elaborated and then in turn synthesized into complex fields. The large variety of simple and complex fields to be found in a single column (Text-fig. 15) suggests that the connexions between cells in a column are highly specific.

We may now begin to appreciate the significance of the great increase in the number of cells in the striate cortex, compared with the lateral geniculate body. In the cortex there is an enormous digestion of information, with each small region of visual field represented over and over again in column after column, first for one receptive-field orientation and then for another. Each column contains thousands of cells, some cells having simple fields and others complex. In the part of the cortex receiving projections from the area centralis the receptive fields are smaller, and presumably more columns are required for unit area of retina; hence in central retinal regions the cortical projection is disproportionately large.

Complex receptive fields

The method of stimulating the retina with small circular spots of light and recording from single visual cells has been a useful one in studies of the cat's visual system. In the pathway from retina to cortex the excitatory and inhibitory areas mapped out by this means have been sufficient to account for responses to both stationary and moving patterns. Only when one reaches cortical cells with complex fields does the method fail, for these fields cannot generally be separated into excitatory and inhibitory regions. Instead of the direct small-spot method, one must resort to a trial-and-error system, and attempt to describe each cell in terms of the stimuli that most effectively influence firing. Here there is a risk of over- or under-estimating the complexity of the most effective stimuli, with corresponding lack of precision in the functional description of the cell. For this reason it is encouraging to find that the properties of complex fields can be interpreted by the simple supposition that they receive projections from simple-field cells, a supposition made more likely by the anatomical findings of Part III.

Compared with cells in the retina or lateral geniculate body, cortical cells show a marked increase in the number of stimulus parameters that must be specified in order to influence their firing. This apparently reflects a continuing process which has its beginning in the retina. To obtain an optimum response from a retinal ganglion cell it is generally sufficient to specify the position, size and intensity of a circular spot. Enlarging the spot beyond the size of the field centre raises the threshold, but even when diffuse light is used it is possible to evoke a brisk response by using an intense enough stimulus. For geniculate cells the penalty for exceeding optimum spot size is more severe than in the retina, as has been shown by comparing responses of a geniculate cell and an afferent fiber to the same cell (Hubel & Wiesel, 1961). In the retina and lateral geniculate body there is no evidence that any shapes are more effective than circular ones, or that, with moving stimuli, one direction of movement is better than another.

In contrast, in the cortex effective driving of simple-field cells can only be obtained with restricted stimuli whose position, shape and orientation are specific for the cell. Some cells fire best to a moving stimulus, and in these the direction and even the rate of movement are often critical. Diffuse light is at best a poor stimulus, and for cells in the area of central representation it is usually ineffective at any intensity.

An interesting feature of cortical cells with complex fields may be seen in their departure from the process of progressively increasing specificity. At this stage, for the first time, what we suppose to be higher-order neurones are in a sense less selective in their responses than the cells which feed into them. Cells with simple fields tend to respond only when the stimulus is both oriented and positioned properly. In contrast, the neurones to which they supposedly project are concerned predominantly with stimulus orientation, and are far less critical in their requirements as regards stimulus placement. Their responsiveness to the abstraction which we call orientation is thus generalized over a considerable retinal area.

The significance of this step for perception can only be speculated upon, but it may be of some interest to examine several possibilities. First, neurophysiologists must ultimately try to explain how a form can be recognized regardless of its exact position in the visual field. As a step in form recognition the organism may devise a mechanism by which the inclinations of borders are more important than their exact visual-field location. It is clear that a given form in the visual field will, by virtue of its borders, excite a combination of cells with complex fields. If we displace the form it will activate many of the same cells, as long as the change in position is not enough to remove it completely from their receptive fields. Now we may imagine that these particular cells project to a single cell of still higher order: such a cell will then be very likely to respond to the form (provided the synapses are excitatory) and there will be considerable latitude in the position of the retinal image. Such a mechanism will also permit other transformations of the image, such as a change in size associated with displacement of the form toward or away from the eye. Assuming that there exist cells that are responsive to specific forms, it would clearly be economical to avoid having thousands for each form, one for every possible retinal position, and separate sets for each type of distortion of the image.

Next, the ability of some cells with complex fields to respond in a sustained manner to a stimulus as it moves over a wide expanse of retina suggests that these cells may play an important part in the perception of movement. They adapt rapidly to a stationary form, and continuous movement of the stimulus within the receptive field is the only way of obtaining a sustained discharge (Text-fig. 4H). Presumably the afferent simple-field cells also adapt rapidly to a stationary stimulus; because of their staggered fields the moving stimulus excites them in turn, and the higher-order cell is thus at all times bombarded. This seems an elegant means of overcoming a difficulty inherent in the problem of movement perception, that movement must excite receptors not continuously but in sequence.

Finally, the above remarks apply equally well to displacements of retinal images caused by small eye movements. The normal eye is not stationary, but is subject to several types of fine movements. There is psychophysical evidence that in man these may play an important part in vision, transforming a steady stimulus produced by a stationary object into an intermittent one, so overcoming adaptation in visual cells (Ditchburn & Ginsborg, 1952; Riggs, Ratliff, Cornsweet & Cornsweet, 1953). At an early stage in the visual pathway the effect of such movements would be to excite many cells repeatedly and in turn, rather than just a few continuously. A given line or border would move back and forth over a small retinal region; in the cortex this would sequentially activate many cells with simple fields. Since large rotatory movements are not involved, these fields would have the same axis orientations but would differ only in their exact retinal positions. They would converge on higher-order cells with complex fields, and these would tend to be activated continuously rather than intermittently.

Functional cytoarchitecture

There is an interesting parallel between the functional subdivisions of the cortex described in the present paper, and those found in somatosensory cortex by Mountcastle (1957) in the cat, and by Powell & Mountcastle (1959) in the monkey. Here, as in the visual area, one can subdivide the cortex on the basis of responses to natural stimuli into regions which are roughly columnar in shape, and extend from surface to white matter. This is especially noteworthy since the visual and somatic areas are the only cortical regions so far studied at the single-cell level from the standpoint of functional architecture. In both areas the columnar organization is superimposed upon the well known systems of topographic representation—of the body surface in the one case, and the visual fields in the other. In the somatosensory cortex the columns are determined by the sensory submodality to which the cells of a column respond: in one type of column the cells are affected either by light touch or by bending of hairs, whereas in the other the cells respond to stimulation of deep fascia or manipulation of joints.

Several differences between the two systems will at once be apparent. In the visual cortex the columns are determined by the criterion of receptive-field axis orientation. Presumably there are as many types of column as there are recognizable differences in orientation. At present one can be sure that there are at least ten or twelve, but the number may be very large, since it is possible that no two columns represent precisely the same axis orientation. (A subdivision of cells or of columns into twelve groups according to angle of orientation shows that there is no clear prevalence of one group over any of the others.) In the somatosensory cortex, on the other hand, there are only two recognized types of column.

A second major difference between the two systems lies in the very nature of the criteria used for the subdivisions. The somatosensory cortex is divided by submodality, a characteristic depending on the incoming sensory fibres, and not on any transformations made by the cortex on the afferent impulses. Indeed we have as yet little information on what integrative processes do take place in the somatosensory cortex. In the visual cortex there is no modality difference between the input to one column and that to the next, but it is in the connexions between afferents and cortical cells, or in the interconnexions between cortical cells, that the differences must exist.

Ultimately, however, the two regions of the cortex may not prove so dissimilar. Further information on the functional role of the somatic cortex may conceivably bring to light a second system of columns, superimposed on the present one. Similarly, in the visual system future work may disclose other subdivisions cutting across those described in this paper, and based on other criteria. For the present it would seem unwise to look upon the columns in the visual cortex as entirely autonomous functional units. While the variation in field size from cell to cell within a column is generally of the sort suggested in Text-figs. 9 and 15, the presence of an occasional cell with a very large complex field (up to about 20°) makes one wonder whether columns with similar receptive-field orientations may not possess some interconnexions.

Binocular interaction

The presence in the striate cortex of cells influenced from both eyes has already been observed by several authors (Hubel & Wiesel, 1959; Cornehls & Grüsser, 1959; Burns, Heron & Grafstein, 1960), and is confirmed in Part II of this paper. Our results suggest that the convergence of influences from the two eyes is extensive, since binocular effects could be demonstrated in 84% of our cells, and since the two eyes were equally, or almost equally, effective in 70% (groups 3–5). This represents a much greater degree of interaction than was suggested by our original work, or by Grüsser and Grüsser-Cornehls (see Jung, 1960), who found that only 30% of their cells were binocularly influenced.

For each of our cells comparison of receptive fields mapped in the two eyes showed that, except for a difference in strength of responses related to eye dominance, the fields were in every way similar. They were similarly organized, had the same axis orientation, and occupied corresponding regions in the two retinas. The responses to stimuli applied to corresponding parts of the two receptive fields showed summation. This should be important in binocular vision, for it means that when the two images produced by an object fall on corresponding parts of the two retinas, their separate effects on a cortical cell should sum. Failure of the images to fall on corresponding regions, which might happen if an object were closer than the point of fixation or further away, would tend to reduce the summation; it could even lead to mutual antagonism if excitatory parts of one field were stimulated at the same time as inhibitory parts of the other. It should be emphasized that for all simple fields and for many complex ones the two eyes may work either synergistically or in opposition, depending on how the receptive fields are stimulated; when identical stimuli are shone on corresponding parts of the two retinas their effects should always sum.

Although in the cortex the proportion of binocularly influenced cells is high, the mixing of influences from the two eyes is far from complete. Not only are many single cells unequally influenced by the two eyes, but the relative eye dominance differs greatly from one cell to another. This could simply reflect an intermediate stage in the process of mixing of influences from the two eyes; in that case we might expect an increasing uniformity in the eye preference of higher-order cells. But cells with complex fields do not appear to differ, in their distribution among the different eye-dominance groups, from the general population of cortical cells (Text-fig. 12). At present we have no clear notion of the physiological significance of this incomplete mixing of influences from the two eyes. One possible hint lies in the fact that by binocular parallax alone (even with a stimulus too brief to allow changes in the convergence of the eyes) one can tell which of two objects is the closer (Dove, 1841; von Recklinghausen, 1861). This would clearly be impossible if the two retinas were connected to the brain in identical fashion, for then the eyes (or the two pictures of a stereo-pair) could be interchanged without substituting near points for far ones and vice versa.

Comparison of receptive fields in the frog and the cat

Units in many respects similar to striate cortical cells with complex fields have recently been isolated from the intact optic nerve and the optic tectum of the frog (Lettvin, Maturana, McCulloch & Pitts, 1959; Maturana, Lettvin, McCulloch & Pitts, 1960). There is indirect evidence to suggest that the units are the non-myelinated axons or axon terminals of retinal ganglion cells, rather than tectal cells of efferent optic nerve fibers. In common with complex cortical cells, these units respond to objects and shadows in the visual field in ways that could not have been predicted from responses to small spots of light. They thus have "complex" properties, in the sense that we have used this term. Yet in their detailed behaviour they differ greatly from any cells yet studied in the cat, at any level from retina to cortex. We have not, for example, seen "erasible" responses or found "convex edge detectors." On the other hand, it seems that some cells in the frog have asymmetrical responses to movement and some have what we have termed a "receptive-field axis."

Assuming that the units described in the frog are fibres from retinal ganglion cells, one may ask whether similar fibres exist in the cat, but have been missed because of their small size. We lack exact information on the fibre spectrum of the cat's optic nerve; the composite action potential suggests that non-myelinated fibres are present, though in smaller numbers than in the frog (Bishop, 1933; Bishop & O'Leary, 1940). If their fields are different from the well known concentric type, they must have little part to play in the geniculo-cortical pathway, since geniculate cells all appear to have concentric-type fields (Hubel & Wiesel, 1961). The principal cells of the lateral geniculate body (those that send their axons to the striate cortex) are of fairly uniform size, and it seems unlikely that a large group would have gone undetected. The smallest fibres in the cat's optic nerve probably project to the tectum or the pretectal region; in view of the work in the frog, it will be interesting to examine their receptive fields.

At first glance it may seem astonishing that the complexity of third-order neurones in the frog's visual system should be equalled only by that of sixth-order neurones in the geniculo-cortical pathway of the cat. Yet this is less surprising if one notes the great anatomical differences in the two animals, especially the lack, in the frog, of any cortex or dorsal lateral geniculate body. There is undoubtedly a parallel difference in the use each animal makes of its visual system: the frog's visual apparatus is presumably specialized to recognize a limited number of stereotyped patterns or situations, compared with the high acuity and versatility found in the cat. Probably it is not so unreasonable to find that in the cat the specialization of cells for complex operations is postponed to a higher level, and that when it does occur, it is carried but by a vast number of cells, and in great detail. Perhaps even more surprising, in view of what seem to be profound physiological differences, is the superficial anatomical similarity of retinas in the cat and the frog. It is possible that with Golgi methods a comparison of the connexions between cells in the two animals may help us in understanding the physiology of both structures.

Receptive fields of cells in the primate cortex

We have been anxious to learn whether receptive fields of cells in the monkey's visual cortex have properties similar to those we have described in the cat. A few preliminary experiments on the spider monkey have shown striking similarities. For example, both simple and complex fields have been observed in the striate area. Future work will very likely show differences, since the striate cortex of the monkey is in several ways different morphologically from that of the cat. But the similarities already seen suggest that the mechanisms we have described may be relevant to many mammals, and in particular to man.

SUMMARY

1. The visual cortex was studied in anaesthetized cats by recording extracellularly from single cells. Light-adapted eyes were stimulated with spots of white light of various shapes, stationary or moving.

2. Receptive fields of cells in the visual cortex varied widely in their organization. They tended to fall into two categories, termed "simple" and "complex."

3. There were several types of simple receptive fields, differing in the spatial distribution of excitatory and inhibitory ("on" and "off") regions. Summation occurred within either type of region; when the two opposing regions were illuminated together their effects tended to cancel. There was generally little or no response to stimulation of the entire receptive field with diffuse light. The most effective stimulus configurations, dictated by the spatial arrangements of excitatory and inhibitory regions, were long narrow rectangles of light (slits), straight-line borders between areas of different brightness (edges), and dark rectangular bars against a light background. For maximum response the shape, position and orientation of these stimuli were critical. The orientation of the receptive-field axis (i.e. that of the optimum stimulus) varied from cell to cell; it could be vertical, horizontal or oblique. No particular orientation seemed to predominate.

4. Receptive fields were termed complex when the reponse to light could not be predicted from the arrangements of excitatory and inhibitory regions. Such regions could generally not be demonstrated; when they could the

laws of summation and mutual antagonism did not apply. The stimuli that were most effective in activating cells with simple fields—slits, edges, and dark bars—were also the most effective for cells with complex fields. The orientation of a stimulus for optimum response was critical, just as with simple fields. Complex fields, however, differed from simple fields in that a stimulus was effective wherever it was placed in the field, provided that the orientation was appropriate.

5. Receptive fields in or near the area centralis varied in diameter from $\frac{1}{2}$–$1°$ up to about 5–6°. On the average, complex fields were larger than simple ones. In more peripheral parts of the retina the fields tended to be larger. Widths of the long narrow excitatory or inhibitory portions of simple receptive fields were often roughly equal to the diameter of the smallest geniculate receptive-field centres in the area centralis. For cells with complex fields responding to slits or dark bars the optimum stimulus width was also usually of this order of magnitude.

6. Four fifths of all cells were influenced independently by the two eyes. In a binocularly influenced cell the two receptive fields had the same organization and axis orientation, and were situated in corresponding parts of the two retinas. Summation was seen when corresponding parts of the two retinas were stimulated in identical fashion. The relative influence of the two eyes differed from cell to cell: for some cells the two eyes were about equal; in others one eye, the ipsilateral or contralateral, dominated.

7. Functional architecture was studied by (a) comparing the responses of cells recorded in sequence during micro-electrode penetrations through the cortex, (b) observing the unresolved background activity, and (c) comparing cells recorded simultaneously with a single electrode (multiple recordings). The retinas were found to project upon the cortex in an orderly fashion, as described by previous authors. Most recordings were made from the cortical region receiving projections from the area of central vision. The cortex was found to be divisible into discrete columns; within each column the cells all had the same receptive-field axis orientation. The columns appeared to extend from surface to white matter; cross-sectional diameters at the surface were of the order of 0.5 mm. Within a given column one found various types of simple and complex fields; these were situated in the same general retinal region, and usually overlapped, although they differed slightly in their exact retinal position. The relative influence of the two eyes was not necessarily the same for all cells in a column.

8. It is suggested that columns containing cells with common receptive-field axis orientations are functional units, in which cells with simple fields represent an early stage in organization, possibly receiving their afferents directly from lateral geniculate cells, and cells with complex fields are of higher order, receiving projections from a number of cells with simple fields within the same column. Some possible implications of these findings for form perception are discussed.

ACKNOWLEDGMENT

We wish to thank Miss Jaye Robinson and Mrs. Jane Chen for their technical assistance. We are also indebted to Miss Sally Fox and to Dr. S. W. Kuffler for their helpful criticism of this manuscript. The work was supported in part by Research Grants B-2251 and B-2260 from United States Public Health Service, and in part by the United States Air Force through the Air Force Office of Scientific Research of the Air Research and Development Command under contract No. AF 49 (638)–713. The work was done during the tenure of a U.S. Public Health Service Senior Research Fellowship No. SF 304-R by D.H.H.

REFERENCES

Bishop, G. H. (1933). Fiber groups in the optic nerve. *Amer. J. Physiol.* **106**, 460–474.

Bishop, G. H. & O'Leary, J. S. (1940). Electrical activity of the lateral geniculate of cats following optic nerve stimuli. *J. Neurophysiol.* **3**, 308–322.

Bishop, P. O., Burke, W. & Davis, R. (1959). Activation of single lateral geniculate cells by stimulation of either optic nerve. *Science*, **130**, 506–507.

Burns, B. D., Heron, W. & Grafstein, B. (1960). Response of cerebral cortex to diffuse monocular and binocular stimulation. *Amer. J. Physiol.* **198**, 200–204.

Cornehls, U. & Grüsser, O.-J. (1959). Ein elektronisch gesteuertes Doppellichtreizgerät. *Pflüg. Arch. ges. Physiol.* **270**, 78–79.

Daniel, P. M. & Whitteridge, D. (1959). The representation of the visual field on the calcarine cortex in baboons and monkeys. *J. Physiol.* **148**, 33P.

Ditchburn, R. W. & Ginsborg, B. L. (1952). Vision with stabilized retinal image. *Nature Lond.*, **170**, 36–37.

Dove, H. W. (1841). Die Combination der Eindrücke beider Ohren und beider Augen zu einem Eindruck. *Mber. preuss. Akad.* **1841**, 251–252.

Erulkar, S. D. & Fillenz, M. (1958). Patterns of discharge of single units of the lateral geniculate body of the cat in response to binocular stimulation. *J. Physiol.* **140**, 6–7P.

Erulkar, S. D. & Fillenz, M. (1960). Single-unit activity in the lateral geniculate body of the cat. *J. Physiol.* **154**, 206–218.

Grüsser, O.-J. & Sauer, G. (1960). Monoculare und binoculare Lichtreizung einzelner Neurone im Geniculatum laterale der Katze. *Pflüg. Arch. ges. Physiol.* **271**, 595–612.

Hayhow, W. R. (1958). The cytoarchitecture of the lateral geniculate body in the cat in relation to the distribution of crossed and uncrossed optic fibers. *J. comp. Neurol.* **110**, 1–64.

Hubel, D. H. (1957). Tungsten microelectrode for recording from single units. *Science,* **125**: 549–550.

Hubel, D. H. (1958). Cortical unit responses to visual stimuli in nonanesthetized cats. *Amer. J. Ophthal.* **46**, 110–121.

Hubel, D. H. (1959). Single unit activity in striate cortex of unrestrained cats. *J. Physiol.* **147**: 226–238.

Hubel, D. H. (1960). Single unit activity in lateral geniculate body and optic tract of unrestrained cats. *J. Physiol.* **150**, 91–104.

Hubel, D. H. & Wiesel, T. N. (1959). Receptive fields of single neurones in the cat's striate cortex. *J. Physiol.* **148**, 574–591.

Hubel, D. H. & Wiesel, T. N. (1960). Receptive fields of optic nerve fibres in the spider monkey. *J. Physiol.* **154**, 572–580.

Hubel, D. H. & Wiesel, T. N. (1961). Integrative action in the cat's lateral geniculate body. *J. Physiol.* **155**, 385–398.

Jung, R. (1960). Microphysiologie corticaler Neurone: Ein Beitrag zur Koordination der Hirnrinde und des visuellen Systems. *Structure and Function of the Cerebral Cortex*, ed. Tower, D. B. and Schadé, J. P. Amsterdam: Elsevier Publishing Company.

Kuffler, S. W. (1953). Discharge patterns and functional organization of mammalian retina. *J. Neurophysiol.* **16**: 37–68.

Lettvin, J. Y., Maturana, H. R., McCulloch, W. S. & Pitts, W. H. (1959). What the frog's eye tells the frog's brain. *Proc. Inst. Radio Engrs., N. Y.,* **47**, 1940–1951.

Maturana, H. R. Lettvin, J. Y., McCulloch, W. S. & Pitts, W. H. (1960). Anatomy and physiology of vision in the frog (*Rana pipiens*). *J. gen. Physiol.* **43**, part 2, 129–176.

Minkowski, M. (1913). Experimentelle Untersuchungen über die Beziehungen der Grosshirnrinde und der Netzhaut zu den primären optischen Zentren, besonders zum Corpus geniculatum externum. *Arb. hirnanat. Inst. Zürich,* **7**, 259–362.

Mountcastle, V. B. (1957). Modality and topographic properties of single neurons of cat's somatic sensory cortex. *J. Neurophysiol.* **20**, 408–434.

O'Leary, J. L. (1941). Structure of the area striata of the cat. *J. comp. Neurol.* **75**, 131–164.

Polyak, S. (1957). *The Vertebrate Visual System,* ed. Klüver, H. The University of Chicago Press.

Powell, T. P. S. & Mountcastle, V. B. (1959). Some aspects of the functional organization of the cortex of the postcentral gyrus of the monkey: a correlation of findings obtained in a single unit analysis with cytoarchitecture. *Johns Hopk. Hosp. Bull.* **105**, 133–162.

Riggs, L. A., Ratliff, F., Cornsweet, J. C. & Cornsweet, T. N. (1953). The disappearance of steadily fixated visual test objects. *J. opt. Soc. Amer.* **43**, 495–501.

Silva, P. S. (1956). Some anatomical and physiological aspects of the lateral geniculate body. *J. comp. Neurol.* **106**, 463–486.

Talbot, S. A. (1942). A lateral localization in the cat's visual cortex. *Fed. Proc.* **1**, 84.

Talbot, S. A. & Marshall, W. H. (1941). Physiological studies on neural mechanisms of visual localization and discrimination. *Amer. J. Ophthal.* **24**, 1255–1263.

Thompson, J. M., Woolsey, C. N. & Talbot, S. A. (1950). Visual areas I and II of cerebral cortex of rabbit. *J. Neurophysiol.* **13**, 277–288.

von Recklinghausen, F. (1861). Zum körperlichen Sehen. *Ann. Phys. Lpz.* **114**, 170–173.

RECEPTOR MECHANISMS
IN HUMAN VISION

George Wald

HARVARD UNIVERSITY

Source *Reprinted from the* **Proceedings of the 13th** *International Physiological Congress, Tokyo, 1965, 69–79, with permission of the author and the Excerpta Medica Foundation. Parts of the paper have been revised for this volume by the author.*

The rods and cones of the vertebrate retina are derived embryonically from such ciliated cells as typically line the ventricles of the brain. It is the swollen and otherwise modified shaft of a presumptive cilium that forms the rod or cone outer segment (Tokuyasu and Yamada, 1960; De Robertis, 1960; Dowling and Gibbons, 1961). The latter has a layered structure, characteristically different in rods and cones (Fig. 1). In rods the lamellae take the form of a pile of flattened sacs, each bordered by a more rigid, differentiated rim, all enclosed within the plasma membrane. In the cones of fishes and amphibia the transverse layers consist of repeated infoldings of the plasma membrane on the side away from the ciliary process (Sjöstrand, 1959, 1961). In primate cones, however, one finds much the same structural arrangements as in the rods, except that in cones the flattened sacs lack the differentiated rim (Cohen, 1961; Dowling, 1965). In both rods and cones the lamellar membranes are about 50 Å thick, about as thick therefore as the diameter of a molecule of cattle rhodopsin, provided it is spherical in shape.

The visual pigments of vertebrates share a common chemistry (Wald, 1960, 1961). Each consists of a specific type of protein, an opsin, bearing as chromophore a particular configuration of retinaldehyde (vitamin A aldehyde, formerly retinene), the 11-*cis* isomer. *The only action of light in vision is to isomerize this chromophore* from the 11-*cis* to the all-*trans* configuration (Hubbard and Kropf, 1958). All other changes—chemical, physiological, indeed psychological—are "dark" consequences of this single light reaction.

The first light product—all-*trans* retinaldehyde bound to as yet unmodified opsin—in the case of rhodopsin called prelumirhodopsin, is highly unstable at ordinary temperatures (Yoshizawa and Wald, 1964). In the dark it is transformed rapidly over a series of intermediates—lumirhodopsin, metarhodopsin I and metarhodopsin II (Matthews, Hubbard, Brown, and Wald, 1963), hydrolyzing finally to a mixture of opsin and free all-*trans* retinaldehyde (Fig. 2). This last reaction is too slow to play a part in visual excitation, which must depend therefore upon one of the earlier intermediates. The latter represent progressive stages in the unfolding of the opsin structure, in the course of which new groups are exposed, including two sulfhydryl (-SH) groups and one H^+-binding group with pK about 6.6 (histidine?).

In vertebrate retinas, owing to the presence of the enzyme, alcohol de-

[1] Investigations from our laboratory were supported in part with funds from the U.S. National Science Foundation and the Office of Naval Research. More detailed reviews and more adequate references to earlier developments will be found in *Life and Light* (W. D. McElroy and B. Glass, ed.), Baltimore, Johns Hopkins Press (1961), p. 724; and *J. opt. Soc. Amer.*, 1963, 53 (20).

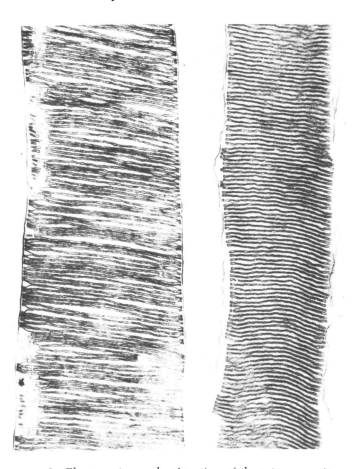

FIGURE 1   *Electron micrographs of portions of the outer segments of a rod (left) and a foveal cone (right) of the rhesus monkey, Macaca mulata ($\times$ 75,000). In both types of receptor the transverse layers consist of flattened sacs, differing only slightly in arrangement and dimensions. In the rod, however, each double-membraned disc is bounded by a special, somewhat thickened and relatively rigid rim, absent in the cones. (From Dowling, 1965.) (Reduced 40% for reproduction.)*

hydrogenase, the retinaldehyde released by the bleaching of visual pigments is reduced to retinol (vitamin A). To regenerate a visual pigment, retinol must be reoxidized to retinaldehyde, and either molecule or both must be exchanged for or isomerized to the active 11-*cis* configuration.

To these general arrangements, which they share with other vertebrates, primates add two special features: the presence of a central yellow patch, or macula lutea; and color vision, which, though distributed widely among vertebrates and arthropods, is peculiarly accessible in primates and particularly in man.

Human rods contain a typical rhodopsin (Wald and Brown, 1958). Its

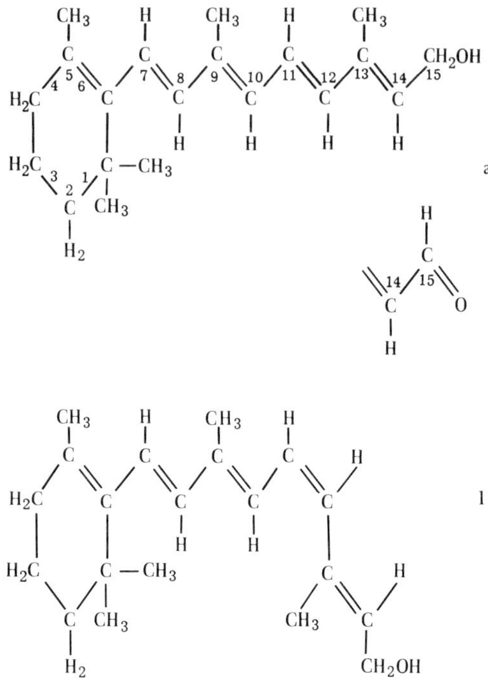

all-*trans* Vitamin A

Retinene

11-*cis* (*neo*-b)

FIGURE 2 *Structures of all-trans and 11-cis retinol (vitamin A) and retinaldehyde (retinene).*

absorption spectrum, measured in suspensions of rod outer segments or by the microspectrophotometry of human retinas (Brown and Wald, 1963), has λ_{max} about 500 mμ, and accounts precisely for the spectral sensitivity of human rod vision, whether this is measured in normal subjects and corrected for ocular transmission, or measured without correction in lensless eyes. Human rhodopsin, extracted into aqueous solution, bleaches in the usual way to opsin and all-*trans* retinaldehyde, and can be regenerated in solution from opsin and 11-*cis* retinaldehyde. Rhesus monkey rhodopsin exhibits much the same properties. In both man and monkey the rhodopsin molecules are oriented in the rod outer segments much as in frogs and cattle (Brown and Wald, 1963).

After a century of speculation, we have recently begun to obtain reliable data on the spectra of the human cone pigments concerned with color vision. Difference spectra of the red- and green-sensitive pigments of the cones have been measured by the direct microspectrophotometry of human and monkey foveas (Brown and Wald, 1963). The spectra of patches of fovea 0.2 mm. wide were measured first in the dark, then after exhaustive bleaching with deep red light, and finally after complete bleaching at shorter wavelengths. The red-sensitive pigment was found to have λ_{max} 565–570 mμ, the green-sensitive pigment λ_{max} 535–540 mμ (Fig. 4). Both pigments are regenerated on adding 11-*cis* retinaldehyde to the medium, showing this to be their common chromophore, joined to different opsins.

Recently it has proved possible to make such measurements in single parafoveal rods and cones of man and monkey (Marks, Dobelle and Mac-Nichol, 1964; Brown and Wald, 1964). Recording spectra in such exceedingly small fields inevitably involves some bleaching of the visual pigments. Marks *et al.* incorporate a monitored correction for this factor in their measurements. In our experiments the pigments sometimes bleached up to 20–30 per cent in the course of a single scan. By recording the spectrum in both directions—from red to violet and back from violet to red—and averaging the results, one can nevertheless obtain spectra that are not greatly distorted in shape or position.

Such measurements of the difference spectra of the visual pigments in single human cones reveal the presence of (at least) three groups of cones, red-, green-, and blue-sensitive (Fig. 5). These data provide the first direct evidence of the existence of such groups of cones, reasonably consistent in their properties with the hypothetical components of trichromatic theory. Too few cones have yet been measured in this way to define the absorption maxima reliably. A central problem awaiting such measurements is whether each type of cone contains a single visual pigment or whether some of them contain mixtures of pigments.

We have recently determined by direct microspectrophotometry the absorption spectra of human and monkey maculas (Brown and Wald, 1963). Some years ago the human macular pigment was shown to be a carotenoid, apparently lutein or leaf xanthophyll, $C_{40}H_{54}(OH)_2$ (Wald, 1954, 1949).

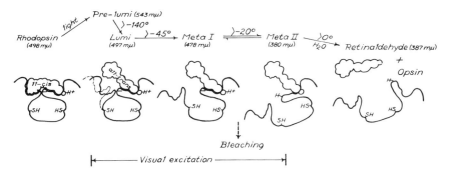

FIGURE 3 *Stages in the bleaching of rhodopsin. Rhodopsin has as chromophore 11-cis retinaldehyde, which fits closely a section of the opsin structure. The only action of light is to isomerize retinaldehyde from the 11-cis to the all-trans configuration (pre-lumirhodopsin). Then the structure of opsin opens in stages (lumirhodopsin, metarhodopsin I and II), until finally the retinaldehyde is hydrolyzed away from opsin. Bleaching occurs in the transition from metarhodopsin I to II; and by this stage visual excitation must also have occurred. The opening of the opsin structure exposes new groups, including two -SH groups and one H⁺-binding group. The absorption maxima shown are for pre-lumirhodopsin at − 190°C., lumirhodopsin at − 65°, and the other pigments at room temperature.*

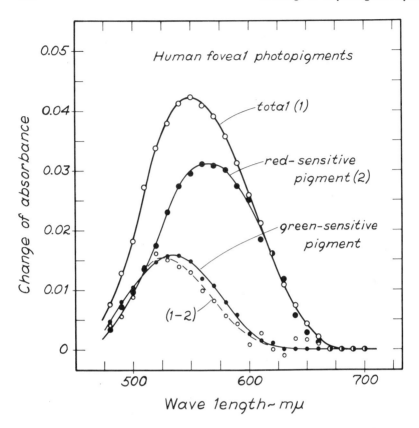

FIGURE 4 *Difference spectra of visual pigments of the human fovea. The foveal spectrum was first recorded in darkness, then after exhaustive bleaching in deep red light, finally after complete bleaching at shorter wavelengths. The difference between the first two spectra measures the red-sensitive pigment (λ_{max} 565–570 m); that between the second and third spectra measures the green-sensitive pigment (λ_{max} 535–540 mμ); that between the first and last spectra measures the total foveal pigment (λ_{max} ca. 550 mμ). At wavelengths longer than about 630 mμ the red-sensitive pigment accounts almost wholly for the total absorption. Subtracting the spectrum of the red-sensitive pigment from the total should yield an estimate of the spectrum of the green-sensitive pigment; this difference, shown as a broken line, approximates the directly-measured spectrum of the green-sensitive pigment. (From Brown and Wald, 1963.)*

Monkey maculas appear to possess the same pigment. A patch of human or monkey macula yields in the microspectrophotometer a typical carotenoid spectrum, with absorption maxima at about 430, 455, and 484 mμ (Fig. 6). The average absorbance at 455 mμ in eight series of measurements of human maculas was 0.49, representing an average absorption at this wavelength of 68 per cent. When allowance is made for ocular and macular absorptions, the absorption spectrum of the total pigments of the human fovea accounts exactly for the foveal spectral sensitivity (Brown and Wald, 1963).

A simple psychophysical procedure was recently devised for measuring the spectral sensitivities of the human color vision pigments (Wald, 1964). The spectral sensitivity of the dark-adapted fovea represents the composite action spectrum of all the foveal photopigments. By re-measuring the spectral sensitivity on intense colored backgrounds, one can isolate the action spectra of the individual pigments. So for example, determining visual thresholds throughout the spectrum, superimposed on a steady background illumination of intense blue light, reveals the action spectrum of the red-sensitive pigment. In effect the blue background selectively bleaches the

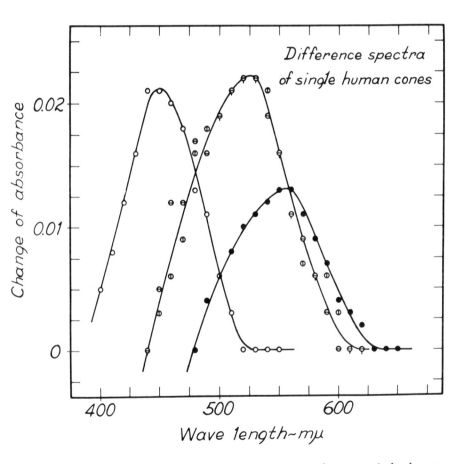

FIGURE 5 *Difference spectra of the visual pigments in single cones of the human parafovea. In each case the absorption spectrum was recorded in the dark, then again after bleaching with a flash of yellow light. The differences between these spectra are shown. They involve one blue-sensitive cone, two green-sensitive cones, and one red-sensitive cone. In making these measurements light passed through the cones axially, in the direction of incidence normal in the living eye.* (From Brown and Wald, 1964.)

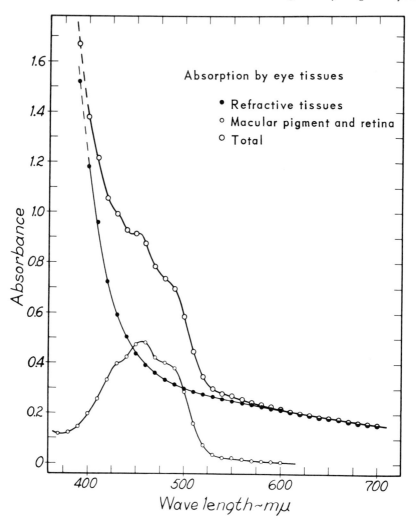

FIGURE 6   *Average absorption by the dioptric tissues of the human eye (cornea to retinal surface) and of the macula lutea in the foveal region (average of eight eyes). (From Brown and Wald, 1963; Wald, 1964.)*

blue- and green-sensitive pigments to such levels that the foveal thresholds are due to the red-sensitive pigment alone. Similarly exposure to bright yellow light isolates the action spectrum of the blue-sensitive pigment; and exposure to a mixture of red and blue, hence purple light, isolates the spectrum of the green-sensitive pigment (Fig. 7).

Measured at the level of the cornea such action spectra vary from one person to another, owing to differences in ocular and macular transmission. The uncorrected spectral sensitivity curves for the blue-, green- and red-sensitive pigments are maximal at 440–450 mμ, 540–550 mμ, and 575–580 mμ.

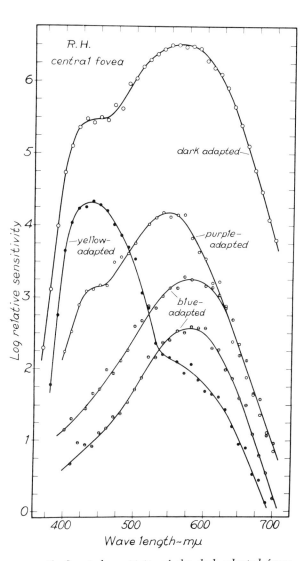

FIGURE 7 *Spectral sensitivity of the dark adapted fovea and action spectra of a single color-vision pigments, measured in terms of light incident on the cornea of the eye of subject R. H. The dark adapted fovea is most sensitive at about 562 mμ. Adaptation to yellow light virtually isolates the action spectrum of the blue-sensitive pigment (λ_{max} 438 mμ). Adaptation to a mixture of violet and red, hence purple light, exposes the green-sensitive pigment (λ_{max} 548 mμ); and adaptation to blue light isolates the red-sensitive pigment (λ_{max} 580 mμ). The results of two different blue adaptations demonstrate the invariance of such action spectra with the conditions of adaptation. Ordinates are log relative sensitivity (log 1/threshold), expressed as relative numbers of photons per flash incident upon the cornea of the eye. Absolute sensitivities can be judged from the fact that the threshold of the dark adapted fovea at about 560 mμ is about 10^4 photons in this observer. (From Wald, 1964.)*

The procedures used in obtaining these curves are closely related to those introduced some years ago by Stiles for the analysis of human color vision (Stiles, 1949, 1959, 1964). The present spectra of the blue- and green-sensitive pigments agree reasonably well with the sensitivity curves of Stiles's blue-mechanisms (π_1–π_3) and his green-mechanism (π_4). Stiles's red-mechanism (π_5), however, forms an almost exact envelope of the action spectra of the red- and green-sensitive pigments shown in Figure 7. The criteria by which Stiles measured these functions were directed more toward isolating physiological mechanisms than individual pigments, and this characteristic of the π_5 function may mean that one of the physiological unit mechanisms in color vision may involve the operation of both the red- and green-sensitive pigments.

After correction for ocular and macular transmission, these action spectra become invariant, and now have the force of absorption spectra of the color vision pigments. Their maxima lie at about 430, 540, and 575 mμ. They are closely related also to the spectral sensitivities of response mechanisms in the human retina (Motokawa, 1949), and single responding units in the primate lateral geniculate (de Valois and Jones, 1961) and visual cortex (Motokawa, Taira and Okuda, 1962).

The spectral sensitivities of the three color vision pigments, measured at the corneal level, add up to yield the average photopic luminosity curve when the maxima are in the proportions, B:G:R = 0.018:0.58:0.54. Corrected for ocular and macular transmissions, hence as though at the level of the cones, these ratios become about 0.09:0.59:0.52 (Fig. 8) (Wald, 1964).

The selective color-adaptation procedure has recently been used in an analysis of defective color vision. Normal vision involves the operation of three independent variables, hence is *trichromatic*. The most obvious expression of this condition is that normal persons need to mix three primary colors in various proportions to match all the hues they see. The great bulk of colorblind persons are *dichromats;* they can match all the hues they see with mixtures of two primaries. There is also a rare class of *monochromats,* who can match all colors with one another by adjusting the brightness. Finally, there are the *anomalous trichromats,* who require three primaries to match all colors, but whose mixtures differ in proportion from those of normal trichromats and from one another.

For this investigation the selective adaptation procedure was standardized so as to yield comparable data throughout. The background fields were the same as used earlier, but their brightnesses were adjusted arbitrarily so as to make the maximum sensitivities of the individual color mechanisms about equal in the average normal subject. Typical results of these measurements are shown in Fig. 9 (Wald, 1966).

In 9 normal observers, there was no difficulty in demonstrating the presence of the three usual color-vision pigments. The average $\lambda_{\max}$ of the dark adapted fovea (D) fell at 559 mμ., and that of B, G and R at 442, 546 and 571 mμ. In 8 protans, however, (5 protanopes, 3 protanomalous),

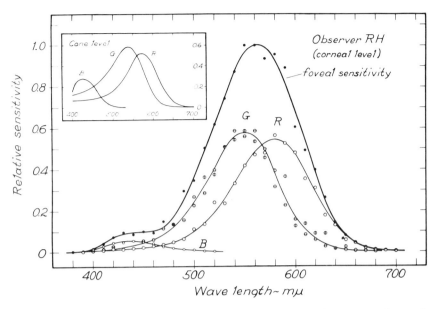

FIGURE 8 *Contributions of the individual color-receptor mechanisms to the total foveal sensitivity of observer R. H. The main graph shows measurements at the corneal level, the inset corresponding curves corrected for ocular and macular transmission, hence as though measured at the level of the cones. In R. H., who is particularly blue-sensitive, when the foveal sensitivity is given a maximal height of 1.0, the heights of the blue-, green-, and red-sensitive components are as B:G:R: = 0.053:0.575:0.542 at the corneal level, and 0.28:0.59:0.52 at the level of the cones. In the average observer the blue-component is only about ⅓ as high. (From Wald, 1964.)*

though the blue- and green-sensitive pigments were readily measured, every attempt to measure the red-sensitive pigment yielded instead the green-sensitive pigment again at a lower level of sensitivity. In protanopes, therefore, the red-component is lacking; they are in this sense red-blind. The absence of the red-receptor also distorts the total luminosity function of the fovea. It is narrower than normal, owing to the sharp decline of sensitivity in the red, and for the same reason is displaced toward considerably shorter wavelengths, the average λ_{max} appearing at about 548 mμ.

In a first attempt to understand the mechanism of color blindness on the basis of data already in the literature (Wald, 1964), I had taken up Willmer's earlier suggestion (1955) that there are two classes of deuteranope, one lacking the green-sensitive pigment (a "loss" mechanism); the other possessing all three color-vision pigments in normal proportions, and hence a normal spectral sensitivity function, but with matters so arranged that the red- and green-sensitive pigments excite a single sensation (a "fusion" mechanism). Not finding an example of such a "fusion" mechanism among the first deuteranopes I examined, I went on until I had measured

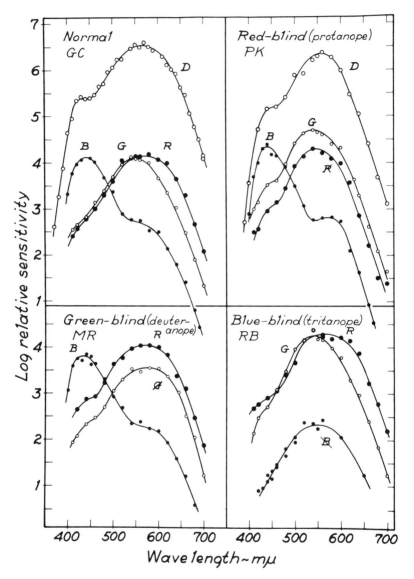

FIGURE 9 *Measurements of spectral sensitivity with a standardized procedure in a normal subject, a red-blind (protanope), a green-blind (deuteranope) and a blue-blind (tritanope). Each of the colorblinds reveals the operation of only two of the three color-vision pigments; in each case the attempt to measure the third pigment reveals only one of the former pigments at a lower level of sensitivity. D; dark adapted fovea. B, G, R: blue-, green- and red-sensitive pigments, measured on bright yellow, purple or blue back-grounds. These letters crossed out represent unsuccessful attempts to measure the corresponding pigments in colorblind eyes.*

in all 20 deutans (13 deuteranopes, 7 deuteranomals). All of them exhibited the type of result shown at the lower left in Fig. 9. In every case the selective adaptation procedure revealed normal blue- and red-sensitive pigments; but every attempt to find the green-receptor yielded instead only the red-receptor again at a lower level of sensitivity. All these deutans appear to lack the green-sensitive pigment, and are in this sense green-blind.

Similarly, 2 tritanopes who were examined, a mother and son, exhibited normal red- and green-receptors, but no trace of the blue-receptor. In this sense such tritanopes are blue-blind (Fig. 9).

In this procedure anomalous trichromats (protanomals and deuteranomals) yielded results indistinguishable from those of dichromats. Clearly these subjects possess a third receptor, but so low in sensitivity compared with the normal that it could not be found by this method. To account for the abnormal color-matching of anomalous trichromats, something more is needed than diminished sensitivity in this missing receptor; it must also possess a sensitivity curve displaced in the spectrum, as pointed out many years ago by König and Dieterici (1892).

The discovery of a subject who in addition to being a tritanope is also deuteranomalous provided a unique opportunity to reveal this type of mechanism directly. Selective adaptation showed that this subject, in addition to a normal red-receptor, possesses a green-receptor of abnormally low sensitivity and displaced considerably toward the red, so that its λ_{max} falls at about 555 mμ.

Though color blindness is widely stated to be inherited as a sex-linked recessive, that is true only of the more prevalent red- and green-blindness. Blue-blindness appears to be an autosomal character, as evidenced by the fact that it involves females almost as often as males (Kalmus, 1955).

On the basis of genetic information alone, it has not been possible to decide whether red- and green-blindness involve one or two loci on the X-chromosome. As stated above, however, regeneration experiments show the human red- and green-sensitive pigments to differ only in their protein components, their opsins. That two different proteins are involved in forming these pigments is good presumptive evidence that they are determined by two distinct genes. The simplest assumption is that at two loci on the X-chromosome genes exist which determine the amino acid sequences of the opsins of the normal red- and green-sensitive pigments. A mutation in either of these genes may block the formation of the corresponding pigment, resulting in either red- or green-blindness. It is known that the corresponding color-anomalous conditions, protanomaly and deuteranomaly, breed true. They seem to represent other mutations at the same gene loci, which rather than blocking altogether the synthesis of a color-vision pigment, permit the synthesis of a modified pigment in abnormally small amount. That is, at each of these loci there is a series of at least three allelic genes, representing the normal, color-anomalous, and color-blind conditions, their dominance decreasing in that order.

REFERENCES

Brown, P. K., Gibbons, I. R., and Wald, G.: *J. Cell Biol.*, 1963. **19** (79).

Brown, P. K., and Wald, G.: *Nature (Lond.)*, 1963, **200** (37).

Brown, P. K., and Wald, G.: *Science*, 1964, **144** (45).

Cohen, A. I.: *Exp. Eye Res.*, 1961, **1** (128).

De Robertis, E.: *J. gen. Physiol.*, 1960, 43/Suppl. 2 (1).

De Valois, R. L., and Jones, A. E.: In: *The Visual System*, Jung, R., and Kornhuber, H., editors, Springer, Berlin, 1961 (178).

Dowling, J. E.: *Science*, 1965, **147** (57).

Dowling, J. E., and Gibbons, I. R.: In: *The Structure of the Eye*, Smelser, G. K., editor, Academic Press, New York, 1961 (85).

Hubbard, R., and Kropf, A.: *Proc. nat. Acad. Sci. USA*, 1958, **44** (130).

Kalmus, H., *Ann. Human Genetics*, **20** 39 (1955).

König, A., and C. Dieterici, Z. *Psych. u. Physiol. Sinnesorgane*, **4**, 241 (1892).

Marks, W. B., Dobelle, W. H., and MacNichol Jr., E. F.: *Science*, 1964, **143** (1181).

Matthews, R. G., Hubbard, R., Brown, P. K., and Wald G.: *J. gen. Physiol.* 1963, **47** (215).

Motokawa, K.: *J. Neurophysiol.*, 1949, **12** (291).

Motokawa, K., Taira, N., and Okuda, J.: *Tohoku J. exp. Med.*, 1962, **78** (320).

Sjöstrand, F. S.: *Erg. Biol.*, 1959, **21** (128).

Sjöstrand, F. S.: *Rev. Mod. Phys.*, 1959, **31** (301).

Sjöstrand, F. S.: In: *The Structure of the Eye*, Smelser, G. K., editor, Academic Press, New York, 1961 (1).

Stiles, W. S.: *Ned. T. Natuurk.*, 1949, **15** (125).

Stiles, W. S.: *Proc. nat. Acad. Sci. USA*, 1959, **45** (100).

Stiles, W. S.: *Science*, 1964, **145** (1016).

Tokuyasu, K., and Yamada, E.: *J. biophys. biochem. Cytol.*, 1960, **7** (187).

Wald, G.: *Science*, 1945, **101** (653).

Wald, G.: *Docum. ophthal. (Den Haag)*, 1949, **3** (94).

Wald, G.: *Science*, 1964, **145** (1007).

Wald, G.: *Proc. nat. Acad. Sci. USA*, 1966, **55** (1347).

Wald, G., and Brown, P. K.: *Science*, 1958, **127** (222).

Wald, G., Brown, P. K., and Gibbons, I. R.: In: *Biological Receptor Mechanisms*, Beament, J., editor, Cambridge Univ. Press, 1962 (32).

Wald, G., Brown, P. K., and Gibbons, I. R.: *J. opt. Soc. Amer.*, 1963, **53** (20).

Willmer, E. N.: *Docum. ophthal. (Den Haag)*, 1955, **9** (235).

Yamada, E., Tokuyasu, K., and Iwaki, S.: *J. Kurume med. Ass.*, 1958, **21** (1979).

Yoshizawa, T., and Wald, G.: *Nature (Lond.)*, 1963, **197** (1279).

Yoshizawa, T., and Wald, G.: *Nature (Lond.)*, 1964, **201** (340).

Yoshizawa, T., and Wald, G.: in press.

Arousal,
Emotion,
Attention

PRELIMINARY ANALYSIS OF FUNCTIONS OF THE TEMPORAL LOBES IN MONKEYS

Heinrich Klüver and Paul C. Bucy

UNIVERSITY OF CHICAGO

Editors Note   This is a classical and germinal study. Since its publication a great deal of work has been done on the parts of the brain involved—the temporal lobe, amygdala, and hippocampus. There is still no complete agreement on the functions of these various parts of the brain, although perceptual, memory, motivational evaluation, and act sequencing or "planning" functions have all been proposed by various investigators. This reading is the first of a series on the temporal lobes and associated structures which are reprinted in the present collection. The others, by Penfield (No. 25), Scoville and Milner (No. 26), and Kimble and Pribram (No. 27), give a sample of the history of experimental refinement and reinterpretations concerning the functions of this part of the brain.

It is hoped that these readings will provide an example of the way research has progressed in the task of mapping psychological functions of the brain. While comparable studies have been done on other parts of the brain, e.g. the frontal lobes, it seemed more instructive, given space limitations, to present an historical series such as this rather than a number of unrelated articles on various sections of the brain.

Source   Reprinted from the Archives of Neurology and Psychiatry, December, 1939, 42, 979–1000, with permission of the authors and the American Medical Association. Copyright 1939.

In previous communications[1] we pointed out that the chief symptoms following bilateral temporal lobectomy in the rhesus monkey consist in "psychic blindness" (*Seelenblindheit*) or visual agnosia, strong "oral" tendencies and profound emotional changes. Our results were primarily based on an analysis of the behavioral symptoms of a female rhesus monkey which had been studied for a period of four months following the operations. The type of disturbance analyzed in that case seemed to be similar to the "associative mind blindness" of Lissauer.[2] It is true that the diagnosis "agnosia" can be only of practical importance and merely serves to raise a number of questions. A review of the clinical literature indicates that the more carefully a case is studied the more difficult it may be to decide whether there is really an "agnostic" or merely a "visual" defect, that is, whether the variety of "agnostic" symptoms can be reduced to disturbances of "elementary" or "higher" visual functions. Von Monakow[3] and Mourgue[4] even raised the question whether the disturbances in the process of recognition commonly referred to as "agnosia" are the result of an emotional indifference of the subjects, or, in other words, whether "agnostic" symptoms represent merely disturbances in the affective sphere. In view of this situation, we can consider the "psychic blindness" and related symptoms, as described in our first report, merely the starting point for further analysis. It seemed desirable to produce, if possible, the same symptoms in a larger number of cases and to extend the behavioral analysis in certain directions in order to gain a better understanding of the nature of the disturbance following removal of both temporal lobes.

TESTING PROCEDURES

In addition to general observations on locomotion, drinking, eating, sleeping and other forms of activity displayed by the animals while kept in cages, we made use of a variety of special tests. Most of these procedures represent methods or modifications of methods previously devised by one of us for analyzing the behavior of subhuman primates.[5] With the exception of our first monkey,[1b] which

[1] Klüver, H., and Bucy, P. C.: (*a*) "Psychic Blindness" and Other Symptoms Following Bilateral Temporal Lobectomy in Rhesus Monkeys, Am. J. Physiol. **119**: 352–353, 1937; (*b*) An Analysis of Certain Effects of Bilateral Temporal Lobectomy in the Rhesus Monkey, with Special Reference to "Psychic Blindness," J. Psychol. **5**: 33–54, 1938.

[2] Lissauer, H.: Ein Fall von Seelenblindheit nebst einem Beitrage zur Theorie derselben, Arch. f. Psychiat. **21**: 222–270, 1890.

[3] von Monakow, C.: Die Lokalisation im Grosshirn und der Abbau der Funktionen durch kortikale Herde, Wiesbaden, J. F. Bergmann, 1914.

[4] Mourgue, R.: Neurobiologie de l'hallucination: Essai sur une variété particulière de désintégration de la fonction, Bruxelles, Maurice Lamertin, 1932.

[5] Klüver, H.: (*a*) Behavior Mechanisms in Monkeys, Chicago, University of Chicago

was observed previous to the operations only generally, all animals were tested before and after operation. In case the operation was performed in two or more stages, the animal was also subjected to interoperative tests. In the following sections, we shall briefly indicate the procedures and test situations employed. A detailed description of the tests will be published later.

1. **Investigation of Sensory and Motor Factors.** In addition to utilizing conditioned differential reactions as indicators (see "Differential Reactions"), we recorded the reactions of the animal to various stimuli and test situations. Although in most instances quantitative data were not obtained, the tests were designed to enable us to determine at least the presence of gross sensory and motor defects. The procedures used have been briefly described in our first report.[1b] The investigation of visual reactions was confined to the following items: visual reflexes; the ability to appreciate differences in brightness, size, shape, distance or position of objects; and visual field defects. For example, in obtaining data on visual acuity we utilized pulling-in reactions; the caged-in animal was required to pull in black or white threads a fraction of a millimeter in diameter and lying on a black or white ground or on surfaces exhibiting complex visual patterns. In determining visual field defects, various methods of "food perimetry" and the "hemianopic testing board"[5c] were used. The application of the pulling-in technic[5a] made it possible to obtain data on the speed of motor reactions, handedness and various motor habits.

2. **Determination of Lateral Tendencies.** Two or more similar objects were placed before the experimental cage. In reacting to objects in a row, any monkey may display strong right or left tendencies; that is, it may tend to pick up or pull in such objects as pieces of food, strings or boxes from the right to the left or vice versa. The test situations employed have been extensively used in a previous study of hemianopic monkeys.[6]

3. **Multiple Object Tests.** Different objects were placed in a row on a table on a piece of cardboard or were suspended from a horizontal string running parallel with the front of the cage and then brought within reach of the animal. In some tests the animal could view the objects before they were placed within reach; in others they were kept out of view until presented. The rows of objects contained either one or more pieces of food or none at all. The objects presented included such items as objects made of glass, wood, paper or metal; feces; live animals; toys; spots of moisture, and drawings made with ink or chalk. In most tests each object was different, but in some tests two or more of the inedible objects were alike.

4. **Investigation of Reactions When Monkey was Free in Room.** The animal was turned loose in a large room which contained pieces of apparatus and furniture, and on the floor of which had been placed various objects, including several pieces of food. During a thirty minute period the reactions were observed by the experimenter and an assistant, who sat in different corners of the room.

5. **"Concentration" Test.** The apparatus, previously described,[7] consists essentially of a rotating platform on which the center of a board, 180 cm. long and 3.5 cm. wide, is fastened. The positions of the apparatus and the experi-

Press, 1933; (b) An Auto-Multi-Stimulation Reaction Board for Use with Sub-Human Primates, J. Psychol. 1: 123–127, 1935; (c) Certain Effects of Lesions of the Occipital Lobes in Monkeys, ibid. 4: 383–401, 1937.
[6] Klüver,[5c] pp. 386 and 387.
[7] Klüver and Bucy.[1b] Klüver.[5a]

mental cage were so adjusted that the monkey was able to reach one end of the rotating board for a short time every thirty seconds. A piece of food was placed on one end of the board and a nail or metal nut on the other. The animal could, therefore, obtain one edible and one inedible object per minute.

6. **Pulling-in Tests.** The tests either represented "string experiments"[5a] or required the pulling in of a box under different conditions. One, several or all of the strings lying within easy reach of the monkey were baited with food or some inedible object. Different "string configurations" were obtained by varying the number, position, length, direction and distance of the strings from each other.

7. **Differential Reactions Established by Training.** The technics used, which have been previously described, included: (a) the "form board," for establishing reactions to visual differences;[8] (b) the automultistimulation reaction board," with two plates for establishing reactions to differences in sound,[5b] and (c) the pulling-in technic, with movable stimulus boxes for establishing reactions to differences in weight.[5a] It should be remarked that "form boards" with one as well as with two holes were used. In tests with the one hole "form board" the animal simply had to push aside the stimulus object, for instance, a circle, to gain access to the food. Differential reactions were established only in 4 of the 8 animals with bilateral temporal lobectomy and in monkey 16 (see "Subjects"). This was done partly in view of Munk's results with dogs. It was thought desirable to have available a series of animals which had not been subjected to systematic training procedures. Monkeys 1, 5 and 6 were trained to respond positively to a circle and negatively to a square of the same size. In critical trials following the training, groups of equivalent and nonequivalent stimuli were determined. Monkey 8 was trained to react negatively to a sound, the sound being produced by a Cenco impulse counter, and positively to "silence." Monkey 6 was trained to react positively to the lighter of two weights in the 1,050 and 350 Gm. pair. Finally, monkey 16 was trained to respond positively to a circle instead of a square and to respond positively to a 1,150 instead of a 350 Gm. weight.

8. **Investigation of Reactions in the Presence of Animate and Inanimate Objects.** The response of the animal to the presentation of single objects likely to elicit characteristic forms of behavior, especially emotional reactions, was studied. We employed such objects as a snake, a cat, a dog, a rat, a mirror, a metal stick (such as is used in transferring a monkey from one cage to the other) and a catcher (used in catching monkeys).

9. **Investigation of Implement-Using Behavior.** Analysis of the ability to utilize objects as "tools," as previous studies have indicated,[9] seems worth while only in the case of Cebus monkeys. The present series includes 1 Cebus monkey (case 5); all the other animals were macaques. Implement-using behavior was studied only in the case of the Cebus monkey.

SURGICAL PROCEDURES

We shall briefly indicate the procedures employed in temporal lobectomy. In all cases anesthesia was induced by intraperitoneal injection of pentobarbital

[8] Klüver.[5c] Klüver and Bucy.[1b]

[9] Klüver, H.: Re-Examination of Implement-Using Behavior in a Cebus Monkey After an Interval of Three Years, Acta psychol. 2: 347–397, 1937; footnote 5a.

sodium. A temporal osteoplastic flap was reflected downward from over the temporal lobe. The pia-arachnoid membrane was coagulated and then cut with the Bovie high frequency current just below and parallel to the sylvian vessels and transversely across the temporal lobe at the level of the anastomotic vein of Labbé, if it occupied its usual position, or at a point just posterior to the lower end of the central sulcus. A blunt spatula was then inserted along these lines of incision and the lobe, including its medial surface, removed. Bleeding was controlled with the Bovie cautery. Whenever possible, the tissue was removed in a single block, weighed and preserved for histologic examination. The wound was carefully dried and the bone flap replaced. Muscle and scalp were closed with several layers of silk sutures.

Some of the animals have been killed, while others are still being studied. The brains of the animals killed have been or are being serially sectioned, and the sections have been stained both for myelinated fibers (by Weil's method) and for cellular elements (with cresyl violet).

A preliminary microscopic examination, for instance, of the brain of monkey 4 has shown that the extirpation included Brodmann's areas 22, 21 and 20, with the exception of the upper part of area 22 lying anterior to area 19. The uncus and almost the entire hippocampus were removed. Throughout the extent of the lesion only a thin dorsomedial strip of the hippocampus remained. Posteriorly, as the hippocampus turns dorsally toward the hippocampal commissure, about one fifth of this structure remained. The basal ganglia were not damaged except for the amygdala, which had been largely removed, and the tail of the caudate nucleus, which had been removed or seriously damaged.

SUBJECTS

In the following list we have indicated the species, the sex and weight of the animal, the type and date of the operation and the date of death, if it has occurred. In 7 of the 8 cases of bilateral temporal lobectomy the operation was performed in two stages. In 1 case both lobes were removed simultaneously (case 8). Cases 9 to 15 represent animals in which the temporal lobes were severed from either the frontal or the occipital lobes or in which one or portions of one or of both temporal lobes were removed. In case 16 one temporal lobe was extirpated subsequent to removal of both prefrontal areas.

Case 1. A female rhesus monkey (Macaca mulatta), weighing 6.3 Kg., underwent extirpation of the left temporal lobe on Dec. 7, 1936 and extirpation of the right temporal lobe on Jan. 25, 1937. The animal was killed on Dec. 7, 1938.

Case 2. A male rhesus monkey, weighing 3.8 Kg., underwent extirpation of the left temporal lobe, on Feb. 1, 1937 and extirpation of the right temporal lobe on Feb. 23, 1937. The animal was killed on July 8, 1937.

Case 3. A male rhesus monkey, weighing 3.42 Kg., underwent extirpation of the right temporal lobe on Feb. 4, 1937 and extirpation of the left temporal lobe on Sept. 17, 1937. The animal was killed on Oct. 27, 1937.

Case 4. A female rhesus monkey, weighing 3.36 Kg., underwent extirpation of the right temporal lobe on Feb. 11, 1937 and extirpation of the left temporal lobe on February 23, 1937. The animal was killed on March 18, 1937.

Case 5. A male Cebus monkey (Cebus capucina), weighing 2.82 Kg., underwent extirpation of the left temporal lobe on Sept. 17, 1937 and extirpation of the right temporal lobe on Oct. 15, 1937. The animal is still living.

Case 6. In a male rhesus monkey, weighing 2.72 Kg., the olfactory tracts were cut on July 22, 1938. The right temporal lobe was extirpated on Nov. 25, 1938 and the left temporal lobe on Jan. 27, 1939. The animal is still living.

Case 7. In a male rhesus monkey, weighing 4.65 Kg., the left temporal lobe was extirpated on Dec. 20, 1938 and the right temporal lobe on Feb. 6, 1939. The animal is still living.

Case 8. A male rhesus monkey, weighing 4.9 Kg., underwent simultaneous bilateral extirpation of the temporal lobes on Jan. 23, 1939. The animal is still living.

Case 9. A male rhesus monkey, weighing 4.04 Kg., underwent extirpation of the first convolution of the left temporal lobe on April 14, 1938 and extirpation of the first convolution of the right temporal lobe on July 8, 1938. The animal is still living.

Case 10. A female rhesus monkey, weighing 3.17 Kg., underwent extirpation of the second and third convolutions of the right temporal lobe on May 26, 1938 and extirpation of the second and third convolutions of the left temporal lobe on July 16, 1938. The animal is still living.

Case 11. In a female Java monkey, weighing 1.4 Kg., the connections between the temporal and the frontal lobe were severed, i.e., the anterosuperior margin of the lesion produced by temporal lobectomy was duplicated, on the left side on April 18, 1938. Connections between the temporal and the frontal lobe on the right side were severed on July 19, 1938. The animal is still living.

Case 12. In a male rhesus monkey, weighing 3.07 Kg., the connections between the temporal and the frontal lobe were severed on the left side on July 12, 1938 and on the right side on Sept. 27, 1938. The animal is still living.

Case 13. In a male rhesus monkey, weighing 3.2 Kg., the connections between the temporal and the occipital lobe were severed, i. e., the posterior margin of the lesion produced by temporal lobectomy was duplicated, on the right side on July 13, 1938. The connections between the temporal and the occipital lobe on the left side were severed on Sept. 29, 1938. The animal is still living.

Case 14. A female rhesus monkey, weighing 4.36 Kg., underwent extirpation of the left temporal lobe on Feb. 4, 1937 and was killed on May 17, 1937.

Case 15. A male rhesus monkey, weighing 4.2 Kg., underwent extirpation of the second and third convolutions of the left temporal lobe on April 15, 1938. The animal was killed on April 23, 1938.

Case 16. A female rhesus monkey, weighing 4.22 Kg., underwent extirpation of the left prefrontal area on Feb. 11, 1937, of the right prefrontal area on May 12, 1938 and of the left temporal lobe on Jan. 30, 1939. The animal is still living.

EFFECTS OF BILATERAL TEMPORAL LOBECTOMY

We shall describe the polysymptomatic picture as observed in the "bilateral temporal" monkey. It should be said first that the present investigation has essentially confirmed the results[1b] obtained in case 1. Such symptoms as were exhibited in case 1 can be observed immediately after extirpation of the second temporal lobe or after simultaneous removal of the two lobes, and although certain changes occur in the course of time, it is worthy of note that the picture found in case 1 about two years after the operations is in most of its characteristic features essentially the same as can be observed in the bilateral temporal monkey as early as twenty-four hours after the operations. We shall first describe forms of behavior which seem to indicate that the ability to recognize and detect the meaning of objects on the basis of visual criteria alone is either lost or seriously disturbed, although the animal exhibits no, or at least no gross, defect in the ability to discriminate visually. We have summarized this group of symptoms under the term "psychic blindness."

"Psychic Blindness." The bilateral temporal monkey shows a strong tendency to approach animate and inanimate objects without hesitation. This tendency appears even in the presence of objects which previously called forth avoidance reactions, extreme excitement and other forms of emotional response. The animal tends to contact every object in sight and to examine it by mouth rather than by hand. In multiple object tests, the caged-in monkey, even when hungry, will pick up objects indiscriminately either one after the other or, by using both hands, two at a time. After an oral examination, the object, if inedible, such as a nail, a glass, a live mouse, feces or a piece of sealing wax, is discarded, but if edible is immediately consumed. In general, all available objects are examined, even though the first object examined may be the only piece of food present among the objects presented and even though the row of objects lying before the cage may contain no food at all. In a given test situation, an inedible object which has been discarded after a first examination may be reexamined several times. If the row of objects contains, let us say, one piece of food and four inedible objects, the reexamination of such an object as an electric bulb or a socket may take place before or after the food has been picked up. If the same objects are presented again in the next test or on succeeding days the animal examines them as if they were being presented for the first time. In such a way, a given object may be examined again and again in the course of several months as if it had never been responded to before. The animal tends to examine all available objects, even if two or more of the objects lying in a row are alike. If the inedible objects are not removed after each test, the animal may frequently reexamine them not only between tests but also while a new series of objects is lying before the cage.

Although it has been our endeavor to present as great a variety of objects as possible in the various multiple object situations, we have not succeeded in finding any object which the bilateral temporal monkey did not want to examine. Objects are examined, no matter whether they are very large or very small, dead or alive, edible or inedible, moving or stationary, silent or noisy, solid or figures printed on paper. The monkey seems to be just as eager to examine the tongue of a hissing snake, the mouth of a cat, feces, a wire cage or a wagon as a piece of food.

The tendency to respond indiscriminately to various objects not only appears in the multiple object tests but may be just as strong when the animal is left to itself in its home cage or when it is turned loose in a room. When in its home cage the animal may examine at random pieces of food, the food pan itself, stones, cigaret stubs and wires lying among the pieces of food, the head of a screw in the wall of the cage and a chain hanging down from the door. If free in a large room the animal may contact and examine more than 100 objects in thirty minutes and may pass the pieces of food lying on the floor many times before picking them up. The examination includes such heterogeneous objects as a steel nut in a motor, an iron pipe, the tail of a monkey, a windowpane, the fingers, shoes and stopwatch of the experimenter and a piece of soap. When free in a room, the monkey again tends to reexamine most objects at intervals, so that a given object, let us say an iron pipe, may be examined a dozen times in the course of half an hour. It is worthy of note that the monkey never changes the position of any of the objects in the room and that even very small objects are not carried around. Occasionally an object may be picked up for examination, but then is dropped at the same place. The animal in moving about behaves as if all available objects belonged to one general class, as if they were merely "something to be approached and examined."

In the "concentration" test, in which a piece of food or a metal object passes the experimental cage every thirty seconds, the monkey picks up both the food and the metal object until it ceases reacting to both. The food is eaten, whereas the nail or the steel nut is discarded after an examination by mouth. In some experimental period, both the food and the inedible object are picked up in 100 percent of the trials. Even after as many as 260 successive trials the monkey may remove the nail each time it passes, so that finally more than a hundred nails may lie on the floor of its cage. As a rule, however, the monkey is not content with removing and examining the metal object in all, or practically all, trials; it will frequently pick up a nail or a steel nut from the floor of the cage in the intervals between removing an object every thirty seconds. It should be pointed out that the normal monkey in this test situation will let the nail pass by in all trials or pick it up only the first few times.

In pulling-in tests, the animal tends to pull in the strings indiscriminately, no matter whether edible or inedible objects or no objects are attached to them. In fact, the monkey may first examine the cardboard on which the strings are lying, then one string after the other and, finally, after the pulling-in, the object fastened to the string. Again, the strings and objects already pulled in may be examined between trials. When pulling in boxes, the monkey may examine the string repeatedly during the pulling-in and the box itself before reaching into it.

Oral Tendencies. There exists a strong tendency to examine all objects by mouth. The fact that in the multiple object tests and in other test situations we have not discovered any kind of object the monkey did not want to examine means, therefore, that we have found no object the animal was not prone to examine orally. This oral examination consists in putting the object into the mouth, biting gently, chewing, licking, touching with the lips and "smelling" by holding the object before the nostrils. At times the object is first put into the mouth and then "smelled;" sometimes the "smelling" occurs first. Either reaction is rarely absent in examining an object. Oral tendencies are present not only in the sense that the animal examines the object orally but also in that it tends to contact the object directly by mouth instead of using its hands. Even in the multiple object tests, in which the objects are lying before the cage, the animal may often attempt to press its head through the bars to establish direct contact with its mouth. Since this is not possible, the monkey is forced to pick up the objects for oral examination. "Objects" which cannot be picked up, such as spots of moisture, drawings made on the table or designs on wallpaper, are frequently touched, rubbed or scratched after futile attempts have been made to pick them up. Such reactions are frequently followed by holding the hand or one finger before the nostrils. The "smelling" of fingers is also observed if an object is beyond reach so that no contact can be established by hand or mouth. Occasionally this "smelling" even precedes the touching or picking up of an object within reach. The monkey may repeatedly stick out its tongue to contact a metal object moving back and forth before the cage, although such an object can be easily reached by hand. The tendency to examine objects orally is not interfered with, of course, when the animal is turned loose in a room. The monkey will run from one object to another and contact and examine the various objects, or parts of them, by mouth. At times the reaction seems to be confined merely to "smelling" glass, metal or other objects, since the mouth does not come in direct contact with the object. When transferred to another cage, the monkey frequently first makes an oral examination of the door, chain, galvanized iron of the floor, heads of nails or other parts of the cage. In the "concentration" test, the hundredth nail picked up is examined orally in the same way as was the first nail removed from the board. In pulling-in tests the monkey examines not only the various objects pulled in but also the stick or the hand of the experimenter used for removing these objects from the experimental cage after completion of the test.

The tendency to examine objects orally is present even though the objects may have acquired "meaning" through previous training. For instance, in the "form board" test the animal is required to choose a circle instead of a square. For the normal monkey which has learned this problem the circle merely points to, or signifies, the presence of food. It is not reacted to for its own sake. It is an object to be pushed aside to gain access to the piece of food. For the bilateral temporal monkey the circle does not signify another object, that is, food, but both circle and square are treated as any other object, that is, as something to be examined. At times both stimulus figures are picked up, examined by mouth and discarded before even an attempt is made to take the piece of food lying in one of the holes. When the automultistimulation reaction board is placed before the cage, the animal may try to contact the apparatus by mouth and, since this is impossible, may at least remove the brass squares, take them into the cage and examine them orally.

It is of great interest that the normal rhesus monkey which gets hold of an inedible object is generally dominated by the tendency to tear it rapidly to pieces by using the hands and mouth. In contrast to this, the bilateral temporal monkey when confronted with a variety of objects evidences a certain lack of aggressiveness toward the objects in the sense that it confines its activities to biting them gently, to licking or to touching them with the mouth; in brief, to examining them orally in different ways. The same type of reaction or, differently expressed, the same lack of aggressiveness toward objects appears when the animal is turned loose in a room. No attempt is made to destroy, break or carry objects around.

The reactions, and especially the oral tendencies, observed in case 6 deserve special comment, as the olfactory tracts of this monkey were cut previous to removing both temporal lobes. After the olfactory tracts were severed, the characteristic gesture of "smelling" an object by holding it before the nostrils was still observed for a week. Thereafter, up to the present, for about ten months, the "smelling," even of pieces of food, has never been observed. After section of the olfactory tracts but prior to removal of the temporal lobes the monkey did not show any tendency to pick up inedible objects; even edible objects, in case the animal was not familiar with them, were frequently not taken. This type of behavior did not change when, after about four months, the right temporal lobe was removed. When the left temporal lobe was extirpated about six months after the olfactory tracts were severed, all of the symptoms characteristic of the bilateral temporal monkey appeared except that no "smelling" was ever observed. Although one of the components in the picture of oral tendencies was absent, it is significant that oral tendencies were present as in any other animal with bilateral temporal lobectomy. The results may be best illustrated by reference to the "concentration" test. After the cutting of the olfactory tracts, the animal picked up the piece of food in 100 percent and the metal object in 2 percent of the trials. There was never any "smelling" of the objects. After removal of the right temporal lobe exactly the same results were obtained. When the left lobe was also removed the "smelling" reactions continued to be absent, but the animal now picked up the nail or the steel nut in 92 percent of the trials and in each case examined the object by mouth before discarding it. In brief, it may be said that the reactions observed in the "concentration" test, the multiple object tests, the pulling-in tests and the other test situations clearly indicated that monkey 6 was not different from any other animal with bilateral temporal lobectomy in its tendency to pick up objects indiscriminately and then examine them by mouth.

"Hypermetamorphosis." Any description of the typical behavior of the bilateral temporal monkey is incomplete without reference to another characteristic reaction tendency. When the reactions of the monkey to animate and inanimate objects are observed, it frequently appears to the observer as if the animal were acting under the influence of some "compulsory" or "irresistible" impulse. It behaves as if it were "forced" to react to objects, events and changes in the environmental stimulus constellation. Thus, it may be said that in the bilateral temporal monkey there exists an excessive tendency to take notice of and to attend and react to every visual stimulus. The symptom described here has been given various names by neurologists and psychiatrists, for instance, by Wernicke, Sommer, Leupoldt, Steiner and others. For the sake of brevity, we shall adopt the terminology of Wernicke,[10] who spoke of a "hypermetamorphosis" and a "hypermetamorphic impulse to action."

The monkey immediately attends to and takes in quickly the various details of a visual situation. The close visual inspection is not confined to objects within reach. The objects singled out for inspection may include such items as an eyelet in a board, a speck of dirt on a mirror, a scratch on the table, a nut in a motor, a stone in a ring, the foot of a toy monkey, a whiff of smoke, cuff buttons, a wrist watch and the mouth of the experimenter. When confronted with a series of objects, the monkey frequently looks from one object to the other before seizing one and often picks up two at a time. In the "concentration" test the animal may almost constantly attend to the end of a moving board and in such a way succeed in removing an object every thirty seconds for more than two hours. It seems clear, therefore, that a "paresis of attention" or similar defects cannot be assumed to account for the picture of "psychic blindness."

[10] Wernicke, C.: Gundriss der Psychiatrie, Leipzig, Georg Thieme, 1906.

The outstanding characteristic of the various reactions is not that the monkey attends visually to such a variety of stimuli and evinces such great curiosity in all kinds of objects and events. The most impressive feature is that the presentation of any visual object will, whenever possible, immediately lead to a motor response. For the bilateral temporal monkey the most heterogeneous objects, varying from a dot in a necktie to the tongue of a hissing snake, have become equivalent in the sense that they evoke the same typical forms of motor behavior. Expressed differently, certain properties of the objects, their being "dangerous," "inedible" or "indifferent," have suddenly become ineffective in determining visually guided reactions. The monkey seems to be dominated by only one tendency, namely, the tendency to contact every object as quickly as possible. The speed with which contact is established is especially great when only a single object is presented. Noticing an object and performing the requisite motor response for contact seem to be a continuous process. When turned loose in a room, the monkey often behaves as if it were ceaselessly "pulled" from one object to another. When the experimenter or a stranger enters the laboratory, the animal may be seen standing in its cage as near to the door as possible and with an arm extended in the direction of the person entering. If the monkey is prevented from establishing contact with an object by the experimenter keeping the object out of reach, it may start examining the objects available in its cage.

The "hypermetamorphic impulse to action" is set off by almost any kind of object. It seems, therefore, that the fact of an object being an object, that is, a "segregated whole," a "discrete something" different from its surroundings, is in itself sufficient for eliciting this impulse. The multiple object tests and other tests demonstrate the strong tendency of the animal to respond to every available object, no matter what its character, and to reexamine it whenever it is noticed again. Whether or not an object is noticed, however, seems to depend on various factors. For instance, every attempt to remove one of the discarded objects from the cage may be immediately followed by grabbing and examining this or some other object or the hand of the experimenter. The monkey, which picks up, let us say, a nail for the hundredth time to examine it, is examining the same object, i.e., a nail, but the very fact that something is presented within reach, either by the experimenter or by an apparatus, makes possible what was impossible a few seconds ago, namely, a transformation of the "hypermetamorphic impulse to action" into action. At any rate, on appearance of the nail the monkey responds by picking it up.

Sensory and Motor Factors. The question may be raised whether the picture of "psychic blindness," oral tendencies and "hypermetamorphosis" results from a combination of various sensory and motor defects. It appears that defects in "elementary" sensory functions either do not exist or are of a kind not apt to account for the typical behavior of the monkey.

In cases of visual agnosia the attempt must be made to determine whether visual defects of various kinds can in some way account for the reactions observed. One of us[5e] has shown that visual field defects alone, even if they should exist, cannot be considered sufficient to produce the picture of "psychic blindness." It was found that the various differential responses to visual stimuli established by training were not lost, or were only slightly disturbed, after unilateral occipital lobectomy or bilateral destruction of the macular cortex. In these cases Brodmann's areas 18 and 19 were also injured. Since in these cases even very extensive damage to the visual system did not lead to inability to recognize objects visually, it is difficult to understand why such a defect should appear as a consequence of much smaller field defects, as found in some of our bilateral temporal animals. In some cases of temporal lobectomy no field defects can be demonstrated. Yet the previously described symptoms following bilateral temporal lobectomy are the same in animals with and in those without visual field defects. In case 7 the tests indicate the existence of right homonymous hemianopia. The ability to appreciate differences in brightness, size, shape, distance, position and movement is as little impaired in this monkey as it is in monkeys with the left occipital lobe removed.

Our previous analysis of case 1 made the existence of defects in the upper quadrants highly probable.[1b] Since then, the existence of these defects has been supported by anatomic investigation of the brain. When microscopically examined, the right hemisphere showed interruption of the ventral half of the visual radiation close to its origin in the lateral geniculate body. There was presumably a defect involving the upper homonymous quadrant of the left halves of the visual fields, extending probably as far as the horizontal meridians and including the macula. The functional defect to be postulated on the basis of an examination of the left hemisphere was far less extensive and was probably confined to the upper part of the temporal crescent of the right eye. Despite the defects in the upper left quadrants, the monkey would jump without hestiation from the floor to high stands or tables. Anatomic investigation of the brain in case 4 indicates that one must postulate a defect confined to the upper parts of the temporal crescents. Anatomic data on other cases are not as yet available.

In studying visually induced reactions, the question is of interest whether the sequence of reactions in multiple object tests and other test situations is determined by strong lateral tendencies. Such right or left tendencies appear in normal animals, but especially in hemianopic monkeys when series of similar objects are presented. Lateral tendencies also occur at times in cases of bilateral temporal lobectomy, but our observations in multiple object tests and other tests, in which dissimilar objects are introduced, do not support the view that strong right or left tendencies, combined with an excessively strong impulse to action, enforce on the animal a certain sequence of reactions.

The temporal lobes have been of interest chiefly because of their importance for auditory function. In studying the anatomic relationship of the medial geniculate body to the cerebral cortex, Walker[11] has found that in the rhesus monkey the medial geniculate body projects only to a small area on the superior surface of the first temporal convolution. It is of historical interest that work on the functional significance of the temporal lobes has really been concerned with this small area. In our operations no attempt was made to remove this area, since our interest in temporal lobe functions was aroused by the discovery of one of us (Klüver) that the injection of mescaline or chemically related substances into monkeys produces peculiar chewing and licking movements as well as convulsions, in other words, symptoms resembling those found in the "uncinate group of fits" described by Hughlings Jackson and Stewart.[12] It was thought desirable, therefore, to remove the temporal lobes, including the uncus. In pass-

---

[11] Walker, A. E.: The Primate Thalamus, Chicago, University of Chicago Press, 1938.
[12] Jackson, J. H., and Stewart, P.: Epileptic Attacks with a Warning of a Crude Sensation of Smell and with the Intellectual Aura (Dreamy State) in a Patient Who Had Symptoms Pointing to Gross Organic Disease of the Right Temporo-Sphenoidal Lobe, Brain 22: 534–549, 1899.

ing, it should be noted that the symptoms produced by mescaline are the same in the bilateral temporal monkey as in the normal monkey.

The bilateral temporal monkeys in our series did not exhibit any disturbance in auditory function if judged by the motor reactions to various sounds. Although quantitative data are lacking, it seems justifiable to assume that at least gross defects were absent. The anatomic data so far available support this view. In case 1 only the caudal tips of the medial geniculate bodies were degenerated. In case 4 the posterior one fourth or one third of the medial geniculate bodies was degenerated, the degeneration being more extensive on the right side. For several weeks, and even months, these animals do not vocalize; no sound is uttered in response to other monkeys. The monkey is likely to remain silent even if it is attacked or if the whole colony is shouting at feeding time. The vocal behavior which appears thereafter seems to differ from that of the normal monkey. The fact that the animals respond to and yet do not seem to recognize the meaning of sounds suggests the possibility of "agnosia" in the auditory field.

The possibility of a tactile agnosia must also be considered, although we failed to detect changes in cutaneous sensitivity in most cases. None of the monkeys was satisfied with touching, grasping or manipulating the objects. Seizing an object was merely preparatory to transporting it to the mouth. With the methods at our disposal, it was difficult to obtain reliable data on the gustatory and the olfactory sense, but it is noteworthy that inedible objects were never swallowed. Inedible objects were always discarded after an oral examination, although even feces were often chewed several times before being removed. Nevertheless, the type and speed of removing objects, such as feces, a piece of food soaked in quinine or a wooden or metal object, were often strikingly different. In view of the fact that the lesions involved all or the greater part of the hippocampus and uncus, it is of special interest that the "smelling" of objects and the characteristic gesture of holding an object before the nostrils represent some of the most typical reactions of the bilateral temporal monkey. It is significant that such reactions were absent in case 6, which the olfactory tracts had been cut.

The motor reactions involved in grasping, holding, picking up and pulling in objects were essentially the same as in normal monkeys. In some cases abnormalities of gait were observed. Although the tendency to approach and contact every object seemed equally strong in all animals, there were considerable differences in the amount of spontaneous activity. All of the more active monkeys tended to perform "antics," not only when they could not get certain objects beyond reach but also when they were left to themselves in their home cages. In our previous description of case 1 it was pointed out that we frequently observed a "sequence of gesticulations, involving arms, head and most of the body."[1b] These gesticulations and similar movement patterns in other cases are difficult to describe. The many peculiar movements executed by the animal while sitting, lying, jumping or hanging from the top or sides of the cage frequently arouse the mirth of a casual observer. The monkey may repeatedly put both feet, or one foot and one hand, simultaneously behind its neck. It may jump around on the floor of the cage while holding on to one foot with one hand and then without letting the foot go may jump to the seat of the cage. In jumping from the seat to the floor, it may seize the wire mesh at the top of the cage first with its hands, then with its feet, and then may drop to the floor, landing on its hands first. It may swing and perform peculiar twists of its body while hanging with its feet from the top of the cage. It may grab one forearm with one hand and move both arms up and down. It may hang with its hands from the top of the cage and, after pulling its body through the space between its arms, may swing back and forth with its feet almost touching the floor of the cage. It may repeat such movement patterns many times and combine them in different ways. In fact, the general picture is that of a witzelsucht of the extremities.

Emotional Changes. In the bilateral temporal monkey we find either profound changes in emotional behavior or complete absence of all emotional reactions in the sense that the motor and vocal reactions generally associated with anger and fear are not exhibited. This change in affectivity is especially remarkable in view of the fact that care has been taken to use only "wild," aggressive monkeys in this work.

The fact that the monkey approaches every object without hesitation, no matter whether it be a catcher, a large bull snake or a strange person, represents in itself a striking deviation from normal behavior. Even bodily contact with an object does not produce avoidance reactions or other forms of behavior indicative of fear. Movements, for instance, of a live animal when being examined, or other forms of sensory stimulation may, because of their suddenness, lead to retreat, but often immediately thereafter a new attempt is made to establish contact with the object.

The typical reaction of a "wild" monkey when suddenly turned loose in a room consists in getting away from the experimenter as rapidly as possible. It will try to find a secure place near the ceiling or hide in an inaccessible corner where it cannot be seen. If seen, it will either crouch and, without uttering a sound, remain in a state of almost complete immobility or suddenly dash away to an apparently safer place. This behavior is frequently accompanied by other signs of strong emotional excitement. In general, all such reactions are absent in the bilateral temporal monkey. Instead of trying to escape, it will contact and examine one object after another or parts of objects, including the experimenter, strangers or other animals. The experimenter may walk over to it, touch and stroke and even pick it up. The monkey often confines itself almost entirely to examining objects which are on or can be reached from the floor. After being attacked and bitten by another animal, it may approach this animal again and again in an attempt to examine it.

While this is the general picture of emotional behavior, individual animals present differences. Expressions of emotions, such as vocal behavior, "chattering" and different facial expressions, are generally lost for several months, but they may reappear. In some cases the loss of anger and fear reactions is complete. In case 6, for instance, the animal is restlessly active most of the time, constantly attending to and responding to numerous stimuli, never resenting any form of handling, always eager to engage in playful activities with the experimenter or to follow him around the room. In fact, it may be said that the picture of normal "wildness" has been replaced by that of "hypomania." The bodily expressions of emotions associated with aggressive tendencies can be observed in some monkeys after a few months. Although such a monkey, with teeth bared and ears laid back, may jump toward the experimenter as if to attack him, it will merely lick or otherwise examine the fingers of the experimenter.

The animal may exhibit expressions of intense emotional excitement in case the floor is swept near its cage or a wagon rolled by, but the moment the monkey is allowed to contact and to examine the broom or the wagon, the anger expressions will immediately subside. It seems that emotional behavior, when it occurs, occurs chiefly in connection with events preceding or following the oral examination of an object, especially when the attempt to contact an object is thwarted.

Changes in Sexual Behavior. In some monkeys the increase in sexual activity is so marked and the manifestations of sexual behavior are so diverse that we are forced to include sexual changes among the symptoms produced by bilateral temporal lobectomy. Such changes are not immediately apparent. We have noticed them first three to six weeks after the operation. It should be noted that 2 of the monkeys in our series were killed before this period. Our observations are, therefore, chiefly concerned with male macaques.

The monkeys appear hypersexed, not only when with other animals but also when alone. The reactions to be recorded either are overt sexual responses or represent forms of behavior involving some sexual element. When the monkey is confined alone in a cage, the following states and activities can be observed: frequent erection of the penis, often without previous manipulation, the glans penis being clearly visible, or semierection, even while the animal is sitting quietly; long-continued licking and sucking of the penis, the animal at times apparently falling asleep with the penis in the mouth; manipulating or pulling at the penis or scrotum, even while the animal is standing; "yawning" (as seen in copulatory reactions) and, at the same time, manipulation of the genitalia while lying on the back or side; oral and manual exploration of the genitalia while the animal is in all kinds of positions, for instance, biting of the penis while swinging back and forth with the feet suspended from the top of the cage and with the hands pressed against the hindquarters; long-continued biting of the fingers, toes, feet, legs and other parts of the body; grabbing the bars of the cage and pressing the hindquarters rhythmically against them, and "presenting reactions" on approach of an observer. Grabbing the finger of the observer may be immediately followed by general bodily activity and penile erection.

Whenever other monkeys are put into the same cage, various forms of heterosexual and homosexual behavior can be observed. The monkey may, for instance, copulate almost continuously for half an hour. It may leave the female only to mount again immediately. If two bilateral temporal male monkeys are put together, sexual behavior may take forms which make it necessary to separate the animals. One of the monkeys while lying on the seat of the cage may reach with one hand toward the floor to grab the erect penis of the other monkey and practically lift the animal from the floor. The animal which is being lifted may do nothing but utter a grunt. Or one monkey may grab the tail of the other and in pulling it across the edge of the seat incidentally break the tail. While one monkey mounts the other and performs copulatory movements, the other one may be seen standing with erect penis. Or both monkeys may lie on the floor and mutually explore each other's genitalia. One monkey may ride on the back of the other and at the same time suck one of its ears. Although they frequently bite each other's legs, arms or tail, fights never develop, and injuries are merely the by-product of heightened sexual activity.

Since such striking manifestations of sexual behavior are completely absent in the normal animals of our colony and do not appear in unilateral temporal monkeys kept on the same diet and under the same conditions, or in monkeys with differently situated lesions, we feel justified in assuming that these sexual changes are dependent on removal of the second temporal lobe or simultaneous removal of both lobes.[13]

GENERAL CONSIDERATION OF BEHAVIORAL CHANGES

Munk failed to produce "psychic blindness" in rhesus monkeys, and although he thought that he had succeeded in producing it in dogs, it was subsequently shown by a number of investigators that visual disturbance and field defects could account for the behavior of the animals. We have found a picture of "psychic blindness" following bilateral temporal lobectomy in the monkey. The importance of this result lies, first of all, in the fact that such a picture can be produced by a cortical operation in animals. At the start, questions such as the duration of the symptoms or the exact nature of the lesions are of secondary importance.

In studying the various reactions and reaction tendencies, we have arrived at a group of symptoms which we may consider "typical" for the bilateral temporal monkey. We are aware that the picture may be modified by a variety of factors. The animals in the present series were studied for varying periods, ranging from three weeks to about two years from the date of the operation. They differed in age, weight, sex and other factors. Nevertheless, in all cases the typical symptoms, which we have briefly summarized under "psychic blindness," oral tendencies, "hypermetamorphosis" and emotional changes, appeared almost immediately and remained remarkably constant for the periods of observation indicated. It is true that changes occurred, but that these changes were not more marked deserves special emphasis. For instance, the experimenter could at all times touch, stroke or slap 6 of the 8 monkeys. Such treatment of the other 2 animals was not possible after several months, but their emotional behavior remained profoundly altered. Monkey 1, which was studied for about 2 years, tended during the last few months, in multiple object tests, to pick up food first and then to examine the remaining objects, but was inclined to pick up objects indiscriminately again when they were kept out of view until presented or when injections of mescaline were given. It should be remembered that many of the objects used in these tests had been presented again and again in the course of previous experiments. In brief, even the long-continued study in this case revealed little change

[13] It is perhaps significant that in case 1 typical "presenting reactions" were frequently observed after a period of one and a half years in spite of the fact that the uterus and both ovaries had been previously removed. This animal, as well as 3 other monkeys that had had similar operations, were supplied to us by Dr. G. W. Bartelmez. Two of these animals were even "wilder" and more "vicious" than the average untamed rhesus monkey. Only 1 of these 4 animals was used in the present study (case 1).

in the general picture presented by "psychic blindness," oral tendencies, "hypermetamorphosis" and emotional changes.[13a]

In considering the polysymptomatic picture following bilateral temporal lobectomy, the question may be raised whether the various symptoms point to one basic defect or disturbance. Conceivably, any of the symptoms described may be indicative of a disturbance in some fundamental mechanism, so that all other symptoms could be understood by reference to one factor. At present, however, any attempt to reduce the variety of behavioral manifestations to one simple formula seems rather hopeless. To determine the mechanisms operative in the behavior of these monkeys further analysis is needed. Preliminary information was obtained in studying various conditioned differential reactions.

In the "form board" test, the monkey was required to react positively to a circle instead of a square. The normal monkey may learn this without even making one error if the tests are preceded by a few trials with a one hole form board. We shall briefly state the results in cases 1, 5 and 6. In case 1 training was started after removal of both temporal lobes. The animal acquired the differential response only with difficulty and after hundreds of trials. For a long time stimulus figures and food were responded to indiscriminately, but finally an errorless performance was reached. Monkeys 5 and 6, which had been trained before the operations, showed a marked disturbance of the differential response after removal of both lobes, but it was possible to reestablish the response through training. The same marked disturbance occurred in the reactions of monkey 8, which had previously been trained to respond negatively to a sound. However, when vibratory stimulation was included by use of a buzzer or a bell fastened below the floor of the cage instead of the original source of sound (a Cenco impulse counter placed at a considerable distance from the cage), the animal immediately obtained food in 100 per cent of the trials by opening the proper receptacle of the automultistimulation reaction board. Only one of the responses established preoperatively was found intact after bilateral temporal lobectomy, namely, the response in case 6 to the lighter weight in the 1,050 and 350 Gm. pair.

More important than these findings, perhaps, is the fact that we were able to demonstrate that the animals had not lost the ability to "generalize" when responding to visual stimuli. In the "form board" tests the properties of the stimuli were changed by introducing variations in size, brightness, color and even shape (by presenting, for instance, an ellipse and a triangle instead of a circle and a square) or by substituting "figures" drawn on cardboard for the circle and the square. Despite these changes, all 3 mon-

[13a] In checking on possible changes in dietary habits, we recently found that the rhesus monkeys with bilateral temporal lobectomy which are still living (monkeys 6, 7 and 8) eat animal foods, such as bacon, liver sausage, boiled ham, boiled tongue, smoked whitefish, ground beef and broiled lamb chops. We have never seen normal rhesus monkeys accept such articles of diet.

keys continued to react positively to the circle or responded immediately to the curvilinear figure.

It may be said that the ability to respond to different objects in terms of such relations as "larger than," "brighter than" or "nearer than," or such properties as "angular" or "curvilinear" implies "generalizations" of a very primitive order. It can be readily understood that adaptive behavior, as long as it occurs at all, presupposes the effectiveness of such properties or the existence of such primitive forms of "generalization," and it is apparently for this reason that investigators have frequently insisted that the *Beziehungsfunktion* cannot really be destroyed by cerebral lesions.

In view of this situation, the results obtained in the Cebus monkey (case 5) are of special interest. The "form board" tests gave no evidence that the ability to "generalize" in responding to visual stimuli was impaired. At the same time, the ability to utilize objects as "tools" in obtaining food was completely lost. It is apparently one thing to recognize that a stick is "longer than" another one or "nearer than" a piece of food; it is another thing to recognize the "tool" character of a stick. As previous work indicates,[9] being "longer than" and being a "tool" are properties which become effective at different levels of adaptive behavior. At any rate, monkey 5 was unable to solve even the simplest problem in which a piece of food lying beyond reach on the floor could be obtained by using a stick lying near the food and within reach of the animal. The response consisted in repeatedly making an oral examination of the stick and again and again reaching for the food with one hand. When different objects were available at the same time, such as a stick, a sack, a wire or a leather belt, the monkey, instead of seizing one of them to obtain food in a few seconds, as it would have done in preoperative tests, repeatedly reached for the food and walked around for half an hour or longer examining one object after another. None of the objects was ever carried around. It is of great theoretic interest to learn whether these results will be confirmed by future work on suitable animals.

EFFECTS OF OTHER LESIONS

The behavioral changes following the removal of one temporal lobe were studied in 8 monkeys (cases 1 to 7 and 14) for periods ranging from about two weeks to seven months. The extirpation of one lobe produced none of the symptoms characteristic of the bilateral temporal monkey. In some cases, however, there was a change in the direction of greater "tameness." This seems significant in view of the fact that we have failed to observe a similar change in monkeys with occipital, parietal or frontal lesions. There was no disturbance in differential responses established before the operation.

Furthermore, the forms of behavior typical of monkeys with both temporal lobes removed did not appear after (1) bilateral removal of the first temporal convolution (case 9); (2) unilateral or bilateral removal of the second and third temporal convolutions (cases 10 and 15); (3) severing the connections between the temporal and the frontal lobes (cases 11 and 12), or (4) severing the connections between the temporal and the occipital lobes (case 13). Only in case 13 was there uncertainty as to whether at least some of the symptoms existed in an attenuated form.

Of special interest are the results in case 16. The chief effect of removing the left temporal lobe subsequent to removal of both prefrontal areas was disappearance of the restlessness and the hyperactivity characteristic of the prefrontal monkey and a marked change in the direction of greater "tameness."[14]

COMMENT

In view of the fact that the anatomic study of the brains has not yet been completed, a detailed discussion of the relations between behavioral and neural mechanisms is out of the question. At this point it seems worth while, however, to relate some of the results of our behavioral analysis to data furnished by human pathology.

We may consider the outstanding characteristic of the behavioral changes following bilateral temporal lobectomy to be that they affect the relation between animal and environment so deeply. A monkey which approaches every enemy to examine it orally will conceivably not survive longer than a few hours if turned loose in a region with a plentiful supply of enemies. We doubt that a monkey would be seriously hampered under natural conditions, in the wild, by a loss of its prefrontal region, its parietal lobes or its occipital lobes, as long as small portions of the striate cortex remained intact.

The fact that removal of both temporal lobes in the monkey may result in such profound behavior changes, particularly in the emotional sphere, becomes of special interest in view of the insistence of previous writers, such as Anglade, Takase and Marburg, that the temporal lobes in man are in some way concerned with emotions or "affective tonus."[15] The possible significance of the temporal lobes for emotional behavior has also been brought out in recent discussions of the nonolfactory functions of the "olfactory" cortex. It should be recalled that our extirpations include structures generally represented as subserving some phase of olfactory function. Her-

[14] Spontaneous activity was registered by utilizing vacuum tube amplification. The floor of the cage was covered with pieces of galvanized iron separated by gaps of about 1.5 cm. A minute current passing through the body of the animal operated a relay control whenever the animal walked or ran across these gaps. In such a way the number of circling movements or other movements from one part of the cage to the other could be automatically recorded by an electric counter.

[15] von Economo, C., and Koskinas, G. N.: Die Cytoarchitektonik der Hirnrinde des erwachsenen Menschen, Berlin, Julius Springer, 1925.

rick[16] expressed the view that the olfactory cortex may serve as a nonspecific activator for all cortical activities and that it may act on "the internal apparatus of general bodily attitude, disposition and affective tone." In studying the rhinencephalon of the dolphin, Addison[17] found that the hippocampus, fornix, mamillary bodies and habenular and amygdaloid nuclei are present, although the olfactory bulbs and tracts are lacking. Langworthy[18] made similar observations in the porpoise. It is of interest that the parolfactory cortex, which Edinger termed a center for the *Oralsinn*, was present in both forms. In the opinion of Langworthy, "the fact that the hippocampus, fornix, and mamillary bodies persist . . . suggests that they must have functions other than olfactory."

The nonolfactory functions of these structures have recently been emphasized in a different connection by Papez,[19] who attempted to find an "anatomic basis of the emotions" by correlating anatomic, clinical and experimental data of various kinds. He stated:

It is proposed that the hypothalamus, the anterior thalamic nuclei, the gyrus cinguli, the hippocampus and their interconnections constitute a harmonious mechanism which may elaborate the functions of central emotion, as well as participate in emotional expression.

Papez suggested that "the central emotive process of cortical origin" may be built up in the hippocampus and transferred to the mamillary body and thence through the anterior nuclei of the thalamus to the cortex of the cingular gyrus, from which the process may spread to other regions in the cerebral cortex. He found "no clinical or other evidence" to support the view that these structures mediate olfactory function.

In our experiments, the cortical circuit proposed by Papez has been definitely interrupted by removal of the hippocampus. The fact that none of the typical symptoms appeared in animals in which the hippocampus was left intact may also be interpreted as lending further support to Papez' theory. As pointed out before, the behavioral reactions characteristic of the bilateral temporal monkey were absent when only the first convolution or the second and third convolutions of the temporal lobes were removed, or when the connections between the frontal and the temporal lobes or between the occipital and the temporal lobes were severed. Whether the hippocampal formation and its connections play such a decisive role in emotional behavior, as suggested by Papez, can only be determined by subsequent experimentation. To throw further light on the symptomatology of the bilateral temporal monkey, it will be necessary to study not only

[16] Herrick, C. J.: The Functions of the Olfactory Parts of the Cerebral Cortex, Proc. Nat. Acad. Sc. **19:** 7–14, 1933.

[17] Addison, W. H. F.: On the Rhinencephalon of Delphinus Delphis, L., J. Comp. Neurol. **25:** 497–522, 1915.

[18] Langworthy, O. R.: A Description of the Central Nervous System of the Porpoise (Tursiops Truncatus), J. Comp. Neurol. **54:** 437–499, 1932.

[19] Papez, J. W.: A Proposed Mechanism of Emotion, Arch. Neurol. & Psychiat. **38:** 725–743 (Oct.) 1937.

the effects of differently situated subtotal lesions but also the changes following a resection of the fornix or an isolated removal of the hippocampus. Herrick[16] has called attention to the fact that most ablation operations performed in connection with studies of behavior have involved only the neopallium, leaving the olfactory cortex entirely intact or but slightly injured. He pointed out the necessity for removing the various parts of the olfactory cortex in an isolated manner, although this may involve "difficult, but probably not impossible surgical operations."

Kleist[20] has advanced ideas similar to those of Papez in proposing an anatomic substratum for enteroceptive functions, i. e., drives, attitudes, personality traits, moods and emotions. Spatz[21] expressed doubt that the highly developed *Orbitalhirn* of Kleist and the primitive allocortical olfactory region are intimately related and emphasized the importance of the "basal cortex" of the temporal and the frontal lobe for personality changes. He advanced the opinion that no other disease is more important for advancing knowledge of cortical localization than Pick's disease. In this disease there are not only fundamental changes in personality and character but also such symptoms as echolalia, echopraxia and palilalia.[22] Even in the last stages of the disease the patient may still visually attend to everything that is going on and seize every object within reach to put it into his mouth.[23]

In considering the "hypermetamorphosis" and "hypermetamorphic impulse to action" in the bilateral temporal monkey, we commented on the "compulsory" nature of the reactions. The question may be raised whether the lack of inhibition displayed in seizing every object and the tendency to respond to the same object again and again find their parallel in the symptomatology in cases of lesions in the human temporal lobe. It is perhaps significant that the analysis of speech disorders led Pick[24] to the view that the temporal lobes form the anatomic basis of inhibition, the absence of which leads to logorrhea, various echo symptoms (echolalia, echographia, echopraxia) and paraphasia. According to him, the speech utterances accompanying the epileptic aura or the "dreamy states" of Hughlings Jackson also involve the same mechanism of disinhibition.

In studying the similarities of catatonic and encephalitic disturbances in motility, Steiner[25] found postencephalitic children who touched and ex-

[20] Kleist, K.: Breicht über die Gehirnpathologie in ihrer Bedeutung für Neurologie und Psychiatrie, Ztschr. f. d. ges. Neurol. u. Psychiat. **158**: 159–193, 1937.

[21] Spatz, H.: Ueber die Bedeutung der basalen Rinde, Ztschr. f. d. ges. Neurol. u. Psychiat. **158**: 208–232, 1937.

[22] Benedek, L., and Lehoczky, T.: The Clinical Recognition of Pick's Disease: Report of Three Cases, Brain **62**: 104–122, 1939.

[23] von Braunmühl, A., and Leonhard, K.: Ueber ein Schwesternpaar mit Pickscher Krankheit, Ztschr. f. d. ges. Neurol. u. Psychiat. **150**: 209–241, 1934.

[24] Pick, A.: Aphasie, in Bethe, A.; von Bergmann, G.; Embden, G., and Ellinger, A.: Handbuch der normalen und pathologischen Physiologie, Berlin, Julius Springer, 1931, vol. 15, pt. 2, pp. 1416–1524.

[25] Steiner, G.: Encephalitische und katatonische Motilitätsstörungen, Ztschr. f. d. ges. Neurol u. Psychiat. **138**: 553–561, 1922.

amined every object in sight by hand without uttering a word. He expressed the view that a "hypermetamorphosis" which takes the form of touching and tactually examining every object is closely related to echopraxia and echolalia. It is of interest that Leyser,[26] Lotmar[27] and others stated that "hypermetamorphosis," profound changes in affectivity and changes in sexual behavior are the outstanding symptoms in cases of epidemic encephalitis.

The fact that a picture of "psychic blindness," as described by Munk, should result from lesions of the temporal lobe is not readily explained at present. The close relation of aphasic and agnostic symptoms has been frequently emphasized. It is known from Walker's study of the thalamocortical projection of the rhesus monkey that the temporal lobe has few or no thalamic connections except from the medial geniculate body.[11] The functional significance of this observation is not clear, but it seems that the elaboration of impulses relayed from the periphery by way of the thalamus cannot be one of the chief functions of the temporal lobes. The importance of the corticifugal fiber connections of the temporal region, as studied by Mettler,[28] must also be considered. Niessl von Mayendorf[29] has advanced the theory that visual agnosia is due to lesions of the left macular bundle of the visual radiation or of the cortical representation of the macula in the left hemisphere. We consider it safe to assume that the picture of "psychic blindness," as found in the bilateral temporal monkey, is not due to such lesions. The anatomic investigation, for instance, of the brain of monkey 4 has clearly demonstrated that both macular bundles are intact. The behavioral tests applied to animals still living definitely suggest that visual field defects do not exist in the majority of cases.

SUMMARY

The behavioral effects of the removal of both temporal lobes, including the uncus and the greater part of the hippocampus, were studied in macaques. The monkeys exhibited the following symptoms: (1) forms of behavior which seem to be indicative of "psychic blindness"; (2) strong oral tendencies in examining available objects (licking, biting gently, chewing, touching with the lips, "smelling"); (3) a strong tendency to attend and react to every visual stimulus ("hypermetamorphosis"); (4) marked changes in emotional behavior or absence of emotional reactions in the sense

[26] Leyser, E.: Untersuchungen über die Charakterveränderungen nach Encephalitis epidemica, Arch. f. Psychiat. **72**: 552–609, 1925.

[27] Lotmar, F.: Die Stammganglien und die extrapyramidal-motorischen Syndrome, in Foerster, O., and Wilmanns, K.: Monographien aus dem Gesamtgebiete der Neurologie und Psychiatrie, Berlin, Julius Springer, 1926, no. 48, pp. 1–169.

[28] Mettler, F. A.: Corticifugal Fiber Connections of the Cortex of Macaca Mulatta: The Temporal Region, J. Comp. Neurol. **63**: 25–47, 1935.

[29] Niessl von Mayendorf, E.: Beiträge zur Lehre von der Seelenblindheit: VIII, Ztschr. f. d. ges. Neurol. u. Psychiat. **159**: 326–344, 1937.

that the motor and vocal reactions generally associated with anger and fear are not exhibited, and (5) an increase in sexual activity. These symptoms also appeared if the olfactory tracts were cut previous to removing both temporal lobes. Even the oral tendencies, except for the "smelling," were present.

The symptoms typical of monkeys with both temporal lobes removed did not appear after (1) bilateral removal of the first temporal convolution; (2) bilateral removal of the second and third temporal convolutions; (3) severing the connections between the temporal and the frontal lobes, i.e., duplicating the anterosuperior margin of the lesion produced by temporal lobectomy; (4) severing the connections between the temporal and the occipital lobes, i. e., duplicating the posterior margin of the lesion produced by temporal lobectomy. The symptoms also did not appear after unilateral temporal lobectomy, except that there was in some cases a change in the direction of greater "tameness." This "tameness" was also observed when after previous extirpation of both prefrontal areas one temporal lobe was removed.

Differential reactions to visual stimuli established preoperatively were seriously disturbed after bilateral temporal lobectomy, but it was possible to reestablish the response through training. The ability to "generalize" in responding to visual stimuli did not seem to be impaired.

ACKNOWLEDGMENT

This research has been aided by a grant from the Committee for Research in Dementia Praecox, founded by the Supreme Council, Thirty-Third Degree, Scottish Rite, Northern Masonic Jurisdiction, U.S.A.

BEHAVIORAL AND EEG CHANGES FOLLOWING CHRONIC BRAIN STEM LESIONS IN THE CAT

D. B. Lindsley, L. H. Schreiner,
W. B. Knowles, and H. W. Magoun

NORTHWESTERN UNIVERSITY

Source   Reprinted from **Electroencephalography and**
Clinical Neurophysiology, *1950, 2, 483–498, with permis-*
sion of the authors and the Elsevier Publishing
Company.

Each twenty-four hours of their existence, in periods that often correspond approximately with daylight and darkness, man and most animals are alternately aware of environmental changes and respond more or less purposefully to them, in a state called wakefulness, or are out of touch with the world about and lie inert and, except for internal processes, motionless, in a state called sleep. It is apparent that pronounced alterations in central neural activity underly these contrasting conditions. Electroencephalography, which has provided a means of sampling this activity directly, has revealed that alert wakefulness is associated with low voltage, fast discharge of the cerebral cortex, while high voltage slow waves characterize electrocortical activity in drowsiness and sleep.

The present approach to study of central neural alterations in sleep and wakefulness had its inception in the discovery that exciting the reticular core of the brain stem and the basal diencephalon abolished existing electrocortical synchrony and substituted low voltage, fast activity in its place, thus reproducing the EEG change seen in spontaneous awakening or in the arousal reaction to natural stimuli (Moruzzi and Magoun, 1949). In the waking "encéphale isolé" acute brain stem lesions in a position to interrupt this reticular activating system were next found to abolish the EEG pattern of wakefulness and to result in recurring slow waves and spindle bursts, like those of sleep or barbiturate anesthesia (Lindsley, Bowden and Magoun, 1949).

With this background, it seemed desirable to determine to what extent correlated behavioral and EEG observation of animals with chronic lesions of the brain stem would support the seemingly important role of its reticular activating system in the induction and maintenance of the waking state. With every attempt to make the operated animal's situation a natural one, EEGs were repeatedly recorded during the survival period and, when the animal was drowsy or asleep, the arousing effect of sensory stimulation was tested.

METHODS

In a series of cats, electrolytic lesions were placed in the brain stem under aseptic precautions with the Horsley-Clarke technique. The animals were followed for survival periods between three weeks and two months, receiving all the postoperative care necessary to maintain them.

EEGs were repeatedly recorded with a Grass model III amplifier and inkwriter. Pickup electrodes consisted of the balled tips of silver wires implanted in the calvarium so as to rest upon the dura. They were either

[1] Aided by a grant from the Commonwealth Fund.

embedded in a threaded plastic cylinder screwed into a tapped trephine opening (Ingram, Knott and Wheatley, 1949), or were forced into a small burr hole, with the insulated length of the wire passing under the skin to emerge from the back of the neck (Rheinberger and Jasper, 1937). The latter type was most often used, three electrodes being inserted over each hemisphere and records being obtained between pairs of them.

RESULTS

Before presenting the consequences of lesions of the brain stem, the EEG events associated with wakefulness and sleep in the normal cat may briefly be described. The records shown in figure 1 are selections from a run in which the normal animal, initially awake, arranged itself in a comfortable reclining position, drowsed for a time, occasionally opening its eyes, then went unmistakably to sleep, ultimately to reawaken. During wakefulness, its EEG was marked by low voltage, fast activity (fig. 1,

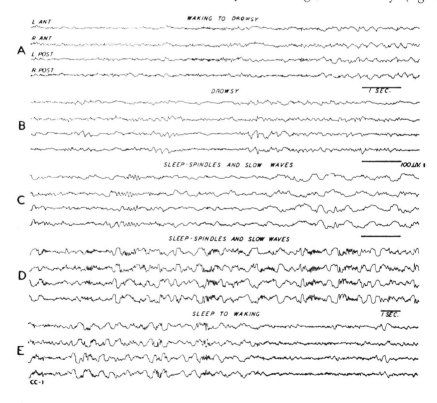

FIGURE 1   *The EEG of a normal cat in wakefulness and sleep. The animal is initially awake (A), drowses (B), goes to sleep (C and D) and reawakens (E). Channels record activity in the anterior and posterior parts of the left and right hemisphere, as indicated. Speed in D and E is half that in A-C. The strips are not continuous.*

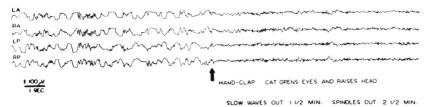

FIGURE 2   *Activation of the EEG of a normal sleeping cat by auditory stimu-*
lation (hand-clap) at arrow. Pickup as in Figure 1.

A). With drowsiness, large slow waves appeared at random in the record
and more moderate amplitude synchrony was present between them (fig.
1, A and B). With sleep, slow waves were larger and slower than before,
and often preceded and followed spindle bursts of 10–15/sec. waves (fig.
1, C–E). Upon awakening, these varieties of EEG synchrony gave way
once more to a low voltage, fast record (fig. 1, E).

The desynchronization of the EEG observed in spontaneous awakening
from sleep (fig. 1, E) could be produced by any stimulus that aroused
the animal to alertness or attention. In the instance shown in figure 2,
with the normal cat asleep, a clap of the hands caused opening of the
eyelids and raising of the head, with concomitant cessation of slow waves
and spindle bursts in the EEG and the appearance and prolonged maintenance of low voltage, fast activity.

In considering, next, the extent to which sleep and wakefulness, and
the EEG alterations associated with them, were influenced by injury to
the rostral brain stem, the results following interruption of the ascending
reticular activating system (A) may be compared with those observed
when this system was spared while other relevant functional components
were destroyed (B).

A. Lesion of the reticular activating system

INJURY TO THE PONTO-MIDBRAIN TEGMENTUM   The most caudal of the
lesions in the reticular formation interrupted most of the tegmentum of
the brain stem, in a plane passing ventrally through the front of the pons,
while sparing more lateral structures (fig. 3).

During the first week, the cat exhibited recurring bouts of running movements and extensor hypertonus, increased by handling. Running movements
were absent during the second and third weeks of its 22 days survival
and, when undisturbed during this period, the animal lay on its side, with
eyes almost closed, and was motionless except for occasional arching of
the back and extension of the legs, augmented by nociceptive stimulation.
Its head was elevated and it appeared awake at the start of six EEG
tests between the third and eighteenth days and, on the third and eighth
days, it was impossible to get the animal to sleep. At these times its EEG
was characterized by small fast waves, slightly more synchronous than

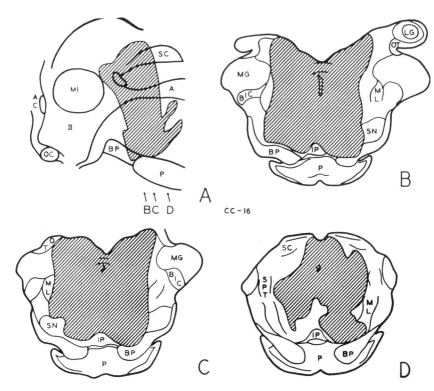

FIGURE 3 *Large lesion of the ponto-midbrain tegmentum whose distribution is projected upon a reconstruction of the midsagittal plane (A) and is shown in transverse sections (B-D), the levels of which are indicated at the base in A.*

Abbreviations for all figures are as follows: A aqueduct, AC anterior commissure, AD anterodorsal nucleus, AM anteromedial nucleus, BIC brachium inferior colliculus, BP basis pedunculi, BRC brachium conjunctivum BSC brachium superior colliculus, C nucleus centralis, CA caudate nucleus, CER cerebellum, CL nucleus centralis lateralis, CM centre median, CT central tegmental tract, D dentate nucleus, EN entopedunclar nucleus, GP globus pallidus, H habenulo-peduncular tract, IC internal capsule, IP interpeduncular nucleus, L lateral thalamic nucleus. LL lateral lemniscus, LG lateral geniculate body, M medial nucleus, MB mammillary body, MF medial longitudinal fasciclus, MG medial geniculate body, MI massa intermedia, ML medial lemniscus, MP mammillary peduncle, OC optic chiasma, OT optic tract, P pons, PC posterior commissure, PL pulvinar, PY pyramid, R restiform body, RN red nucleus, SC superior colliculus, SN substantia nigra, SPT lateral spino-thalamic tract, SVN spinal fifth tract, THAL thalamus, VA veutralis anterior, VL ventralis lateralis, VM ventralis medialis, VPL ventralis posterolateralis, VPM ventralis posteromedialis, III third ventricle, IV fourth ventricle.

those of a normal waking record. With the passage of time, in the remainder of these tests and in others, the animal's head sank to the table and irregular slow waves appeared in the EEG, which was usually lacking in spindle bursts, and contained more sharp, fast waves than are normally present during sleep (fig. 4). When such EEG synchrony was established, both somatic and auditory stimuli abolished it and introduced variable periods of low voltage fast activity (fig. 4, A and B).

LESION MIDBRAIN TEGMENTUM

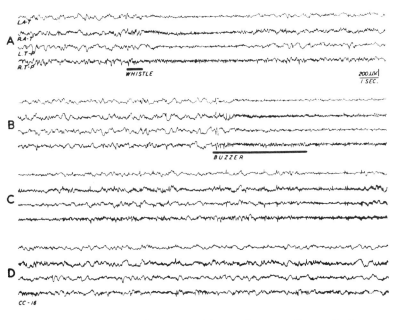

FIGURE 4 *EEG of cat with tegmental lesion shown in Figure 3. Arousing effects of whistle (A) and buzzer (B) on 13th postoperative day. Period of stimulation indicated by a heavy line. Channels pickup between left anterior-temporal, right anterior-temporal, left temporal-posterior and right temporal-posterior regions. Strips B-D are continuous.*

LESION OF MIDBRAIN TEGMENTUM In this case also, most of the extent of the tegmentum was interrupted but at a somewhat more rostral level immediately behind the diencephalon (figs. 5, 6*). Again lateral afferent paths and the diencephalon itself were largely spared.

This animal, when unmolested, lay motionless on its side, with eyes closed, as though deeply asleep, throughout its 21 days of survival. Its resting EEG consisted of large, recurring, slow waves, with spindle bursts often interposed between them (figs. 7, 20B,* B1). During the first four post-operative days, ordinary stimulation had no effect upon the animal's somnolence or its EEG. Thereafter, either auditory or somatic stimulation blocked EEG synchrony and promptly introduced low voltage, fast activity in its place (fig. 7, A–C). Such typical activation was characteristically maintained only for the duration of the stimulus or for a few seconds thereafter, and the instances shown in figure 7 illustrate some of the longer lasting examples observed. Increasing the intensity of stimulation did not greatly prolong the duration of EEG arousal, which might occur without any behavioral counterpart or, when a nociceptive stimulus was employed, be accompanied by raising or shaking of the head and growling.

HYPOTHALAMIC DESTRUCTION The lesion seen in figures 8 and 9

* Fig. 6 has been omitted in reprinting. (Ed.)

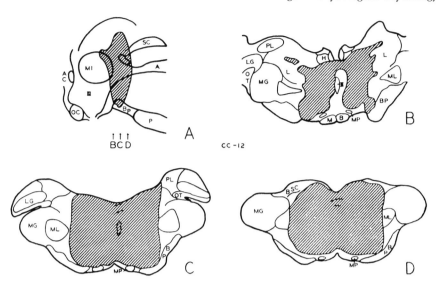

FIGURE 5 *Large lesion at the anterior end of the midbrain tegmentum, projected upon a reconstruction of the midsagittal plane (A) and shown in transverse sections (B-D).*

LESION MIDBRAIN TEGMENTUM

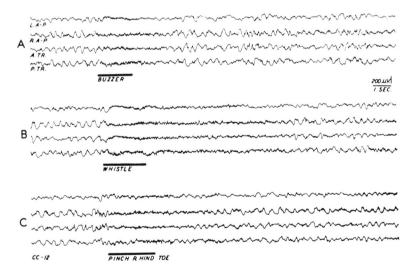

FIGURE 7 *EEG of cat with tegmental lesion seen in Figures 5 and 6. Arousing effects of buzzer (A), whistle (B) and pinch (C) on 7th postoperative day. Channels record activity in left anterior-posterior, right anterior-posterior, left-right, anterior (transcortical) and left-right posterior regions.*

[Fig. 9 omitted in reprinting (Ed.)] almost completely destroyed the hypohalamus and invaded the medial subthalamus and ventromedial part of the halamus, which was otherwise spared.

When unmolested during its 25 day survival, the cat lay on its side, omnolent or asleep, and inert except for occasional slight movements of he extremities. Placed on its feet, it slowly collapsed to a prone position. Gradual tension in cranial muscles developed on auditory stimulation, and he animal responded to nociceptive stimulation by growling and baring its teeth or spitting. By the third week, its EEG was usually characterized by moderate amplitude 3–5/sec. waves, which tended to wax and wane n runs (fig. 10). Earlier, and at times then, spindle bursts of larger amplitude and double this frequency occurred, together with larger slow waves, and the record looked more like that of normal sleep. Against whatever background of EEG synchrony tests were made, both auditory and somatic stimulation introduced excellent low voltage, fast activity, which usually terminated promptly with the cessation of the stimulus (fig. 10, A and B) but, with more intense irritation, might persist for several seconds longer (fig. 10, C).

LESION OF JUNCTION OF HYPOTHALAMUS WITH THALAMUS   In the instance seen in figure 11, injury to the ventromedial thalamus and dorsal hypothalamus was in a position to interrupt any connections entering the thalamus from below in the walls of the third ventricle.

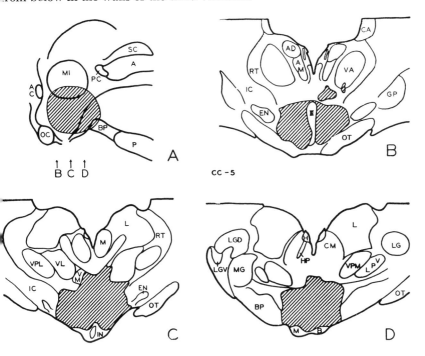

FIGURE 8   *Large lesion of hypothalamus projected upon a midsagittal reconstruction (A) and shown in transverse sections (B-D).*

HYPOTHALAMIC   DESTRUCTION

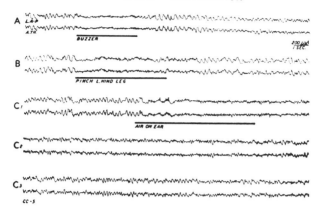

FIGURE **10**   *EEG of cat with the hypothalamic lesion seen in Figures 8 and 9. Arousal induced by buzzer (A), pinch (B) and air on ear (C), on 25th postoperative day. Channels pick-up between left anterior-posterior and left-right anterior region. Strips C 1-3 are continuous.*

A week after operation, the cat lay wherever it was placed, with eyes closed, and except for occasional stepping movements of the extremities initiated no activity. Afferent stimulation was still capable of arousing the animal and activating its EEG, but the duration of these effects was much reduced from those seen in preoperative tests obtained in this case. In

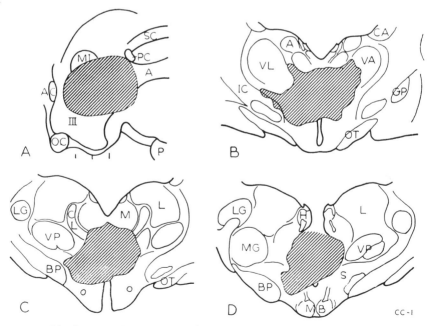

FIGURE **11**   *Lesion of junction of hypothalamus with thalamus projected on reconstruction of midsagittal plane (A) and shown in transverse sections (B-D).*

EEG desynchronization evoked by a buzzer, spindle bursts were abolished for 40 sec. before (fig. 12, A) and for 10 sec. after operation (fig. 12, B). Before operation, hearing another cat meow faintly abolished regular slow waves for 30 sec. (fig. 12, C) while postoperatively, blowing air in the cat's ear, a stimulus which provoked spitting, several stereotyped yowls and piloerection, prevented slow waves for only 10 succeeding seconds (fig. 12, D).

Though varying in degree, the common behavioral result of each of these lesions in a position to block much or all of the cephalic end of the reticular activating system was a postoperative somnolence or lethargy and hypokinesia, in which the animal displayed little or no spontaneous activity of a purposeful sort and seemed unaware of ordinary environmental stimuli. The EEG associated with this state either exhibited the large slow waves and spindle bursts of natural sleep or other prominent synchrony, and low voltage fast activity was conspicuously absent.

In the chronic period, startling auditory or nociceptive stimulation were clearly able both to arouse the animal behaviorally and to activate its EEG. Motor effects were usually limited to opening of the eyelids and raising the head, though, if the midbrain were intact, vocalization might be added. The desynchronization of electrocortical activity was quite as

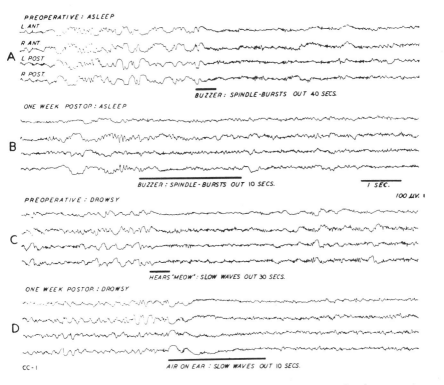

FIGURE 12   EEG of the cat with the lesion seen in Figure 11. The duration of pre- and postoperative arousal is compared (A and B; C and D).

pronounced as that exhibited by a normal animal, but differed from the normal in the respects that the intensity of the arousing stimulus needed to be high and that activation was short-lived, disappearing immediately or soon after cessation of the stimulus that had provoked it. Many instances could be added to those shown, in which, upon the cessation of moderate stimuli, low voltage, fast activity gave way within a second or two to the higher voltage slow waves that marked the initial record. Even when the arousing stimulus was intense, only a few seconds usually elapsed before EEG synchrony returned. It should be emphasized, however, that during afferent stimulation and for a brief period thereafter, low voltage fast activity was just as low and just as fast as though mesencephalic or hypothalamic components of the reticular activating system had not been interrupted.

B. Lesion sparing the reticular activating system

LESIONS OF THE PERIAQUEDUCTAL GREY were produced in two cases, one destroying its caudal and the other its rostral part. The caudal of these lesions, which also injured the medial part of the cerebellum extensively (fig. 13, A–C), left the animal awake and alert from the first postoperative

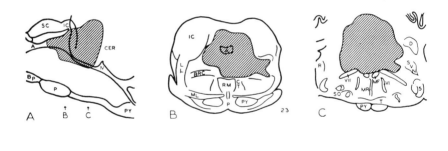

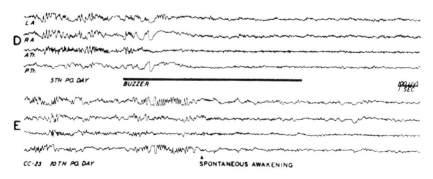

FIGURE 13　*Lesion destroying periaqueductal grey and medial cerebellum projected upon midsagittal plane (A) and shown in transverse sections (B and C).*
　　EEGs show arousal by buzzer (D) and spontaneous awakening (E) on 5th and 10th postoperative days. Channels pickup from left anterior, right anterior, left-right anterior, and left-right posterior of the hemisphere.

day, with no greater disposition to sleep than that exhibited by a normal cat. When the animal was asleep, wakefulness could readily be induced by afferent stimulation (fig. 13, D) and often occurred spontaneously (fig. 13, E). Once present, an activated EEG and the behavioral alertness associated with it were characteristically maintained for long periods.

The rostral lesion destroyed the cephalic portion of the central grey and invaded the caudal part of the thalamus (fig. 14, A–C). During the first postoperative week, the animal appeared asleep or drowsy, exhibited little or no spontaneous activity and could not be aroused by afferent stimulation. At this time, its EEG resembled that of sleep, with large slow waves and spindle bursts, and could not be activated. Thereafter, the cat became progressively more wakeful and active and, two and three weeks after operation, its EEG consisted for the most part of low voltage fast activity. When drowsiness or sleep occurred, arousal by afferent stimulation was readily provoked and was prolonged (fig. 14, D–F).

In the chronic period after destruction either of the caudal or rostral part of the periaqueductal grey, therefore, normal sleep-waking behavior was present and EEG activation by afferent stimulation showed no impairment.

LESION OF SENSORY PATHS   In two animals, lateral mesencephalic injury

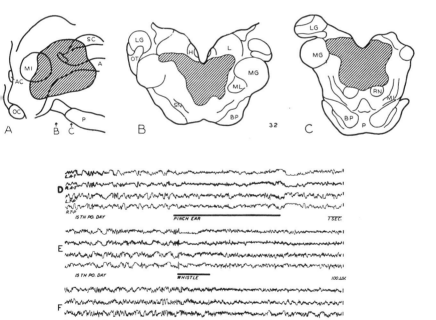

FIGURE 14 *Lesion of anterior periaqueductal grey and caudal thalamus and projected on the midsagittal plane (A) and shown in transverse section (B,C).*

EEGs show arousal to pinch (D), whistle (E) and buzzer (F) on 15th and 21st postoperative days. Channels pick up between left anterior-temporal, right anterior-temporal, left temporal-posterior and right temporal-posterior regions.

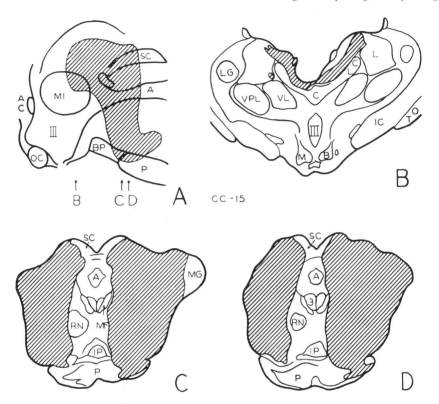

FIGURE 15 *Lesion of sensory paths in lateral midbrain projected upon reconstruction of midsagittal plane (A) and shown in transverse section (B-D).*

severed long afferent paths and adjacent structures, immediately behind
the diencephalon, while sparing the medial tegmental region in which
the reticular activating system is distributed (figs. 15, 16,* 18). These
animals were followed for two months and in the chronic period were
able to stand and walk, though often standing on the dorsum of the foot
and displaying other abnormalities. One exhibited compulsive walking and
both were usually awake during the day (fig. 20 A).* These animals could
sleep, however, and both the behavioral and EEG features of their repose
appeared completely normal (figs. 17, 19).

When asleep, both auditory and somatic stimuli were still capable of
awakening each of these animals. In the representative instance shown
in figure 17, a series of blasts on a police whistle aroused the animal
from sleep, the large slow waves and spindle bursts in its EEG giving
way to characteristic low voltage, fast activity (fig. 17, A and B). Seven
minutes later the animal was still awake (fig. 17, C) and, 15 minutes
after arousal, the first "drowsy waves" appeared (fig. 17, D). Seventeen

* Omitted in reprinting. (Ed.)

minutes after awakening, the cat had returned to sleep (fig. 17, E). The only unusual feature of the EEG arousal was the rather long latency of its initiation, for a period of from 2 to 3 sec. from the beginning of auditory stimulation ensued before an activation pattern became fully established. Though not always as prolonged, such latency was seen on most occasions.

High intensity of stimulation was not essential for arousal, however. It might be provoked by a buzzer and figure 19 shows an instance of awakening, in the second of these cats, induced simply by the sound of one of the investigators (L. H. S.) walking in the room. Awakening and EEG arousal, identical with the examples seen in figures 17 and 19, could also be induced by somatic stimulation in each of these animals.

In terminal experiments, click stimuli failed to evoke potentials in the auditory or other parts of the cortex in either of these cases. In one, single shock stimuli to the sciatic nerve induced contralateral cortical potentials, presumed to be secondary responses, shown by Morison and Dempsey (1942) to be conducted through the central portion of the midbrain. Terminal stimulation of the bulbar reticular formation readily desynchronized

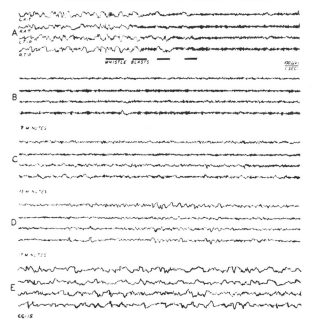

FIGURE 17   *EEG of cat with lateral midbrain lesions shown in Figures 15 and 16. Arousal by whistle blasts on 12th postoperative day. Strips A and B are continuous, C is 7 min. after A, D, 15 min. after A, and E, 17 min. after A. Channels pickup between left anterior-temporal, right anterior-temporal, left temporal-posterior and right temporal-posterior regions.*

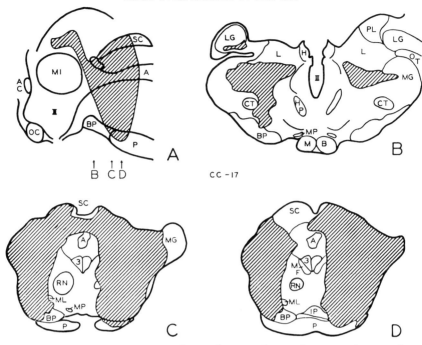

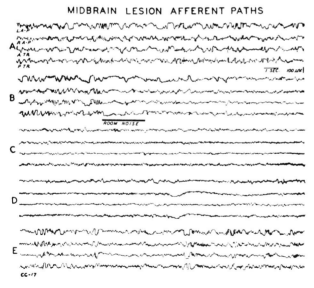

FIGURE 18 *Lesions of sensory paths in the second animal, projected upon the midsagittal plane (A) and shown in transverse section (B-D).*

MIDBRAIN LESION AFFERENT PATHS

FIGURE 19 *EEG of animal with lesion seen in Figure 18, showing arousal from sleep induced by sound of one of the investigators walking in room on 21st postoperative day. Strips are continuous except for a 7 sec. interval between D and E. Channels pickup between left anterior-posterior, right anterior-posterior, left-right anterior and left-right posterior regions.*

the EEG, as in the acute experiments of Moruzzi and Magoun (1949), in which only the central mesencephalon connected the lower brain stem with the cerebrum.

In the chronic period, therefore, following interruption of known auditory and somatic afferent pathways immediately behind the diencephalon, while sparing the central midbrain tegmentum, the animals showed no disposition to pathological somnolence. When tested during sleep, both auditory and somatic stimulation readily evoked behavioral arousal and activation of the EEG. The latter often required a second or two to develop but exhibited no other abnormality and, once induced, was characteristically prolonged.

DISCUSSION

Present conceptions of sleep date from 1935, when Bremer discovered that the forebrain isolated from lower portions of the nervous system, by mesencephalic transection, exhibits electrical activity identical with that in natural sleep or anesthesia. From this, Bremer concluded that sleep is the consequence of functional deafferentation of the cerebrum for, at that time, the only known corticipetal influences to whose interruption the results could be attributed were those conducted in classical sensory paths. More recently, Moruzzi and Magoun (1949) identified an activating system ascending through the brain stem reticular formation, whose direct stimulation induced EEG changes simulating those of wakefulness. At the same time, Lindsley, Bowden and Magoun (1949) determined that acute injury to the upper end of this reticular activating system was the factor responsible for the sleep changes in the cerebrum which Bremer had earlier described.

The present study has verified this finding in animals with chronic lesions of the brain stem for, when the anterior end of the reticular activating system is interrupted in the mesencephalic tegmentum or basal diencephalon, the EEG is characterized by the large slow waves and spindle bursts of normal sleep, or by other synchrony, while low voltage fast activity associated with wakefulness is lacking (fig. 20, B').* Behaviorally, such animals appear asleep and, when unmolested, persist in this state throughout their postoperative survivals (fig. 20 B).* Conversely, in the chronic period after brain stem lesions which leave this reticular system uninjured, while destroying the periaqueductal grey or long sensory paths, the animals appear behaviorally awake much of the day (fig. 20, A),* and their EEG is characterized by low voltage fast activity (fig. 20 A').* These findings are in complete accord with Bremer's fundamental observation that sleep in the cerebrum ensues upon interrupting ascending influences from the brain stem, but they indicate that it is the absence of ascending influences

* Omitted in reprinting. (Ed.)

of the reticular activating system, and not those conducted by classical sensory paths, that is of importance.

The commonplace experience that afferent stimulation will induce and contribute to wakefulness, while its absence favors sleep, seems opposed to this conclusion until the possibility is considered that collaterals from afferent paths may terminate in the reticular activating system and exert their influence indirectly by modifying its activity. The chronic animals of the present study served also to test this possibility for, in each of them, the arousing effect of somatic and auditory stimulation was repeatedly tested against a background of drowsiness or sleep.

It may be said first that positive indication was obtained for such collateral excitation of the reticular activating system for, when both somatic and auditory paths were chronically interrupted at the front of the midbrain, somatic and auditory stimuli were still regularly capable of arousing the sleeping animal and activating its EEG. The alteration had a little longer latency than usual but was otherwise typical and, once aroused, the animals usually remained awake for long periods. In our opinion, such arousal was mediated by collaterals from afferent paths terminating in the brain stem reticular formation below the lesion and exerting their cephalic influence indirectly through its ascending relays. Anatomical evidence favoring this possibility has recently been presented by Morin and O'Leary (1950).

It should next be pointed out that when the front end of the reticular activating system is interrupted by large mesencephalic or hypothalamic lesions, it is also possible to induce a degree of behavioral arousal and to activate the EEG by auditory and somatic stimulation. EEG activation was excellent but differed from normal in that it characteristically terminated almost immediately upon the cessation of the arousing stimulus and, even when this was intense, never persisted for more than a few succeeding seconds. From these observations, it appears that afferent stimulation can activate the EEG both by collateral excitation of the reticular formation below the mesencephalon and, additionally, by the direct arrival of afferent impulses at some site above the midbrain or hypothalamus. It is possible that activation occurs upon the arrival of afferent impulses finally at the cortex, as is generally believed. It seems more likely that such activation develops upon arrival of afferent impulses at the thalamus, at which site presumably the ascending influences of the reticular activating system are elaborated for corticipetal transmission. If this latter were the case, the identity of EEG activation by whichever route the afferent impulses inducing it are conducted, could more readily be understood.

Wherever it is located, the site at which EEG activation is induced by afferent impulses coursing past the brain stem reticular formation, in long sensory paths, is evidently cephalad to the neural focus at which self-propagating activity continues to preserve the waking state for long periods after the arousing stimulus initiating it has ceased. For, as remarked, arousal in the animals under discussion was only brief and, being so directly dependent for maintenance upon the continued application of the arousing stimulus, failed to serve the animal usefully. Stated in anatomical terms, interconnections between the thalamus and cortex, and the hypothalamus as well, are not by themselves capable of preserving the waking state beyond the immediate period of their bombardment by afferent impulses from the periphery. It thus appears that maintained wakefulness following the cessation of an arousing stimulus depends upon excitation within the reticular activating system below the diencephalon.

In these animals with large hypothalamic or midbrain tegmental lesions, the excellence of the EEG activation induced by afferent stimulation contrasted sharply with the poverty of associated behavioral arousal and the lesions appeared, in fact, to have dissociated these two features of the waking state. This suggests that in addition to the cephalic influence of the reticular activating system upon the electrocortical activity, which has so far been emphasized here, attention should be focussed also upon caudally directed influences of this reticular formation which are known to be capable of providing a facilitatory background favoring motor performance (Rhines and Magoun, 1946; Austin and Jasper, 1950). There now seem to be sufficient data to suggest that influences of the reticular activating system are directed both cephalically upon the cerebrum and caudally upon levels of motor outflow, and to propose that the presence or absence of the caudal influence of this activating system is as important in contributing to the behavioral differences exhibited in wakefulness and sleep as are variations in its cephalic influences in modifying electrocortical activity in these contrasting states.

SUMMARY

The effect upon behavior and the EEG of chronic lesions in the rostral brain stem has been studied in a series of cats.

Of lesions in sensory paths, in the periaqueductal grey, or in the midbrain tegmentum and basal diencephalon, only the latter, in a position to interrupt the ascending reticular activating system, were followed by chronic somnolence and EEG synchrony.

Activation of the synchronized EEG by somatic and auditory stimulation was still possible either after the reticular activating system or after long sensory paths had been interrupted immediately behind the thalamus. Collateral sensory excitation of the reticular activating system in the lower brain stem, and the direct arrival of afferent impulses at some site above the midbrain, thus serve equally well to induce EEG arousal, but only in the former instance does prolonged wakefulness follow.

Poverty of behavior after lesions of the reticular activating system suggests that its influences may be directed both cephalically to activate the EEG and caudally to facilitate motor activity, in maintaining the waking state.

Addendum. In a recent abstract Ingram, W. R., Knott, J. R. and Wheatley, M. D. Electroencephalograms of cats with hypothalamic lesions. (*EEG Clin. Neurophysiol.,* 1949, 1: 523), Ingram and his associates state that "depression of slow high voltage waves associated with total and subtotal hypothalamic destruction, in response to arousal stimuli, indicates that relatively normal records may be briefly seen in these preparations." The present results confirm these observations.

REFERENCES

Austin, G. and Jasper, H. Diencephalic mechanisms for facilitation and inhibition. *Fed. Proc.,* 1950, 9: 6.

Bremer, F. Cerveau isolé et physiologie du sommeil. *C. R. Soc. Biol., Paris,* 1935, 118: 1235–1242.

Ingram, W. R., Knott, J. R. and Wheatley, M. D. Electroencephalograms of cats under various experimental conditions. *Anat. Rec.,* 1949, 103: 157.

Lindsley, D. B., Bowden, J. and Magoun, H. W. Effect upon the EEG of acute injury to the brain stem activating system. *EEG Clin. Neurophysiol.,* 1949, 1: 475–486.

Morin, F. and O'Leary, J. L. Ascending tracts of the anterolateral white column in Macaca mulatta. *Anat. Rec.,* 1950, 106: 60.

Morison, R. S. and Dempsey, E. W. A study of thalamo-cortical relations. *Amer. J. Physiol.,* 1942, 135: 281–292.

Moruzzi, G. and Magoun, H. W. Brain stem reticular formation and activation of the EEG. *EEG Clin. Neurophysiol.,* 1949, 1: 455–473.

Rheinberger, M. B. and Jasper, H. H. Electrical activity of the cerebral cortex in the unanesthetized cat. *Amer. J. Physiol.,* 1937, 119: 186–196.

THE RELATION OF EYE
MOVEMENTS DURING SLEEP
TO DREAM ACTIVITY:
AN OBJECTIVE METHOD
FOR THE STUDY OF DREAMING

William Dement and Nathaniel Kleitman

UNIVERSITY OF CHICAGO

Editor's Note   *In recent years, Dement and others have established that the sleeping state is considerably more complex than was once thought. There appear to be two distinct kinds of sleep, one involving rapid eye movements as a symptom, the other not. There is increasing evidence that the two kinds of sleep may serve different biological and psychological functions. In the reading reprinted here, Dement and Kleitman show that the rapid eye movement sleep is associated with dreaming. It was the methodology and observations reported here that opened the way to the later differentiation of the two sleep states.*

Source   Reprinted from the **Journal of Experimental Psychology,** *1957,* **53,** *(5), 339–346, with permission of the authors and the American Psychological Association.*

The study of dream activity and its relation to physiological variable during sleep necessitates a reliable method of determining with precision when dreaming occurs. This knowledge, in the final analysis, always de pends upon the subjective report of the dreamer, but becomes relatively objective if such reports can be significantly related to some physiologica phenomena which in turn can be measured by physical techniques.

Such a relationship was reported by Aserinsky and Kleitman (1) who observed periods of rapid, conjugate eye movements during sleep and found a high incidence of dream recall in Ss awakened during these periods and a low incidence when awakened at other times. The occurrence of these characteristic eye movements and their relation to dreaming were confirmed in both normal Ss and schizophrenics (4), and they were shown to appear at regular intervals in relation to a cyclic change in the depth of sleep during the night as measured by the EEG (5).

This paper represents the results of a rigorous testing of the relation between eye movements and dreaming. Three approaches were used: (*a*) Dream recall during rapid eye movement or quiescent periods was elicited without direct contact between *E* and *S*, thus eliminating the possibility of unintentional cuing by *E*. (*b*) The subjective estimate of the duration of dreams was compared with the length of eye movement periods before awakening, reasoning that there should be a positive correlation if dreaming and eye movements were concurrent. (*c*) The pattern of the eye movements was related to the dream content to test whether they represented a specific expression of the visual experience of dreaming or merely a random motor discharge of a more active central nervous system.

METHOD

The Ss for the experiments were seven adult males and two adult females. Five were studied intensively while the data gathered from the other four were minimal with the main intent of confirming the results on the first five.

In a typical experiment, S reported to the laboratory a little before his usual bedtime. He was instructed to eat normally but to abstain from alcoholic or caffeine-containing beverages on the day of the experiment. Two or more electrodes were attached near the eyes for registering changes in the corneoretinal potential fields as the eyes moved. Two or three electrodes were affixed to the scalp for recording brain waves as a criterion of depth of sleep. The S then went to bed in a quiet, dark room. All electrode lead wires were further attached to the top of the head and from there to the lead box at the head of the bed in a single cord to minimize the possibility of entanglement and allow

[1] Aided by a grant from the Wallace C. and Clara A. Abbott Memorial Fund of the University of Chicago.

Table 1. Summary of Experiments

Ss	Nights Slept	Awakenings	Average Nightly Awakenings	Average Sleeping Time
DN	6	50	8.3	7:50
IR	12	65	5.4	4:20
KC	17	74	4.4	6:00
WD	11	77	7.0	6:30
PM	9	55	6.1	6:20
KK	2	10	5.0	6:00
SM	1	6	6.0	6:40
DM	1	4	4.0	7:00
MG	2	10	5.0	6:10
Totals	61	351	5.7	6:00

S a free range of movement. The potentials were amplified by a Model III Grass Electroencephalograph in an adjoining room. The electroencephalograph was run continuously throughout the sleep period at a paper speed of 3 or 6 mm. per sec. which allowed easy recognition of eye-movement potentials. A faster speed (3 cm./sec.) was used for detailed examination of the brain waves although the slower speed permitted at least an approximate estimation of the gross pattern. The criteria of eye-movement potentials and their differentiation from brain wave artifacts have been discussed at length elsewhere (1, 4).

At various times during the night Ss were awakened to test their dream recall. The return to sleep after such an awakening invariably took less than 5 min. Table 1 is a summary of the experiments showing the number of nights each S slept and the number of awakenings. In all, 21% of the awakenings fell in the first 2 hr. of sleep, 29% in the second two, 28% in the third two, and 22% in the fourth two.

RESULTS

THE OCCURRENCE OF RAPID EYE MOVEMENTS[2] Discrete periods during which their eyes exhibited rapid movements were observed in all nine Ss every night they slept. These periods were characterized by a low-voltage, relatively fast pattern in the EEG. The interspersed periods in which rapid eye movements were absent showed EEG patterns indicative of deeper sleep, either a predominance of high-voltage, slow activity, or frequent, well-defined sleep spindles with a low-voltage background. No REM's were ever observed during the initial onset of sleep although the EEG always passed through a stage similar to that accompanying the rapid eye movement periods occurring later in the night. These findings

[2] In most of the remaining text the following abbreviations will be used: REM's (rapid eye movements) and NREM's (no rapid eye movements).

concerning associated EEG patterns were identical with previous observations on uninterrupted sleep (5).

An accurate appraisal of the mean duration of the REM periods was impossible since most were terminated artificially by an awakening. However, those that were not so terminated varied between 3 and 50 min. in duration with a mean of about 20 min., and they tended to be longer the later in the night they occurred. The eyes were not constantly in motion during such periods; rather, the activity occurred in bursts of one or two, up to fifty or a hundred movements. A single movement was generally accomplished in .1–.2 sec. and was followed by a fixational pause of varying duration. The amount, pattern, and size of the movements varied irregularly from period to period.

The REM periods occurred at fairly regular intervals throughout the night. The frequency of occurrence seemed to be relatively constant and characteristic for the individual. DM and WD averaged one eye-movement period every 70 min. and every 75 min. respectively. KC averaged one eye-movement period every 104 min. The other Ss fell between these two extremes. The average for the whole group was one REM period every 92 min.

Despite the considerable disturbance of being awakened a number of times, the frequency and regularity with which REM periods occurred was almost exactly comparable to that seen previously in a study of uninterrupted sleep (5). If the awakening occurred during a NREM period, the return to sleep was never associated with REM's, nor was the time of onset of the next REM period markedly changed from that which would have been expected in the absence of an awakening. An awakening during an REM period generally terminated the REM's until the next period, and the sequence of EEG changes, excluding the brief period of wakefulness, was the same as that following an REM period that ended spontaneously. Exceptions occurred when S was awakened during an REM period in the final hours of sleep when the period was likely to be quite long if uninterrupted. On these occasions, the REM's sometimes started up again when S fell asleep. It seemed as though a period of heightened CNS activity had not run its normal course and, although S was able to fall asleep, he continued to dream.

EYE MOVEMENT PERIODS AND DREAM RECALL   For all awakenings to elicit dream recall, the arousing stimulus was the ringing of an ordinary doorbell placed near the bed and sufficiently loud to ensure immediate awakening in all levels of sleep. The Ss then spoke into a recording device near the bed. They were instructed to first state whether or not they had been dreaming and then, if they could, to relate the content of the dream. When S had finished speaking E, who could hear their voices, occasionally entered the room to further question them on some particular point of the dream. There was no communication between S and E in any instance, it must be emphasized, until S had definitely committed himself. The Ss were considered to have been dreaming only if they could relate a coherent, fairly detailed description of dream content. Assertions that they had dreamed without recall of content, or vague, fragmentary impressions of content, were considered negative.

The awakenings were done either during REM periods or at varying increments of time after the cessation of eye movements during the interspersed periods of NREM's. The Ss, of course, were never informed when awakened whether or not their eyes had been moving.

Table 2 shows the results of the attempts to recall dreams after the various awakenings. The REM or NREM awakenings for PM and KC were chosen according to a table of random numbers to eliminate any possibility of an unintentional pattern. For DN, a pattern was followed: first three REM awakenings, then three NREM awakenings, and so on. WD was told he would be awakened *only* when the recording indicated that he was dreaming, but REM and NREM awakenings were then interspersed randomly. The type of awakenings for IR was chosen according to the whim of E.

The Ss uniformly showed a high incidence of dream recall following REM awakenings and a very low incidence of recall following awakenings during periods of NREM's regardless of how the awakenings were chosen. In particular, DN was not more accurate than the others although there was a pattern he might have learned, and WD was not less accurate although he was deliberately misled to expect to have been dreaming every time he was awakened. Over a narrow range, some Ss appeared better able to recall dreams than others.

Table 3 compares the results of the first half of the series of REM awakenings with the last half. Practice was certainly not a significant factor

Table 2. Instances of Dream Recall after Awakenings During Periods of Rapid Eye Movements or Periods of No Rapid Eye Movements

S	Rapid Eye Movements		No Rapid Eye Movements	
	Dream Recall	No Recall	Dream Recall	No Recall
DN	17	9	3	21
IR	26	8	2	29
KC	36	4	3	31
WD	37	5	1	34
PM	24	6	2	23
KK	4	1	0	5
SM	2	2	0	2
DM	2	1	0	1
MG	4	3	0	3
Totals	152	39	11	149

*Table 3. Comparison of First Half of Series of Rapid
Eye Movement Awakenings with Second Half*

	First Half		Second Half	
S	Dream Recall	No Recall	Dream Recall	No Recall
DN	12	1	5	8
IR	12	5	14	3
KC	18	2	18	2
WD	19	2	18	3
PM	12	3	12	3
Totals	73	13	67	19

as only one S showed any degree of improvement of recall on later nights as compared with the early ones.

The incidence of dream recall dropped precipitously almost immediately upon cessation of REM's. In 17 NREM awakenings that were done within 8 min. after the end of a REM period, 5 dreams were recalled. Although small, this was a much higher incidence of dream recall than occurred when the NREM awakenings followed the end of REM periods by *more* than 8 min. In the latter category only 6 dreams were recalled in 132 awakenings.

In general, Ss were best able to make an emphatic statement that they had not been dreaming when the NREM awakenings were done during an intermediate stage of sleep as indicated by a brain-wave pattern of spindling with a low-voltage background. When aroused during a deep stage of sleep characterized by high-voltage, slow waves in the EEG, Ss often awoke somewhat bewildered. In this state they frequently felt that they must have been dreaming although they could not remember the dream or, on the other hand, that they had not been asleep at all. They sometimes had a great variety of feelings to describe—such as pleasantness, anxiety, detachment, etc., but these could not be related to any specific dream content.

Most of the instances of inability to recall dreaming after awakenings during REM periods occurred in the early part of the night. Of 39 negative reports in the entire study, 19 occurred after awakenings during REM periods falling in the first 2 hr. of sleep, 11 after REM awakenings during the second 2 hr., 5 in the third 2 hr., and 4 in the last 2 hr. There was no such variation relating to awakenings during the interspersed periods of ocular quiescence, the incidence of dream recall being uniformly low, regardless of whether the early or late part of the night was being considered.

LENGTH OF RAPID EYE MOVEMENT PERIODS AND SUBJECTIVE DREAM-DURATION ESTIMATES   If the length of the REM periods were proportional to the subjectively estimated duration of the dreams, it would further help to establish the relatedness of the two and would give some information about the rate at which dreaming progresses.

At first, Ss were awakened at various increments of time after the REM's had begun and were requested to estimate to the nearest minute the amount of time they had been dreaming. This proved to be too difficult, although the estimates were always of the same order of magnitude as the lengths of the REM periods, and were occasionally exactly right.

A series was then done in which Ss were awakened either 5 or 15 min. after the onset of REM's and were required on the basis of their recall of the dream to decide which was the correct duration. The 5- or 15-min. periods were chosen on the basis of a random series. Table 4 shows the results of these awakenings. All Ss were able to choose the correct dream duration with high accuracy except DN. This S, however, made most of his incorrect choices by estimating 15 min. to be 5 min. This is consistent with the interpretation that the dream was longer, but he was only able to recall the latter fraction and thus thought it was shorter than it actually was.

In addition to depending on the amount of actual dreaming, the lengths of the dream narratives were undoubtedly influenced by many other factors as, for example, the loquacity or taciturnity of S. However, the lengths of the dream narratives still showed a significant relationship to the duration of REM periods before awakening. Table 5 shows the correlations between minutes of REM's and lengths of dream narratives for each S. The number of words in the narrative was the measurement of length. Of the 152 dreams recalled, 26 were not included because poor recording did not allow complete transcription. Dream narratives recalled after 30 or as much as 50 min. of REM's were not a great deal longer than those after 15 min. although Ss had the impression that they had been dreaming for an unusually long time. This was perhaps due to inability to remember all the details of very long dreams.

SPECIFIC EYE-MOVEMENT PATTERNS AND VISUAL IMAGERY OF THE DREAM
The quality and quantity of the REM's themselves showed endless variation. There was much or little movement, big or small movements, and so on.

Table 4. Results of Dream-Duration Estimates After 5 or 15 Min. of Rapid Eye Movements

S	5 Minutes		15 Minutes	
	Right	Wrong	Right	Wrong
DN	8	2	5	5
IR	11	1	7	3
KC	7	0	12	1
WD	13	1	15	1
PM	6	2	8	3
Totals	45	6	47	13

Table 5. Correlation Between Duration of REM Periods in Minutes and Number of Words in Dream Narratives

Subjects	Number of Dreams	r	P
DN	15	.60	< .02
IR	25	.68	< .001
KC	31	.40	< .05
WD	35	.71	< .001
PM	20	.53	< .02

As has been stated, the movements occurred in bursts of activity separated by periods of relative inactivity. However, the brain-wave stage during the whole period remained the same whether there was much or little movement at any given moment of the period.

It was hypothesized that the movements represented the visual imagery of the dream, that is, that they corresponded to where and at what the dreamer was looking. An attempt to account for every movement by having S state chronologically in what directions he had gazed in the dream proved futile. The Ss could not recall the dream with such a high order of detail and precision.

In a slightly different approach, Ss were awakened as soon as one of four predominant patterns of movement had persisted for at least 1 min. and were asked to describe in detail the dream content just before awakening. The four patterns were : (a) mainly vertical eye movements, (b) mainly horizontal movements, (c) both vertical and horizontal movements, and (d) very little or no movement. The prevalence of the horizontal or vertical components was determined by placing leads both vertically and horizontally around the eyes.

A total of 35 awakenings was accumulated from the nine Ss. Periods of either pure vertical or horizontal movements were extremely rare. Three such periods of vertical movements were seen. After each of these the dream content involved a predominance of action in the vertical plane. One S dreamed of standing at the bottom of a tall cliff operating some sort of hoist and looking up at climbers at various levels and down at the hoist machinery. Another S dreamed of climbing up a series of ladders looking up and down as he climbed. In the third instance the dreamer was throwing basketballs at a net, first shooting and looking up at the net, and then looking down to pick another ball off the floor. Only one instance of pure horizontal movement was seen. In the associated dream S was watching two people throwing tomatoes at each other. On 10 occasions Ss were awakened after 1 min. of little or no eye movement. In these, the dreams all had the common property that the dreamer was watching something at a distance or just staring fixedly at some object.

In two of these awakenings in different Ss the patterns were the same, as follows: about a minute of ocular inactivity followed by several large movements to the left just a second or two before the awakening. Both instances, interestingly enough, were virtually identical as regards dream content. In one case S was driving a car and staring at the road ahead. He approached an intersection and was startled by the sudden appearance of a car speeding at him from the left as the bell rang. In the other, the dreamer was also driving a car and staring at the road ahead. Just before the awakening he saw a man standing on the left side of the road and hailed him as he drove past.

In the 21 awakenings after a mixture of movements Ss were always looking at things close to them, objects or people. Typical reports were of talking to a group of people, looking for something, fighting with someone, and so forth. There was no recall of distant or vertical activity.

In order to confirm the meaningfulness of these relationships, 20 naive Ss as well as 5 of the experimental Ss were asked to observe distant and close-up activity while awake. Horizontal and vertical electrodes were attached. The eye-movement potentials in all cases were comparable in both amplitude and pattern to those occurring during dreaming. Furthermore, there was virtually no movement, as indicated by the eye potentials, when viewing distant activity, and much movement while viewing close-up activity. Vertical eye-movement potentials were always at a minimum except for the upward movements accompanying blinking, and in a few cases when E tossed a ball in the air for them to watch.

DISCUSSION

The results of these experiments indicate that dreaming accompanied by REM's and a low-voltage electroencephalogram occurred periodically in discrete episodes during the course of a night's sleep. It cannot be stated with complete certainty that some sort of dream activity did not occur at other times. However, the lack of recall and also the fact that the brain waves were at the lightest level of sleep only during REM periods and at deeper levels at all other times, makes this unlikely. The few instances of dream recall during NREM periods are best accounted for by assuming that the memory of the preceding dream persisted for an unusually long time. This is borne out by the fact that most of these instances occurred very close, within 8 min., after the end of REM periods.

Other workers have attempted to relate dreaming to physiological phenomena during sleep. Wada (12) felt that dreaming and gastric contractions occurred simultaneously. However, this conclusion was based on only seven awakenings in two Ss. One was unable to recall dream content although he felt he had been dreaming and the other remembered dream content in 3 of 4 awakenings. Scantlebury, Frick, and Patterson (11) also studied gastric activity and dreaming. They felt, on the basis of three

instances of dream recall out of seven awakenings, that the two were probably related, but judiciously stated that "the exact time during which a
dream occurs is elusive of record." The occurrence of dreaming during
a series of foot twitches occurring immediately after the onset of sleep
was postulated by McGlade (9). However, he based this conclusion mainly
on dreams recalled on the morning after the experiments which is highly
unreliable, and only 3 out of the 25 Ss studied exhibited foot twitches.

Incidental observations have been made on the occurrence of dreaming
by investigators studying brain waves during sleep (2, 3, 6, 7, 8). All
stages of brain waves were related to dreaming in these five papers, but
no mention was made of whether or not actual dream content was recalled,
and the number of reports by sleepers was generally very small.

In other studies of dreaming, excellently reviewed by Ramsey (10),
attempts were made to localize dream activity by simply awakening Ss
at various times during the night. In general it was found that dreams
might be recalled at any time during the night, but that most were recalled
in the later hours of sleep. This would correspond to the statistical incidence
of REM's as previously reported (1, 4), and is also consistent with the
finding in this study that, even when the awakenings occurred during
REM periods, recall was still more difficult earlier in the night.

It was stated herein that all Ss showed periods of REM's *every* night
they slept. This was also the case in another briefly reported series of
experiments involving 16 Ss who were observed a total of 43 nights (5).
It is felt on the basis of these and other studies which are unreported
that periods of REM's and dreaming and the regularity with which they
occur are an intrinsic part of normal sleep. In view of this, the failure
to observe REM's in occasional Ss reported in earlier work (1, 4) deserves
some consideration. One explanation is that the recording was done by
sampling rather than continuously. If the REM periods were shorter than
usual, they may have occurred in the intervals between the samples, thus
escaping observation. Another explanation is that a lower amplification
of the REM potentials was employed which, although usually adequate,
did not clearly record very small movements. A third possibility is that
the dreams of these Ss happened to be the sort, such as watching distant
activity, in which eye movement was at a minimum. Since the association
of the characteristic low-voltage, non-spindling EEG was not realized at
the time and thus could not aid in identifying this sort of period, they
very likely would have been overlooked.

There was nothing in the experiments reported in this paper to indicate
that the dreams occurred instantaneously, or with great rapidity, as some
have supposed. Rather, they seemed to progress at a rate comparable to
a real experience of the same sort. An increment in the length of REM
periods was almost invariably associated with a proportional increase in
the length of the dream. This could not have occurred if dreaming were
instantaneous, since any length of REM periods would then easily accommodate a virtually infinite amount of dream activity.

It seems reasonable to conclude that an objective measurement of dreaming may be accomplished by recording REM's during sleep. This stands in marked contrast to the forgetting, distortion, and other factors that are involved in the reliance on the subjective recall of dreams. It thus becomes possible to objectively study the effect on dreaming of environmental changes, psychological stress, drug administration, and a variety of other factors and influences.

SUMMARY

Regularly occurring periods of REM's were observed during every night of experimental sleep in nine adult Ss. A high incidence of dream recall was obtained from Ss when awakened during REM periods and a very low incidence when they were awakened at other times. A series of awakenings was done either 5 or 15 min. after the REM's (dreaming) had begun and Ss judged the correct dream duration with high accuracy. The pattern of the REM's was related to the visual imagery of the dream, and the eye movements recorded in analogous situations while awake corresponded closely in amplitude and pattern to those observed during dreaming.

REFERENCES

1 Aserinsky, E., & Kleitman, N. Two types of ocular motility occurring in sleep. *J. appl. Physiol.*, 1955, **8**, 1–10.

2 Blake, H., Gerard, R., & Kleitman, N. Factors influencing brain potentials during sleep. *J. Neurophysiol.*, 1939, **2**, 48–60.

3 Davis, H., Davis, P., Loomis, A. L., Harvey, E. N., & Hobart, G. A. Human brain potentials during the onset of sleep. *J. Neurophysiol.*, 1938, **1**, 24–38.

4 Dement, W. Dream recall and eye movements during sleep in schizophrenics and normals. *J. nerv. ment. Dis.*, 1955, **122**, 263–269.

5 Dement, W., & Kleitman, N. Incidence of eye motility during sleep in relation to varying EEG pattern. *Fed. Proc.*, 1955, **14**, 216.

6 Henry, C. E. Electroencephalographic individual differences and their constancy. I. During sleep. *J. exp. Psychol.*, 1941, **29**, 117–132.

7 Knott, J. R., Henry, C. E., & Hadley, J. M. Brain potentials during sleep; a comparative study of the dominant and non-dominant alpha groups. *J. exp. Psychol.*, 1939, **24**, 157–168.

8 Loomis, A. L., Harvey, E. N., & Hobart, G. A. Cerebral states during sleep as studied by human brain potentials. *J. exp. Psychol.*, 1937, **21**, 127–144.

9 McGlade, H. B. The relationship between gastric motility, muscular twitching during sleep and dreaming. *Amer. J. digest. Dis.*, 1942, **9**, 137–140.

10 Ramsey, G. Studies of dreaming. *Psychol. Bull.*, 1953, **50**, 432–455.

11 Scantlebury, R. E., Frick, H. L., & Patterson, T. L. The effect of normal and hypnotically induced dreams on the gastric hunger movements of man. *J. appl. Psychol.*, 1942, **26**, 682–691.

12 Wada, T. An experimental study of hunger and its relation to activity. *Arch. Psychol.*, N. Y., 1922, **8**, No. 57.

EFFECTS OF STIMULATION
OF BRAIN STEM
ON TACHISTOSCOPIC PERCEPTION

Joaquin M. Fuster

UNIVERSITY OF CALIFORNIA, LOS ANGELES

Source *Reprinted from* **Science**, *August 3, 1958,* **127,** *150, with permission of the author and the American Association for the Advancement of Science.*

This report concerns part of a study (*1*) conducted on rhesus monkeys to investigate the effects of electrical stimulation of different sites in the brain on tachistoscopic perception.

For this investigation the animals were first trained to discriminate between stereometric objects presented in pairs, by placing food reward under one of the objects of each pair. After this preliminary training without restriction of exposure duration, each animal was subjected to several series of trials at different exposures; the number of correct responses was noted, and the reaction time was automatically measured. The testing apparatus was a modification of that used by Harlow, which for our purposes was transformed into a tachistoscope (Fig. 1). Its main feature was an argon-mercury bulb which was used to flash briefly a light of controllable duration and constant intensity upon the objects. The pairs of white objects (for example, a cone and a 12-sided pyramid of similar proportions) were placed in a dark field in front of the animal. A brief acoustic signal preceded by 2 seconds the illumination of the objects; this signal was in no case concomitant with the visual stimulus. Selection of the correct member of each pair was always followed by a food reward. The position of the correct member was changed randomly from trial to trial.

Electrodes were implanted in the animals' brains so that the effects of electrical stimulation could be studied. To date, six animals have been used in the investigation. The electrode placements were histologically verified. As a rule, currents were always used that did not cause any apparent effect on the normal behavior of the awake animal, regardless of the placement of the electrodes. A biphasic square wave current, of 300 cy/sec and intensities between 100 and 300 μa, was used as a norm. Each animal was used as its own control. In the experimental series, the electrical stimulation was applied during each trial period, starting 2 seconds in advance of the flash and persisting until the animal had made its choice.

Stimulation of the core of the brain stem at the level of the mesencephalon consistently increased the animals' efficiency at discrimination, as indicated by significantly higher percentages of correct responses and shorter reaction times as compared with the controls (Fig. 2). Stimulation through the same electrodes with intensities higher than the threshold for the elicitation of observable motor effects, such as generalized muscular jerks (startle reaction), eye movements, pupillary oscillations, vocalization, and so forth, had a deleterious effect on the performance of the animals, as indicated by the diminution of correct responses at all exposure durations and prolongation of reaction time. These effects were consistent and reproducible from animal to animal.

The same areas which upon mild stimulation facilitated tachistoscopic discrimination have previously been shown to evoke electroencephalo-

191

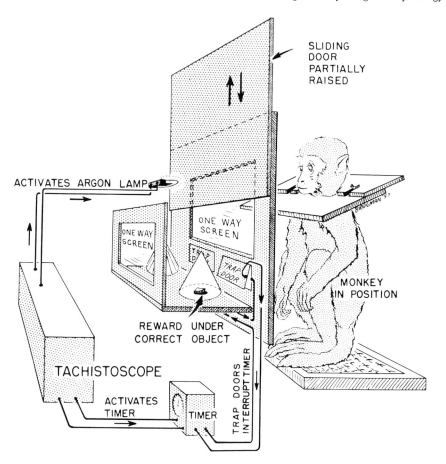

FIGURE 1 *Testing apparatus for visual discrimination. The monkey is shown in one of the plastic collars (schematically represented) by which the animals were permanently held to protect the electrode mount from their hands and to restrict them partially in performing the experimental task.*

graphic and behavioral arousal in the sleeping or relaxed animal (2, 3). These areas are in the rostral part of the brain stem activating system, which is mostly composed of the reticular formation of the midbrain tegmentum. Evoked potentials of long latency to sensory stimuli are also picked up in these areas (4). This was verified in the present investigation, by using the same electrodes for recording.

Both perceptual and motor processes involved in tachistoscopic discrimination appear to be facilitated by stimulation of the reticular activating system. It is difficult to determine whether the effects on reaction time are a direct consequence of the facilitatory effect on perception or independent of it. However, it seems likely that the reticular facilitation is primarily upon "central integrative time," rather than upon peripheral transmission time.

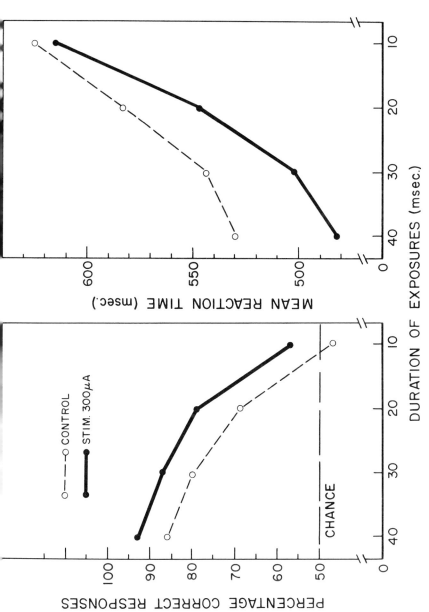

FIGURE 2 *Effects of stimulation of the brain stem on tachistoscopic discrimination. Each plotted point is based on 100 trials.*

These findings give support to the hypothesis that the reticular activating system, whose primary role has been demonstrated to be that of central mediator for the achievement and maintenance of wakefulness by means of activation of the cortex, extends its function to the alert state as a further manifestation of the same physiological role, subserving basic attentive behavior. Its different degrees of excitation underlie the gradation of this function from deep sleep to extreme alertness. Excitation of this brain stem system induces general activity of the cortex (arousal), presumably facilitating its receptivity to the sensory impulses ascending over the classic sensory paths. The facilitation of tachistoscopic discrimination by electrical stimulation of the same system may be considered as an example of such an effect on visual perception.

REFERENCES AND NOTES

1 This work was aided by grants from the following sources: Carnegie Corporation of New York; Office of Naval Research contract NR-144-102, Nonr 233(32); U.S. Public Health Service, grant B-611; Ford Foundation. I am especially indebted, also, to Robert B. Livingston, H. W. Magoun, Donald B. Lindsley, and K. F. Killam for their help and advice throughout the course of this investigation.
2 G. Moruzzi and H. W. Magoun, *Electroencephalog. and Clin. Neurophysiol.* **1**, 455 (1949).
3 J. P. Segundo, R. Arana, J. D. French, *J. Neurosurg.* **6**, 601 (1955).
4 J. D. French, M. Verzeano, H. W. Magoun, *A.M.A. Arch. Neurol. Psychiat.* **69**, 505 (1953).

THE PHYSIOLOGICAL DIFFERENTIATION BETWEEN FEAR AND ANGER IN HUMANS

Albert F. Ax

UNIVERSITY OF WASHINGTON

*Source Reprinted from **Psychosomatic Medicine**, 1953, **15**, No. 5, 433–442, with permission of the author and the Hoeber Medical Division, Harper & Row, Publishers, Incorporated.*

Simultaneous multiple recording of several physiological reactions during emotional changes may serve several purposes. The primary purpose is to add to our understanding of the precise nature of the total emotional reaction, which has not been adequately studied. From the psychological point of view, the details of the physiological state constitute an essential part of the conditions existing at the time of observation.

Multiple recording contributes more than the mere addition of variables for observation. The quantitative patterns of these differentially influenced processes (such as blood pressure, heart rate, sweating, skin temperature) provide a qualitative description of the emotional state at the physiological level and may be diagnostic of the type of emotional reaction. This characteristic of being differentially influenced by varying emotional states was an essential consideration in selecting which variables to record. Other criteria for selecting the variables were that they be available for continuous recording and that recording them would not seriously disturb the subject.

The multiple-variable approach for studying physiological states may provide answers to three different questions: (1) Can individuals be classified in terms of their physiological reaction syndromes, which are paradigmed by the psychosomatic diseases? (2) Can the physiological reactions serve as an emotional or motivational indicator during psychological observation? This is a classical use of physiological reactions made by psychologists. (3) The third approach seeks for patterns of physiological reaction which may be diagnostic of the primary emotional states. It seeks to examine, for example, Cannon's hypothesis that fear and anger are essentially similar physiological reactions.

This paper reports a study of the latter type of polygraph research: that is, the physiological differentiation of two emotional states. Fear and anger were selected for study as being the two emotional states most often described as being identical physiological states. Although Cannon's theory that "fight and flight" excitement states have similar visceral patterns has been demonstrated to be generally true, there has always existed the possibility that a closer inspection of the physiological reaction patterns might reveal a differentiation or subtyping of the excitement states.

There have been hints deriving from both theoretical and experimental sources that question the hypothesis of the undifferentiated physiological state. Magda Arnold,[1] arguing from both neurological evidence and a reconsideration of published experimental data, concluded that fear is a strong arousal state of the sympathetic branch of the autonomic nervous system,

[1] Support for this study was provided by the Laboratory of Social Relations at Harvard University; the Boston Psychopathic Hospital; and the Department of Psychiatry, University of Washington School of Medicine. Dr. and Mrs. Joseph Schachter and Andrew Jensen cooperated in this research.

whereas anger is a strong arousal state of both the sympathetic and para-sympathetic branches of the autonomic nervous system. Wolf and Wolff have described increases in motility, secretion, and vascular dilatation of the viscera associated with anger or resentment and decreases in these functions during anxiety and depression. Mittleman and Wolff, in a study of finger temperature changes during psychoanalytical therapy, reported that decreases in temperature were associated with periods of anxiety and discussions of unpleasant topics, while during sexual excitement there were increases in finger temperature.

None of these studies, however, clearly demonstrated that these reported differences in physiological response might not be due either to different intensities of arousal or merely to the unique response patterns of a single individual. Accordingly, for this study it was planned to select an adequate sample and to record simultaneously with the emotional arousal a number of physiological reactions which could produce "patterns" of response.

PROCEDURE

The variables recorded are shown in Fig. 1 [Omitted in reprinting. (Ed.).] The Grass eight-channel electroencephalograph was used as the main recorder and amplifier. Since the Grass has only A. C. amplifiers, modulated A. C. envelopes were used for all continuous variables. The transducers can be briefly described. (1) The electrocardiogram was re-corded directly from ear and leg leads. (2) The ballistocardiogram, as an index of stroke volume, was produced by a crystal phono pickup im-bedded in a wooden block lying across the subject's ankles. A small lead weight on the end of the stylus converts the pickup into an efficient accel-erometer which responds to the ballistic reaction of the body to ejection of blood from the heart. (3) Respiration was recorded from thorax and abdominal pneumograph tubes activating an inductance tambour. (4 and 5) Face and finger skin temperatures were detected by V-611 Western Electric thermistors in an A. C. bridge using the electroencephalograph for recording the imbalance. (6) The skin conductance, as the index of sweating of the volar surfaces of two fingers of one hand, was also measured by a bridge using 60-cycle A. C. (7) Finally, at the bottom of the chart is the integrated muscle potential index from the frontalis muscle picked up by sponge electrodes and integrated and recorded as a modulated 60-cycle envelope. Systolic and diastolic blood pressures were taken every minute by a nurse. The room temperature was held constant at 23° C. ± 0.1° C.

The subject reclined in the testing room on a rigid table covered by a hair mattress. The nurse and experimenter were also in this room. The polygraph and operator were in an adjacent room.

The subjects were recruited through newspaper advertisements and a state employment agency. The only criteria for inclusion were that they must be free from any illness and within the age limits of 21 and 55 years. The average age was 27 years; 22 were men and 21 women. They were paid $3.00 for 2 hours. Only those whose blood pressure did not exceed 140/90 after 20 minutes' rest were included.

The subjects were told that this was a study of the physiological differences between people with hypertension and those without hypertension, that their only task was to relax on the bed and listen to their preferred music for about an hour. A rest period of 25 minutes preceded the stimulus periods. The stimulation periods of fear and anger were alternated so that 22 subjects received the fear stimulation first and 21 subjects received the anger stimulation first.

The fear stimulus consisted of a gradually increasing intermittent shock stimulus to the little finger which never reached an intensity sufficient to cause pain. When the subject reported the sensation, the experimenter expressed surprise, checked the wiring, pressed a key which caused sparks to jump near the subject, then exclaimed with alarm that this was a dangerous high-voltage short circuit. The experimenter created an atmosphere of alarm and confusion. After five minutes from the time the subject reported the shock, the experimenter removed the shock wire, assuring the subject that all danger was past, that the short circuit had been found and repaired. A ten- to fifteen-minute recovery period with music separated the fear and anger stimuli.

The polygraph operator was the key figure for the anger situation. He was described to the subject as not the regular operator but one who had been fired for incompetence and arrogance, but due to the sickness of the regular operator he had to be employed for that day. Thus he was labeled as a suitable target for hostility by the subject.

At the beginning of the anger stimulus, the operator entered the room stating he must check the wiring because some of the calibrations might be off. The experimenter objected but agreed to go into the other room and operate the polygraph. The operator shut off the music, criticized the nurse, and told the subject sarcastically that it would have helped if he had been on time. He checked the electrodes, roughly adjusted the subject, and criticized him for moving, noncooperation, and other behavior. After five minutes of abuse, the operator left and the experimenter returned, apologizing for this rude behavior. The experimenter reassured the subject and urged him to relax once more. After ten minutes the experimenter interviewed the subject for a five-minute period, questioning his memory and feelings for the first interruption; following another ten-minute rest period, the experimenter questioned him about the second interruption.

Remarks made by subjects either just after the stress stimulus or during the interviews illustrate their feeling states. Just after the operator left the room following the "anger" stimulus, one female subject said, "Well! It's easy to see he is not an educated man." A male subject said, "Say, what goes on here? I was just about to punch that character on the nose." Examples of fear reactions were also clearly genuine. One woman kept pleading, "Please take the wires off. Oh! Please help me." Another said during the interview that she had prayed to be spared during the fear episode. A man said, "Well, everybody has to go sometime. I thought this might be my time."

Some subjects used rather far-fetched rationalizations to limit or prevent fear. One man with great assurance said, "I wasn't really worried because I knew these wires were much too small to be dangerous." One subject did not report the shock for several minutes. The experimenter noticed an involuntary twitching and asked about it. The subject said, "Oh, I thought that was just part of the experiment."

The records for 6 subjects were not included in this study because it was immediately decided, purely on the basis of the interview and observation before seeing the polygraph data, that these subjects did not become either sufficiently angry or frightened to justify comparison.

ANALYSIS OF DATA

For all variables the maximum rises and falls during the stimulus period and the following two minutes (a total of seven minutes) were recorded as deviations from the resting level just prior to the stimulus period. Systolic and diastolic *blood pressures* recorded every minute were scored in millimeters of mercury. The *heart rate* was averaged for a six-second interval in selecting the maximum and minimum points. The *ballistocardiograph* score was the average voltage for approximately ten beats, covering exactly either two or three complete respirations.

Respiration was scored for changes in rate, amplitude, and inspiration /respiration ratio. Five consecutive breaths whose volume was judged to be maximum were selected for measurement. The I/R ratio and amplitude showed no significant difference for fear and anger. An index of volume, composed of the product of rate times amplitude, showed a significant difference which, however, was less significant than rate alone. Hence, rate was chosen as the variable to represent respiration.

Both *face temperature and hand temperature* were expressed in log units with the zero of the scale at 15° C., which is approximately 1° C. below the wet bulb thermometer temperature for the conditions of the experiment. Thus, if the finger were covered with perspiration and blood flow were zero, the temperature on the log units scale would approximate zero.

The *sweating index* was the skin conductance, which is the reciprocal of the resistance component of the impedance. Two aspects of conductance were scored: (1) the skin conductance rise as the maximum increase in conductance above the resting level just prior to the experimental period; (2) the number of increments per unit time in skin conductance of at least 1 micromho, which must have increased at least one micromho in three seconds.

One score for *muscle tension* was the maximum change in muscle potential which was averaged over a fifteen-second interval. The second muscle tension score was the average number of potential peaks per unit time. A peak was defined as an increment which doubled its size within three seconds.

RESULTS

In Table 1 are tabulated the means, standard deviations, differences of means for anger and fear, the t of the differences, and the null probabilities for the fourteen variables. In Fig. 2, these means are graphed in standard score units. The black bars represent the changes during the anger stimulus, and the white bars the changes during the fear stimulus. The $+$ signs indicate increases in the variable, and the $-$ signs decreases. Seven of the variables show significant differences between anger and fear. Four of the variables—diastolic blood pressure rises ($DBP+$), heart rate falls ($HR-$), number of galvanic skin responses ($\#GSR$), and muscle tension increases ($MT+$)—have greater average reactions for anger. Three variables—skin conductance increases ($SC+$), number of muscle tension peaks ($\#MTP$), and respiration rate increases ($RR+$)—have greater average reactions for fear.

It is of value to combine and express quantitatively these differences between the reactions of anger and fear, and also to provide a means of testing the significance of the combined differences. The difference between fear and anger which we wished to describe was not an amplitude difference but only the qualitative difference, which would be revealed in the profile shape with all average amplitude differences eliminated. Although there was no significant average amplitude difference between the fear and anger profiles, this factor was completely eliminated by the following procedure, illustrated for 1 subject in Table 2.

Standard scores based on the mean and standard deviation for both anger and fear combined were computed for these seven variables for the 43 sub-

Table 1. Characteristics of the Raw Scores

		$DBP+$	$HR-$	$FT-$	$HT-$	$\#GSR$	$MT+$	$BC-$	$BC+$
Means	A	17.83	6.02	.00498	.0497	11.56	4.35	22.6	173.2
	F	14.49	3.98	.00414	.0448	4.74	3.34	18.4	142.8
σ	A	9.33	3.72	.00390	.0320	7.84	3.12	38.9	178.5
	F	7.97	3.41	.00366	.0208	5.08	2.08	40.3	134.4
MA − MF		3.34	2.04	.000842	.00489	6.82	1.01	4.2	31.56
	t	2.47	3.66	1.22	.841	5.60	2.54	.79	1.15
Prob	t	.02	<.01	>.10	>.10	<.01	.02	>.10	>.10

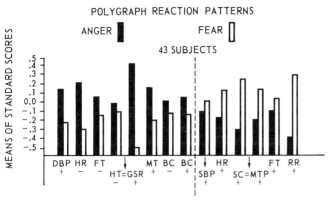

FIGURE 2   *The polygraph reactions, in standard score units, to the two stress situations called "anger" and "fear."*

jects. The scores of each profile were then summed across the seven variables. The difference between these two sums $(F—A)$ was obtained and divided by 7 to obtain the average difference in amplitude for this subject. This average difference was then subtracted from each score of the fear profile to produce the corrected fear profile (Fc). The average amplitude of this corrected fear profile was now identical to the average amplitude of the anger profile. In the next step, each of these corrected fear scores was subtracted from its corresponding anger score $(A—Fc)$. The mean of the differences for the four variables whose average amplitude was greater for anger was obtained $(M_{a>f}$, which for Subject 1 is .702). Likewise, the mean of the differences for the three variables whose average amplitude was less for anger was obtained $(M_{a<f} = -.938)$. This latter mean difference was subtracted from the former $[.702 - (-.938)]$ to produce the *profile difference score of* 1.640, which is a sum composed of the differences $(A—F)$ between those variables which are greater for anger plus the negative differences $-(A—F)$ between those variables which are greater for fear.

It might appear more direct merely to have summed the seven absolute

$SBP+$	$HR+$	$SC+$	$\#MTP$	$FT+$	$RR+$
19.19	25.79	9.41	10.45	.00294	2.31
20.35	30.32	14.81	13.17	.00348	6.00
8.58	14.19	8.88	7.88	.00382	3.99
11.77	17.69	10.42	7.94	.00317	6.50
-1.16	-4.53	-5.40	-2.72	-.00054	-3.69
.68	1.59	5.2	2.19	.87	3.46
>.10	>.10	<.01	.04	>.10	<.01

Table 2. Sample of Method for Computing the Profile Difference Scores

	A > F				A < F				
Subject 1.	DBP+	HR−	MT+	#GSR	SC+	RR+	#MTP		
F	− .470	1.077	− .657	− .700	1.381	− .018	1.146	ΣF	1.759
A	− .696	2.962	− .955	.377	.685	−1.667	.399	ΣA	1.105
Fc	− .563	.984	− .750	− .793	1.288	− .111	1.053	F − A	.654
A − Fc	− .133	1.978	− .205	1.170	− .603	−1.556	− .654	M$_{f\text{-}a}$	.093
	Σ$_{a>f}$		M$_{a>f}$		Σ$_{a<f}$		M$_{a<f}$	M$_{a>f}$ − M$_{a<f}$	
	2.810		.702		−2.813		− .938	1.640	

differences and called it a "profile shape difference score." The difficulty
with such a score is that even by the null hypothesis of no average difference between the shapes of the two profiles, the sum would have a mean
of finite value of unknown distribution. Obtaining its theoretical distribution is complicated by intercorrelation of the variables.

The more useful profile difference score obtained, as described above,
by subtracting the mean $(F > A)$ differences from the mean $(A > F)$
differences produces a distribution with a theoretical mean of zero, assuming the null hypothesis of no difference in shape between the anger and
fear profiles. The reason the theoretical mean of this distribution of *profile
difference scores* is zero is because it is a sum of seven distributions, each
of which has a theoretical mean of zero, each being a distribution of differences of standard scores whose means are zero.

The actual distribution of the *profile difference scores* deviated very
significantly from the theoretical one derived from the null hypothesis.
Forty-two of the forty-three scores were positive, whereas the null expectation is that approximately half would be positive and half negative. The
mean of the distribution was 1.087 with a t of 10.24, which indicates that
the null hypothesis may be rejected with a high degree of confidence.

DISCUSSION

It could be argued that the assignment of variables to the anger-greater-
than-fear category and to the fear-greater-than-anger category on the basis
of their mean differences would, of necessity, produce positive profile difference scores. There are, however, two legitimate methods for assignment
of variables to the category: (1) by an hypothesis independent of this
data; and (2) by inclusion of only those variables which have differences
sufficiently great to establish with confidence their correct category. Both
methods were employed in this study. The data from the first 16 subjects
were examined and found to have the pattern relationships described here
for the total group. The hypothesis is not completely independent, how-

ever, because the original 16 subjects are included in the total. The second principle of including only those variables showing significant differences bears the burden of our thesis. The fact that 50 per cent of the variables show significant differences around the .99 level of confidence constitutes the evidence that there is a difference in physiological reaction pattern to the two stimulus conditions here labeled "anger" and "fear." The individual *profile difference score* is a quantitative measure of the difference in reaction made by the individual for the two stimulus situations. It might be considered an index of emotional differentiation expressed in the physiological reaction.

The differences found can hardly be due to amplitude differences of the two emotional states, since some reactions were greater for fear and others were greater for anger. The differences remained when the profiles were equated for amplitude.

Possible interference effects due to the sequence of one stimulus situation following the other were controlled by stimulating half of the group first to anger and half of the group first to fear.

There was no selection of subjects which could have corrupted the results, since the only subjects eliminated were those 6 deemed not to have been both angered and frightened purely on the basis of the interview and observation, without reference to the physiological reactions.

An argument with some relevance may be raised. Possibly the differences found are not the result of two different emotional reactions, but related somehow to differences in the procedure and behavior of the subject during the two stimulus situations. Possibly there was more talking or small movements during one stimulus period than during the other. The two procedures were made as similar as possible. Close scrutiny of the records and of the wire recordings reveals no such systematic difference.

The use of two aspects of one variable, such as maximum rise in skin conductance ($SC+$) and the number of rises in skin conductance ($\#GSR$), or the maximum change in muscle tension ($MT+$) and the number of peaks in muscle tension ($\#MTP$) might be questioned. If two aspects of one variable were merely reciprocals of each other, they would be equally discriminative of the two states, but the second would contribute no additional discrimination over the first. Product moment correlations between maximum rise in skin conductance and number of rises in skin conductance were $-.05$ for fear and $+.38$ for anger. Correlations of muscle tension change with number of muscle tension peaks were $+.07$ for fear and $+.16$ for anger, which indicates almost a complete lack of dependence between them. The $+.38$ correlation between maximum changes in skin conductance and number of rises in skin conductance during anger probably indicates a small tendency for those subjects with the larger sweating response to make these responses more frequently but only during anger. The complete lack of substantial negative correlation certainly removes any question of these two aspects being merely reciprocals of each other.

A rather surprising finding is the general lack of correlation between

Table 3. Correlations for Anger and Fear for the Variables Which Distinguished Significantly between Anger and Fear

		DBP+	HR−	#GSR	MT+	SC+	#MTP	RR+
DBP+	A		−.17	.32	−.12	.38	.10	.16
	F	.51[a]	−.11	−.10	−.08	−.03	.08	.22
HR−	A			−.09	−.09	−.04	−.16	−.00
	F		.49[a]	−.01	.10	.13	.06	.01
#GSR	A				−.28	.38	.00	−.12
	F			.42[a]	−.06	−.05	.14	−.16
MT+	A					−.17	.16	.24
	F				.64[a]	−.06	.07	−.04
SC+	A						.06	.25
	F					.77[a]	−.09	−.29
#MTP	A							−.01
	F						.52[a]	−.06
RR+	A							.26[a]
	F							

[a] The self-correlations are between anger and fear.

the variables. The intervariable correlations are found in Table 3. Very few approach significance, and those are quite small compared to the self-correlations for fear and anger, which average .53. This lack of correlation among the physiological reactions fits a general hypothesis underlying this study: that is, that there is marked uniqueness in physiological expression of emotion. Evidence which further supports this thesis is the significantly larger between-subjects variance (9.68), as compared with the within-subjects variance (4.00), which has an F ratio of 2.42, significant at the 99 per cent level of confidence. (It was determined that neither distribution differed significantly from normal.) This finding is in essential agreement with results reported by Lacey and by Malmo,[5,6,7,8] in which various types of autonomic responses are described as being characteristic either of the individual or of a special diagnostic group. This well-established specificity of autonomic-response pattern in a sense highlights the present findings of uniformity of response, which is characteristic of a specific emotional state experienced by many different individuals. If the physiological response pattern which is diagnostic of a specific emotional state could be measured for each individual as a deviation from his characteristic response pattern, much greater accuracy of specific emotional diagnosis might be expected.

Another interesting finding was the consistently larger correlations (neglecting sign) between the variables for anger than for fear. The mean of the fear correlations was .090 and for anger .157, the difference being significant at the 96 per cent level of confidence, the t being 2.25 for 20 degrees of freedom. One might interpret this greater tendency for higher correlation of the physiological reactions during anger to indicate a greater organization or integration during anger than during fear. Such an interpretation might be examined in terms of the evolutionary theory of the struggle for survival. Possibly successful attack would usually require greater mobilization and organization of the individual's resources than would flight. The paralysis of extreme fear might exemplify almost complete lack of effective integration.

In speculating as to a possible integrating factor for these two different physiological reaction profiles for fear and anger, it was noticed that the fear profile resembled that produced by an injection of epinephrine while the anger profile more nearly resembled that of a combined epinephrine and nor-epinephrine reaction. Goldenberg reported that injections of nor-epinephrine produce a larger rise in diastolic blood pressure and a larger fall in pulse rate and stroke volume, while epinephrine produces a larger rise in systolic blood pressure, pulse rate, and stroke volume. Since the chief action of nor-epinephrine appears to be that of general vasoconstriction while that of epinephrine is one of increased cardiac output and reflex vasodilatation, we might predict that face temperature and hand temperature falls would be greater in nor-epinephrine, while face temperature rises would be greater for epinephrine. We know of no data which would suggest what to expect for muscle tension, respiration, or sweating changes.

The bar graph (Fig. 2) is arranged so that the eight variables in which the mean reactions were greater for anger are placed left of the dotted vertical line, and the remaining six variables in which the mean reactions were greater for fear are placed right of the dotted vertical line. The only variable in which the empirical data are in reversal to theory (of anger being like nor-epinephrine and fear like epinephrine) is the ballistocardiograph increases. This difference (although not statistically significant) may be explained by the fact that heart rates, on the average, were faster for fear, which could have reduced auricular filling of the heart and thus have reduced the stroke volume for fear as compared to anger. Another possible explanation is that since anger is presumed to be a state of combined epinephrine and nor-epinephrine, the epinephrine may have succeeded in dominating the ballistocardiograph variable.

The patterns obtained for fear and anger argue against the proposal by Arnold that anger differs from fear in that the parasympathetic system is strongly aroused in anger. Our findings that diastolic blood pressure rises and skin temperature falls were greater in anger and that face temperature rises were less in anger are each contrary to that of a general parasympathetic reaction. None of the values obtained, except the insignificantly greater rise of the stroke volume index during anger, on the other hand, is inconsistent with the hypothesis of a combination epinephrine and nor-epinephrine-like reaction for anger and an epinephrine-like reaction for fear.

CONCLUSIONS

The results of this experiment indicate that two stimulus conditions which appeared to the experimenter and to the subjects as being properly termed "anger-producing" and "fear-producing" were accompanied by simultaneously recorded physiological reaction patterns which, on the average, were clearly different for the two stimuli for this sample of 43 subjects. These results do not refute Cannon's hypothesis of a unitary visceral excitement reaction but merely reveal a further differentiation in physiological reaction pattern. The patterns obtained for fear and anger are suggested as being similar to those produced by injections of epinephrine and a combination of epinephrine and nor-epinephrine. The intercorrelations of the physiological variables were significantly higher for anger than for fear, which was interpreted as indicating greater integration during anger.

These results provide further evidence for the psychophysiological unity of the organism in the sense that even the finest nuances of psychological events may be found to have a corresponding differentiation at the physiological level.

SUMMARY

Forty-three subjects were stimulated in the laboratory to "fear" and "anger," during which the following physiological reactions were recorded: (1) heart rate, (2) ballistocardiogram, (3) respiration rate, (4) face temperature, (5) hand temperature, (6) skin conductance, and (7) integrated muscle potential. The scores used were the maximum rise and maximum fall from the preceding resting level and the number of responses of a critical value per unit time. Of the 14 scores thus obtained, 7 showed significant discrimination between anger and fear. Diastolic blood pressure rises, heart rate falls, number of rises in skin conductance, and muscle potential increases, were greater for anger than for fear, whereas skin conductance increases, number of muscle potential increases, and respiration rate increases were greater for fear than for anger. *Profile difference scores,* computed from appropriate combinations of these differences, were found to be greater than zero in 42 of the 43 cases and to have a mean which deviated very significantly from zero, which rejects the null hypothesis that there is no difference in physiological reaction between anger and fear.

The patterns obtained for anger and fear argue against the Arnold proposal that anger is a strong reaction of both the sympathetic and parasympathetic branches of the autonomic nervous systems, whereas fear is but a sympathetic reaction.

Another finding was the very low correlations among the physiological reactions and the significantly higher intercorrelations for anger than for fear, which was interpreted as indicating greater physiological integration during anger.

Between-subject variance was significantly greater than within-subject variance, which supports the findings of Lacey and Malmo that there is considerable specificity in physiological response patterns.

The physiological response patterns of anger were suggested as being similar to those produced by injections of epinephrine and nor-epinephrine combined, and those of fear as being similar to injections of epinephrine.

REFERENCES

1 Arnold, M. "An excitatory theory of emotion." In: Reymert, M. L. (ed.): *Feelings and Emotions*. New York, McGraw-Hill, 1950, Chap. 2.

2 Cannon, W. B. *Bodily Changes in Pain, Hunger, Fear, and Rage*. New York, Appleton, 1920.

3 Goldenberg, M., *et al.* The hemodynamic response of man to nor-epinephrine and epinephrine and its relation to the problem of hypertension. *Am. J. Med.* **5**: 792, 1948.

4 Lacey, J. I. Individual differences in somatic response patterns. *J. Comp. Physiol. Psychol.* **43**: 338, 1950.

5 Malmo, R. B., and Shagass, C. Physiologic studies of reaction to stress in anxiety and early schizophrenia. *Psychosom. Med.* **11**: 9, 1949.

6 Malmo, R. B., Shagass, C., and Davis, H. D. Specificity of bodily reactions under stress. *Proc. A. Res. Nerv. Ment. Dis.* **29**: 231, 1950.

7 Malmo, R. B., Shagass, C., and Heslam, R. M. Blood pressure response to repeated brief stress in psychoneurosis: A study of adaptation. *Canad. J. Psychol.* **5**: 167, 1951.

8 Malmo, R. B., Shagass, C., and Smith, A. A. Responsiveness in chronic schizophrenia. *J. Person.* **19**: 359, 1951.

9 Mittelman, B., and Wolff, H. G. Emotions and skin temperature: Observations on patients during psychotherapeutic (psychoanalytic) interviews. *Psychosom. Med.* **5**: 211, 1943.

10 Wolf, S., and Wolff, H. G. *Human Gastric Function*. New York, Oxford, 1947.

MODIFICATION OF ELECTRIC ACTIVITY IN COCHLEAR NUCLEUS DURING "ATTENTION" IN UNANESTHETIZED CATS

Raúl Hernández-Peón, Harald Scherrer, and Michel Jouvet

UNIVERSITY OF CALIFORNIA, LOS ANGELES, AND VETERANS ADMINISTRATION HOSPITAL, LONG BEACH

Editor's Note Attention is called to the close relation between this reading and that of Galambos' (No. 1).

Source *Reprinted from* **Science**, *February 24, 1956,* **123**, *331–332, with permission of the authors and the American Association for the Advancement of Science.*

Attention involves the selective awareness of certain sensory messages with the simultaneous suppression of others. Our sense organs are activated by a great variety of sensory stimuli, but relatively few evoke conscious sensation at any given moment. It is common experience that there is a pronounced reduction of extraneous sensory awareness when our attention is concentrated on some particular matter. During the attentive state, it seems as though the brain integrates for consciousness only a limited amount of sensory information, specifically, those impulses concerned with the object of attention.

An interference with impulses initiated by sensory stimuli other than those pertaining to the subject of attention seems to be an obvious possibility. It is clear that this afferent blockade might occur at any point along the classical sensory pathways from receptors to the cortical receiving areas, or else perhaps in the recently disclosed extraclassical sensory paths that traverse the brain-stem reticular system (*1*).

Recent evidence indicates the existence of central mechanisms that regulate sensory transmission. It has been shown that appropriate stimulation of the brain-stem reticular system will inhibit afferent conduction between the first- and second-order neurons in all three principal somatic paths (*2–4*). During central anesthesia, the afferent-evoked potentials in the first sensory relays are enhanced. This appears to be due to the release of a tonic descending inhibitory influence that operates during wakefulness and requires the functional integrity of the brain-stem reticular formation.

The possibility that a selective central inhibitory mechanism might operate during attention for filtering sensory impulses was tested by studying (*5*) afferent transmission in the second- or third-order neurons of the auditory pathway (cochlear nucleus) in unanesthetized, unrestrained cats during experimentally elicited attentive behavior. Bipolar stainless steel electrodes with a total diameter of 0.5 mm were implanted sterotaxically in the dorsal cochlear nucleus through a small hole bored in the skull. The electrode was fixed to the skull with dental cement. A minimum of 1 week elapsed between the operation and the first electroencephalographic recordings. Electric impulses in the form of short bursts of rectangular waves (0.01 to 0.02 sec) at a frequency of 1000 to 5000 cy/sec were delivered to a loudspeaker near the cats at an intensity comfortable to human observers in the same environment.

Three types of sensory modalities were used to attract the animal's attention: visual, olfactory, and somatic. As is illustrated in Fig. 1, during presentation of visual stimuli (two mice in a closed bottle), the auditory responses in the cochlear nucleus were greatly reduced in comparison with the control responses; they were practically abolished as long as the visual stimuli elicited behavioral evidence of attention. When the mice were removed,

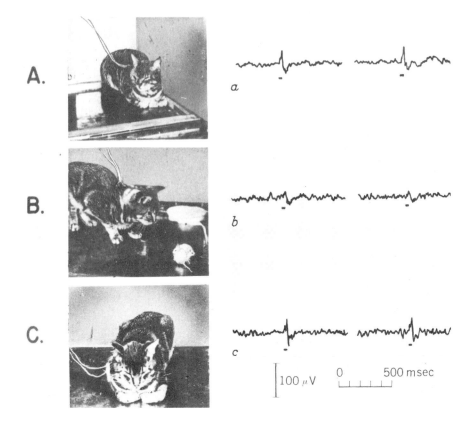

A.

a

B.

b

C.

c

100 μV   0   500 msec

FIGURE 1 *Direct recording of click responses in the cochlear nucleus during three periods; the photographs were taken simultaneously. (Top and bottom) Cat is relaxed; the click responses are large. (Middle) While the cat is visually attentive to the mice in the jar, the click responses are diminished in amplitude.*

the auditory responses returned to the same order of magnitude as the initial controls. An olfactory stimulus that attracted the animal's attention produced a similar blocking effect. While the cat was attentively sniffing tubing through which fish odors were being delivered, the auditory potential in the cochlear nucleus was practically absent (Fig. 2). After the stimulus had been removed and when the cat appeared to be relaxed once more, the auditorily evoked responses in the cochlear nucleus were of the same magnitude as they had been prior to the olfactory stimulation. Similarly, a nociceptive shock delivered to the forepaw of the cat—a shock that apparently distracted the animal's attention—resulted in marked reduction of auditorily evoked responses in the cochlear nucleus.

If this sensory inhibition during attentive behavior, as demonstrated in the auditory pathway, occurs in all other sensory paths except the ones concerned with the object of attention, such an inhibitory mechanism might lead to favoring of the attended object by the selective exclusion of incom-

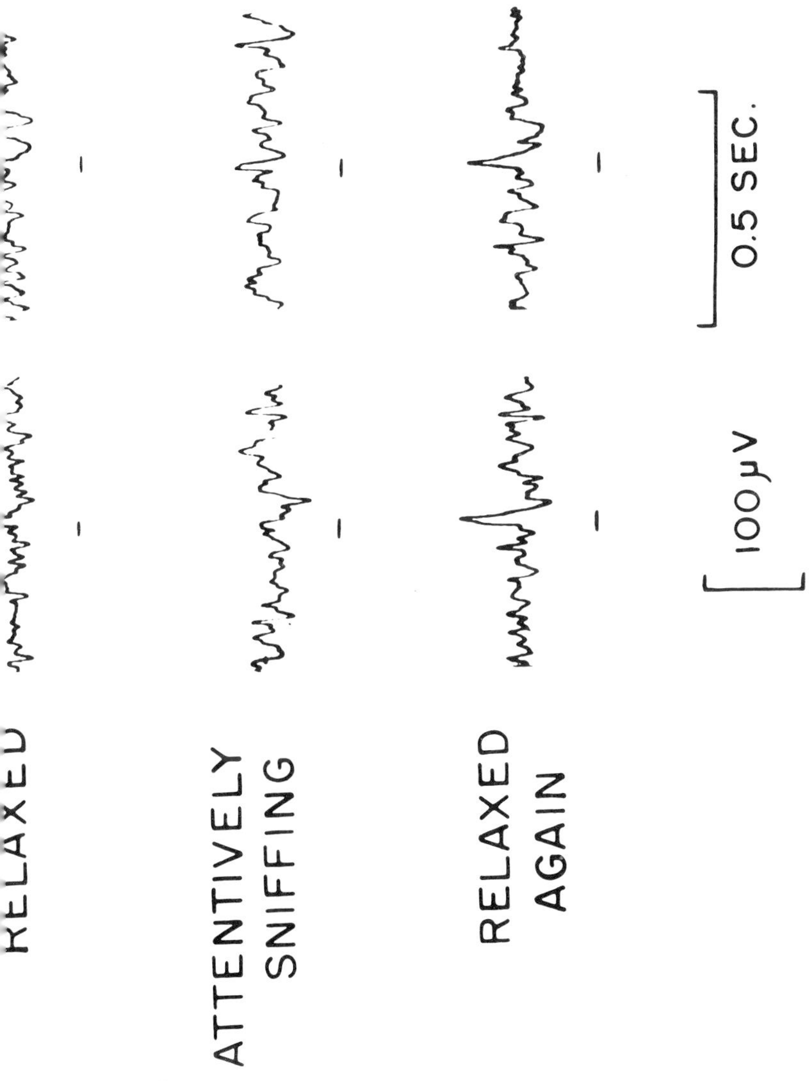

FIGURE 2 *Click responses recorded from the cochlear nucleus of the cat. (Top) cat is relaxed; (middle) cat is attentively sniffing an olfactory stimulus; (bottom) cat is relaxed again. Note the reduced amplitude of the click responses when the animal is sniffing.*

ing signals. It is conceivable not only that such a selective sensory inhibition might operate simultaneously for various sensory modalities, leaving one or more unaffected but that the selectivity could extend to some discrimina ble aspects of any single modality—for example, to one tone and not to others. This suggestion finds support in the recent demonstration that sen sory "habituation" may occur to a particular tone—that is, a slowly develop ing inhibitory effect on auditorily evoked potentials observed in the cochlear nucleus on prolonged repetition of a given tone, an influenc that does not affect other frequencies that are novel to the animal (6) The pathway by which this inhibitory influence acts on incoming auditor impulses remains to be determined, but experiments now in progress have shown that during electric stimulation of the midbrain reticular formation the auditory potential in the cochlear nucleus is depressed (7).

The present observations suggest that the blocking of afferent impulse in the lower portions of a sensory path may be a mechanism whereby sensory stimuli out of the scope of attention can be markedly reduced while they are still in their trajectory toward higher levels of the centra nervous system. This central inhibitory mechanism may, therefore, play an important role in selective exclusion of sensory messages along thei passage toward mechanisms of perception and consciousness. In a recen symposium on brain mechanisms and consciousness, Adrian pointed ou that "the signals from the sense organs must be treated differently when we attend to them and when we do not, and if we could decide where and how the divergence arises we should be nearer to understanding how the level of consciousness is reached" (8).

REFERENCES AND NOTES

1 J. D. French, M. Verzeano, H. W. Magoun, *Arch. Neurol. Psychiat.* **69**, 505 (1953).
2 K.-E. Hagbarth and D. I. B. Kerr, *J. Neurophysiol.* **17**, 295 (1954).
3 R. Hernández-Peón and K.-E. Hagbarth, *ibid.* **18**, 44 (1955).
4 H. Scherrer and R. Hernández-Peón, *Federation Proc.* **14**, 132 (1955).
5 This work was aided by grants from the Commonwealth Fund, the National Institute for Neurological Diseases and Blindness of the U.S. Public Health Service, and El Lilly and Company. This report is based on a paper presented before the American Physiological Society on 12 Apr. 1955.
6 R. Hernández-Peón and H. Scherrer, *Federation Proc.* **14**, 71 (1955); R. Hernández-Peón, M. Jouvet, H. Scherrer, in preparation.
7 M. Jouvet, E. Berkowitz, R. Hernández-Peón, in preparation.
8 E. D. Adrian, in *Brain Mechanisms and Consciousness*, J. F. Delafresnaye, Ed. (Blackwell, Oxford, 1954), p. 238.

Motivation

THE INTERNAL ENVIRONMENT AND BEHAVIOR

PART III. WATER CONTENT

Edward F. Adolph

UNIVERSITY OF ROCHESTER

Editor's Note   *This classic and very important study is somewhat "old-fashioned" in its language and style of presentation. However, it bears patient and careful reading since it establishes a conclusion with quite far-reaching implications: It shows that the nervous system may at times control behavior by effectively computing quantitative requirements for future action.*

Source   *Reprinted from the **American Journal of Psychiatry**, 1941, **97**, 1365–1373, with permission of the author and the publisher.*

Claude Bernard (1878, p. 114) declared: "In animals having free existence there necessarily exists a group of arrangements regulating the losses and the gains in a manner that maintains the quantity of necessary water in the internal medium." That statement expresses in qualitative terms the rule that adjustments of water content of the animal body are relations between losses of water and gains of water. I have recently attempted to obtain, for man and dog, quantitative data from which these relations may be described.

EXCHANGES OF WATER IN WATER EXCESSES   For experimental purposes, a man or dog as ordinarily observed in the laboratory is in water balance. Water content is increased by the planned ingestion of diverse amounts of water (data of Kingsley). Thereafter very many physiological quantities are different from what they were; among them the losses and the gains of water by the body as a whole are first chosen for measurement. The body weight, made excessive by the ingestion, decreases as time goes on, and much more rapidly than without the ingestion. After a lag, the rate of loss is approximately proportional to the excess of water (or positive *load*) present in the body. Rates are greatest at 1 to 1¾ hours, and after 3 to 4 hours nearly all the load has been eliminated. Most of the unusual loss is accounted for as urine.

Choosing to compare the rates of water exchange either in the first one hour or the second one hour after water is drunk, it is found that rates of loss are greater as loads are greater. Simultaneously, rates of gain of water are very small, being limited to that water formed by oxidative metabolism. Load itself may be thought of as a stimulus, and rate of exchange then answers the definition of a response. The response is one that actually accomplishes recovery of water content. It increases the output of water in urine, modifying activities of more tissues than just the kidneys.

EXCHANGE OF WATER IN WATER DEFICITS   In other tests, water content is diminished. Some tests are carried out by consuming only dry foods for 1 to 4 days, hence by partial privation of water intake. In other tests on man the water content is depleted by intense sweating incident to walking for an hour or two in the hot desert, in which period 2 to 4 per cent of the body weight is lost (Adolph and Dill, '38). At a predetermined moment the subjects are allowed to drink water at will. At first they take water rapidly, later much more slowly; and during half an hour much less water is consumed in man than had been previously lost. There is just significantly faster intake in the summer desert as compared with the winter laboratory. In any one test the intake in relation to time follows a regular course corresponding roughly to an exponential equation.

Initial rates of intake are related to initial deficits of water that prevail, in both man and dog (Fig. 1). Regression of rates upon these negative

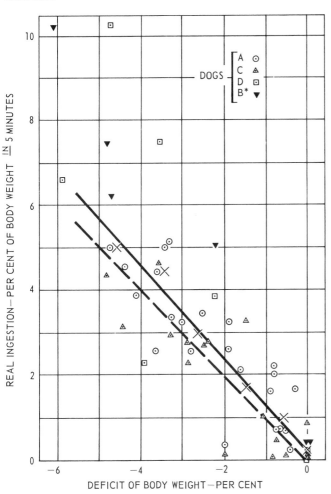

FIGURE 1 *Amounts of water drunk by dogs at the end of water privations that produced diverse deficits of water content. Each test is indicated, and every eight tests taken in order of abscissae are averaged (×) except for those of dog B* in which an esophageal fistula was reconnected by a tube (from Adolph, '39).*

water loads indicates approximate proportionality, but the proportion of the deficit taken in an hour or less is much smaller in man than in dog. This marked diversity between the two species is far outside of any individual variations, and has not yet been related with any better-known feature of mammalian economy.

ADJUSTMENT OF WATER CONTENT BY GAIN AND LOSS The two sorts of water load, excess and deficit, may be compared graphically with loads as abscissae and initial rates of exchange as ordinates (Adolph, '37). Two curves result, one for loss and one for gain. When loss is rapid, gain is slow, and vice versa. The two curves cross in one point, gain equalling loss, which is water *balance*. The point is located at the only water content that is steadily maintained (zero load). At all other water contents initial losses exceed gains, or vice versa. This means a *net* loss (or gain), and the direction of exchange is apparently appropriate to restoration of the original water content.

Intake and output are thus compared in common dimensions. So far as I can judge, adjustments of deficits and of excesses are equally accurate. Output is a physiological behavior exhibited in the continuous flow of urinary water and of evaporative water. Intake is a physiological behavior exhibited in intermittent swallowing and more continuous absorption and distribution of water. If the term behavior be not limited to activities involving known neural structures, then behavior as observed at both ends of the course of water metabolism is concerned in restoring water content. Or, maintenance and restoration of water content of the body, of the internal environment, *is* behavior.

SOME POSSIBLE INTERMEDIARIES Observations of the sort mentioned above raise questions concerning what tissues are employed in those activities. In water excesses the increased urine output or diuresis might be dictated by one or many changes in the body. (1) Complete denervation of the kidneys in dogs does not modify the time relations or precise quantity of urine excreted (Klisiecki *et al.*, '33). Hence, whatever messages are employed in controlling output need no nerves in this part of their transmission. (2) It is now certain that during diuresis in dogs the plasma is diluted. The dilution of the plasma may then be a message in itself. This dilution appears about one-third hour before any diuresis. (3) Special chemical messengers have been sought. Augmented output of something from adrenal glands, and suppressed output of something from hypophysis have been widely suspected, but neither seems to be demonstrated. These three hypotheses represent the sorts of inference that are being tested.

Water deficits are said to be accompanied by "thirst." This term is commonly used in at least three meanings: (*a*) a physiological *state* that may be easily defined as a negative water load. An animal is "subjected to thirst" when it is deprived of water. (*b*) A *sensation*, as set forth by Cannon ('18) that, so far, is known to exist only in man, for no means has been devised of identifying it in any sensory element of other animals. (*c*) An *urge* or craving, that may be studied by finding how much water is drunk.

The last definition can be put to test, and particularly strikingly in dogs with fistula of the esophagus. Water that was drunk then gained no access to the body, and the drinking could be quantitatively measured without long dispelling the urge to drink. Such dogs were rendered poor in water to diverse extents while on diet of uniform daily amount; body weight was a measure of water deficit (Adolph, '39). It was found that on the average the rate of sham-drinking was proportional to the weight deficit (Fig. 2). Hence the urge called thirst is closely correlated with the state called thirst.

The esophageal fistulous dog could also be supplied by stomach (Bel-

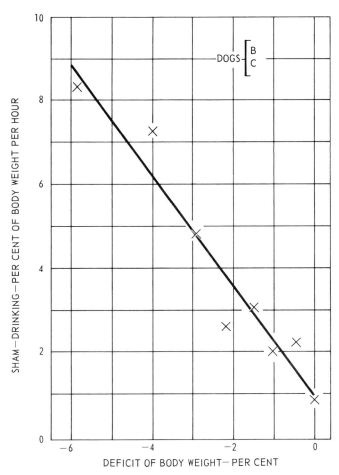

FIGURE 2 *Amounts of water sham-drunk by dogs during steady deficits of water content. Each point represents the average of 12 tests of 24 hours each, taken in order of abscissae (from Adolph, '39).*

lows, '39) with the exact amount of water required to dispel its deficit. This water did not pass through the mouth. If allowed access to water at once the dog sham-drank an equal quantity. After 10 minutes less was drunk, and if forced to wait 15 minutes or more, no water was drunk. This time was presumably required for water in the stomach to accomplish some specific effect, possibly while being absorbed from the gut. Bellows has also shown (new data) that water in the amount of the water deficit, given by stomach tube to a non-fistulous dog is likewise followed by duplicate drinking of the whole amount. The dog has now obtained twice the amount of water craved, for the first water administered did not register on its way to the stomach. This demonstrates two separable factors; one temporary, of passage of water through mouth and esophagus, the other lasting, after water reaches the stomach.

Thirst, is one of many urges that seem to be indispensable for successful survival, but for which no sense organs, neural pathways (Bellows and Van Wagenen, '39), or other structures are identified. Functions that have no known anatomical basis need not be ignored on that account. The suggestion (Cannon, '18) that the throat is one site of origin of sensations of thirst has been widely discussed.

SOME OTHER BEHAVIORS IN WATER EXCESSES   It seems appropriate to mention a few further specific types of overt behavior that are exhibited when water loads are increased. Achelis ('30), measuring the excitability to electrical stimuli in cutaneous nerves, found that after adding water to the body the chronaxie temporarily increased. Larger excesses of water have occasionally been produced in men for various experimental or supposedly therapeutic purposes, and a series of manifestations has been observed in these extreme states, e.g., muscular twitchings, headache, dizziness, restlessness, chills, nausea, vomiting, diarrhea, dyspnea, asthenia, cramps, sweating, positive Babinski reflexes, incoordination of movements, stupor, unconsciousness, dilatation of the pupils, opisthotonus, convulsions and death. Most were seen in two surgical patients who through error received 8 liters of water by rectum within 30 hours (Helwig et al., '35, '38). To the physician these phenomena are symptoms of an unusual state of the human body. They are also to be regarded as responses to this internal state. Intensities and frequencies of each such response need to be precisely measured in relation to water content. Certain of the activities, notably vomiting, diarrhea, dyspnea, and sweating, actually relieve the body of some of its excess of water. It seems arbitrary to say which of the responses are advantageous to the subject while others are unavoidable consequences. Rather, all are part of a syndrome sometimes termed "water intoxication" from which very commonly recovery occurs. All are behaviors characteristically exhibited by men with unusual, high excesses of water content. It is supposed (Rowntree, '26) that intracranial pressure is greater than usual in this state.

The most likely exception to utility in the responses is the urge to drink more water, found by Regnier ('16) and Kunstmann ('33). After consuming about 10 liters of water daily for 8 to 127 days, drinking became an obsession. The subjects often awoke at night and felt impelled to get out of bed in order to drink. Salt was also craved and the mouth was dry, possible indications of inadequate use and distribution of the excess of water already present in the body. Patients having meningioma with high intracranial pressure are generally relieved of symptoms by drinking large volumes of water.

In the uncommon pathological state of diabetes insipidus, men exhibit modified behaviors toward water; the rates of intake and output of water are greatly augmented. It is not known whether a net excess or deficit of water prevails during it as compared with the average water content of normal individuals. When an excess of water is suddenly administered, it is not all promptly excreted (Findley and White, '37). The urge to drink water is overwhelming, yet water taken is lost more rapidly than usual. If the steady loss is retarded by administrations of hypophysial extracts, excessive intake and output of water are usually completely inhibited.

Diverse types of organic and functional nervous disease are characterized by aberrant rates of adjustment of water content. It is also known that faster excretion of water may be induced by suggestion during hypnosis (Hoff and Wermer, '26). Water exchanges respond to conditioned stimuli (Marx, '35). This may mean that adjustments of water content though once imperfect, may be capable of reëstablishment and training.

BEHAVIORS IN WATER DEFICITS States of water deficit may be equally productive of special behaviors. A train of manifestations was described by King (1878) from observations upon a troop of cavalry lost for 4 days in the Texas desert: inability to swallow, dimness of vision, deafness, vertigo, delirium, incoordination of movement, emotional irritability, and hallucinations of feasting and drinking. Food is often refused. The flow of saliva in response to an adequate stimulus is greatly diminished. Restlessness and mental confusion are the rule (McGee, '06). The lone traveler who has run short of water in the desert raves, casts off his clothing, and rushes onward kicking his obsessive but empty water-can ahead of him. Even here it is not possible to judge which of the behaviors are inappropriate to recovery of water content. All are responses correlated with particular deficits of water content; precise measurement of each of them is highly desirable.

Investigators often use the "thirst drive" to increase the intensity or frequency or rate at which various acts are performed, in rats, cats, dogs, and I hope in man. I suggest that the drive or urge be measured in quantitative units, either of the amount of water subsequently consumed *ad libitum*, or of the negative water load with which it is correlated (Figs. 1 and 2). For the latter, it is only necessary to ascertain the shortage of body weight that prevails when the tests are made. Further, a standard type of deficit may be produced by water deprivation upon an otherwise standard diet, rather than many types of deficit by a variety of exposures, drugs and unknowns.

SUMMARY Internal environment and overt behavior present a reciprocal relation, for the constancy of the body's composition and function depends on behavior for its maintenance, and behavior in turn depends on the body's contents and physiological states. With respect to water, elimination of excess and replacement of shortages are symmetrical aspects of recoveries and adjustments of water content. Each is quantitatively related to the other in a kinetic pattern that is but rarely incomplete, even in diseased states.

Bernard said (1878, p. 113): "The fixity of the internal medium presupposes an arrangement in the organism such that the variations are at each instant compensated and equilibrated." This arrangement I have tried to describe.

BIBLIOGRAPHY

Achelis, J. D.: Ueber Umstimmung der Sensibilität. Archiv. gesam. Physiol., **226**: 121, 1930.

Adolph, E. F.: Rates of adjustment of body water content. Science, **86**:(2237), 446, November 12, 1937.

Adolph, E. F., and Dill, D. B.: Observations on water metabolism in the desert. Am. J. Physiol., **123**:(2), 369, August, 1938.

Adolph, E. F.: Measurements of water drinking in dogs. Am. J. Physiol., **125**:(1), 75, January, 1939.

Bellows, R. T.: Time factors in water drinking in dogs. Am. J. Physiol., **125**:(1), 87, January, 1939.

Bellows, R. T., and Van Wagenen, W. P.: The effect of resection of the olfactory, gustatory and trigeminal nerves on water drinking in dogs without and with diabetes insipidus. Am. J. Physiol. **126**:(1), 13, May, 1939.

Bernard, C.: Leçons sur les Phénomènes de la vie communs aux animaux et aux vegetaux. Paris, Baillière, 1878.

Cannon, W. B.: The physiological basis of thirst. Proc. Roy. Soc., 90B: **283**, 1918.

Findley, T., Jr., and White, H. L.: The response of normal individuals and patients with diabetes insipidus to the ingestion of water. J. Clin. Invest., **16**: 197, 1937.

Helwig, F. C., Schutz, C. B., and Curry, D. E.: Water intoxication. Report of a fatal human case, with clinical, pathological and experimental studies. J. Am. Med. Assn., **104**: 1569, 1935.

Helwig, T. C., Schutz, C. B., and Kuhn, H. P.: Water intoxication. J. Am. Med. Assn., **110**: 644, 1938.

Hoff, H., and Wermer, P.: Untersuchungen über den Mechanismus der Diuresehemmung durch Pituitrin beim Menschen. Arch. exp. Path. Pharm., **119**: 153, 1926.

King, J. H.: Brief account of the sufferings of a detachment of U.S. cavalry, from privation of water, etc. Am. J. Med. Sci., **75**: 404, 1878.

Kingsley, H. D., and Adolph, E. F.: Unpublished data.

Klisiecki, A., Pickford, M., Rothschild, P., and Verney, E. B.: The absorption and excretion of water by the mammal. I. The relation between absorption of water and its excretion by the innervated and denervated kidney. Proc. Roy. Soc., **112B**: 496, 1933.

Kunstmann: Ueber die Wirkung der Zufuhr grosser Wassermengen auf den Organismus. Archiv. exp. Path. Pharm., **170**: 701, 1933.

Marx, H.: Der Wasserhaushalt des gesunden und kranken Menschen. Berlin. Springer. 1935.

McGee, W. J.: Desert thirst as disease. Interstate Med. J., **13**: 279, 1906.

Regnier, A.: Ueber den Einfluss diätetischer Massnahmen auf das osmotische Gleichgewicht des Blutes beim normalen Menschen. Z. exp. Path. Therap., **18**: 139, 1916.

Rowntree, L. G.: The effects on mammals of the administration of excessive quantities of water. J. Pharm., **29**: 135, 1926.

THE EFFECT OF INJECTIONS OF HYPERTONIC NaCl-SOLUTIONS INTO DIFFERENT PARTS OF THE HYPOTHALAMUS OF GOATS

Bengt Andersson

KUNGL. VETERINÄRHÖGSKOLAN

Source   *Reprinted from* **Acta Physiologica Scandi-**
navica, 1953, 28, 189–201, with permission of the author
and the publisher.

The cause of the intake of water has never been fully understood. Much evidence has been given against the theory of Cannon (1918) that the sensation of thirst is locally generated by dryness of the mucous membranes of the mouth and throat. Thus the sensation of thirst persists if the nerve supply to the mouth is interrupted (Bellows and Van Wagenen 1939) and the thirst sensation can be inhibited by giving water by stomach tube.

On the other hand the experiments of Gilman (1937) show that an elevation of the osmotic pressure of the blood in dogs by intravenous injection of hypertonic solutions of NaCl gives a much greater intake of water than an equivalent rise in osmotic pressure caused by the injection of urea. This indicates that cellular dehydration is the prime factor in arousing thirst. But the fact that primary polydipsia can be caused by a tumor, a cyst (Fulton and Bailey 1929, Kourilsky 1950) or experimental injuries (Bailey and Bremer 1921, Bellows and Van Wagenen 1938) in the hypothalamus makes it likely that the sensation of thirst generates from this part of the brain. It could thus be postulated that osmoreceptors, situated in the hypothalamus, were involved in the thirst mechanism.

In order to study the effect of an increased osmotic pressure in the hypothalamus injections of hypertonic NaCl-solutions were performed directly into this part of the brain stem of unanaesthetized goats, and a polydipsic effect of such injections was recently reported in two short communications (Andersson 1952). In this paper a full report of the experiments will be given, as well as the results of the histological examinations.

METHODS

In all 19 goats of different age and size were used—some of them for more than one experiment. The operations were performed, with the animals placed in a stand, under local anaesthesia completed with light ether narcosis where the animals reacted to the incision. Hess' technique was applied for fixation and guidance of the cannulae, the length of which varied according to the size of the skulls and the point of stimulation desired. The cannulae used for the injections were, after having been guided into the hypothalamus, screwed up to a holder, earlier fixed on the skull (Fig. 1) [omitted in reprinting]. Injections could thus be performed without displacing the cannulae. These were 0.5 mm in diameter and the injections were performed through a small hole 0.5–1 mm (in the earlier experiments 3–6 mm) from their tip. Thus the injections could either be rostrally or caudally directed.

Body-warm NaCl-solutions of varying concentration were used for the injections, which as a rule were carried out with the animals placed in

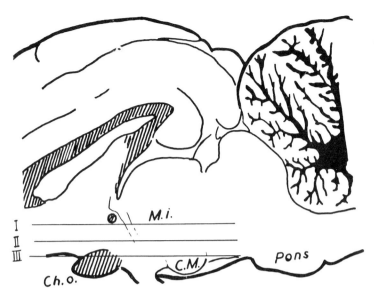

FIGURE 3A. *Diagram of a sagittal section through the brain of a goat.*
I, II and III = Planes of horizontal sections seen in Fig. 3B, 3C, and 3D.

Ch. o. = *Chiasma opticum.*
C. M. = *Corpus mamillare.*
M. i. = *Massa intermedia.*

the same stand as that used for the operations. The animals were offered water from a basin immediately before and after each injection. X-ray pictures of the skull were taken before and during or after each experiment in order to secure and control the position of the cannulae (Fig. 2) [omitted in reprinting].

When the animals had been killed, the heads were perfused, first with saline and then with 8% formaldehyde solution. In some cases a small amount of Evans blue or Indian ink was injected through the cannulae before the animal was killed. Most of the brains were embedded in celloidin, cut in serial sections, 40–60 microns thick, stained with toluidin blue and histologically examined. In this way the localisation of most points of injection could be determined. They are projected here on three diagrams of horizontal sections through the hypothalamus (Fig. 3 B, C and D) corresponding to planes I, II and III in Fig. 3A.

RESULTS

The abbreviated protocols of two experiments are given below, one in which a very large effect was obtained, and another with a negative result.

May 5th 1952. Goat no. 16. Weight about 35 Kg.
11.40–12.20 Operation. The cannula was placed on the caudal part of

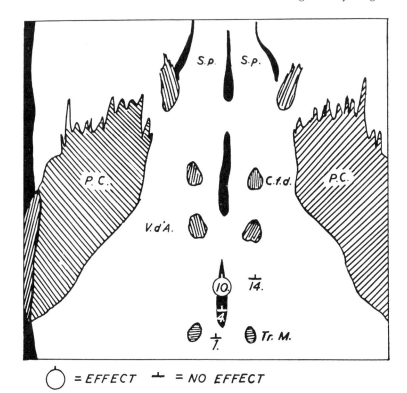

FIGURE 3B *Diagram of a horizontal section as plane I in Fig. 3A.*
Short lines on the symbols indicate the direction of the injections.

C. f. d. = *Columna fornix descendens.*
P. C. = *Pedunculus cerebri.*
S. p. = *Septum pellucidum.*
Tr. M. = *Tractus Meynert.*
V. d'A. = *Tractus Vic. d'Azyr.*

the holder. Two injections of 0.1 cc of 2% NaCl-solution were not
followed by any drinking.

Localisation: The point of injection was situated caudally in the third
ventricle in the dorsal hypothalamic region. It is projected as no.
4 in Fig. 3B.

13.25. A new cannula was placed on the rostral part of the holder.

13.50. Injection of 0.15 cc of 2% NaCl-solution. Half a minute after the
injection the animal drank very greedily 3.1 liters of water. It had
refused to drink immediately before the injection.

13.55. Urine. Amount 50 cc. Sp. gr. 1.035.
20 minutes later the animal was again offered water, and now it
drank in three stages, some minutes between each, 6.1 liters of water.

14.40. Renewed injection as at 13.50 did not induce any further drinking.

14.47. Urine. Amount: 50 cc. Sp. gr. 1.034.

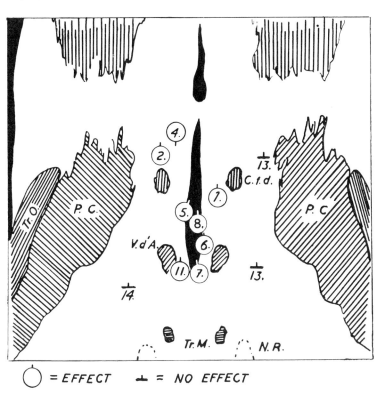

○ = EFFECT   ⊥ = NO EFFECT

FIGURE 3C   *Diagram of a horizontal section as plane II in Fig. 3A. Short lines on the symbols indicate the direction of the injections.*

C. f .d. = *Columna fornix descendens.*
N. R. = *Nucleus ruber.*
P. C. = *Pedunculus cerebri.*
Tr. M. = *Tractus Meynert.*
V. d'A. = *Tractus Vic d'Azyr.*

15.03. Renewed injection without effect.
15.21. Urine. Amount: 33 cc. Sp. gr. 1.033.
16.05. Urine. Amount: 150 cc. Sp. gr. 1.008.
16.30. Urine. Amount: 155 cc. Sp. gr. 1.003. Between 16.30 and 17.10 was collected 490 cc of urine with a specific gravity of 1.002. The course of the polyuria was not followed over night. The animal was killed the next morning.

Localisation: The point of injection was situated in the middle hypothalamic region rostral and somewhat medial to Columna fornix descendens on the left side. It is seen in Fig. 4 [omitted in reprinting. (Ed.)] and is projected as no. 4 in Fig. 3C. The injection was performed in caudal direction and was not seen to have broken through the ventricular wall.

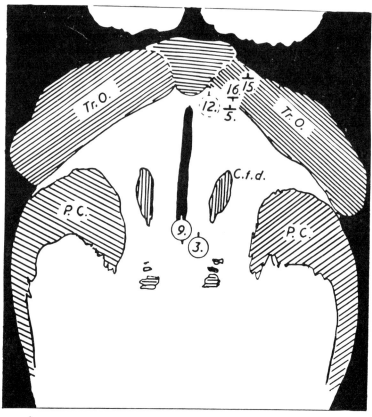

$\bigcirc$ = EFFECT   ⊥ = NO EFFECT

FIGURE 3D   *Diagram of a horizontal section as plane III in Fig. 3A. Short lines on the symbols indicate the direction of the injections.*

C. f. d. = *Columna fornix descendens.*
P. C. = *Pedunculus cerebri.*
Tr. O. = *Tractus opticus.*

August 29th 1952. Animal no. 19.

10.40–11.05. Operation. Three consecutive injections of 0.05–0.1 cc of 2% NaCl-solution induced no drinking, but visibly irritated the animal. The experiment lasted for 2 hours. Just before it ended the animal urinated. Amount: 70 cc. Sp. gr. 1.009.

Localisation: The point of injection was situated on the right side in the region of the optic chiasm. It is projected in Fig. 4D as no. 16. Injection in caudal direction.

The points, where injection of hypertonic NaCl-solution had a polydipsic effect, were all situated medially in the hypothalamus in the vicinity of the third ventricle.

The most obvious effect was obtained in 5 experiments, in three of them the points of injection were near to Columna fornix descendens at a horizontal section approximately through the middle of the hypothalamus. Here the injected solution was not seen to have broken through the ventricular wall.

In 6 out of 7 experiments, where the injections were made into the third ventricle or where the injected solution visibly had broken through the ventricular wall, the injections were followed by water drinking of the animals. However, the polydipsic effect in these cases seemed to be less pronounced, but was more easily repeatable after renewed injections.

In three experiments injection of 0.8–0.9% NaCl-solution caused no drinking, but subsequent injections of 2% NaCl-solution were effective in this respect.

Injections in the lateral part of the hypothalamus and in the vicinity of the optic chiasm did not induce any water drinking, possibly with the exception of one experiment, where injection of strongly hypertonic solution in the rostral part of the median eminence on one occasion was followed by drinking of the animal. Two to four hours after the experiment started an obviously increased urine secretion together with a diminished concentration of the urine was observed in 7 cases. In at least one of them this polyuria was not the consequence of an increased intake of water.

In 6 experiments no increased diuresis was observed, but here the observation of the animals lasted only for 2–3½ hours.

To three of the animals water was administered by stomach tube. In two of these experiments the injection of hypertonic NaCl-solution did not cause any visible change in the subsequent water diuresis. Here the injected salt solution had visibly emerged into the third ventricle and previous injections of the same kind had induced water drinking. In the third experiment, where the point of injection was in the rostral part of the median eminence, injections of 0.1 cc of 4% NaCl-solution were followed by decreased urine flow and a marked concentration of the urine. Any polydipsic effect at this point of injection was very doubtful.

DISCUSSION

The important rôle played by hypothalamic centres in the regulation of water metabolism has been elucidated in several ways. Thus Ranson and coworkers (1938) demonstrated that the supraoptic nuclei are directly involved in the antidiuretic function of the neurohypophysis and it has been shown (Bailey and Bremer 1921, Camus and Roussy 1922, Bellows and Van Wagenen 1938, and others) that injuries to the ventral part of the hypothalamus, without direct damage to the posterior pituitary can lead to temporary and permanent diabetes insipidus. Investigations, especially those of Verney (1947) have also demonstrated the presence of osmotically sensitive cells within the part of the brain which is supplied by the internal carotid arteries. The possible localisation of such cells to the supraoptic and paraventricular nuclei has been postulated. It has also been shown that dehydration as well as overloading of the antidiuretic function by injection of hypertonic sodium chloride solutions in rats leads to a chromatolytic reaction in the nerve cells of both the supraoptic and the magno-cellular portions of the paraventricular nuclei (Hillarp 1949). However, the question of whether the paraventricular nuclei are involved in the regulation of the function of the posterior pituitary is not settled as Harris (1947) showed that electrical stimulation of the supraoptic nuclei caused secretion of antidiuretic hormone from the neurohypophysis, but stimulation of the paraventricular nuclei in the same way did not have this effect.

The rôle played by the hypothalamus in the regulation of the water intake is more obscure. The strong increase of the intake of water seen soon after section of the pituitary stalk and often after other lesions in the hypothalamus seems to be secondary to a preceding polyuria (Richter 1935, Fisher, Magoun and Hetherington 1938 and Fisher, Ingram and Ranson 1938). On the other hand, the polydipsia in some cases of diabetes insipidus (Fulton and Bailey 1929, Kourilsky 1950 and others) or sometimes after experimental hypothalamic injury (Bailey and Bremer 1922, Bellows and Van Wagenen 1938) is not always preceded by a polyuria. These findings would indicate that some hypothalamic structure also is involved in the regulation of water intake. If this structure, however, were identical to the supraoptic nuclei or closely associated with them, the destruction of this region of the hypothalamus would inhibit the normal water intake and produce a state of dehydration. But this seems not to be the case, as Fisher, Ingram and Ranson (1938) showed that the polyuria seen after a severe damage to the supraoptic region was followed by an obvious polydipsia.

On the other hand, rats with bilateral lesions in the ventromedian region of the hypothalamus develop a chronic state of relative dehydration, and this is suggested to be the result of a destruction of neural elements governing the water intake (Stevensen 1949). An experimental support for the eliciting of thirst feelings from this part of the hypothalamus was also given by Brügger (1943), who compiled the results of electrical stimulation in the hypothalamus, earlier obtained by W. R. Hess. He found that hyperphagia was often combined with increased thirst when stimulating within a region near to the ventricular wall in the middle part of the hypothalamus, and considered that this would indicate that the urge to eat and drink are elicited from hypothalamic regions adjacent to each other.

The experiments here described were designed to observe whether a local rise in the osmotic pressure by injection of hypertonic sodium chloride solution into some part of the hypothalamus could produce a sensation of thirst. This seems to have been the case within a region medially in the hypothalamus near to the third ventricle, while injections into the supraoptic region or laterally in the hypothalamus did not seem to have this effect. From these experiments, however, it is not possible to determine from which structure in the medial hypothalamus the effect was elicited, as very little is known about the spread of the injected solutions. Neither do the experiments give any real proof for the existence of cells within this region, reacting specifically to osmotic stimulation, as hypertonic NaCl-solutions of the concentration used, probably have a general stimulating effect on nerve cells.

That the simple mechanical effect of the injections could be of any importance is unlikely, as injections of iso- and hypotonic solutions did not cause any drinking.

Since in most cases injections into the third ventricle were followed by water drinking it further seems as if the tissue from which the thirst was elicited was situated near to the ventricular wall. The thirst stimulation caused by injections into the ventricle was, however, as judged from the amount of water drunk, not as strong as in some other experiments, where the injected solution did not seem to have emerged into the ventricle. Intraventricular injections, on the other hand, probably caused less damage to the tissue, reacting to the stimulus, as the effect here was more easily repeatable.

The experiments thus show that nervous tissue involved in the regulation of the water intake is situated in the hypothalamus somewhere in the vicinity of the third ventricle, and might be taken as a support for the assumption that this tissue consists of cells reacting specifically to a rise in the extracellular osmotic pressure. This could explain why in most cases of diabetes insipidus and of experimental injuries to the hypothalamus the polyuria precedes the polydipsia, though in certain cases quite the contrary is seen. Severe damage to the supraoptic region might leave most of the mechanism eliciting thirst intact. Thus a polydipsia should be seen as a consequence to the polyuria. On the other hand, an injury irritating structures involved in the thirst mechanism, without a simultaneous inactivation of the supraoptico-hypophysial system could cause a primary polydipsia.

As yet, however, the effect of other hypertonic solutions than sodium chloride has not been tried. This would be of interest as recent work has shown that the non-electrolyte sorbitol and sucrose, when injected intravenously, are as effective as NaCl in producing drinking, whereas glucose (Holmes and Gregersen 1950) and urea (Gilman 1937) are much less effective in this respect. Verney (1947) has shown that the stimulating effect of these substances on the osmoreceptors regulating the secretion of antidiuretic hormone is of the same order.

The strongest thirst stimulus from one single intrahypothalamic injection of hypertonic NaCl-solution was obtained in experiment no. 4, where the animal drank more than 9 liters of water. As could be seen from the histological examination the injected salt solution had not caused any damage to the ventricular wall, although some of the injected solution might have diffused into the ventricle. The point of injection was here situated in the middle hypothalamic region rostral to the paraventricular nucleus on the left side (Fig. 4) and the injection was directed caudally. In this case it seems likely that cells within the paraventricular nucleus or close to it have reacted to the osmotic stimulus and elicited the sensation of thirst. The increased activity of cells within this nucleus seen after dehydration (Hillarp 1950) supports this assumption.

The fact that the animal did not drink the whole amount of water at once could either have been due to a temporary inhibition of the thirst from the alimentary tract when a certain amount of water had been drunk, or have depended on a gradual spread of the solution to more and more of the sensitive tissue, or have been the combined result of both. In this experiment two new injections about an hour after the first had no effect. It is possible that the stimulus was not sufficient any more to elicit further drinking since the animal had over-loaded itself with water after the first injection. Another possibility is that the first injection had first stimulated, but then inactivated the sensitive tissue.

This experiment also most obviously shows that an extreme polydipsia can precede a polyuria after hypothalamic stimulation, as earlier shown to be the case sometimes after hypothalamic injuries (Bailey and Bremer 1921, Bellows and Van Wagenen 1938).

The increased diuresis seen in these experiments have, however, not always been preceded by a polydipsia and it seems very possible that a polyuria would have occurred in some of the experiments even if the animals had not been offered water after the injections. The onset (2–4 hours after the hypothalamic incision) and the course of this polyuria very much resembles that seen in the temporary phase of experimental diabetes insipidus (Bellows and Van Wagenen 1938).

Only three experiments were performed, where intrahypothalamic injections of hypertonic sodium chloride solution were made into previously hydrated animals and of this hardly any conclusions can be drawn. In the single experiment where an inhibition of the water diuresis was seen as a consequence to the injections, the point of injection was situated in the rostral part of the median eminence. A spread of the injected solution to the supraoptic region is possible, but, as in this case strongly hypertonic NaCl-solution (4%) was used, it is just as likely that the supraoptico-hypophysial tract was directly stimulated. A stimulation of the posterior pituitary as a consequence to the fixation of the cannula in its position must also be suspected here, as the water diuresis did not appear until $4\frac{1}{2}$ hours after the animal had been strongly hydrated.

SUMMARY

In goats intrahypothalamic injections of hypertonic NaCl-solutions, within a region medially in the vicinity of the third ventricle, induced drinking of the animals. The most obvious effect was obtained in experiments, where the injection was performed in the middle hypothalamic region near to the paraventricular nucleus.

Injections of iso- or hypotonic solutions had not this effect.

Injections of hypertonic NaCl-solution in the lateral parts of the hypothalamus and in the vicinity of the optic chiasm did not induce any drinking.

In seven experiments an obviously increased diuresis together with a diminished concentration of the urine was observed 2–4 hours after the experiments had started. This polyuria was not in every case the consequence of an increased intake of water.

REFERENCES

Andersson, B., Experentia. 1952. *VIII*/4. 157.
———— Nord. Med. 1952. **47**. 663.
Bailey, P., and F. Bremer, Arch. Int. Med. 1921. **28**. 773.
Bellows, R. T., and W. P. Van Wagenen, J. nerv. ment. Dis. 1938. **88**. 417.
Bellows, R. T., and W. P. Van Wagenen, Amer. J Physiol. 1939. **126**. 13.
Brügger, M., Helv. Physiol. Acta 1943. **1**. 183.
Cannon, W. B., Proc. Roy. Soc., Lond. B. 1918. **90**. 283.
Camus, J., and G. Roussy, Rev. neurol. 1922. **30**. 622.
Fisher, C., W. R. Ingram and S. W. Ranson, Diabetes insipidus and the neuro-hormonal control of water balance. 1938. Ann. Arbor, Edwards Bros., Inc.
Fisher, C., H. W. Magoun and A. Hetherington, Amer. J. Physiol. 1938. **121**. 112.
Fulton, J. F., and P. Bailey, J. nerv. ment. Dis. 1929. **69**. 1, 145, 261.
Gilman, A., Amer. J. Physiol. 1937. **120**. 323.
Harris, G. W., Phil. Trans. Roy. Soc., Lond. B. 1947. **232**. 386.
Hess, W. R., Das Zwischenhirn. 1949. Benno Schwabe & Co. Basel.
Hillarp, N.-Å., Acta endocrinol. 1949. **2**. 33.
Holmes, J. H., and M. I. Gregersen, Amer. J. Physiol. 1950. **162**. 326.
Kourilsky, R., Proc. Roy. Soc. Med. 1950. **43**. 842.
Richter, C. P., Amer. J. Physiol. 1935. **112**. 481.
Stevensen, J. A. F., L. G. Welt and J. Orloff, Amer. J. Physiol. 1950. **161**. 35.
Verney, E. B., Proc. Roy. Soc., Lond. B. 1947. **135**. 25.

REWARD EFFECTS OF FOOD VIA STOMACH FISTULA COMPARED WITH THOSE OF FOOD VIA MOUTH

Neal E. Miller and Marion L. Kessen

YALE UNIVERSITY

Source   Reprinted from the **Journal of Comparative and Physiological Psychology**, 1952, **45**, 555–564, with permission of the authors and the American Psychological Association.

Motivation and reward are closely related. For example, if an animal is not motivated by the drive of hunger, food is not an effective reward. Furthermore, the food that rewards the hungry animal so that it learns, also tends to reduce the strength of its hunger drive so that it eventually becomes satiated. These functional relationships have led to the drive-reduction hypothesis of reinforcement which states that a prompt reduction in the strength of a drive has the effect of rewarding immediately preceding responses (2, 6, 7). According to this hypothesis the rewarding effects of food are due to the fact that it reduces the strength of the hunger drive, and the relative ineffectiveness of food as a reward after the animal has become satiated is due to the fact that little if any drive is present to be reduced.

The present experiment is one of a series designed to analyze the mechanism of satiation and its relationship to the rewarding effects of food. The first two experiments in this series compared the hunger-reducing effects of food via stomach fistula with those of food via mouth. The measure of hunger in the first of these, Kohn (4), was the rate of performance of an instrumental response (panel-pushing) periodically reinforced by food; in the second, Berkun, Kessen, and Miller (1), it was a consummatory response (amount of milk drunk). Both measures showed exactly the same pattern of results: (*a*) 14 cc. of isotonic saline injected by fistula directly into the stomach of hungry albino rats produced relatively little effect, (*b*) a similar volume of enriched milk injected directly into the stomach produced a prompt reduction in the rate of performance of the instrumental response and the amount of the consummatory response, and (*c*) the same volume of enriched milk taken normally by mouth produced an even greater reduction in the responses. From these results it seems reasonable to conclude that milk injected directly into the stomach produces a prompt reduction in the strength of hunger and that milk taken normally by mouth produces an even greater reduction.

If milk injected directly into the stomach produces a prompt reduction in the strength of hunger, the drive-reduction hypothesis of reinforcement demands that it should act as a reward to produce the learning of new responses. That food injected directly into the stomach may indeed serve as a reward is suggested by the results which Hull *et al.* (3) secured in an exploratory experiment on a dog with an esophageal fistula. Unfortunately, the original data of this experiment were lost, but the authors' notes indicate that the animal learned to choose the side of a simple maze

[1] This study was supported by funds from the Institute of Human Relations. A preliminary report of it was given as part of a paper read at the 1951 meetings of the APA (8).

where it received food through the esophageal fistula in preference to the side where a catheter was inserted but no food injected.

The main purpose of the present experiment was to determine whether food injected via fistula directly into the stomach of hungry albino rats would serve as a reward to reinforce the learning of a simple habit. The essential procedure involved giving hungry rats with small plastic fistulas sewn into their stomachs injections of enriched milk when they made the correct choice on a T maze and an injection of isotonic saline when they made an incorrect choice. Learning the correct choice would demonstrate the reward value of an injection of food; it would also serve as a control to rule out the possibility that the reductions in instrumental and in consummatory responses observed in the first two experiments were caused by nausea motivating conflicting responses rather than by a genuine reduction in the strength of the hunger drive. Finally, such learning would not be expected from the hypothesis, recently advanced by Sheffield (9, 10, 11), that the critical factor in reinforcement is the elicitation of a prepotent consummatory response.

A second purpose of the experiment was to compare the rewarding effects of food injected directly into the stomach with those of food taken normally by mouth. This was accomplished by training a second group of animals that received a dish of milk when they went to the correct side of the T maze and a dish of isotonic saline when they went to the incorrect side. From the fact that food by mouth produces a greater reduction in the strength of hunger than food via fistula, the drive-reduction hypothesis predicts that it should serve as a stronger reward and hence produce faster learning. A similar prediction would also be made from the fact that one would expect the cues involved in oral ingestion to have learned reward value.

Since it might be argued that the effect of reward begins with the first sip, when milk is taken by mouth, but only after a considerable volume of milk has been injected directly into the stomach, a third group was run exactly like the second one except that the presentation of the dishes of milk or saline was delayed 7 min. and 35 sec., the time required to complete an injection.

PROCEDURE

The subjects in this experiment were 17 male, albino rats of Sprague-Dawley strain approximately 150 days old at the start of the experiment. All of them had small plastic fistulas sewn into their stomachs, threaded between the skin and the body wall and projecting approximately ½ in. from the back of the neck. These fistulas were inserted according to the procedure described by Kohn (4).

The apparatus is illustrated in Figure 1. It consisted of a T maze. The starting compartment was painted black; it had a slotted lid through which a small rubber tube descended to the animal's fistula, and a false back which could be pushed forward when it was necessary to force recalcitrant subjects to make a

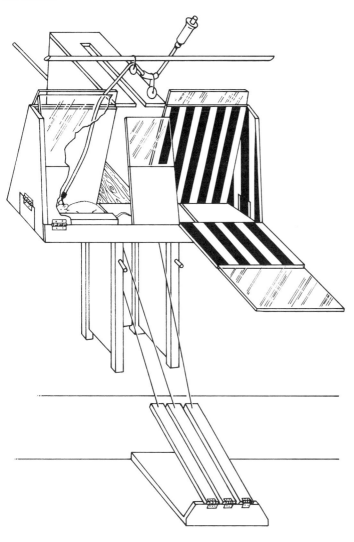

FIGURE 1 *The T maze. The starting box has a false back which can be pushed forward by a rod projecting through the back. The starting box and each of the goal boxes have doors sliding up from below, which are operated by foot pedals. Opening the door to the starting box closes a microswitch and starts a clock which is stopped when the animal steps across the small gap in the floor of either goal box and operates an electronic relay. The top $7\frac{1}{2}$ in. of the front of the apparatus is transparent plastic to allow the experimenter to observe the animal. In the diagram the hinged front of the right goal box is opened; a portion of the left one is cut out so that an animal can be seen being injected with milk via fistula. Hinged doors at the end of each goal box allow dishes of milk or saline to be inserted.*

choice. The two arms of the maze, which also served as the goal boxes, were made quite distinctive (a) so that it would be easy for the cues in the correct one to acquire learned reward value to help compensate for any delay in the effects of the injection, and (b) to minimize the generalization of this learned reward value to the cues in the incorrect goal box (12). The goal box to the left (in the diagram) was painted gray and had a floor consisting of ½-in.-guage wire mesh which was bisected longitudinally by an aluminum covered wooden strip ⅞ in. high and ¾ wide. The goal box to the right was painted with vertical black and white stripes 1 in. wide and had a window-screen floor.

In order to allow a ½-in. opening at the top through which the small rubber tube could descend to the fistula, but to discourage the rats from trying to jump up and poke their heads through this opening, the sides of the two goal boxes slanted inward at a 12° angle toward the top. The front of each goal box was a hinged door through which the animals could be removed. In order to allow the experimenter to observe the animals in the goal boxes, the top 7¼ in. of this hinged front side was made of transparent plastic.

Lowering the door at the front of the starting compartment automatically started an electric clock. When it put one of its front feet across a little break in the metal mesh in the floor 4 in. from the entrance of either goal box, the animal completed a circuit allowing a subthreshold current to actuate an electronic relay which stopped the clock. Then the experimenter closed the door behind it so that the animal was confined in the goal box. The experimenter operated the doors by foot pedals.

A small rubber tube ran from the rat's fistula up through the top of the maze over a pully on the far side of which a light counterweight picked up the slack. Beyond the counterweight the tube was attached to an ordinary hypodermic syringe containing the liquid to be injected.

At the end of each goal box was a small hinged door through which dishes of milk or saline could be inserted. In order to speed up the procedure and to rule out any possibility that drops of spilled milk or the odor of milk could serve as a reward for the injected animals, two pieces of apparatus were used, one for the animals receiving injections via fistula and another for those receiving milk by dish. These T mazes were identical except for the fact that in the first one the striped compartment was on the right and in the second it was on the left. It had originally been planned to reverse the roles of these two pieces of apparatus in the second replication of the experiment as a control on the improbable possibility that differences between them influenced learning. Inasmuch as the results of the first replication were statistically reliable, however, no second one was run.

The diet used in this experiment consisted of milk enriched with cream, starch, casein, vitamins, and minerals according to the formula described in previous articles (1, 4). This supplied 2.1 calories per cc. It was supplemented by a mash of 50 per cent ground Purina Laboratory Chow and 50 per cent water in amounts sufficient to bring the animal's total daily intake to 50 calories.

Habituation. Postoperative care of the animals was similar to that described by Kohn (4). To avoid possible distress (suggested by exploratory work), the experimental animals were first habituated to progressively increasing injections of milk. Each animal was injected with milk twice a day at 11 A.M. and 3 P.M. The first injection was 2 cc. and on each subsequent injection the amount was increased 2 cc. until 12 cc. had been injected. Enough wet mash was given at approximately 4:30 P.M. to bring the total intake to 50 cal. Injections were given on a small perch at the rate the animals normally drank, 1 cc. every 35 sec. The animals to be fed by mouth were habituated in exactly the same way except that they received progressively increasing amounts of milk in dishes in their home cages.

Training. Before habituation the animals were randomly divided into three groups:

1. *Stomach injection* animals received an injection of 14 cc. of enriched milk via fistula when they went to the correct side and 14 cc. of isotonic saline when to the incorrect. For two animals the correct (milk) side was to the right; for three it was to the left. (Seven operated animals were originally prepared for these groups. One, however, was discarded before the first trial because its fistula leaked, and the second had to have a new fistula put in after five training trials, and then died following an operation for a tumor after 26 days of training during which it showed definite signs of learning.) Before being placed in the starting box, the animals had a small rubber tube slipped over their fistula and firmly tied with a thread. In order to avoid injecting air into the animal, this tube was collapsed by gentle suction from a hypodermic syringe after which the free end was sealed off by a little spring clip. As soon as the animal stopped the clock, the door was closed behind it, the syringe containing the proper substance was connected to the tube, the clip was removed, and the first 1 cc. (plus an extra 3.15 cc. required to fill the rubber tube and the plastic fistula) was injected. Thereafter 1 cc. was injected every 35 sec. so that the average rate of injection approximated the rate at which animals had been found to drink normally by mouth. The injection lasted for 7 min. 35 sec.; the animals were allowed to remain in the compartment 3 min. longer and then were removed to their home cages. Approximately 15 min. before the first run each day, while the animals were being weighed, they received an injection of 1 cc. water to clear the fistula and, if the last injection of the day had been milk, another 1 cc. of water was injected before they received their supplementary diet of wet mash.

2. *Mouth, No delay* animals received dishes containing 14 cc. of milk or saline in the correct or incorrect goal boxes, respectively. These dishes were inserted through the hinged door at the end of the sections at the same time that the injections of animals in the preceding group were begun. For three rats the correct side was to the right, and for the other three to the left. The animals in this group remained in the goal boxes the same length of time as those in the first group.

3. *Mouth, Delay* animals received their dishes of 14 cc. of milk for a correct choice or saline for an incorrect one after a delay of 7 min. 35 sec., the time that it normally took to complete an injection. After this delay these animals were left in the goal box with the dish of milk or saline for another period of approximately 7 min. 35 sec. For three of these animals the correct side was to the right, for three to the left.

At approximately 10 A.M. each animal in each of the three groups was given a trial during which it was free to choose either side. As soon as it stepped over the break in the floor of a goal box and stopped the clock, the door was closed behind it and the substance, milk for a correct choice or saline for an incorrect one, was administered. Approximately 4 hr. later, each animal was given a second trial during which the door to the previously chosen side was closed

so that it was forced to turn in the opposite direction and receive the other
kind of substance. If an animal failed to run within 3 min. on any trial, the
false back of the starting box was gradually pushed forward, forcing the animal
to the choice point; if it failed to choose within 7 additional minutes, the false
back was pushed all of the way forward so that the animal was forced out
of the choice point into a goal box. Approximately an hour after the forced
trial the animals were given enough wet mash in their home cages to bring
their daily intake to a total of 50 calories.

Training of the stomach-injection animals was continued for 40 days. Because
the other two groups had already learned, their training was discontinued after
25 days.

In some animals there developed an infection along the side of the fistula.
Cultures showed that the infections contained a typical intestinal bacteria,
Escherichia coli, which presumably seeped through the incision where the fistula
was sewn into the stomach. Such infections were treated by making a pinpoint
incision at the place of infection, draining it and sprinkling powdered sulfathia-
zole on this area. As a preventive measure the animals were given powdered
aureomycin three or four times a week in their diet of wet mash.

RESULTS

Figure 2 shows the percentage of correct choices (to the milk side)
made by the animals in the three groups on the morning trials which
were free choice. It can be seen that all three groups learned. In order
to test the reliability of improvement for the animals which received injections directly into the stomach, the number of correct choices made by

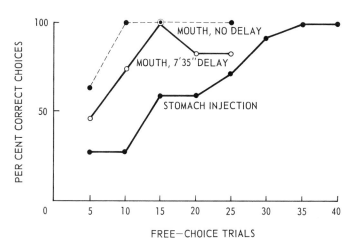

FIGURE 2 *Percentage of choices of the correct (milk) side on
free-choice trials. After making five successive correct choices on
the eleventh to fifteenth trials, one animal in the mouth, delay
group reverted to a consistent position habit on the incorrect side.
This one animal contributed all the errors made by this group after
the first ten trials.*

Table 1. Reliabilities of the Differences between the Groups on Days 1 to 25

Group	Errors in Free-choice	Log Time to Milk Side
Stomach Injection vs. Mouth, No Delay	.001*	.001
Stomach Injection vs. Mouth, Delay	.038	.001
Mouth, Delay vs. Mouth, No Delay	.070	.003

* Probability of getting by chance as large a difference in the predicted direction.

each animal on the first 15 free-choice trials was compared with that on the last 15. Chi-square tests, corrected for discontinuity, showed that the improvement was statistically reliable for each one of the five animals in that group. For the individual animals the probability of securing the observed differences in the predicted direction by chance are: .05, .05, .01, .001, and .001. Furthermore, the three animals tested in the preliminary experiment using a slightly different apparatus (8) also learned to go consistently ($p = .02$, .01, and .001) to the side (two right and one left) on which milk was injected via fistula.

Comparing the different groups shows that milk taken immediately by mouth produced the fastest learning, milk taken by mouth after a delay produced the next fastest learning, and milk injected directly into the stomach produced the slowest learning. In order to test the reliability of these differences each animal was given a score which was the number of correct choices during the first 25 free-choice trials. Then t tests were made. These are summarized in Table 1. It can be seen that the superiority of the animals fed milk by mouth (either immediately or after a delay) over those who received it via fistula is statistically reliable.

Figure 3 shows the mean running speed to milk of the animals in the

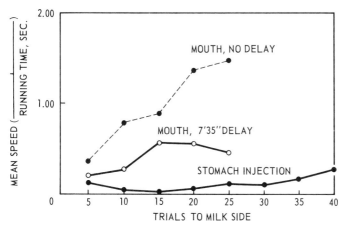

FIGURE 3 *Speed of running to the compartment in which milk was given.*

three groups. When the free choice in the morning was correct, this was the running speed on that trial; when it was incorrect, this was the running speed on the afternoon forced trial to the milk side. It can be seen that the differences among the speed scores of the three groups are exactly the same as those among the error scores. In order to test the reliability of these differences, the time scores of each animal on each trial were converted to logs. This conversion was made to normalize the distribution. Then each animal was given a score consisting of the sum of the log times on the first 25 trials, and t tests were made for the differences among the means of the three groups. These are summarized in Table 1, which shows that all the differences are highly reliable.

Further evidence that the injection of milk directly into the stomach produced learning whereas that of saline did not, is presented in Figure 4. This figure presents the speed of running to the compartment in which milk was injected compared with that to the compartment in which saline was injected. At the beginning of training there was no difference between these two speeds. During the first 15 trials the speed of running to both compartments decreased. It seems probable that this decrease was produced by the extinction of initial exploratory tendencies, but it may have been due to a slight discomfort produced by the injections during the early part of training and gradually adapting out or becoming counteracted

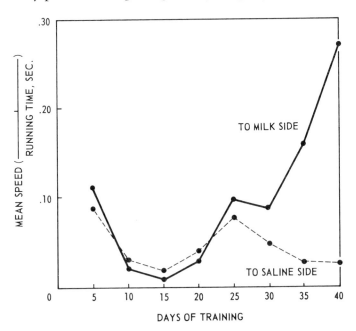

FIGURE 4 *Speed of run to milk versus speed of run to isotonic saline for animals receiving injections via fistula. The curve represented by the solid line in this figure is the same as the bottom curve in Figure 3 except that the scale has been considerably magnified.*

by the reward effects.[2] From the fifteenth trial on there is a progressive increase in the speed of running to the compartment where milk was injected while the speed to the compartment where saline was injected remains at approximately the same low level. The difference in the speeds of running to the milk and saline compartments (as calculated by t tests or the sum of the log times on the last 5 trials to each) would be expected in the predicted direction by chance less than 1 time in 100. It is another indication of the reward effect of injecting milk directly into the stomach.

DISCUSSION

The results show (a) that milk injected directly into the stomach can serve as a reward to produce learning, and (b) that milk taken normally by mouth serves as a stronger reward to produce faster learning. Both results are exactly what was predicted from the drive-reduction hypothesis and the evidence (1, 4) that milk by fistula produces a prompt reduction in the strength of hunger while milk by mouth produces an even greater reduction.

The reward effect of milk injected directly into the stomach would not readily be predicted from Sheffield's (9, 10, 11) hypothesis that reinforcement is critically related to the ability of the goal object to elicit a dependable, prepotent response when presented.

The faster learning of the animals which received milk by mouth would be expected from the fact that this procedure produces a greater reduction in the strength of the drive. It would also be predicted from the fact that one would expect the cues involved in oral ingestion to have learned reward value, but if one holds to a strict drive-reduction hypothesis of learned rewards, this reduces to the same factor of drive-reduction (5, 6, 7). It

That such discomfort can be produced is suggested by the results of a fourth group of five animals which were run as a part of the original design of this experiment but relegated to this footnote because the behavior and results suggested an artifact from discomfort produced by the injection. These animals were run under exactly the same conditions as the first group except that during habituation and training their injection was given almost ten times faster so that 14 cc. required between 45 sec. and 1 min. During the last 15 free-choice trials, chi-square tests showed that three of these animals were consistently going to the saline side (p = .01, .001, .001) and two to the milk side (p = .01 and .001). Because the avoidance of the milk side showed up so early in training, none of the differences between the first and last 15 free-choice trials is reliable for the animals preferring saline, but for the animals chosing milk these differences are reliable at .04 and .001 levels, respectively. The fact that the animals preferring the saline side had to be forced (their average speed to saline on the last five trials was somewhat slower than that of the animals injected at the normal rate, but their average speed to milk was much lower) suggests that they were avoiding milk rather than approaching saline. Because milk curdles and leaves the stomach much more slowly than saline, it seems reasonable to assume that the fast injection of large amounts of milk would be more likely to produce distress than similar injections of isotonic saline.

is also quite possible that the reduction in the strength of drive is not quite as prompt when food is injected into the stomach as when it is taken by mouth.

Finally, the fact that the injected animals learned to choose the milk side serves as a control to rule out the possibility that the effects of the injection of milk into the stomach in the preceding experiments (1, 4) were only the production of nausea rather than a reduction in the strength of the hunger drive.

SUMMARY

1. Seventeen male, albino rats had small plastic fistulas sewn into their stomachs. Then they were given training trials during which they received enriched milk when they went to the correct side of a simple T maze and isotonic saline when they went to the incorrect side. They were divided into three groups trained respectively under the following conditions:

a. The substances, 14 cc. of milk for a correct or saline for an incorrect choice, were injected directly into the stomach at the rate at which the animals normally drank.

b. Dishes containing 14 cc. of milk for a correct or saline for an incorrect choice were inserted into the end of the goal box immediately after the animal had made its choice.

c. Dishes containing 14 cc. of milk or saline were inserted into the end of the goal box after a delay of 7 min. 35 sec., the time required to complete an injection for the animals in *a.*

2. All animals were given two trials a day motivated by hunger. On the first trial the animal was free to go in either direction; this trial was used to measure correct choices. On the second trial, given 4 hr. later, the animal was forced to go in the opposite direction and receive the other substance.

3. The animals which received injections directly into their stomachs learned to choose the milk side within 40 days of training. Both the decrease in errors and the faster speed to the milk side were statistically highly reliable.

4. The animals which received milk by mouth, either immediately or after a delay, learned faster than those which received milk via fistula. The differences in both the speed and error scores were statistically reliable.

5. These results show that milk injected directly into the stomach serves as a reward to produce learning, but that milk taken normally by mouth serves as a stronger reward to produce faster learning. The results confirm the prediction from the drive-reduction hypothesis of reinforcement and fail to confirm the prediction from the prepotent consummatory response hypothesis of reinforcement. They serve as a control to show that the decrements in instrumental and consummatory responses observed in preceding experiments were produced by reductions in hunger rather than by nausea.

REFERENCES

1 Berkun, M. M., Kessen, M. L., & Miller, N. E. Hunger-reducing effects of food by stomach fistula versus food by mouth measured by a consummatory response. *J. comp. physiol. Psychol.*, 1952, **45**, 550–554.

2 Hull, C. L. *Principles of behavior.* New York: D. Appleton-Century, 1943.

3 Hull, C. L., Livingston, J. R., Rouse, R. O., & Barker, A. N. True, sham, and esophageal feeding as reinforcements. *J. comp. physiol. Psychol.*, 1951, **44**, 236–245.

4 Kohn, M. Satiation of hunger from stomach versus mouth feeding. *J. comp. physiol. Psychol.*, 1951, **44**, 412–422.

5 Miller, N. E. Learnable drives and rewards. In S. Stevens (Ed.), *Handbook of experimental psychology.* New York: Wiley, 1951.

6 Miller, N. E. Comments on multiple-process conceptions of learning. *Psychol. Rev.*, 1951, **58**, 357–363.

7 Miller, N. E., & Dollard, J. *Social learning and imitation.* New Haven, Conn.: Yale Univer. Press, 1941.

8 Miller, N. E., Kessen, M. L., & Kohn, M. The drive-reducing and reinforcing effects of food injected via fistula into the stomach. *Amer. Psychologist*, 1951, **6**, 280–281. (Abstract)

9 Sheffield, F. D., & Roby, T. B. Reward value of a non-nutritive sweet taste. *J. comp. physiol. Psychol.*, 1950, **43**, 471–481.

10 Sheffield, F. D., Wulff, J. J., & Backer, R. Reward value of copulation without sex drive reduction. *J. comp. physiol. Psychol.*, 1951, **44**, 3–8.

11 Sheffield, F. D. The contiguity principle in learning theory. *Psychol. Rev.*, 1951, **58**, 362–367.

12 Spence, K. W. The role of secondary reinforcement in delayed reward learning. *Psychol. Rev.*, 1947, **54**, 1–8.

POSITIVE REINFORCEMENT PRODUCED
BY ELECTRICAL STIMULATION
OF SEPTAL AREA
AND OTHER REGIONS
OF RAT BRAIN

James Olds and Peter Milner

MC GILL UNIVERSITY

Editor's Note   This is the initial paper in which Olds and Milner reported the discovery of what Olds has called "pleasure centers" in the brain, i.e., loci in which animals will cause themselves to be electrically stimulated. Since the original publication of this paper, a great deal of further work on this phenomenon has been done, one sample of which is found in the following selection by Hoebel and Teitelbaum. The fairly extensive regions giving positive and/or negative effects have been mapped (the strongest positive effects are usually obtained in the median forebrain bundle). In many loci both positive and negative effects have been found, depending on stimulation parameters. In addition, certain difficulties in interpretation of the effect as the same as natural primary reinforcement have arisen. Notably, self-stimulation appears to extinquish more rapidly than do responses learned for normal reinforcement, and it has been suggested that stimulation in these areas has drive-arousing as well as simple reinforcing effects.

Source   Reprinted from the **Journal of Comparative and Physiological Psychology,** *1954,* **47,** *419–427, with permission of the authors and the American Psychological Association.*

Stimuli have eliciting and reinforcing functions. In studying the former, one concentrates on the responses which come after the stimulus. In studying the latter, one looks mainly at the responses which precede it. In its reinforcing capacity, a stimulus increases, decreases, or leaves unchanged the frequency of preceding responses, and accordingly it is called a reward, a punishment, or a neutral stimulus (cf. 16).

Previous studies using chronic implantation of electrodes have tended to focus on the eliciting functions of electrical stimuli delivered to the brain (2, 3, 4, 5, 7, 10, 12, 14). The present study, on the other hand, has been concerned with the reinforcing function of the electrical stimulation.[2]

METHOD

GENERAL

Stimulation was carried out by means of chronically implanted electrodes which did not interfere with the health or free behavior of Ss to any appreciable extent. The Ss were 15 male hooded rats, weighing approximately 250 gm. at the start of the experiment. Each S was tested in a Skinner box which delivered alternating current to the brain so long as a lever was depressed. The current was delivered over a loose lead, suspended from the ceiling, which connected the stimulator to the rat's electrode. The Ss were given a total of 6 to 12 hr. of acquisition testing, and 1 to 2 hr. of extinction testing. During acquisition, the stimulator was turned on so that a response produced electrical stimulation; during extinction, the stimulator was turned off so that a response produced no electrical stimulation. Each S was given a percentage score denoting the proportion of his total acquisition time given to responding. This score could be compared with the animal's extinction score to determine whether the stimulation had a positive, negative, or neutral reinforcing effect. After testing, the animal was sacrificed. Its brain was frozen, sectioned, stained, and examined microscopically to determine which structure of the brain had been stimulated. This permitted correlation of acquisition scores with anatomical structures.

ELECTRODE IMPLANTATION

Electrodes are constructed by cementing a pair of enameled silver wires of 0.010-in. diameter into a Lucite block, as shown in Figure 1. The parts of

[1] The research reported here was made possible by grants from the Rockefeller Foundation and the National Institute of Mental Health of the U.S. Public Health Service. The authors particularly wish to express their thanks to Professor D. O. Hebb, who provided germinal ideas for the research and who backed it with enthusiastic encouragement as well as laboratory facilities and funds. The authors are also grateful to Miss Joann Feindel, who performed the histological reconstructions reported here.
[2] The present preliminary paper deals mainly with methods and behavioral results. A detailed report of the locus of positive, negative, and neutral reinforcing effects of electrical brain stimulation is being prepared by the first author.

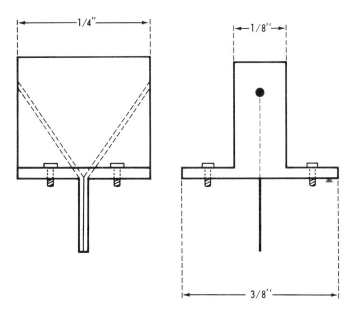

FIGURE 1   *Electrode design (see text for detailed description).*

the wires which penetrate the brain are cemented together to form a needle, and this is cut to the correct length to reach the desired structure in the brain. This length is determined from Krieg's rat brain atlas (11) with slight modifications as found necessary by experience. The exposed cross section of the wire is the only part of the needle not insulated from the brain by enamel; stimulation therefore occurs only at the tip. Contact with the lead from the stimulator is made through two blobs of solder on the upper ends of the electrode wires; these blobs make contact with the jaws of an alligator clip which has been modified to insulate the two jaws from one another. A light, flexible hearing-aid lead connects the clip to the voltage source.

The operation of implantation is performed with the rat under Nembutal anesthesia (0.88 cc/kg) and held in a Johnson-Krieg stereotaxic instrument (11). A mid-line incision is made in the scalp and the skin held out of the way by muscle retractors. A small hole is drilled in the skull with a dental burr at the point indicated by the stereotaxic instrument for the structure it is desired to stimulate. The electrode, which is clamped into the needle carrier of the instrument, is lowered until the flange of the Lucite block rests firmly on the skull. Four screw holes are then drilled in the skull through four fixing holes in the flange, and the electrode, still clamped firmly in the instrument, is fastened to the skull with jeweler's screws which exceed the diameter of the screw holes in the skull by 0.006 in. The electrode is then released from the clamp and the scalp wound closed with silk sutures. The skin is pulled tightly around the base of the Lucite block and kept well away from the contact plates. A recovery period of three days is allowed after the operation before testing. Figure 2 is an X-ray picture of an electrode in place.

TESTING

The testing apparatus consisted of a large-levered Skinner box 11 in. long, 5 in. wide, and 12 in. high. The top was open to allow passage for the stimulating lead. The lever actuated a microswitch in the stimulating circuit so that when it was depressed, the rat received electrical stimulation. The current was obtained from the 60-cycle power line, through a step-down transformer, and was adjustable between 0 and 10 v. r.m.s. by means of a variable potentiometer. In the experiments described here the stimulation continued as long as the lever was pressed, though for some tests a time-delay switch was incorporated which cut the current off after a predetermined interval if the rat continued to hold the lever down. Responses were recorded automatically on paper strip.

On the fourth day after the operation rats were given a pretesting session of about an hour in the boxes. Each rat was placed in the box and on the lever by E with the stimulus set at 0.5 v. During the hour, stimulation voltage was varied to determine the threshold of a "just noticeable" effect on the rat's behavior. If the animal did not respond regularly from the start, it was placed on the lever periodically (at about 5-min. intervals). Data collected on the first day were not used in later calculations. On subsequent days, Ss were placed in the box for about $3\frac{1}{2}$ hr. a day; these were 3 hr. of acquisition and $\frac{1}{2}$ hr. of extinction. During the former, the rats were allowed to stimulate themselves

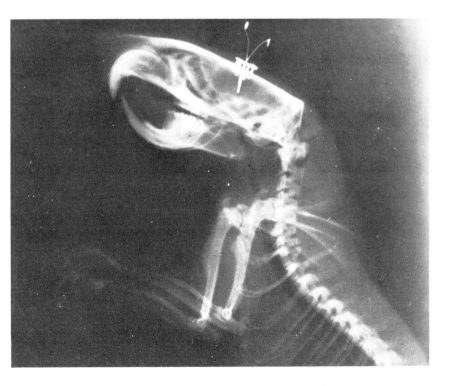

FIGURE 2 *X-ray showing electrode in place in intact animal. There are two wires insulated completely from each other, stimulating the brain with their tips.*

with a voltage which was just high enough to produce some noticeable response in the resting animal. As this threshold voltage fluctuated with the passage of time, E would make a determination of it every half hour, unless S was responding regularly. At the beginning of each acquisition period, and after each voltage test, the animal was placed on the lever once by E. During extinction periods, conditions were precisely the same except that a bar press produced no electrical stimulation. At the beginning of each extinction period, animals which were not responding regularly were placed on the lever once by E. At first, rats were tested in this way for four days, but as there appeared to be little difference between the results on different days, this period was reduced to three and then to two days for subsequent animals. Thus, the first rats had about 12 hr. of acquisition after pretesting whereas later rats had about 6 hr. However, in computing the scores in our table, we have used only the first 6 hr. of acquisition for all animals, so the scores are strictly comparable. In behavioral curves, we have shown the full 12 hr. of acquisition on the earlier animals so as to illustrate the stability of the behavior over time.

At no time during the experiment were the rats deprived of food or water, and no reinforcement was used except the electrical stimulus.

Animals were scored on the percentage of time which they spent bar pressing regularly during acquisition. In order to find how much time the animal would spend in the absence of reward or punishment, a similar score was computed for periods of extinction. This extinction score provided a base line. When the acquisition score is above the extinction score, we have reward; when it is below the extinction score, we have punishment.

In order to determine percentage scores, periods when the animal was responding regularly (at least one response every 30 sec.) were counted as periods of responding; i.e., *intervals of 30 sec. or longer without a response were counted as periods of no responding*. The percentage scores were computed as the proportion of total acquisition or extinction time given to periods of responding.

DETERMINATION OF LOCUS

On completion of testing, animals were perfused with physiological saline, followed by 10 per cent formalin. The brains were removed, and after further fixation in formalin for about a week, frozen sections 40 microns thick were cut through the region of the electrode track. These were stained with cresyl violet and the position of the electrode tip determined. Figure 3 [Fig. 3 has been omitted in reprinting (Ed).] is a photomicrograph showing the appearance of the electrode track in a stained and mounted brain section.

RESULTS

LOCUS

In Table 1, acquisition and extinction scores are correlated with electrode placements. Figure 4 presents the acquisition scores again, this time on three cross-sectional maps of the rat brain, one at the forebrain level, one at the thalamic level, and one at the mid-brain level. The position of a score on the map indicates the electrode placement from which this acquisition score was obtained.

Table 1. Acquisition and Extinction Scores for All Animals Together with Electrode Placements and Threshold Voltages Used during Acquisition Tests

Animal's No.	Locus of Electrode	Stimulation Voltage r.m.s.	Percentage of Acquisition Time Spent Responding	Percentage of Extinction Time Spent Responding
32	septal	2.2–2.8	75	18
34	septal	1.4	92	6
M-1	septal	1.7–4.8	85	21
M-4	septal	2.3–4.8	88	13
40	c.c.	.7–1.1	6	3
41	caudate	.9–1.2	4	4
31	cingulate	1.8	37	9
82	cingulate	.5–1.8	36	10
36	hip.	.8–2.8	11	14
3	m.l.	.5	0	4
A-5	m.t.	1.4	71	9
6	m.g.	.5	0	31
11	m.g.	.5	0	21
17	teg.	.7	2	1
9	teg.	.5	77	81

Key: *c.c.*, *corpus callosum*; *hip.*, hippocampus; *m.l.*, medial lemniscus; *m.t.*, Mammillo-thalamic tract; *m.g.*, medial geniculate; *teg.*, tegmentum.

The highest scores are found together in the central portion of the fore-brain. Beneath the *corpus callosum* and between the two lateral ventricles in section I of Figure 4, we find four acquisition scores ranging from 75 to 92 per cent. This is the septal area. The Ss which produced these scores are numbered 32, 34, M-1, and M-4 in Table 1. It will be noticed that while all of them spent more than 75 per cent of their acquisition time responding, they all spent less than 22 per cent of their extinction time responding. Thus the electrical stimulus in the septal area has an effect which is apparently equivalent to that of a conventional primary reward as far as the maintenance of a lever-pressing response is concerned.

If we move outside the septal area, either in the direction of the caudate nucleus (across the lateral ventricle) or in the direction of the *corpus callosum,* we find acquisition scores drop abruptly to levels of from 4 to 6 per cent. These are definitely indications of neutral (neither rewarding nor punishing) effects.

However, above the *corpus callosum* in the cingulate cortex we find an acquisition score of 37 per cent. As the extinction score in this case was 9 per cent, we may say that stimulation was rewarding.

At the thalamic level (section II of Fig. 4) we find a 36 per cent acquisi-tion score produced by an electrode placed again in the cingulate cortex, an 11 per cent score produced by an electrode placed in the hippocampus, a 71 per cent score produced by an electrode placed exactly in the mammil-

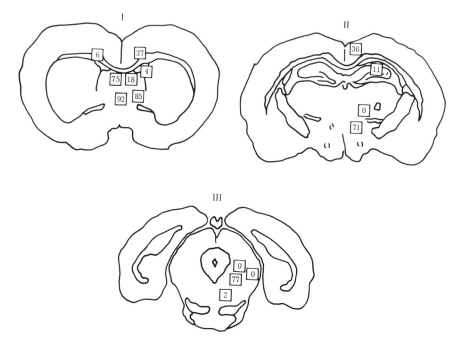

FIGURE 4 *Maps of three sections, (I) through the forebrain, (II) through the thalamus, (III) through the mid-brain of the rat. Boxed numbers give acquisition percentage scores produced by animals with electrodes stimulating at these points. On section I the acquisition scores 75, 88, 92, 85 fall in the septal forebrain area. On the same section there is a score of 4 in the caudate nucleus, a score of 6 in the white matter below the cortex, and a score of 37 in the medial (cingulate) cortex. On section II the acquisition score of 36 is in the medial (cingulate) cortex, 11 is in the hippocampus, 71 is in the mammillothalamic tract, and 0 is in the medial lemniscus. On section III the two zeroes are in the medial geniculate, 2 is in the tegmental reticular substance, 77 falls 2 mm. anterior to the section shown—it is between the posterior commissure and the red nucleus.*

lothalamic tract, and a zero per cent score produced by an electrode placed in the medial lemniscus. The zero denotes negative reinforcement.

At the mid-brain level (section III of Fig. 4) there are two zero scores produced by electrodes which are in the posterior portion of the medial geniculate bodies; here again, the scores indicate a negative effect, as the corresponding extinction scores are 31 and 21 per cent. There is an electrode deep in the medial, posterior tegmentum which produces a 2 per cent score; this seems quite neutral, as the extinction score in this case is 1 per cent. Finally, there is an electrode shown on this section which actually stands 1½ mm. anterior to the point where it is shown; it was between the red nucleus and the posterior commissure. It produced an acquisition score of 77 per cent, but an extinction score of 81 per cent.

This must be a rewarding placement, but the high extinction score makes it difficult to interpret.

BEHAVIOR

We turn our attention briefly to the behavioral data produced by the more rewarding electrode placements.

The graph in Figure 5 is a smoothed cumulative response curve illustrating the rate of responding of rat No. 32 (the lowest-scoring septal area rat) during acquisition and extinction. The animal gave a total of slightly over 3000 responses in the 12 hr. of acquisition. When the current was turned on, the animal responded at a rate of 285 responses an hour; when the current was turned off, the rate fell close to zero.

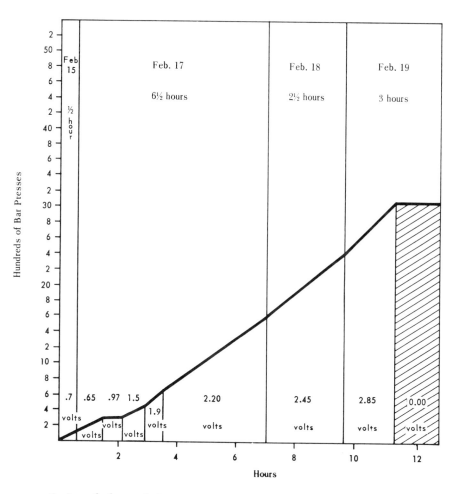

FIGURE 5 *Smoothed cumulative response curve for rat No. 32. Cumulative response totals are given along the ordinate, and hours along the abscissa. The steepness of the slope indicates the response rate. Stimulating voltages are given between black lines. Cross hatching indicates extinction.*

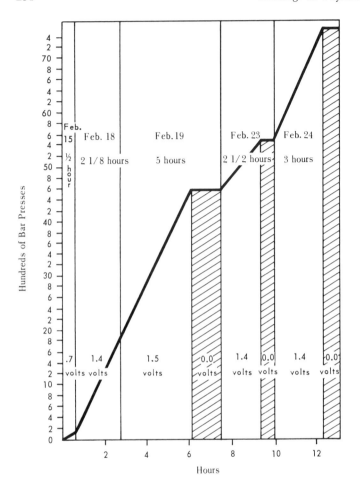

FIGURE 6   *Smoothed cumulative response curve for rat No. 34.*

The graph in Figure 6 gives similar data on rat No. 34 (the highest-scor-ing septal rat). The animal stimulated itself over 7500 times in 12 hr. Its average response rate during acquisition was 742 responses an hour; during extinction, practically zero.

Figure 7 presents an unsmoothed cumulative response curve for one day of responding for rat No. A-5. This is to illustrate in detail the degree of control exercised by the electrical reward stimulus. While this rat was actually bar pressing, it did so at 1920 responses an hour; that is, about one response for every 2 sec. During the first period of the day it responded regularly while on acquisition, extinguished very rapidly when the current was turned off, and reconditioned readily when the current was turned on again. At reconditioning points, E gave S one stimulus to show that the current was turned on again, but E did not place S on the lever. During longer periods of acquisition, S occasionally stopped responding for short periods, but in the long run S spent almost three-quarters of

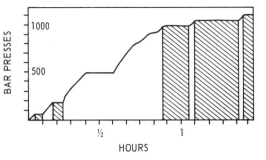

FIGURE 7 *Unsmoothed cumulative response curve showing about ¾ hr. of acquisition and ¾ hr. extinction for rat No. A-5. Shading indicates extinction.*

its acquisition time responding. During the long period of extinction at the end of the day, there was very little responding, but S could be brought back to the lever quite quickly if a stimulus was delivered to show that the current had been turned on again.

DISCUSSION

It is clear that electrical stimulation in certain parts of the brain, particularly the septal area, produces acquisition and extinction curves which compare favorably with those produced by a conventional primary reward. With other electrode placements, the stimulation appears to be neutral or punishing.

Because the rewarding effect has been produced maximally by electrical stimulation in the septal area, but also in lesser degrees in the mammillothalamic tract and cingulate cortex, we are led to speculate that a system of structures previously attributed to the rhinencephalon may provide the locus for the reward phenomenon. However, as localization studies which will map the whole brain with respect to the reward and punishment dimension are continuing, we will not discuss in detail the problem of locus. We will use the term "reinforcing structures" in further discussion as a general name for the septal area and other structures which produce the reward phenomenon.

To provide an adequate canvass of the possible explanations for the rewarding effect would require considerably more argument than could possibly fit within the confines of a research paper. We have decided, therefore, to rule out briefly the possibility that the implantation produces pain which is reduced by electrical stimulation of reinforcing structures, and to confine further discussion to suggestions of ways the phenomenon may provide a methodological basis for study of physiological mechanisms of reward.

The possibility that the implantation produces some painful "drive stimulus" which is alleviated by electrical stimulation of reinforcing structures does not comport with the facts which we have observed. If there were some chronic, painful drive state, it would be indicated by emotional signs in the animal's daily behavior. Our Ss, from the first day after the operation, are normally quiet, nonaggressive; they eat regularly, sleep regularly, gain weight. There is no evidence in their behavior to support the postulation of chronic pain. Septal preparations which have lived healthy and normal lives for months after the operation have given excellent response rates.

As there is no evidence of a painful condition preceding the electrical stimulation, and as the animals are given free access to food and water at all times except while actually in the Skinner boxes, there is no explicitly manipulated drive to be reduced by electrical stimulation. Barring the possibility that stimulation of a reinforcing structure specifically inhibits the "residual drive" state of the animal, or the alternative possibility that the first electrical stimulus has noxious after-effects which are reduced by a second one, we have some evidence here for a primary rewarding effect which is not associated with the reduction of a primary drive state. It is perhaps fair in a discussion to report the "clinical impression" of the Es that the phenomenon represents strong pursuit of a positive stimulus rather than escape from some negative condition.

Should the latter interpretation prove correct, we have perhaps located a system within the brain whose peculiar function is to produce a rewarding effect on behavior. The location of such a system puts us in a position to collect information that may lead to a decision among conflicting theories of reward. By physiological studies, for example, we may find that the reinforcing structures act selectively on sensory or motor areas of the cortex. This would have relevance to current S-S versus S-R controversies (8, 9, 13, 16).

Similarly, extirpation studies may show whether reinforcing structures have primarily a quieting or an activating effect on behavior; this would be relevant to activation versus negative feedback theories of reward (6, 13, 15, 17). A recent study by Brady and Nauta (1) already suggests that the septal area is a quieting system, for its surgical removal produced an extremely active animal.

Such examples, we believe, make it reasonable to hope that the methodology reported here should have important consequences for physiological studies of mechanisms of reward.

SUMMARY

A preliminary study was made of rewarding effects produced by electrical stimulation of certain areas of the brain. In all cases rats were used and stimulation was by 60-cycle alternating current with voltages ranging from $\frac{1}{2}$ to 5 v. Bipolar needle electrodes were permanently implanted at various points in the brain. Animals were tested in Skinner boxes where they could stimulate themselves by pressing a lever. They received no other reward than the electrical stimulus in the course of the experiments. The primary findings may be listed as follows: (*a*) There are numerous places in the lower centers of the brain where electrical stimulation is rewarding in the sense that the experimental animal will stimulate itself in these places frequently and regularly for long periods of time if permitted to do so. (*b*) It is possible to obtain these results from as far back as the tegmentum, and as far forward as the septal area; from as far down as the subthalamus, and as far up as the cingulate gyrus of the cortex. (*c*) There are also sites in the lower centers where the effect is just the opposite: animals do everything possible to avoid stimulation. And there are neutral sites: animals do nothing to obtain or to avoid stimulation. (*d*) The reward results are obtained more dependably with electrode placements in some areas than others, the septal area being the most dependable to date. (*e*) In septal area preparations, the control exercised over the animal's behavior by means of this reward is extreme, possibly exceeding that exercised by any other reward previously used in animal experimentation.

The possibility that the reward results depended on some chronic painful consequences of the implantation operation was ruled out on the evidence that no physiological or behavioral signs of such pain could be found. The phenomenon was discussed as possibly laying a methodological foundation for a physiological study of the mechanisms of reward.

REFERENCES

1 Brady, J. V., & Nauta, W. J. H. Subcortical mechanisms in emotional behavior: affective changes following septal forebrain lesions in the albino rat. *J. comp. physiol. Psychol.*, 1953, **46**, 339–346.

2 Delgado, J. M. R. Permanent implantation of multilead electrodes in the brain. *Yale, J. Biol. Med.*, 1952, **24**, 351–358.

3 Delgado, J. M. R. Responses evoked in waking cat by electrical stimulation of motor cortex. *Amer. J. Physiol.*, 1952, **171**, 436–446.

4 Delgado, J. M. R., & Anand, B. K. Increase of food intake induced by electrical stimulation of the lateral hypothalamus. *Amer. J. Physiol.*, 1953, **172**, 162–168.

5 Dell, P. Correlations entre le système vegetatif et le système de la vie relation: mesencephale, diencephale, et cortex cerebral. *J. Physiol.* (Paris), 1952, **44**, 471–557.

6 Deutsch, J. A. A new type of behavior theory. *Brit. J. Psychol.*, 1953, **44**, 304–317.

7 Gastaut, H. Correlations entre le système nerveux vegetatif et le système de la vie de relation dans le rhinencephale. *J. Physiol.* (Paris), 1952, **44**, 431–470.

8 Hebb, D. O. *The organization of behavior.* New York: Wiley, 1949.

9 Hull, C. L. *Principles of behavior.* New York: D. Appleton-Century, 1943.

10 Hunter, J., & Jasper, H. H. Effects of thalamic stimulation in unanaesthetized animals. *EEG clin. Neurophysiol.*, 1949, **1**, 305–324.

11 Krieg, W. J. S. Accurate placement of minute lesions in the brain of the albino rat. *Quart. Bull., Northwestern Univer. Med. School*, 1946, **20**, 199–208.

12 MacLean, P. D., & Delgado, J. M. R. Electrical and chemical stimulation of fronto-temporal portion of limbic system in the waking animal. *EEG clin. Neurophysiol.*, 1953, **5**, 91–100.

13 Olds, J. A neural model for sign-gestalt theory. *Psychol. Rev.*, 1954, **61**, 59–72.
14 Rosvold, H. E., & Delgado, J. M. R. The effect on the behavior of monkeys of electrically stimulating or destroying small areas within the frontal lobes. *Amer. Psychologist*, 1953, **8**, 425–426. (Abstract)
15 Seward, J. P. Introduction to a theory of motivation in learning. *Psychol. Rev.*, 1952, **59**, 405–413.
16 Skinner, B. F. *The behavior of organisms.* New York: D. Appleton-Century, 1938.
17 Wiener, N. *Cybernetics.* New York: Wiley, 1949.

HYPOTHALAMIC CONTROL OF
FEEDING AND SELF-STIMULATION

Bartley G. Hoebel and Philip Teitelbaum

UNIVERSITY OF PENNSYLVANIA

*Editor's Note   A great deal of work has been done
on the control of eating behavior by centers in the
hypothalamus. For example, there is a well-known phenomenon of hyperphagia—overeating—which results
from injury to the ventro-medial nucleus of the hypothalamus. Teitelbaum and others have investigated this
effect in detail and have found that it apparently involves damage to the mechanism by which satiation
is detected rather than to an increased liking for food.
In the present article Hoebel and Teitelbaum relate
the feeding motivation effects of these centers to their
self-stimulation effects.*

Source   Reprinted from Science, *February 2, 1962*
135, *375–376, with permission of the authors and the
American Association for the Advancement of Science.
Copyright 1962.*

Abstract. Hypothalamic sites which control feeding exert a corresponding control over lateral hypothalamic self-stimulation. This was demonstrated in rats bearing four, intrahypothalamic electrode-cannulas for electrical stimulation or chemical injection. Self-stimulation of the lateral hypothalamus was inhibited by ventromedial excitation or by excessive feeding. Both self-stimulation and feeding were accelerated (disinhibited) by ventromedial ablation or anesthetization. Thus food acts via the ventromedial hypothalamus to inhibit not only feeding, but also lateral hypothalamic self-stimulation.

Feeding is under the control of a dual neural mechanism in which the lateral hypothalamus excites feeding and the ventromedial hypothalamus inhibits it (*1*). In the lateral hypothalamus, electrical (*2, 3*) or chemical stimulation (*4, 5*) induces feeding, and anesthetization (*4*) or destruction of this region (*1*) depresses it. In the ventromedial hypothalamus the situation is reversed; stimulation (*3, 6*) suppresses feeding, and anesthetization (*4*) or destruction (*7*) augments it.

Stimulation in certain areas of the brain is reinforcing; in other areas it induces aversion. For instance, a rat will press a lever repeatedly to stimulate its lateral hypothalamus, but will work to avoid stimulation of its ventromedial hypothalamus (*8*). Thus, the tissue in the lateral hypothalamus which excites feeding lies within a system where stimulation is reinforcing, whereas the inhibitory "satiety center" lies within an aversive region. This anatomical overlap suggests that there might be a functional correlation between feeding and self-stimulation. If so, the hypothalamic systems which regulate feeding should exert a similar control over self-stimulation; moreover, food should decrease the rate of self-stimulation as it satiates hunger.

To explore these possibilities, we devised an electrode-cannula assembly which made it possible to excite or depress the medial and lateral hypothalamus, both bilaterally and simultaneously, in waking rats. Monopolar, hollow electrodes, insulated except at the tip, were constructed from 24-gauge platinum tubing (*9*). Four tubes were implanted simultaneously in the hypothalamus of each rat. Implantation was perpendicular to the surface of the cortex in a frontal plane 6 mm anterior to the ear bars of the stereotaxic instrument. The lateral hypothalamic electrode-cannulas were 2 mm lateral to the midsagittal sinus and 7.5 mm below the surface of the cortex (symbolized: A-6, L-2, D-7.5). Ventromedial electrode-cannulas were implanted at A-6, L-0.75, D-8.5. An indifferent electrode was secured under the scalp.

The electrical stimulus was a 0.5-second train of 100-cy/sec, monophasic, negative, 0.1-msec pulses from a Tektronix 161 square-wave generator. The intensities used were between 0.1 ma and 0.6 ma per electrode. Chemical injections were made from a remote microsyringe via a length of PE-10 tubing fitted onto a 31-guage stainless-steel tube which was inserted inside the full length of the platinum electrode. The chemical injections used were 5 to 10 μl of a 2- to 5-percent solution of sodium chloride for local excitation, and 5 to 10 μl of 1-percent procaine hydrochloride for local anesthetization.

In this report "self-stimulation" always means lever pressing to trigger electrical stimulation of the lateral hypothalamus. Figure 1 summarizes the effects upon feeding and self-stimulation which were obtained by exciting or depressing the hypothalamus. Each arrow represents the results of experiments on five or more female, Sherman albino rats. In brief, when feeding was elicited or increased, so was self-stimulation. When feeding was inhibited, self-stimulation was also inhibited.

The lower-right quadrant in Fig. 1 indicates that unilateral or bilateral electrical stimulation of the lateral hypothalamus caused the rats to eat. This effect was observed from the time stimulation was begun on the day after implantation. Eating was stimulus-bound: satiated rats began to eat within 10 seconds of stimulus onset and continued eating for only a few seconds after the stimulus was turned off. The same rats did not begin self-stimulation until approximately a week after the electrodes were implanted. Once they began, the rate of self-stimulation by rats fed ad libitum was typically 3000 lever presses per hour.

The upper-right quadrant in Fig. 1 indicates that the rats stopped eating when they were stimulated in the ventromedial hypothalamus. They were induced to eat either by 2 days of starvation or by stimulation of the lateral hypothalamus; under both conditions they voraciously ate a liquid diet (10) or Purina laboratory chow until medial stimulation was applied. During weak medial stimulation, on either side of the brain, eating slowed or stopped completely. The same was true for self-stimulation; the rats stopped lever pressing when each press stimulated the medial as well as the lateral area. Higher currents induced aversion and simply disrupted feeding or self-stimulation.

The lower-left quadrant in Fig. 1 indicates that unilateral anesthetization or destruction of the tissue under the self-stimulation electrode stopped self-stimulation. Bilateral destruction produced aphagia.

	ABLATION ANESTHETIZATION		ELECTRICAL STIMULATION	
	FEEDING	SELF-STIM	FEEDING	SELF-STIM
MEDIAL HYPO-THALAMUS	↑	↑	↓	↓
LATERAL HYPO-THALAMUS	↓	↓	↑	↑

FIGURE 1 *The relationship between hypothalamic control of feeding and self-stimulation. An upward arrow means start or increase of feeding or self-stimulation, as indicated; a downward arrow means stop or decrease of these activities. Each hypothalamic manipulation that had an effect on feeding had a similar effect on lateral hypothalamic self-stimulation.*

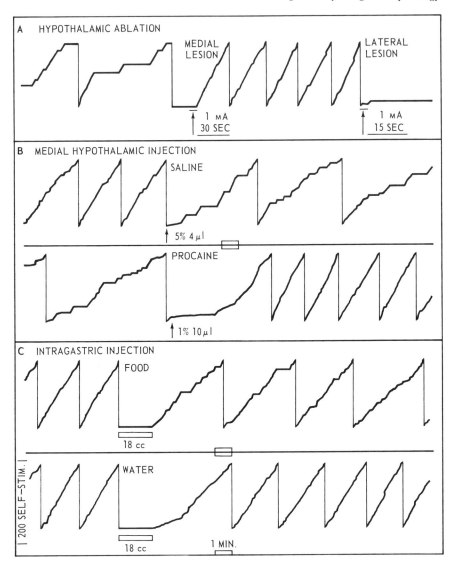

FIGURE 2   *Representative cumulative-recorder records showing the changes in lateral hypothalamic self-stimulation rate produced by experimental influence of the hypothalamus or by feeding. A, Acceleration of self-stimulation caused by destruction of both ventromedial regions. B, Inhibition of self-stimulation by chemical excitation of both ventromedial regions, and subsequent disinhibition of self-stimulation by anesthetization of these regions. C, Prolonged inhibition of self-stimulation by tube feeding a liquid diet (top) but only transient inhibition by tube feeding an equal volume of water (bottom).*

Most interesting is the fact that anesthetization or ablation of the ventro-medial hypothalamus accelerated not only feeding, but also self-stimulation (upper-left quadrant in Fig. 1). Data illustrating this result are shown in records A and B of Fig. 2. The rate of lateral hypothalamic self-stimulation was increased after destruction of the ventromedial hypothalamus on both sides of the brain (first arrow in A). This effect is emphasized in record B in which lateral self-stimulation was suppressed by injecting hypertonic saline into the ventromedial regions; then the effect was com-pletely reversed by ventromedial anesthetization; indeed, self-stimulation was accelerated to a new high.

In such experiments the effect of bilateral anesthetization lasted 5 to 30 minutes. In three rats, unilateral depression of the ventromedial region, even contralateral to the self-stimulating electrode, produced a transient, 3- to 5-minute acceleration of self-stimulation. Therefore, destruction or anesthetization of a site at which a rat will avoid stimulation (8) can enhance self-stimulation at a distant, reward site. This suggests that the normal neural activity of an aversive system can inhibit a reward system. Like feeding, self-stimulation is under inhibitory control.

Does this correlation between hypothalamic control of hunger and self-stimulation extend to the natural effects of food? Does food decrease the rate of self-stimulation as it satiates hunger? Record C (Fig. 2) shows that self-stimulation was slowed to about half the normal rate by a stomach load of 18 ml of liquid diet. The same amount of water had only a transient effect, suggesting that some consequence of food intake other than taste or stomach distension was responsible for prolonged inhibition. This agrees with the finding of Margules (11) and Olds (12) that hungry rats press faster for hypothalamic self-stimulation than satiated ones. In our experi-ment inhibition of self-stimulation typically lasted ½ to 2 hours. Sometimes lever pressing decreased relatively uniformly; other times, as in records B and C, there were repeated interruptions of self-stimulation by other activities such as grooming or rubbing the chin along the floor. In some cases, self-stimulation stopped completely. The inhibition of self-stimulation produced by food in the stomach could be eliminated within 2 minutes by destroying or anesthetizing the ventromedial hypothalamus. This suggests that the inhibitory effect of food on self-stimulation is exerted by way of the ventromedial hypothalamus.

We conclude from these results (13) that within the medial and lateral hypothalamus, the feeding systems control self-stimulation in a man-ner analogous to their control of feeding. Stimulation of the ventromedial area or satiety induced by excessive feeding inhibits lateral hypothalamic self-stimulation; ventromedial destruction disinhibits it. When an animal is hungry, lateral hypothalamic self-stimulation is more reinforc-ing; when satiated, it is less so. It may be that the pleasure of lateral hypothalamic self-stimulation is similar to the gratification obtained by eating.

REFERENCES AND NOTES

1 B. K. Anand and J. R. Brobeck, *Yale J. Biol. and Med.* **24**, 123 (1951).
2 M. Brugger, *Helv. Physiol. et Pharmacol. Acta* **1**, 183 (1943); S. Larsson, *Acta Physiol. Scand. Suppl.* **32**, 115 (1954); N. E. Miller, *Science* **126**, 1271 (1957); P. J. Morgane, *ibid.* **133**, 887 (1961).
3 O. A. Smith, *Anat. Record* **124**, 363 (1956).
4 A. N. Epstein, *Am. J. Physiol.* **199**, 969 (1960).
5 S. P. Grossman, *Science* **132**, 301 (1960).
6 W. Wyrwicka and C. Dobrzecka, *ibid.* **132**, 805 (1960).
7 J. R. Brobeck, J. Tepperman, C. N. H. Long, *Yale J. Biol. and Med.* **15**, 831 (1943).
8 J. Olds, *Am. J. Physiol.* **199**, 965 (1960).
9 Details of electrode-cannula construction will be sent upon request.
10 P. Teitelbaum and B. A. Campbell, *J. Comp. and Physiol. Psychol.* **51**, 135 (1958).
11 D. L. Margules, paper delivered at meeting of Eastern Psychol. Assoc. (1961).
12 J. Olds, *J. Comp. and Physiol. Psychol.* **51**, 320 (1958).
13 A 10-minute movie is available. It shows the major effects that have been reported here. Special thanks are extended to Drs. Alan N. Epstein and Eliot Stellar for their valuable suggestions. This research was supported by the National Science Foundation (grant No. G-9792).

EATING OR DRINKING ELICITED BY DIRECT ADRENERGIC OR CHOLINERGIC STIMULATION OF HYPOTHALAMUS

S. P. Grossman

YALE UNIVERSITY

Source   Reprinted from Science, July 29, 1960, 132, 301–302, with permission of the author and the American Association for the Advancement of Science.
Copyright 1960.

Reading **20**

Abstract. A double cannula system, allowing repeated stimulation of central structures with crystalline chemicals, was developed. This technique was employed to study the effects of adrenergic and cholinergic[1] stimulation of the lateral hypothalamus of rats. Drug-specific effects on the feeding and drinking mechanisms, respectively, were observed.

The exploration of the central nervous system by means of electrical stimulation has provided a wealth of information of great interest to physiologists and psychologists alike. The usefulness of this technique is limited, however, because the effects of stimulation are not restricted to synaptic junctions but affect fibers of passage, causing conduction in both normal and antidromic directions.

It has long been recognized that chemical stimulation avoids these problems, but the technique has in the past been plagued by the problem of uncontrolled spread, which raises a serious objection to the injection of chemicals in solution. Attempts to control for this factor by minimizing the injected quantities have apparently not been completely successful in preventing the escape of the fluid along the shank of the needle, following the path of least resistance.

Depositing chemicals in solid form has been shown to reduce this problem greatly (1), but this method has not allowed repeated stimulation of a selected locus. In the present study, a technique was developed which avoids this objection.

A double cannula system, consisting of two modified syringe needles, was permanently implanted unilaterally, by means of a stereotaxic instrument, into the lateral hypothalamus of each of 12 albino rats. Histological verification of the intended placements showed the tip of the cannula to be located in a circumscribed perifornical region at the same rostrocaudal coordinate as the ventromedial nucleus (see Fig. 1) [Omitted in reprinting. (Ed.)], an area corresponding to the ventral portion of Anand and Brobeck's "feeding area" of the lateral hypothalamus (2).

After 5 days of postoperative recuperation, the inner cannula was removed and minute amounts (1 to 5 μg) of crystalline chemicals were tapped into its tip before it was returned to its usual position. Successive treatments were administered to all animals in a counterbalanced order, with a minimum of 3 days between injections. Both food and water were

[1 Adrenergic and cholinergic refer to actions of chemicals which resemble the action of the two neuro-transmitter substances, acetyl-choline and adrenalin, respectively.(Ed.)]

freely available throughout the experiment. The food and water consumption of satiated rats was recorded for 1 hour immediately following stimulation and compared with the consumption in a comparable period immediately preceding the injection. Daily food and water consumption records were maintained.

None of the animals ever consumed food or water in measurable quantities during the prestimulation period. The injection of epinephrine or norepinephrine resulted in highly significant ($p < .01$), food consumption beginning 5 to 10 minutes after stimulation and persisting with variable intensity for 20 to 40 minutes. Food consumption averaged 3.0 gm under epinephrine and 4.3 gm under norepinephrine.

The injection of acetylcholine (capped by physostigmine) or carbachol into the identical loci in the same animals resulted in highly significant drinking ($p < .01$), the latency, duration, and magnitude of the effect being

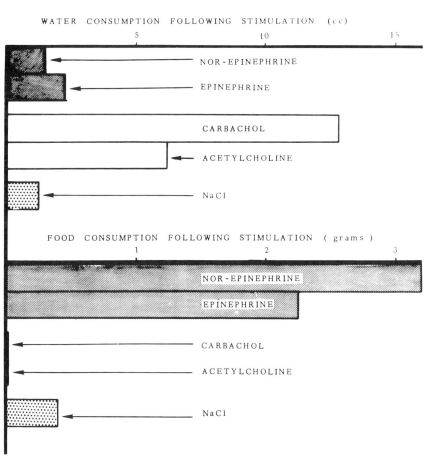

FIGURE 2   *Food and water intake during 1 hour following stimulation. (The intake during a comparable control period was zero in all cases and is not shown.)*

comparable to those obtained for eating after the injection of adrenergic substances. Water consumption averaged 7.4 ml after the injection of acetylcholine and 12.8 ml after the injection of carbachol, this difference being highly significant ($p < .01$). There was no significant food consumption after cholinergic stimulation (see Fig. 2).

The injection of adrenergic substances resulted in significantly less water intake than cholinergic stimulation ($p < .01$). Since in all but one animal the drinking occurred only after a considerable amount of dry food had been consumed, water consumption seemed to be secondary to the food intake rather than a direct consequence of stimulation. To establish further the specificity of the adrenergic effect, norepinephrine was deposited in the lateral hypothalamus of six food- and water-satiated animals, which were then placed in observation cages containing only water. For 30 minutes after the injection none of the animals consumed measurable quantities of water, though four of them repeatedly sampled the drinking tube very briefly. Food was then introduced, and all animals ate almost immediately, though total food consumption was lower than that normally observed, since the food was introduced only toward the end of the period previously established as the duration of the adrenergic effect.

In order to control for the effect of osmotic stimulation, comparable amounts of NaCl were deposited in all the animals. No significant food or water intake was observed. In order to control for general excitation effects, strychnine in comparable quantities was deposited in six animals which also showed the above-described effects of adrenergic and cholinergic stimulation. No consumatory behavior was observed following this stimulation.

The daily consumption records indicate that the amount of food or water consumed during the 1-hour period after stimulation, totaling as much as 40 percent of the animal's normal daily intake, appeared to be consumed above and beyond the normal daily intake. Because of the variability of these records, no statistical evaluation of this effect can be presented, but the conclusion is supported, at least for eating, by the consistent weight gain observed on the day following adrenergic stimulation.

A control for the specificity of the localization of the observed effects was obtained in a preliminary study designed to yield optimal stereotaxic coordinates for the study reported here. It was found that very small deviations from the optimal position, shown in Fig. 1, sufficed to eliminate the effects completely.

The results of this investigation indicate that (i) cell concentrations active in the regulation of both food and water intake are present in the lateral hypothalamus; (ii) cell concentrations exerting this control appear to be highly localized but not clearly separate from each other, since stimulation of "identical" loci in the same animal can evoke both forms of behavior; and (iii) the feeding mechanism appears to be selectively activated by adrenergic stimulation, while the drinking mechanisms appear to respond selectively to cholinergic stimulation (3).

REFERENCES AND NOTES

1 P. D. MacLean, *A.M.A. Arch. Neurol. Psychiat.* **78**, 113 (1957).
2 B. K. Anand and J. R. Brobeck, *Proc. Soc. Exptl. Biol. Med.* **77**, 323 (1951).
3 This investigation was supported by a Public Health Service research fellowship (MF-10, 597), as well as by funds from Dr. Neal E. Miller's grant (M647) from the National Institute of Mental Health, U.S. Public Health Service.

CENTRAL STIMULATION AND OTHER NEW APPROACHES TO MOTIVATION AND REWARD

Neal E. Miller

YALE UNIVERSITY

Editor's Note *This paper was originally given as an address before a meeting of the American Psychological Association, in which Miller reviewed work on the central physiology underlying motivation.*

Source *Reprinted from the* **American Psychologist,** *1958,* **13,** *100–108, with permission of the author and the American Psychological Association.*

The preceding, characteristically brilliant paper by Fred Skinner (marred by a few minor theoretical and statistical aberrations) has shown you the important effects of schedules of reinforcement, and the relatively direct application of these effects to practical situations. The focus of my paper will be on quite a different problem: that of determining how motivations and rewards produce their effects. While the immediate practical implications will not be so obvious, it is a well-known fact that the deeper understanding of basic phenomena almost always leads to significant practical applications, frequently being the necessary foundation for radical innovations.

You are well aware that problems of motivation and reward, which incidentally shade off into mood and temperament, have wide clinical, social, and educational implications. I believe we are at last developing new techniques for getting inside of the organism, manipulating and measuring some of the simpler, more basic things that are going on there, and thus are laying the foundations for fundamental advances in our understanding of the mechanisms of motivation and reward.

COMBINATION OF BEHAVIORAL AND PHYSIOLOGICAL TECHNIQUES

The recent spurt of fruitful research on the mechanisms of motivations has emerged as a result of the convergence of two lines of development. Physiologists, pharmacologists, and biochemists have been developing new and subtler tools for radically affecting and measuring organic processes. At the same time, experimental psychologists have been developing a variety of more effective techniques for measuring drives. The combination of techniques from these two sources is beginning to yield results which have exciting potentialities.

In this brief presentation I can only sample a few of these results. I shall include some pictures to give you a firsthand impression of the work.

An early study of hunger

Using the improved electrolytic technique for making lesions deep in the more primitive structures of the brain, Hetherington and Ranson (12) found that lesions in the region of the ventromedial nuclei of the hypothalamus would cause albino rats to overeat enormously so that, as Fig. 1 shows, they became very fat. But Bailey, Stevenson, and I (25) used be-

[1] The preparation of this paper, as well as most of the author's studies cited in it, was supported by a research grant M 647 from the National Institute of Mental Health, United States Public Health Service.

FIGURE 1 *Effects of overeating produced by lesions in the region of the ventro-medial nuclei of the hypothalamus. (Picture by J. A. F. Stevenson.)*

havioral tests to show that these lesions do not necessarily always potentiate hunger. Although our rats would eat more, they would not work as hard for food. Furthermore, they were stopped by smaller doses of quinine. Thus the additional behavioral tests did not support the original inference of increased hunger drawn from the measure of amount of food consumed. It seemed more reasonable to assume that the lesion interfered with complete satiation.

In the foregoing study, the single test of amount of food consumed disagreed with the rate of bar pressing and a number of other behavioral measures. Other studies, summarized elsewhere (18), show that certain circumstances can affect the rate of bar pressing, so the results of this test will disagree with those of a number of different tests. Discrepancies among tests purporting to measure the same thing raise important problems which the aptitude testers have long since explored: namely, problems of general versus specific factors, and of the purity of various measures of such factors.[2] But our main point for the moment is that it is prudent and extremely fruitful to use a variety of behavioral tests in studying a drive such as hunger. We are just beginning to cash in on the potentialities of these tests; to date most studies of the physiological mechanisms of hunger are still limited to the single measure of the amount of food consumed (17).

Sample of other brain-lesion studies

Lesions in the same general region as those producing overeating can markedly change the temperament of the rat. Anand and Brobeck (1) found that such lesions in the hypothalamus could make rats far more aggressive (a finding which Bailey, Stevenson, and I confirmed on our fingers) and that lesions in the region of the amygdala could abolish this hyperaggressiveness. Similarly, Brady and Nauta (6) have shown that lesions in the septal region can produce heightened startle responses and, with the interesting exception of conditioned suppression (CER), a variety of other indications of increased emotionality. An abstract by King (13) indicates that his paper shows that such emotionality can also be counteracted by lesions in the amygdaloid complex.

In addition to making the animals much tamer, lesions in the region of the amygdala can also produce marked hypersexuality. This is part of the classical Klüver-Bucy (14) syndrome which has been one of the points of departure for many excellent studies of the effects of brain lesions on motivation (e.g., 28, 30, 31, 33).

In the past, the combination of the ablation technique with behavioral tests has been found to be a powerful method for studying sensory, perceptual, and motor functions of the brain. The same combination is becoming a powerful technique for studying also the motivational and emotional functions of the brain. I have cited only a small sample out of the increasingly impressive population of sophisticated studies by able men in this field.

Drive elicited by electrical stimulation

Electrical stimulation of specific points has been another classical technique for studying brain function. Originally, this technique was used to study motor effects on anaesthetized animals. In his classic work, Hess (11) refined this technique by permanently implanting electrodes in the brains of cats so that they could be stimulated in the normal unanaesthetized state. In addition to eliciting complex motor and postural responses, which were less like reflexes and more like acts, Hess discovered that stimulation in the hypothalamus produced a variety of apparently motivational effects such as rage, flight, and eating. His trail-blazing results, which

[2] For a discussion of the design required, but seldom used, to test for the unity and generality of intervening variables such as drives, see (20).

were limited to naturalistic observation, have provided an excellent point of departure for recent studies using a variety of more rigorous behavioral tests.

Let me illustrate by brief excerpts from a film joined together by pieces of black leader to form a series of animated slides. First we see a cat with electrodes permanently implanted in his brain. As soon as he is stimulated, he lowers his head and starts lapping up water. This cat has Delgado-type electrodes ending in subminiature radio sockets so that the wires can be plugged into his head. The demonstration of drinking is very effective. But when the dish is moved a few inches to one side, the cat lowers his head and licks the floor. This simple test shows that we obviously are not eliciting normal thirst, but only a reflex licking response. Other less extreme examples require considerably more subtle tests.

Turning now to some work in collaboration with E. E. Coons, we see in Fig. 2 [omitted in reprinting. (Ed.)] a rat with electrodes placed in a region where stimulation elicits eating. This rat has been thoroughly satiated on food. Soon after stimulation is turned on, the rat starts to eat; soon after it is turned off, he stops. Again, the demonstration is very effective.

But Fig. 3 [Omitted in reprinting] shows that these rats, like Hess's cats, will sometimes also gnaw at inedible objects such as pieces of wood. Therefore, we wonder whether the centrally elicited eating has the properties of normal hunger or is mere reflex gnawing. As a test, we thoroughly trained rats, when thirsty, to get water from a spout above; and, when hungry, to get food by pushing aside a little hinged door below. Then, after thorough satiation, we tested the effects of electrical stimulation. In Fig. 4 you can see that the stimulation can cause a moderately thirsty rat to leave the water spout where he has been drinking and go to a different place to perform the instrumental response of pushing back the hinged door which he has learned as a means of getting food. The fact that the rat stops drinking shows that the effects of stimulation are not mere indiscriminate activation. The fact that the stimulation elicits the

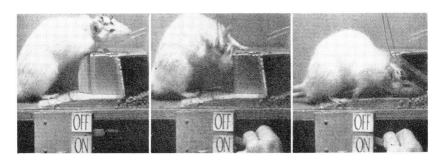

FIGURE 4   *In a critical test, electrical stimulation of the brain causes a moderately thirsty rat to stop drinking at a water spout and go to a different place to perform a learned response, pushing back a hinged door to get food.*

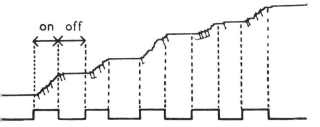

on off

FIGURE 5 *Stimulation in the hypothalamus elicits the learned response of bar pressing in a satiated rat. Each bar press moves the pen up a little. The rat has been trained on a variable-interval schedule; each spike below the record indicates when a bar press actually delivers food.*

learned response of pushing aside the hinged door shows that it has at least some of the more general motivating properties of normal hunger.

In order to make the results completely official, we also trained the rats, when hungry, to secure food by pressing a Skinner bar which delivered small pellets on a variable-interval schedule. Fig. 5 shows the effects of brain stimulation on a thoroughly satiated rat. (Each time the rat presses the bar, the recording lever moves upwards slightly. Each time a bar press actually delivers food, the pen draws a downward spike.) Horizontal sections of the cumulative record show that the satiated rat did relatively little work at the bar during two minute periods of nonstimulation. The upward steps show that, during the two minutes when the stimulation was on, the rat worked at the bar which occasionally delivered food. Thus we have further evidence that electrical stimulation in the areas that induce eating will also motivate the performance of learned instrumental responses that have been reinforced by food. The results are convincing pictorially; they also are statistically reliable.

Continuing our program of testing point-by-point whether the motivation elicited by the electrical stimulation of the brain has all of the properties of normal hunger, Coons and I found that its effects were not limited to the gnawing of solid foods; it caused a satiated rat to drink milk. In control tests the stimulation did not elicit similar sustained drinking of water. Furthermore, the stimulation could be used to motivate the rat to run a T maze with the termination of the stimulation serving as a reward to produce highly reliable choice of the endbox in which the stimulation was turned off. In short, the termination of centrally stimulated "hunger" by turning off the switch seems to have the same rewarding effects as the eating of food which ordinarily terminates normally elicited hunger.

Let us turn now to a different type of motivation: a pain-fear-like emotional disturbance which can be elicited by electrical stimulation in a number of regions deep in the brain (8). Does this emotional reaction have all of the functional properties of normally aroused pain and fear? Some of these properties are: (*a*) Pain and fear can motivate, and their termina-

FIGURE 6 *Electrical stimulation of a pain-fear area in a cat's brain elicits a learned response: rotating a wheel which turns off the stimulation. Stimulation is turned on between the first and second pictures. (From a motion picture by Miller, Delgado, and Roberts, shown by the author at the 1953 meeting of the APA.)*

tion reinforce, trial-and-error learning. (*b*) They can be used to establish a conditioned response. (*c*) They can serve as a punishment to establish an approach-avoidance conflict so that a hungry animal will avoid food.

The purpose of the experiments is to demonstrate point-by-point that central stimulation of the critical places in the brain has all of the foregoing properties.

Figure 6 illustrates the first of these experiments. It shows a cat with chronic Delgado-type electrodes ending in subminiature tube sockets into which are plugged the wires bearing the stimulation. This cat first learned to rotate a paddle wheel to turn off electric shock. Then he was tested with brain stimulation. As soon as the stimulation was delivered, the cat became active and, after a few irrelevant responses, rotated the wheel which turned off the stimulation and thus rewarded the response of rotating the wheel. After a few trials, facilitated by transfer from the previous training, the cat learned to rotate the wheel as soon as the stimulation was turned on. Fig. 6 shows him performing this habit motivated by electrical stimulation of the brain.

In the next experiment, preliminary tests showed that a tone was a neutral stimulus which produced no obvious response. Then for a number of trials the tone was immediately followed by the brain stimulation which elicited wheel turning. After a few such trials, the wheel turning was conditioned: the tone alone, without brain stimulation, caused the cat to turn the wheel.

In the final experiment, we found that stimulation in the sensorimotor area of a hungry control cat, which was eating, produced a violent withdrawal from food; but even after repeated stimulation, the control animals promptly returned to eat. By contrast, experimental cats, stimulated once or twice with a lower voltage in the critical area of the brain, learned to avoid the food.

These experiments have shown that brain stimulation at critical points can have a number of the significant properties of normally elicited pain and fear. In addition to illustrating a general approach to the problem of investigating motivational factors elicited by electrical stimulation of the brain, experiments of the foregoing type may yield information which will help us in knowing where to place lesions in order to relieve certain hitherto hopeless patients from the acute misery of intractable pain.

Similar experiments on centrally aroused aggression have elicited a spectacular and relatively well-integrated cluster of symptoms of rage—hissing, spitting, clawing, etc.—which suggest that rage contains some integrated motor components different from fear (24). So far, however, Warren Roberts and I have confirmed Masserman's results (16) in that we have not been able to condition such responses. This raises an interesting question. Is anger a distinctive drive whose mechanisms we have simply failed to date to locate, or are the motor components involved in rage organized without any separate, distinctive drive so that they must be motivated by other drives such as fear, hunger, or sex?

The results of these experiments are enough to illustrate that the combination of the physiological technique of electrical stimulation with various behavioral techniques for measuring the effects of such stimulation is turning out to be a powerful new tool for investigating the motivational functions of the brain.

Reward effects of electrical stimulation

The combination of the techniques for stimulating the brains of unanaesthetized animals with those of exact behavioral testing led Olds and Milner (27) to a completely unexpected discovery. They found that electrical stimulation of certain areas of the brain would act as a powerful reward. This reward could be used to cause animals to choose the correct side of a T maze or to press a bar in a Skinner box. Often in the history of science, the unexpected discovery of a novel phenomenon, such as X-rays or radioactivity, has forced drastic revisions in current theory and ultimately led to important practical developments. While it is too early to be certain exactly how important will be the effects of this unexpected discovery by Olds and Milner, I suspect they will be considerable.

On the theoretical front, the rewarding effect of central stimulation tends to revive hedonistic theories of reinforcement. As I have pointed out elsewhere, however, the results known to date can be fitted in fairly well with any of the current theories of reinforcement, and the drive-reduction hypothesis suggests a number of interesting lines of investigation in the area of centrally rewarding effects (22). The important thing is that we have here a genuinely novel phenomenon and a completely new technique for investigating the mechanism of reward and its relationship to various drives.

This new discovery has touched off a flurry of research which is still mounting with positive acceleration. Olds (26) has shown that there are certain regions of the hypothalamus where the rate of bar pressing increases with hunger much as it would if the animals were receiving a food reward. In a slightly different area, the rate of bar pressing varies positively with sex—being reduced by castration and increased by androgen therapy. Furthermore, different drugs, such as tranquilizers, seem to have differential effects on the reward phenomenon elicited by stimulation in different parts of the brain. Thus, we probably have here a technique for learning more about how drugs affect different parts of the brain and also for screening drugs in order to discover ones that have more specific psychological effects.

Paradoxical dual effects

The experiments which I performed in collaboration with Delgado and Roberts (8) showed that stimulation of certain points in the brain can serve as a punishment. The experiments by Olds and Milner (27) showed that stimulation at other points of the brain can serve as a reward. One of my students, Roberts (29), has recently shown that stimulation in other places may paradoxically function first as a reward and then as a punishment. Bower and I (5) have described further work along this line.

Figure 7 [omitted in reprinting] shows pictures of a rat with electrodes at a point in the anterior portion of the medial forebrain bundle which elicits these paradoxical dual effects. Pressing the bar turns the stimulation on. As you can see, immediately after having pressed the bar the rat turns away and goes to rotate a wheel which terminates the stimulation, then he returns to press the bar again, continuing to repeat the sequence. I believe that this phenomenon may conceivably give us a technique for studying drugs that accentuate the positive rewarding function of the brain and minimize the negative punishing ones.

Motivational effects of drugs

One of my students, Robert Kirschner, used an apparatus much like the one illustrated in Fig. 7 except that the bar and wheel were replaced by two bars diagonally across a corner from each other in order to equalize the skill and effort required to turn the stimulation on or off. Studying the effects of methamphetamine and chlorpromazine, he found that 2 mg/k of the former and 4 mg/k of the latter produced roughly equivalent reductions in the total number of bar presses.

But, when the rewarding and aversive effects were analyzed separately, these two drugs had strikingly different effects. The methamphetamine increased the time to turn the stimulation off while decreasing the time to turn it on. By contrast, the chlorpromazine produced a great increase in the time to turn the stimulation on and also some increase in the time to turn it off. One interpretation of these results is that methamphetamine was accentuating the positive rewarding effects and minimizing the negative punishing ones—a result congruent with its clinical euphoric effects. Chlorpromazine seemed to be reducing reward more than the aversion—a result congruent with the fact that it sometimes causes patients to feel depressed.

The organic chemists are turning out thousands of new compounds and are able to produce at will slight modifications in known drugs. Similarly, the biochemists are learning more about vital hormones, enzymes, enzyme inhibitors, and other powerful agents of metabolism. But one of the chief bottlenecks to the discovery of superior psychotropic drugs is the difficulty in efficiently and safely testing for the psychological effects of all these new compounds. Perhaps this test, along with many other ingenious ones recently devised by experimental psychologists, will help us in finding drugs which have more potent therapeutic effects with fewer harmful side effects. Although the current enthusiasm for the tranquilizing drugs may have the same rocketing rise and frustrating fall as other "wonder cures" for schizophrenia, I believe that the recent signs of vigorous growth of a new infant science of psychopharmacology afford a reasonable ground for eventual hope.

For the rapid growth of psychopharmacology to be healthy, however, I believe that it should soon advance beyond the stage where a single test is widely used for screening merely on the basis of its face validity. The standards and methods of modern aptitude testing should be adapted to this new area. Batteries of tests should be tried out and validated, first by the criterion of internal consistency and eventually by the criterion of predicting clinically useful effects. Both screening tests and drugs might eventually be factor analyzed. At the same time that we are refining our screening instruments, we should also be conducting pure-science studies to analyze how well-known drugs achieve their psychological effects. We need to discover fundamental laws to develop a basic science of psychopharmacology. Such a science should provide a rational basis for practical applications to mental hygiene in the same way that organic chemistry provides a basis for the analysis and synthesis of new compounds (21).

In connection with the problem of drugs, let me emphasize that there is no necessary incompatibility between organic and functional approaches to the problem of mental disease.[3] As you know, I find it useful to describe neurosis and psychotherapy in terms of learning theory. But the book (9) which Dollard and I wrote on this topic contains a chapter on drugs and brain lesions. It is entirely possible that people differ, for example, in the strength of the innate mechanisms for fear, guilt, and anxiety just as they vary in physical size and strength. A person with unusually strong emotional mechanisms of this kind would be especially susceptible to learning strong fears and guilts by traumatic incidents. These unusually strong fears and guilts might directly elicit certain psychosomatic symptoms, produce strong conflicts, or motivate the learning of functional symptoms. It is quite conceivable that chronic medication by suitable drugs could reduce

[3] For a more detailed discussion, see (19).

this special susceptibility to irrationally strong fears and guilts much as insulin enables the diabetic to tolerate a diet containing more carbohydrates.

Furthermore, drug effects have the great advantage over certain other forms of organic intervention in that they are reversible. Some interesting results have already been secured by combining the use of barbiturates with psychotherapy. It is conceivable that a superior drug will be produced which will be a much more effective aid to emotional reeducation. Indeed, it is conceivable that radically improved results with certain forms of mental disease may be achieved by an unconventional combination of drug therapy, individual therapy, group therapy, training in social skills, and temporary manipulation of the environment.

Biochemical stimulation

In addition to electrical techniques of stimulation, new biochemical techniques (which obviously have implications also for psychopharmacology) have recently been exploited. For example, Andersson (2) has shown that minute injections of salt solution into the region of the third ventricle can cause excessive drinking in goats. Conversely, our group has shown that minute injections of water into the brain can cause a thirsty cat to stop drinking. Furthermore, we have shown that the minute salt injections increase, while the water ones decrease, the rate of performing a learned response to get water. Therefore, these minute injections into the brain have some of the more general effects of normal increases or reductions of thirst (23).

Similarly, Alan Fisher (10) has shown that a minute injection of male hormone into a specific site in the brain can induce complex sexual, and in some instances maternal, behavior as though it had a motivating effect. Since similar effects were not produced by electrical stimulation of the same sites, there is reason to believe that, in some instances at least, the chemical stimulation may be more effective and selective than the electrical technique. Here again, we have a powerful new tool, the potentialities of which are just beginning to be explored.

Electrical recording of brain activity

The converse of the stimulation technique is that of recording electrical activity of the brain and other parts of the nervous system. This technique has been used with great success in tracing sensory systems and has recently produced some quite exciting results which may help to explain the mechanism for the relationship between motivation and attention. For example, it has been found that stimulation of the reticular system in the brain can actually reduce the transmission of sensory impulses from the end organs and through lower relay centers, thus partially shielding the brain from certain sources of stimulation. As Livingston (15) has pointed out, this finding produces a radical change in our previous notions of sensory neurophysiology.

Can these new techniques be applied to other motivational phenomena? For example, Pavlov reports that, when a somewhat painful stimulus is made the conditioned stimulus for food, all of the obvious emotional responses to pain seem to drop out. By using suitable recording techniques, could we demonstrate that the pain impulses themselves are reduced before they reach the highest centers? Would we have an experimental method for producing and studying a phenomenon analogous to hysterical anaesthesia?

Although techniques for recording the electrical activity of the nervous system have been used very successfully in the study of sensory mechanisms, they have not been used much in the study of drive and reward. Here seems a promising new area of application, although there are technical difficulties to overcome. For example, if an animal's motor responses (which disturb electrical recording) were eliminated by one of the improved curare derivatives, such as flaxidil, would we find that the electrical activity in different tracts and centers of the brain is altered when the animal is hungry, thirsty, or suffering painful stimulation? What would be the effects of rewards such as water injected directly into the blood stream of a thirsty animal, if indeed it can be demonstrated that such injections function as a reward? Would there be any effects specific to stimulation of the brain at points where such stimulation is rewarding and different from those at points where it is neutral or aversive? Any such differences are likely to give us significant clues to the basic mechanisms of motivation and reward (22).

OTHER PROMISING APPROACHES

Now fasten your seat belts for a final spurt through a number of different approaches for which the brevity of listing does not mean any inferiority in merit.

Recently Roger Russell's group has been studying the effects of what might be called biochemical lesions of the brain, while David Krech and Mark Rosenzweig have been pursuing the relationships among brain chemistry, heredity, and behavior. While these new lines of work have been aimed chiefly at cognitive functions, they could easily turn up facts which would lead directly into problems of motivation and reward.

Most of the studies I have sampled thus far have involved relatively direct approaches to the brain. The combination of exact behavioral tests with various "intermediate" techniques has also proved fruitful. Some of the techniques used in this way have been a fistula into the stomach, a cannula into a vein, a subcutaneous saline injection, enzyme inhibitors, and unusual substances which are similar to a metabolite in one respect but different in others. Programs involving such work are well under way in Mayer's laboratory at Harvard (3), Stellar's (32) at Pennsylvania, and our own laboratory at Yale (24). Simiarly, Beach (4) and his students are introducing a greater variety of behavioral techniques into the study of sex.

Thus far, various approaches usually have been used in relative isolation. Additional advances may be expected when more use is made of systematic combinations of these approaches. For example, appropriately placed lesions might be used in the analysis of the systems involved in the drive or reward effect of brain stimulation or of the different effects of distending the stomach with either food or a balloon.

Finally, a completely different and highly promising development has been the use of behavioral techniques to bring new drives into the laboratory: first fear, then curiosity, and most recently social deprivation. We can and should extend the range of drives experimentally studied. But that is another story (20).

REFERENCES

1 Anand, B. K., & Brobeck, J. R. Food intake and spontaneous activity of rats with lesions in the amygdaloid nuclei. *J. Neurophysiol.*, 1952, **15**, 421–430.

2 Andersson, B. The effect of injections of hypertonic NaCl solutions into different parts of the hypothalamus of goats. *Acta Physiol., Scand.*, 1953, **28**, 188–201.

3 Anliker, J., & Mayer, J. The regulation of food intake: Some experiments relating behavioral, metabolic and morphologic aspects. *Amer. J. clin. Nutr.*, 1957, **5**, 148–153.

4 Beach, F. A. Characteristics of masculine "sex drive." In M. R. Jones (Ed.), *Nebraska symposium on motivation*. Lincoln: Univer. Nebraska Press, 1956.

5 Bower, G., & Miller, N. E. Paradoxical rewarding and aversive effects from stimulating the same place in a rat's brain. *Amer. Psychologist*, 1957, **12**, 464. (Abstract)

6 Brady, J. V., & Nauta, W. J. H. Subcortical mechanisms in emotional behavior: The duration of affective changes following septal and habenular lesions in the albino rat. *J. comp. physiol. Psychol.*, 1955, **48**, 412–420.

7 Brown, J. The generalization of approach responses as a function of stimulus intensity and strength of motivation. *J. comp. Psychol.*, 1942, 33, 209–226.

8 Delgado, J. M. R., Roberts, W. W., & Miller, N. E. Learning motivated by electrical stimulation of the brain. *Amer. J. Physiol.*, 1954, **179**, 587–593.

9 Dollard, J., & Miller, N. E. *Personality and psychotherapy: An analysis in terms of learning, thinking and culture*. New York: McGraw-Hill, 1950.

10 Fisher, A. Maternal and sexual behavior induced by intracranial chemical stimulation. *Science*, 1956, **124**, 228–229.

11 Hess, W. R. *Das Zwischenhirn: Syndrome, Lokalisationen, Functionen.* (2nd ed.) Basel: Schwabe, 1954.

12 Hetherington, A. W., & Ranson, S. W. The relation of various hypothalamic lesions to adiposity in the rat. *J. comp. Neurol.*, 1942, **76**, 475–499.

13 King, F. A. Effects of amygdaloid lesions upon septal hyperemotionality in the rat. *Amer. Psychologist*, 1957, **12**, 466. (Abstract)

14 Klüver, H., & Bucy, P. C. Preliminary analysis of functions of the temporal lobes in monkeys. *Arch. Neurol. Psychiat.*, 1939, **42**, 979–1000.

15 Livingston, R. B. Central control of afferent activity. In H. H. Jasper, et al. (Ed.), *Henry Ford hospital international symposium: Reticular formation of the brain.* Boston: Brown, in press.

16 Masserman, J. H. Is the hypothalamus a center of emotion? *Psychosom. Med.,* 1941, **3**, 3–25.

17 Miller, N. E. Shortcomings of food consumption as a measure of hunger: Results from other behavioral techniques. *Ann. N.Y. Acad. Sci.,* 1955, **63**, 141–143.

18 Miller, N. E. Effects of drugs on motivation: The value of using a variety of measures. *Ann. N.Y. Acad. Sci.,* 1956, **65**, 318–333.

19 Miller, N. E. A psychologist speaks. In H. D. Kruse (Ed.), *Integrating the approaches to mental disease.* New York: Paul B. Hoeber, 1957.

20 Miller, N. E. Liberalization of basic S-R concepts: Extensions to conflict behavior and social learning. In S. Koch (Ed.), *Psychology: A study of a science.* Vol. II. *General systematic formulations, learning and special processes.* New York: McGraw-Hill, in press.

21 Miller, N. E. Objective techniques for studying motivational effects of drugs on animals. In S. Garatini & V. Ghetti (Eds.), *Psychotropic drugs.* Amsterdam: Elsevier; New York: Van Nostrand, 1957.

22 Miller, N. E. Comments on the implications of the Olds reward effect for theories of reinforcement. In D. E. Sheer (Ed.), *Electrical stimulation of the brain: Subcortical integrative systems.* Houston: Univer. Texas Press, in press.

23 Miller, N. E. Learning and performance motivated by direct stimulation of the brain. In D. E. Sheer (Ed.), *Electrical stimulation of the brain: Subcortical integrative systems.* Houston: Univer. Texas Press, in press.

24 Miller, N. E. Experiments on motivation: Studies combining psychological, physiological, and pharmacological techniques. *Science,* 1957, **126**, 1271–1278.

25 Miller, N. E., Bailey, C. J., & Stevenson, J. A. F. Decreased "hunger" but increased food intake resulting from hypothalamic lesions. *Science,* 1950, **112**, 256–259.

26 Olds, J. Self-stimulation of the brain: Used to study local effects of hunger, sex and drugs. *Science,* in press.

27 Olds, J., & Milner, P. Positive reinforcement produced by electrical stimulation of septal area and other regions of rat brain. *J. comp. physiol. Psychol.,* 1954, **47**, 419–427.

28 Pribram, K. H., & Weiskrantz, L. A comparison of the effects of medial and lateral cerebral resections on conditioned avoidance behavior in monkeys. *J. comp. physiol. Psychol.,* 1957, **50**, 77–80.

29 Roberts, W. W. Both rewarding and punishing effects from stimulation of posterior hypothalamus with same electrodes at same intensity. *J. comp. physiol. Psychol.,* in press.

30 Rosvold, H. E., Mirsky, A. F., & Pribram, K. H. Influence of amygdalectomy on social behavior in monkeys. *J. comp. physiol. Psychol.,* 1954, **47**, 173–178.

31 Schreiner, L., & Kling, A. Rhinencephalon and behavior. *Amer. J. Physiol.,* 1956, **184**, 486–490.

32 Stellar, E. Physiological psychology. In P. R. Farnsworth (Ed.), *Annual review of psychology.* Vol. 8. Palo Alto, Calif.: Annual Reviews Inc., 1957.

33 Waterhouse, I. K. Effects of prefrontal lobotomy on conditioned fear and food responses in monkeys. *J. comp. physiol. Psychol.,* 1957, **50**, 81–88.

Learning and Memory:
Locus of the Trace

IN SEARCH OF
THE ENGRAM

K. S. Lashley

HARVARD UNIVERSITY AND THE
YERKES LABORATORIES OF PRIMATE BIOLOGY

*Editor's Note   This is a very famous paper in which
the great neuropsychologist Lashley summarized many
years of his work in attempting to find the locus of
the record of learning in the brain of monkeys and
rats. Lashley, more than any other man, was responsible
for the development of the method of using brain lesions
and laboratory training of animals to explore the functions of the brain. The program of research which he
initiated, and which continues under his many students,
was to plot the function of the parts of the brain by
their systematic destruction. While his own results were
largely negative in terms of discrete localization, further
work has been much more "successful." Particularly as
better methods of studying behavior have evolved, more
and more localization of psychological function has been
established, as some of the succeeding readings indicate.*

*Source   Reprinted from **Society of Experimental Biology Symposium No. 4: Physiological Mechanisms in
Animal Behavior** (Cambridge University Press), 1950,
478–505, with permission of The Company of Biologists
Limited.*

When the mind wills to recall something, this volition causes the little [pineal gland, by inclining successively to different sides, to impel the animal spirit toward different parts of the brain, until they come upon that part where th traces are left of the thing which it wishes to remember; for these traces ar nothing else than the circumstance that the pores of the brain through whic┃ the spirits have already taken their course on presentation of the object, hav┃ thereby acquired a greater facility than the rest to be opened again the sam┃ way by the spirits which come to them; so that these spirits coming upo┃ the pores enter therein more readily than into the others.

So wrote Descartes just three hundred years ago in perhaps the earlies┃ attempt to explain memory in terms of the action of the brain. In th┃ intervening centuries much has been learned concerning the nature of th┃ impulses transmitted by nerves. Innumerable studies have defined conditions under which learning is facilitated or retarded, but, in spite of sucl progress, we seem little nearer to an understanding of the nature of th┃ memory trace than was Descartes. His theory has in fact a remarkably modern sound. Substitute nerve impulse for animal spirits, synapse for pore and the result is the doctrine of learning as change in resistance of synapses. There is even a theory of scanning which is at least more definite as to the scanning agent and the source of the scanning beam┃ than is its modern counterpart.

As interest developed in the functions of the brain the doctrine of the separate localization of mental functions gradually took form, even while the ventricles of the brain were still regarded as the active part. From Prochaska and Gall through the nineteenth century, students of clinical neurology sought the localization of specific memories. Flechsig defined the association areas as distinct from the sensory and motor. Aphasia, agnosia, and apraxia were interpreted as the result of the loss of memory images, either of objects or of kinesthetic sensations of movements to be made. The theory that memory traces are stored in association areas adjacent to the corresponding primary sensory areas seemed reasonable and was supported by some clinical evidence. The extreme position was that of Henschen, who speculated concerning the location of single ideas or memories in single cells. In spite of the fact that more critical analytic studies of clinical symptoms, such as those of Henry Head and of Kurt Goldstein, have shown that aphasia and agnosia are primarily defects in the organization of ideas rather than the result of amnesia, the conception of the localized storing of memories is still widely prevalent (52).

While clinical students were developing theories of localization, physiologists were analysing the reflex arc and extending the concept of the reflex to include all activity. Bechterew, Pavlov and the behaviourist school in America attempted to reduce all psychological activity to simple associations or chains of conditioned reflexes. The path of these conditioned reflex circuits was described as from sense organ to cerebral sensory area, thence through associative areas to the motor cortex and by way of the pyramidal paths to the final motor cells of the medulla and cord. The discussions of this path were entirely theoretical, and no evidence on the actual course of the conditioned reflex arc was presented.

In experiments extending over the past 30 years I have been trying to trace conditioned reflex paths through the brain or to find the locus of specific memory traces. The results for different types of learning have been inconsistent and often mutually contradictory, in spite of confirmation by repeated tests. I shall summarize today a number of experimental findings. Perhaps they obscure rather than illuminate the nature of the engram, but they may serve at least to illustrate the complexity of the problem and to reveal the superficial nature of many of the physiological theories of memory that have been proposed.

I shall have occasion to refer to training of animals in a variety of tasks, so shall give a very brief description of the methods used. The animals studied have been rats and monkeys with, recently, a few chimpanzees. Two lines of approach to the problem have been followed. One is purely behavioural and consists in the analysis of the sensory excitations which are actually associated with reactions in learning and which are effective in eliciting the learned reactions. The associated reactions are similarly analysed. These studies define the patterns of nervous activity at receptor and effector levels and specify certain characteristics which the memory trace must have. The second approach is by surgical destruction of parts of the brain. Animals are trained in various tasks ranging from direct sensory-motor associations to the solution of difficult problems. Before or after training, associative tracts are cut or portions of the brain removed and effects of these operations on initial learning or postoperative retention are measured. At the termination of the experiments the brains are sectioned and the extent of damage reconstructed from serial sections. The brains are also analysed for secondary degeneration, so far as available histological methods permit.

ELIMINATION OF THE MOTOR CORTEX

I first became sceptical of the supposed path of the conditioned reflex when I found that rats, trained in a differential reaction to light, showed no reduction in accuracy of performance when almost the entire motor cortex, along with the frontal poles of the brain, was removed. This observation led to a series of experiments designed to test the part played by the motor cortex or Betz cell area in the retention of various habits. The matter can be tested either by removing the motor cortex or by severing its connexions with the sensory areas of the brain. Both methods have been used with the rat and the monkey.

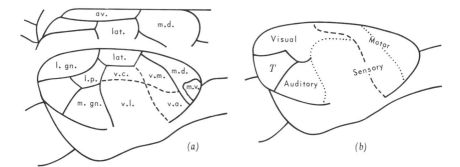

(a)   (b)

FIGURE 1 *Functional divisions of the rat's brain. (a) The projection fields of the principal thalamic nuclei: av., anteroventral; lat., lateral; l.gn., lateral geniculate; l.p., lateral, pars posterior; m.d., median dorsal; m.gn., median geniculate; m.v., median ventral; v., the various divisions of the central nucleus. The projection fields of the median nuclei (m.d., m.v.) correspond to the prefrontal areas of primates. (b) Location of visual, auditory, and overlapping sensory-motor areas. (After Lashley, 44.) The region marked T is probably homologous with the temporal association area of primates.*

The sensory and motor areas of the brains of these animals have been mapped by anatomic methods and by electric stimulation. Figure 1 shows the principal areas of the rat's brain, the separate auditory and visual areas and the overlapping sensory and motor areas. Figure 2 is a composite from several sources of the chief sensory and motor areas of the brain of the macaque monkey.

Incisions were made through the cortex and underlying fibres of the rat's brain such as to sever the visual areas more or less completely from the motor regions of the brain. The rats were then trained in what I have called the conditional reaction. They are taught to jump to a white triangle and to avoid a white $\times$ when both figures are on a black background, but to choose the $\times$ and avoid the triangle if the background is striped; the direction of choice is conditional upon the character of the background. This is the most difficult visual generalization that we have been able

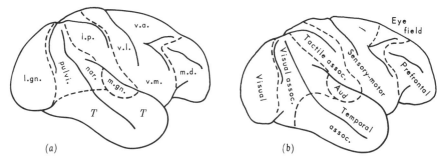

(a)   (b)

FIGURE 2 *Functional divisions of the monkey's brain. (a) The projection of the principal thalamic nuclei. Abbreviations as in Fig. 1. The homologies between the divisions of the central and lateral nuclei are uncertain. (b) Location of functional areas.*

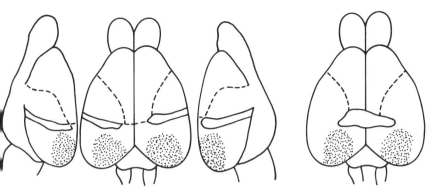

FIGURE 3 *Lesions partially separating the visual area (stippled) from the motor areas (outlined by dashes) of the rat's brain without disturbing visual learning.*

to teach the rat. Animals with incisions like those shown in Fig. 3, which practically separate the motor regions from the visual, were able to learn this reaction as quickly as did normal controls (42).

Monkeys were trained to open various latch boxes. The motor areas were then removed, as shown in Fig. 4. Note that these lesions involved both the Betz cell area and the premotor area, including parts of the eye fields around the arcuate sulcus. This operation produces a temporary paralysis, but after 8 to 12 weeks this paralysis recovers to such an extent that the animals are capable of the movements required to open the boxes. During this recovery period they did not have access to the training boxes. When sufficiently recovered, they were tested and opened the boxes promptly without random exploratory movements. The tasks require both visual recognition of the latches and semiskilled movements, such as turning a crank. Removal of the motor areas did not produce a loss of memory for the movements (33). Jacobsen has since confirmed these observations with a chimpanzee from which the motor cortex was removed (24).

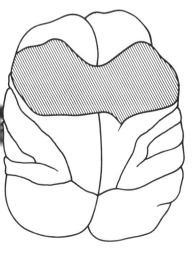

FIGURE 4 *Extent of cortical lesion which did not abolish latch-box habit. The lesion is bounded caudally by the central fissure and extends forward to include the arcuate sulcus.*

These experiments seem to rule out the motor cortex or Betz cell area as containing any part of the conditioned-reflex arc. The traditional view of the function of this area regards it as the region of final integration of skilled voluntary movements. My own interpretation, to which few neurologists would subscribe, is that it has no direct concern with voluntary movement, but is a part of the vast reflex postural system which includes the basal nuclei, cerebellar and vestibular systems. Certainly there is no evidence that it forms a part of the conditioned reflex circuit.

For the rat the experiments rule out the whole frontal region of the brain from participation in visual habits. In the monkey there remains another possibility. The so-called visual associative area (area 18) has direct connexion with the cortex of the arcuate sulcus (area 8), and this in turn with the premotor cortex (area 6). This last area is also motor and perhaps equivalent in function with the Betz cell area (5). The cortex of the arcuate sulcus and of a considerable surrounding area was removed from five monkeys that had been trained in a variety of visual discriminative reactions. After the operations they showed perfect retention of all their visual habits (45). Jacobsen (24) has reported loss of certain latch-box habits in monkeys after removal of area 6, but there are indications that this may be a kinesthetic-sensory area (17, 57), and the loss cannot be ascribed to disturbance of its function as a final common motor path. I have removed it in combination with area 4 without disrupting motor habits (33).

I have occasionally seen the type of defect reported by Jacobsen after prefrontal lobe lesions, as also reported by Kennard (27), but it has not occurred consistently and its occurrence remains unexplained. I did not find it after removal of area 6 in conjunction with the Betz cell area.

TRANSCORTICAL CONDUCTION

There is evidence, not only that the motor cortex does not participate in the transmission of the conditioned-reflex pattern, but also that the transmission of impulses over well-defined, isolated paths from one part of the cortex to another is inessential for performance of complicated habits. The maze habit of the rat almost certainly involves the utilization of several sensory modalities, visual, tactile and kinesthetic. In a rather complicated set of experiments I attempted to test the importance of connexions across the cortex for maze performance. Rats were trained on the maze, then knife cuts were made through the cortex and underlying fibres, separating different functional areas or cutting through functional areas. The incisions were long, averaging half of the entire length of the cerebral hemispheres. After recovery the animals were tested in retention of the maze habit. In other experiments the incisions were made before training and their effect upon the rate of initial learning was tested. In neither initial learning nor in retention could any certain effect of separating the various parts of the cortex be demonstrated. If the incisions interrupted sensory tracts to the cortex, there was loss of the habit, but uncomplicated separation of cortical areas produced no effect on performance.

Both the anatomic evidence of Le Gros Clark (7) and the physiological evidence from strychninization of the cortex (4) show that the primary visual area has direct axon connexions only with the immediately adjacent cortex. In experiments which I shall report in more detail in considering the function of associative areas, I removed the greater part of this band of cortex surrounding the visual areas from five monkeys that had been trained in a variety of visual habits (Fig. 5). This operation almost certainly destroyed all the relay connexions across the cortex from the macular fields. It produced no loss of visual habits based on discrimination of the colour, brightness, or form of objects (45).

Miss Wade trained monkeys in habits which are abolished by destruction of the frontal lobes and which require visual, tactile and kinesthetic adjustments. I cut the transcortical fibres of the frontal lobes in these animals, leaving only the projection fibres for the area. There was no disturbance of performance after the operations (unpublished experiments).

Such results are certainly puzzling. They leave us with almost no understanding of the function of the associative fibres which extend across from one part of the cortex to another. The results are difficult to accept, yet they are supported by various other lines of evidence. Smith (54) and Akelaitis (1) have reported careful studies of human patients in whom the corpus callosum (the great commissure of fibres connecting the two hemispheres) had been severed in an effort to stop the spread of Jacksonian epilepsy. These investigators were not able to demonstrate any effects of the operation except a slight slowing of reaction time, which was equally great, whether the reaction was on the same or opposite side of the body to that stimulated. Sperry (55) has divided the arm motor and sensory areas of the monkey's brain into a number of small square divisions (Fig.

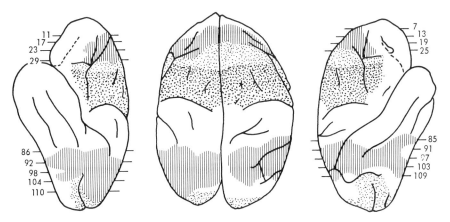

FIGURE 5 *Lesions, marked by hatching, which destroyed the greater part of the so-called visual associative areas in a monkey without affecting visual functions.*

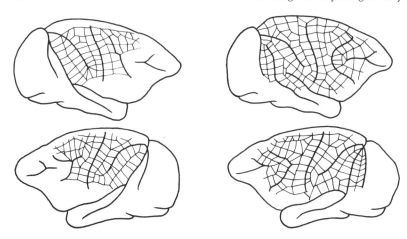

FIGURE 6   *Pattern of incisions in the motor and sensory areas of two monkeys which did not produce incoordination movements. (After Sperry, 55.)*

6) by careful subpial section. Although the operations were intended to sever only the intrinsic fibres of the cortex, they actually destroyed most of the longer loop fibres as well. Such animals do not show any postoperative incoordination of the movements of the different segments of the arm and use the arm efficiently in the performance of habitual movements.

It is difficult to interpret such findings, but I think that they point to the conclusion that the associative connexions or memory traces of the conditioned reflex do not extend across the cortex as well-defined arcs or paths. Such arcs are either diffused through all parts of the cortex, pass by relay through lower centres, or do not exist.

There is the possibility that the chief associative connexions between functional areas of the cortex are by connexions through the thalamus. I doubt this for two reasons. The techniques that have been used to demonstrate cortical efferents to the thalamus, the Marchi stain and strychninization of the cortex, are unreliable indices of the direction of fibres. The supposed cortico-thalamic fibres follow the paths of the afferent fibres and may not be efferent. Secondly, in the rat at least there is little evidence of an elaborate system of intrathalamic association fibres. After a cortical injury thalamic nuclei degenerate completely without leaving a residue of internuncial cells. The question of the importance of intrathalamic association is not settled, and none of the available anatomic or physiological techniques is capable of giving conclusive evidence.

A few experiments by Ingebritsen (23) on the spinal cord suggest that the essential pattern of a learned reaction can be transmitted by a diffuse nervous network. Ingebritsen made double hemisections of the spinal cord of rats, severing one half at the second, the other at the fifth cervical level. These lesions cut all long fibres connecting the brain with the spinal motor centres of the limbs. Nevertheless, such rats retained maze habits and were able to learn to operate latch boxes requiring that they rise on the hindfeet and depress a lever with the forepaws. . . . There are no long fibres, either sensory or motor, crossing over between the two levels of these sections. Habit patterns cannot be acquired by the isolated spinal cord (26). Somehow, the control of the motor pattern essential for the performance of the complex acts traverses the network of short internuncial cells of the spinal cord.

THE PROBLEM OF THE "ASSOCIATION AREAS"

In anatomic theories of the memory trace the association areas of the cortex have played a major part. Frontal, parietal, occipital and temporal associative areas have been distinguished as regions of the cortex, relatively lacking in massive connexions with the lower centres of the brain. On the basis of some clinical evidence, but chiefly because of their anatomic relations, these areas have been considered as associative and as the store-houses of memory images of sensations derived from the adjacent sensory areas. Thus areas 18 and 19 of Brodmann's questionable divisions have been called the visual associative areas, areas 5 and 7 tactile associative, and areas 20, 21, and 22 of the temporal lobe the auditory association areas. The prefrontal area was considered by Hitzig to be a higher integrative region because he believed that it showed the greatest evolutionary growth in the primate brain. Special memory functions were also ascribed to it, however.

S. I. Franz reported that the removal of the frontal association areas of cats destroyed recently formed habits but left old, well-established habits unaffected (15). The actual observation was that the cats lost their habits of opening latch boxes but would still come when called. His operations destroyed much of the motor areas as well as the prefrontal cortex. I later trained monkeys on latch boxes and removed the prefrontal cortex, in an experiment designed to test the influence of the operation on learning ability. During the period allowed for recovery one of the animals found the experimental boxes piled in the corner of the room and promptly opened them. Tests of the other animals showed perfect retention of the manipulative habits. There was no indication that the recently acquired habits had been lost. Jacobsen took up the problem at this point and carried it further. He found that visual discriminative habits and simple habits of latch-box manipulation are unaffected by loss of the prefrontal association areas. Habits requiring a series of acts, such as opening a box with several independent latches, may be lost. This is not, however, a simple removal of memory traces. The animals are incapable of relearning the functions which they have lost. They fail because of a difficulty in going on from one task to the next, not from loss of memory of the individual items of the task (25).

Loss of the delayed reaction after removal of the prefrontal lobes of the monkey has been interpreted as a loss of immediate memory. However, this task and others, which are affected by prefrontal injury, all involve a series of conflicting actions. Difficulty in maintaining a constant set or attitude is the real basis of the loss. Such an interpretation fits better with clinical findings than does the hypothesis of memory defect.

We have recently been testing the relation of other associative areas to memory functions in the monkey. Five spider monkeys were trained on a variety of visual tasks. A band of cortex surrounding the primary visual areas and including the visual associative areas of Campbell and Brodmann was then removed (Fig. 6), and the animals were tested for retention of habits based on discrimination of colours, of geometric forms, and of a number of familiar objects, such as visual recognition of their home cages, of the caretaker, and the like. No loss of any visual memories could be demonstrated (45).

Similar experiments with habits of tactile discrimination are now being completed. The monkeys are required to reach through a hole in a partition and to distinguish variously shaped covers of food dishes by touch alone. They learn readily such tasks as to choose a cylinder and reject a prism, if both are smooth, but to choose the prism, if both are coated with sandpaper. When they had reached a standard criterion of accuracy, the parietal associative areas (Brodmann's areas 5 and 7) were removed. No animal has shown significant loss of the habits based on tactile discrimination after removal of these areas alone (Dr. Josephine Blum).

Removal of the lateral surfaces of the temporal lobes alone has also not affected visual or tactile habits.

A number of experiments with the rat have shown that habits of visual discrimination survive the destruction of any part of the cerebral cortex except the primary visual projection area. Similarly for auditory habits and the auditory cortex. There is no indication of specialized memory areas outside the primary sensory fields. Although there are not clearly distinguished associative areas in the rat's cortex, I have become somewhat sceptical of the existence of any great difference in the extent of associative areas, as between the rat and monkey. The best anatomic index that we have of the functional differentiation of a cortical area is its connexions with the thalamus. The prefrontal cortex of man is the projection field of the dorsomedial and ventromedial nuclei. The corresponding nuclei in the rat's thalamus project to a large frontal region, perhaps proportionately as large as the prefrontal lobes of man (40). This region also includes the electrically excitable points for the head and part of that for the forelegs. It has therefore been classed as motor, but it is equally justifiable to class it as corresponding to the human prefrontal cortex.

It has been claimed that the differentiation of a number of cerebral areas contributes to man's superior intelligence by avoiding confusion of functions, but, if the anatomic relations in man and the rat were reversed, it would be concluded with equal assurance that, because intellectual activity requires close integration of different functions, the advantage lies with he brain in which functional areas are not sharply set off. Such *post hoc* arguments based on anatomic grounds alone have little value for functional nterpretations. Many current conceptions of cerebral physiology are based upon just such dubious inferences from anatomic data.

The outcome of the experiments involving removal of the associative areas of the monkey was unexpected, in spite of the fact that it confirms he earlier results with the rat. The conclusion, which seems to be forced by the accumulated data, runs counter to the accepted tradition concerning he organization of the cerebral cortex. Memory traces, at least of simple sensory-motor associations, are not laid down and stored within the associative areas; at least not within the restricted associative area supposedly concerned with each sense modality. Memory disturbances of simple sensory habits follow only upon very extensive experimental destruction, including almost the entire associative cortex. Even combined destruction of the prefrontal, parietal, occipital and temporal areas, exclusive of the primary sensory cortex, does not prevent the animal from forming such habits, although preexisting habits are lost and their reformation is greatly retarded.

These results, showing that the so-called associative areas are not essential to preservation of memory traces, have been obtained with rats and monkeys. Is there a greater cortical differentiation in anthropoid apes and man? We have experimental data only on the prefrontal associative cortex of the chimpanzee and of man. Bilateral removal of the entire prefrontal granular cortex in five chimpanzees in our laboratory has not resulted in any memory defect. One two-year-old animal, lacking prefrontal and parietal areas, removed in early infancy, falls well within the normal range in all aspects of development. Adult chimpanzees, trained in such complicated habits as choosing an object, like a model shown, retain the habits after removal of the entire prefrontal cortex. We have not been able to demonstrate loss of any memory or, in fact, of any function after such operations.

Clinical data, with amnesias following apparently small lesions, seem to contradict such experimental findings. However, lesions in the human brain are mostly the result either of tumor growth or of severe traumatism, both of which probably produce widespread changes in addition to the local injury. The surgical removal of parts of the frontal lobes in the recent topectomy studies has not produced such severe defects as usually result from traumatic destruction of the lobes (51).

THE ROLE OF SUBCORTICAL STRUCTURES

Perhaps we have been looking in the wrong place for the conditioned-reflex arcs or memory traces. Are they formed somewhere else than in the cortex? Experiments on the thalamus and other subcortical structures are technically difficult, and there is little direct evidence on this question.

Since the classical experiments of Goltz a number of investigators have
studied the capacity of the totally decorticate animal to learn. The outcome
of these experiments is that such animals can form simple sensory-motor
associations, although with extreme slowness in comparison with the rate
of the normal animal (18, 53). We must ask, however, whether such learning occurs when the cortex is intact.

When the sensory or associative areas of the cerebral cortex are
destroyed, the corresponding nuclei of the neo-thalamus degenerate, so this
portion of the subcortex is eliminated from consideration by the same
experiments which rule out the cortical association areas. The only experiments bearing upon the participation of other subcortical centres suggest
that subcortical learning does not occur when the cortex is functioning.

Fischel (14) has maintained, solely from comparative psychological
studies, that the basal ganglia are the seat of the space-coordinate elements
of motor habits. I have destroyed the greater part of these structures in
rats, trained in the discrimination box, without producing loss of orientation. The animals may perform forced circus movements but, in spite of
this, they maintain their orientation in the problem box (31). The basal
ganglia in man are subject to various degenerative diseases. The symptoms
of such diseases are, in general, tremors and other disturbances of coordination at a primitive level, but without evidence of apraxia or other disorder
of the learned patterns of motor coordination. The evidence seems conclusive that in mammals the basal nuclei are not an essential link in the
patterning of learned activities.

It has been widely held that although memory traces are at first formed
in the cerebral cortex, they are finally reduced or transferred by long practice to subcortical levels. The evidence for this has been the apparently
greater fragility of recently formed habits than of old habits; the supposedly
greater resistance of the latter to brain injuries. The amnesias following
electroshock therapy indicate that it is the age of the trace and not the
amount of practice that has built it up which determines its survival, and
a difference of a few minutes in the age of memories may suffice to determine their loss or survival. This is scarcely evidence for reduction to lower
levels of the nervous system. The chief argument for the dropping out
of memory traces from the cortex has seemingly run somewhat as follows:
Consciousness is a function of the cerebral cortex; long-practised habits
become automatic and are performed without conscious control; therefore
they are no longer mediated by the cerebral cortex. Both premises of this
syllogism are probably false, and the conclusion would not follow if they
were true.

When rats are trained in a habit based upon the discrimination of intensities of light, to choose a brightly lighted alley and avoid a dimly lighted
one, the removal of the striate cortex completely abolishes the habit. The
animals are able to relearn the reaction and require as much practice
as they did for initial learning. One group of animals was trained in this
habit and given 1,200 trials of overtraining, daily practice for a period

of 3 months. Their behaviour strongly suggested automatization of the habit. The striate areas were then removed. The habit was lost, just as in the case of animals which are operated as soon as they give evidence of the presence of the habit. The long overtraining did not eliminate the participation of the cortex (30).

This visual habit can be formed in the absence of the visual cortex, and the rates of learning with and without the visual area are exactly the same. The average for 100 normal animals is 125 trials; for nearly 100 without the visual areas it is 123 trials. After such animals, lacking the visual cortex, have learned the brightness reaction, any other part of the cerebral cortex may be destroyed without disturbing the habit. Apparently no other part of the cortex takes over the learning function (32). If, in addition to removal of the striate areas, the pretectile region of the thalamus and the optic tectum are destroyed, the animals cannot learn the discrimination reaction (37). These facts indicate that, in the absence of the visual cortex, the learning of the brightness reaction is carried out by the optic tectum. However, so long as the visual cortex is intact, removal of the tectum has no effect whatever upon the performance of visual habits. The tectum apparently does not participate in visual learning so long as the cortex is intact (37).

Dunlap (8) has advanced the hypothesis that complex serial habits, such as those of maze running, playing a musical passage, or speaking a sentence, are at first chains of sensory-motor reactions in which excitations from muscular contractions in one movement of the series serve as stimuli to elicit the next. He holds that, with continued practice, there is a short-circuiting of these conditioned reflex pathways through the cerebellum and that the peripheral elements drop out. McCarthy and I (47) attempted to test this hypothesis by training rats in the maze, removing the cerebellum, and testing for retention. The operations greatly disturbed the motor coordination of these animals. Some of them practically rolled through the maze, but they rolled without entering the blind alleys. There was no loss of memory of the sequence of turns in the maze.

These few experiments are, of course, by no means conclusive. They constitute, however, the only direct evidence available, and they definitely point to the conclusion that, if the cerebral cortex is intact, the associative connexions of simple conditioned reflexes are not formed in the subcortical structures of the brain.

The studies which I have reported thus far point to the conclusion that habits based upon visual discrimination are mediated by the striate areas, by the primary visual cortex, and do not involve the activity of any other part of the cerebral cortex. The conduction of impulses is from the retina to the lateral geniculate nuclei, thence to the striate areas, and from them down to some subcortical nervous mechanism. The path beyond the striate cortex is unknown. It may be direct to the spinal cord. There is some evidence that the pyramidal paths contain many fibres from all parts of the cerebral cortex, not from the Betz cell area only.

It seems probable that the same restriction of simple discriminative habits to the primary sensory areas holds also for other sensory modalities. The evidence is less complete, but what there is is consistent with the data on the visual system.

The evidence thus indicates that in sensory-motor habits of the conditioned reflex type no part of the cerebral cortex is essential except the primary sensory area. There is no transcortical conduction from the sensory areas to the motor cortex, and the major subcortical nuclear masses, thalamus, striatum, colliculi and cerebellum, do not play a part in the recognition of sensory stimuli or in the habit patterning of motor reactions.

THE ENGRAM WITHIN SENSORY AREAS (EQUIPOTENTIAL REGIONS)

The experiments reported indicate that performance of habits of the conditioned reflex type is dependent upon the sensory areas and upon no other part of the cerebral cortex. What of localization within the sensory areas? Direct data upon this question are limited, but point to the conclusion that so long as some part of the sensory field remains intact and there is not a total loss of primary sensitivity, the habit mechanism can still function. Thus, in a series of experiments attempting to locate accurately the visual cortex of the rat, parts of the occipital lobes were destroyed in a variety of combinations. In these experiments it appeared that, so long as some part of the anterolateral surface of the striate cortex (the projection field of the temporal retina corresponding to the macula of primates) remained intact, there was no loss of habit. Any small part of the region was capable of maintaining the habits based on discrimination of intensities of light (37).

In a later experiment an attempt was made to determine the smallest amount of visual cortex which is capable of mediating habits based upon detail vision. The extent of visual cortex remaining after operation was determined by counting undegenerated cells in the lateral geniculate nucleus. Discrimination of visual figures could be learned when only one-sixtieth of the visual cortex remained (39). No comparable data are available on postoperative retention, but from incidental observations in other experiments I am confident that retention would be possible with the same amount of tissue.

In an early study by Franz (16) the lateral surfaces of the occipital lobes of the monkey were destroyed after the animals had been trained in pattern and colour discrimination. These operations involved the greater part of what is now known to be the projection field of the macula. There was no loss of the habits. I have destroyed the cortex of the retrocalcarine fissure (the perimacular field) without destroying visual memories. The results with monkeys thus support the more ample data for the rat; the visual memory traces survive any cortical lesion, provided some portion of the field of acute vision remains intact.

This lack of definite habit localization might really have been predicted from psychological data alone. Analysis of the effective stimuli in discriminative learning reveals that the association is independent of particular sensory nerve fibres. It is a response to a pattern of excitation which may vary widely in position on the sensory surface and consequently in cortical projection. The reactions involved in motor habits show the same sort of functional equivalence; a motor habit is not a predetermined set of muscular contractions but is a series of movements in relation to bodily posture and to the complex pattern of the environment. The writing of one's name, for example, is not a stereotyped series of contractions of particular muscles but is a series of movements in relation to the body planes which can be performed with any motor organ and with any degree of amplitude.

I have not time here to report in detail the experiments which justify the conclusion that neither the afferent path nor the efferent is fixed by habit. The mass of evidence accumulated by gestalt psychologists shows conclusively that it is the pattern and not the localization of energy on the sense organ that determines its functional effect. Similar motor equivalence is demonstrated by a variety of less systematic evidence. The psychological studies, like the more limited direct experiments on the brain, point to the conclusion that the memory trace is located in all parts of the functional area; that various parts are equipotential for its maintenance and activation.

FACILITATIVE FUNCTIONS IN LEARNING AND RETENTION (MASS ACTION)

The experiments thus far reported have been concerned almost entirely with discriminative habits requiring only an association between a single sensory stimulus and a motor response. A very different picture develops in experiments with other types of learning. If rats are trained in the maze and then have portions of the cortex removed, they show more or less loss of the habit. If a small amount of cortex is destroyed, 5 to 10 per cent, the loss may be scarcely detectable. If large amounts, say 50 per cent or more, are destroyed, the habit is completely lost, and relearning may require many times as much practice as did initial learning. The amount of loss, measured in terms of the practice required for relearning, is, on the average, closely proportional to the amount of cortex destroyed. Figure 7 shows the relation for one group of rats on a relatively difficult maze with eight culs de sac. There is some evidence that the more difficult the task, the greater the relative effect of the larger lesions (34, 48). Similar results have been obtained with latch-box learning and retention (36). So far as it is possible to analyse the data from more than 200 diverse operations, the amount of loss from a given extent of cortical destruction is about the same, no matter what part of the cerebral hemispheres is

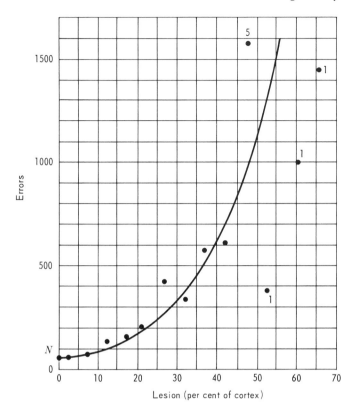

FIGURE 7 *The relation of errors in maze learning to extent of cerebral damage in the rat. The extent of brain injury is expressed as the percentage of the surface area of the isocortex destroyed. Data from 60 normal and 127 brain-operated animals are averaged by class intervals of 5 per cent destruction. The curve is the best fitting one of logarithmic form. For lesions above 45 per cent the number of cases (indicated by numerals on the graph) is too small for reliability. (After Lashley and Wiley, 48.)*

destroyed, provided that the destruction is roughly similar in both hemispheres.

The explanation of this quantitative relationship is difficult. In learning the maze the rat certainly employs a variety of sensory cues, visual, tactile kinesthetic, olfactory, possibly auditory. Brain injuries destroy various sensory fields and the larger the lesion the greater the reduction in available sense data. The production of different amounts of sensory deficit would thus appear to be the most reasonable explanation of the quantitative relation between habit loss and extent of lesion (13, 22). Sensory deficit certainly plays a role in it. In the experiment on effects of incisions through the cortex, which was described earlier, the severity of loss of the maze habit correlated highly with the interruption of sensory pathways, as determined from degeneration of the thalamus.

However, sensory loss will not account for all of the habit deterioration. here is evidence which shows that another more mysterious effect is involved. In the first place, destruction of a single sensory area of the cortex roduces a far greater deficit in maze or latch-box performance than does ss of the corresponding sense modality. A comparison was made of the fects on retention of the latch-box habits of combined loss of vision, brissae touch, and the anesthesia to touch and movement produced by ctioning the dorsal half of the spinal cord at the third cervical level. his latter operation severs the columns of Gall and Burdach, which convey ctile and kinesthetic impulses, and also severs the pyramidal tracts which ave a dorsal position in the rat. The combined peripheral sense privation nd section of the pyramids produced less loss of the latch-box habits an did destruction of a single sensory area of the cortex (36). Secondly, hen blind animals are trained in the maze, the removal of the primary isual cortex produces a severe loss of the habit with serious difficulty relearning, although the animals could have used no visual cues during e initial learning (43).

A possible explanation of this curious effect was that the rat forms concepts of spatial relations in visual terms, as man seems to do, and that e space concepts are integrated in the visual cortex. The visual cortex ight then function in the formation of spatial habits, even when the nimal loses its sight. To test this Tsang (56) reared rats blind from birth, ained them as adults in the maze, then destroyed the visual cortex. The sultant loss of the maze habit by these animals was as severe as in nimals which had been reared with vision. The hypothesis concerning e formation of visual space concepts was not confirmed.

Our recent studies of the associative areas of the monkey are giving milar results to those gained with rats. Visual and tactile habits are not isturbed by the destruction singly, either of the occipital, parietal, or teral temporal regions, so long as the primary sensory fields remain. However, combined destruction of these regions, as shown in Fig. 8, does

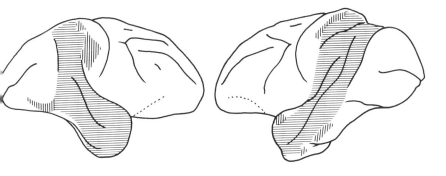

FIGURE 8 *Minimal lesion which produces disturbances in tactile or visual memory n the monkey.*

produce a loss of the habits with retarded relearning. Higher level func tions, such as the conditional reaction, delayed reaction, or solution c the multiple stick problem, show deterioration after extensive damage i any part of the cortex. The capacity for delayed reaction in monkey for example (to remember in which of two boxes food was placed), ma be seriously reduced or abolished by removal either of the prefrontal lobe or of the occipital associative cortex or of the temporal lobes. That i small lesions, embracing no more than a single associative area, do nc produce loss of any habit; large lesions produce a deterioration whic affects a variety of habits, irrespective of the sensory-motor element involved.

Results such as these have led me to formulate a theory of mass actio or mass facilitation. It is, essentially, that performance of any functio depends upon two variables in nervous activity. The reaction mechanism whether of instinctive or of learned activity, is a definite pattern of inte grated neurons with a variable threshold of excitability. The availabilit of such patterns, the ease with which they can be activated, is depender upon less specific facilitative effects. This facilitation can come from variety of sources. Some instinctive behaviour seems to require hormonε activation, probably a direct chemical effect upon specific nervous ele ments. Emotional facilitation may produce a temporary activation. Cor tinued activity of related mechanisms may facilitate the whole group c associated reactions; a sort of warming-up effect.

There are indications (28), although little systematic evidence, that th severity of postoperative amnesia varies with the intensity of motivatior Rats trained in a discrimination without punishment with electric shoc for errors may show loss of the habit after lesions which do not produc loss in animals which were trained with punishment. The greater effect of cortical lesions in monkeys than in rats may be in part a result o the greater difficulty in getting consistent motivation in the higher animals In man an amnesia often seems to be a difficulty rather than impossibilit of recall; recall may be possible but only with extreme effort and fatigue I believe that the evidence strongly favours the view that amnesia fron brain injury rarely, if ever, is due to the destruction of specific memor traces. Rather, the amnesias represent a lowered level of vigilance, a greate difficulty in activating the organized patterns of traces, or a disturbance of some broader system of organized functions.

In interpreting apparent loss of memory after cerebral damage, extrem caution is necessary. The poor performance in tasks may be due to th destruction of specific associative connexions, but is instead generally, believe always, the result rather of interference with a higher level func tional patterning. Some experiments of Dr. Klüver's (personal communica tion) illustrate this point. Monkeys were trained in a variety of discrimina tive reactions calling for use of different sense modalities by a method that required them to pull in the stimulus objects by attached strings

Extensive lesions in different cortical areas all caused loss of these habits. The monkeys simply pulled the strings at random. They were retrained in the discrimination of weights. When this was learned, the habits based on other sense modalities (reactions to intensities of light, for example) returned spontaneously. What had been disturbed by all the operations was the set or attitude to compare stimuli, not the specific memory of which one was correct.

This example perhaps illustrates at a primitive level the characteristic of amnesias as seen clinically. Apparent loss of memory is secondary to a disorder in the structuring of concepts. Some physiological mode of organizing or integrating activity is affected rather than specific associative bonds.

THE COMPLEXITY OF THE MEMORY TRACE

The experiments that I have reviewed deal with only a small part of the whole problem of the memory trace; with those aspects which can most readily be studied in experiments with animals. Immediate memory presents a different type of problem. It is highly probable that immediate memory is maintained by some sort of after-discharge of the originally excited neurons. Such persistent activity can scarcely be the basis of more permanent memory, although Ebbecke (10) and Edgell (11) have formulated theories of memory in terms of persistent states of excitation. It is by no means certain that all memory is mediated by a single type of mechanism; that motor skills and eidetic images, for example, have any physiological properties in common. The attempt to account for all memory by any single theory involves assumptions which are not supported by any evidence now available.

Much of learning theory has been based upon supposedly isolated and simple instances of association, on the assumption that these represent a primitive prototype of all memory. However, an analysis of even the conditioned reflex indicates that it is not the simple, direct association of stimulus and response that it has been thought to be. I served as experimenter and subject for several years in experiments employing both the salivary method of Pavlov and the motor reactions of Bechterew. The experience convinced me that, far from being a simple sensory-motor reaction, the conditioned reflex is very complicated (29). The S-R diagram is misleadingly schematic. The effective stimulus is not only the object which the experimenter designates as S, but a whole background of other objects constituting the situation in which the experiment is conducted. Every stimulus has a space setting. When, for example, the rat is trained to react to a triangle, he fails to respond if the figure is rotated through more than 10 to 15 degrees (12). This means that the memory trace of the figure is tied in with the space coordinates of the animal's postural system. This system of space coordinates is a part of the postural reflex system which pervades every aspect of behaviour. There is scarcely a memory which does not have spatial orientation, either with reference to the planes of the body or to external space in addition.

Most skilled acts, from running a maze to playing a musical phrase or speaking a sentence, involve a timed series of actions which cannot be accounted for as a simple chain of conditioned reflexes (46). The serial timing of actions is among the most important and least studied of behavioural problems. Almost all memories except those of automatized motor habits are dated, as Bergson (3) has emphasized; that is, they have a temporal position in the series of memories which constitutes the individual's past. The memory trace is associated with this series as well as with the particular objects which make up its central core.

The conditioned reflex also includes an element of affective reinforcement. Corresponding to the nature of the conditioning stimulus, there is fear of electric shock, objectively demonstrable by cardiac and respiratory changes, anticipation of acid in the mouth with slight nausea, or expectation of food (29). Unless this affective element is aroused, the conditioned reflex does not occur. So-called extinction of the conditioned reflex is not a weakening of the specific association, but a waning of this affective reinforcement. Other types of association also have dynamic aspects. The amnesic aphasias seem to be due less to a weakening of specific associations than to a reduction in some general form of facilitation. Henry Head has expressed this as a reduction of "vigilance," without attempting to define further the nature of the function which is disturbed.

A variety of evidence (50) shows that, in a memorized series of nonsense syllables, associations are formed, not only between adjacent words but also between words remote from each other in the series. This, I believe, is an illustration at a primitive level of the fact that every memory becomes part of a more or less extensive organization. When I read a scientific paper, the new facts presented become associated with the field of knowledge of which it is a part. Later availability of the specific items of the paper depends upon a partial activation of the whole body of associations. If one has not thought of a topic for some time, it is difficult to recall details. With review or discussion of the subject, however, names, dates, references which seemed to be forgotten rapidly become available to memory. Head (20) has given instances of such recall by multiple reinforcement in his studies of aphasia. Although there are no systematic experiments upon this "warming-up" effect, it is a matter of common experience and is evidence, I believe, that recall involves the subthreshold activation of a whole system of associations which exert some sort of mutual facilitation.

All this is by way of indicating the probable complexity of the memory trace of even the simplest associations. The engram of a new association, far from consisting of a single bond or neuron connexion, is probably a reorganization of a vast system of associations involving the interrelations of hundreds of thousands or millions of neurons.

SOME QUANTITATIVE CONSIDERATIONS

It has been customary to assume that, since the nervous system contains so many millions of neurons, there must be a large reservoir of cells or of synaptic connexions which can be modified and reserved for specific memory functions. Dunlap (9) has expressed the view that every individual has far more brain cells than he is ever called upon to use, and has urged this as an argument against any congenital restriction of ability. A similar view has been implied in the identification of intelligence as the individual's number of unpreempted and available memory bonds. However, only the vaguest sort of anatomic data have been available to support such theories. Analysis of actual cell numbers involved in a reaction system gives little indication of a reserve of unused connexions and raises a very difficult question as to the way in which the same system can mediate different functions.

I have counted or estimated the number of cells at different levels in the visual system of the rat. The numbers, which I believe are correct within approximately 10 per cent, are given in Table 1. You will note that there is a marked concentration of paths from the retinal myoids to the lateral geniculate nucleus, such that an average of nearly 300 myoids feed into each thalamo-cortical path. At the cortical level there is some dispersion, but it is not great. In the receptive layer (lamina iv) there are fewer than four neurons for each afferent fibre, and in the whole visual cortex there are only nineteen neurons for each afferent fibre.

The rat's maximal visual acuity is about 30 min. of arc, as determined

Table 1. The Number of Neurons at Each Level in the Visual System of the Rat (Unilateral)

Level	Total no. of neurons	Ratio to fibres in radiation
Retinal cells:		
Rods	9,180,000	273.0
Cones	120,000	
Bipolar	3,530,000	104.0
Ganglion	260,000	13.1
Lateral geniculate	34,000	1.0
Cortical cells:		
Lamina vii	68,800	2.0
Lamina vi	135,400	4.0
Lamina v	147,700	4.3
Lamina iv (granular)	127,000	3.7
Laminae ii–iii	176,000	5.2
Total cortical	654,900	19.2

by behavioural tests and from the resolving power of the lens system. Because of the extreme curvature of the cornea and lens the visual field of one eye subtends about 210 degrees. If acuity were uniform throughout the retina, it would require more than 80,000 fibres to represent each acuity unit of the retina by one central fibre. The concentration of ganglion cells falls off from 130 per hundredth square millimetre at the fixation point to 65 at the ora serrata (35). Assuming that acuity decreases proportionately, some 40,000 separate paths are required to represent each acuity unit at the cortex by a single afferent fibre. This corresponds fairly well to the 34,000 geniculo-striate paths actually counted. Since acute vision is continuous under light stimulation, it follows that all of the geniculo-striate cells must be firing constantly when the eye is stimulated by the usual lighted environment. Further, since there are not more than nineteen neurons in the visual area for each afferent fibre, it is almost certain that every cell in the striate cortex is firing during light stimulation. Certainly there is no large reserve of cells which can be set aside for excitation only in specific habits.

Corresponding counts of cells in the visual system of the monkey have recently been made by Chow and Blum (personal communication). The number of neurons in the lateral geniculate nucleus and visual cortex is enormously greater than in the rat, about 1 and 140 millions respectively, but the ratio of cortical cells to central pathways is only 140 to 1, so again there is no great reserve of cells for mnemonic purposes.

The rat is capable of retaining scores, probably hundreds, of visual habits involving discrimination of complex figures (38), and retention may sometimes be demonstrated a year after training. As I reported earlier, there is good evidence that visual habits are dependent upon the striate cortex and upon no other part of the cerebral cortex. The efferent path from the striate cortex is not known. It is not via cortico-tectile fibres. If by cortico-thalamic fibres, there are far fewer neurons within the thalamic nuclei than in corresponding cortical areas, and there is certainly no reserve of cells there for the storing of memories. There seems to be no justification for assuming that the specific shunting of nervous impulses constituting various memories occurs at some level beyond the visual cortex or that memory traces are stored elsewhere than in the cortex.

If the data on the restriction of visual memory to the striate cortex are correct, and they are supported by a variety of experiments, the conclusion seems inevitable that the same cells which bear the memory traces are also excited and play a part in every other visual reaction of the animal. In all probability, the same sort of quantitative relations holds for the other sense modalities.

Even if the associative areas are functional in memory, they do not provide the supposed excess of cells. The visual cortex is directly connected only to a band of cortex directly adjacent, the visuopsychic area of Campbell. The boundaries of this are indeterminate, but it certainly contains no more cells than does the striate area, probably fewer. There is no geometrical multiplication of cells and pathways. Many millions of cells of the striate cortex must be firing constantly into the adjacent area, so that its cells also must be constantly bombarded with nervous impulses and constantly firing. The conclusion is justified, I believe, by such considerations and is supported by electrical studies, that all of the cells of the brain are constantly active and are participating, by a sort of algebraic summation, in every activity. There are no special cells reserved for special memories.

Lorente (49) has shown that each neuron may bear a hundred or more end-feet or separate synapses. However, considering the enormous complexity of the nervous activity involved in performance of even the simplest habit, it is doubtful that even the multiplication of cell number by a hundredfold will provide separate connexions that function only for single specific memories.

The alternative to the theory of preservation of memories by some local synaptic change is the postulate that the neurons are somehow sensitized to react to patterns or combinations of excitation. It is only by such permutations that the limited number of neurons can produce the variety of functions that they carry out. Local changes in the cell membrane, such that combined excitation by several synapses excite the cell, would provide a possible mechanism for such response to patterns, but speculation about this mechanism without direct evidence is likely to be as futile as speculation concerning changes in resistance in the synapse has been.

SUMMARY

This series of experiments has yielded a good bit of information about what and where the memory trace is not. It has discovered nothing directly of the real nature of the engram. I sometimes feel, in reviewing the evidence on the localization of the memory trace, that the necessary conclusion is that learning just is not possible. It is difficult to conceive of a mechanism which can satisfy the conditions set for it. Nevertheless, in spite of such evidence against it, learning does sometimes occur. Although the negative data do not provide a clear picture of the nature of the engram, they do establish limits within which concepts of its nature must be confined, and thus indirectly define somewhat more clearly the nature of the nervous mechanisms which must be responsible for learning and retention. Some general conclusions are, I believe, justified by the evidence.

1. It seems certain that the theory of well-defined conditioned reflex paths from sense organ via association areas to the motor cortex is false. The motor areas are not necessary for the retention of sensory-motor habits or even of skilled manipulative patterns.

2. It is not possible to demonstrate the isolated localization of a memory trace anywhere within the nervous system. Limited regions may be essential for learning or retention of a particular activity, but within such regions

the parts are functionally equivalent. The engram is represented throughout the region.

3. The so-called associative areas are not storehouses for specific memories. They seem to be concerned with modes of organization and with general facilitation or maintenance of the level of vigilance. The defects which occur after their destruction are not amnesias but difficulties in the performance of tasks which involve abstraction and generalization, or conflict of purposes. It is not possible as yet to describe these defects in the present psychological terminology. Goldstein (19) has expressed them in part as a shift from the abstract to the concrete attitude, but this characterization is too vague and general to give a picture of the functional disturbance. For our present purpose the important point is that the defects are not fundamentally those of memory.

4. The trace of any activity is not an isolated connexion between sensory and motor elements. It is tied in with the whole complex of spatial and temporal axes of nervous activity which forms a constant substratum of behaviour. Each association is oriented with respect to space and time. Only by long practice under varying conditions does it become generalized or dissociated from these specific coordinates. The space and time coordinates in orientation can, I believe, only be maintained by some sort of polarization of activity and by rhythmic discharges which pervade the entire brain, influencing the organization of activity everywhere. The position and direction of motion in the visual field, for example, continuously modify the spinal postural adjustments, but, a fact which is more frequently overlooked, the postural adjustments also determine the orientation of the visual field, so that upright objects continue to appear upright, in spite of changes in the inclination of the head. This substratum of postural and tonic activity is constantly present and is integrated with the memory trace (46).

I have mentioned briefly evidence that new associations are tied in spontaneously with a great mass of related associations. This conception is fundamental to the problems of attention and interest. There are no neurological data bearing directly upon these problems, but a good guess is that the phenomena which we designate as attention and interest are the result of partial, subthreshold activation of systems of related associations which have a mutual facilitative action. It seems impossible to account for many of the characters of organic amnesias except in such general terms as reduced vigilance or reduced facilitation.

5. The equivalence of different regions of the cortex for retention of memories points to multiple representation. Somehow, equivalent traces are established throughout the functional area. Analysis of the sensory and motor aspects of habits shows that they are reducible only to relations among components which have no constant position with respect to structural elements. This means, I believe, that within a functional area the cells throughout the area acquire the capacity to react in certain definite patterns, which may have any distribution within the area. I have elsewhere

proposed a possible mechanism to account for this multiple representation. Briefly, the characteristics of the nervous network are such that, when it is subject to any pattern of excitation, it may develop a pattern of activity, reduplicated throughout an entire functional area by spread of excitations, much as the surface of a liquid develops an interference pattern of spreading waves when it is disturbed at several points (41). This means that, within a functional area, the neurons must be sensitized to react in certain combinations, perhaps in complex patterns of reverberatory circuits, reduplicated throughout the area.

6. Consideration of the numerical relations of sensory and other cells in the brain makes it certain, I believe, that all of the cells of the brain must be in almost constant activity, either firing or actively inhibited. There is no great excess of cells which can be reserved as the seat of special memories. The complexity of the functions involved in reproductive memory implies that every instance of recall requires the activity of literally millions of neurons. The same neurons which retain the memory traces of one experience must also participate in countless other activities.

Recall involves the synergic action or some sort of resonance among a very large number of neurons. The learning process must consist of the attunement of the elements of a complex system in such a way that a particular combination or pattern of cells responds more readily than before the experience. The particular mechanism by which this is brought about remains unknown. From the numerical relations involved, I believe that even the reservation of individual synapses for special associative reactions is impossible. The alternative is, perhaps, that the dendrites and cell body may be locally modified in such a manner that the cell responds differentially, at least in the timing of its firing, according to the pattern of combination of axon feet through which excitation is received.

REFERENCES

1 Akelaitis, A. J. A study of gnosis, praxis and language following section of the corpus callosum and anterior commissure, *J. Neurosurgery*, 1944, **1**, 94–102.

2 Bailey, P., Bonin, G. v., Davis, F. W., Garol, H. W., and McCulloch, W. S. *J. Neuropath. exp. Neurol.*, 1944, **3**, 413–415.

3 Bergson, H. *Matière et mémorie*. Paris: 1896.

4 Bonin, G. v., Garol, H. W., and McCulloch, W. S. The functional organization of the occipital lobe, *Biol. Symp.*, 1942, **7**, 165–192.

5 Bucy, P. C. The relation of the premotor cortex to motor activity, *J. nerv. ment. Dis.*, 1934, **79**, 621–630.

6 Bucy, P. C., and Fulton, T. F. Ipsilateral representation in the motor and premotor cortex of monkeys, *Brain*, 1933, **56**, 318–342.

7 Clark, W. E. L. Observations on the associative fibre system of the visual cortex and the central representation of the retina, *J. Anat., Lond.*, 1941, **75**, 225–236.

8 Dunlap, K. The short-circuiting of conscious responses, *J. Phil. Psychol. sci. Meth.*, 1927, **24**, 253–267.

9 Dunlap, K. Psychological hypotheses concerning the functions of the brain, *Sci. Mon., N.Y.*, 1930, **31**, 97–112.

10 Ebbecke, U. *Die kortikalen psychophysischen Erregungen.* Leipzig: Barth, 1919.

11 Edgell, B. *Theories of memory.* Oxford: Clarendon Press, 1924.

12 Fields, P. E. Studies in concept formation: I. The development of the concept of triangularity by the white rat, *Comp. Psychol. Monogr.*, 1932, 9 (2).

13 Finley, C. B. Equivalent losses in accuracy of response after central and after peripheral sense deprivation, *J. comp. Neurol.*, 1941, 74, 203–237.

14 Fischel, W. *Die höheren Leistungen der Wirbeltiergehirne,* Leipzig: Barth, 1948.

15 Franz, S. I. On the functions of the cerebrum: the frontal lobes, *Arch. Psychol.*, 1907, (2).

16 Franz, S. I. On the functions of the cerebrum: the occipital lobes, *Psychol. Monogr.*, 1911, 13 (4).

17 Gay, J. R., and Gellhorn, E. Cortical projection of proprioception, *Amer. J. Physiol.*, 1948, 155, 437.

18 Girden, E., Mettler, F. A., Finch, G., and Culler, E. Conditioned responses in a decorticate dog to acoustic, thermal, and tactile stimulation, *J. comp. Psychol.*, 1936, 21, 367–385.

19 Goldstein, K. *Human nature in the light of psychopathology.* Cambridge, Mass.: Harvard Univ. Press, 1940.

20 Head, H. *Aphasia and kindred disorders of speech.* New York: Macmillan, 1926. Vol. II.

21 Herrick, C. J. *Brains of rats and men.* Chicago: Univ. Chicago Press, 1926.

22 Hunter, W. S. A consideration of Lashley's theory of the equipotentiality of cerebral action, *J. gen. Psychol.*, 1930, 3, 455–468.

23 Ingebritsen, O. C. Coordinating mechanisms of the spinal cord, *Genet. Psychol. Monogr.*, 1933, 13, 485–553.

24 Jacobsen, C. F. Influence of motor and premotor area lesions upon the retention of skilled movements in monkeys and chimpanzees, *Proc. Ass. Res. nerv. ment. Dis.*, 1932, 13, 225–247.

25 Jacobsen, C. F. Studies of cerebral function in primates, *Comp. Psychol. Monogr.*, 1936, 13 (3).

26 Kellogg, W. N., Deese, J., Pronko, N. H., and Feinberg, M. An attempt to condition the chronic spinal dog, *J. exp. Psychol.*, 1947, 37, 99–117.

27 Kennard, M. A. Alterations in response to visual stimuli following lesions of frontal lobe in monkeys, *Arch. Neurol. Psychiat., Chicago,* 1939, 41, 1153–1165.

28 Krechevsky, I. Brain mechanisms and brightness discrimination, *J. comp. Psychol.*, 1936, 21, 405–445.

29 Lashley, K. S. The human salivary reflex and its use in psychology, *Psychol. Rev.*, 1916, 23, 446–464.

30 Lashley, K. S. Studies of cerebral function in learning: II. The effects of long continued practice upon cerebral localization, *J. comp. Psychol.*, 1921, 1, 453–468.

31 Lashley, K. S. Studies of cerebral function in learning: III. The motor areas, *Brain*, 1921, 44, 256–286.

32 Lashley, K. S. Studies of cerebral function in learning: IV. Vicarious function after destruction of the visual areas, *Amer. J. Physiol.*, 1922, 59, 44–71.

33 Lashley, K. S. Studies of cerebral function in learning: V. The retention of motor habits after destruction of the so-called motor areas in primates, *Arch. Neurol. Psychiat., Chicago,* 1924, 12, 249–276.

34 Lashley, K. S. *Brain mechanisms and intelligence.* Chicago: Univ. Chicago Press, 1929.

35 Lashley, K. S. The mechanism of vision: V. The structure and image-forming power of the rat's eye, *J. comp. Psychol.*, 1932, 13, 173–200.

36 Lashley, K. S. Studies of cerebral function in learning: XI. The behavior of the rat in latch-box situations, *Comp. Psychol. Monogr.*, 1935, 11, 1–42.

37 Lashley, K. S. The mechanism of vision: XIII. Nervous structures concerned in

the acquisition and retention of habits based on reactions to light, *Comp. Psychol. Monogr.*, 1935, **11**, 43–79.

38 Lashley, K. S. The mechanism of vision: XV. Preliminary studies of the rat's capacity for detail vision, *J. genet. Psychol.*, 1938, **18**, 123–193.

39 Lashley, K. S. The mechanism of vision: XVI. The functioning of small remnants of the visual cortex, *J. comp. Neurol.*, 1939, **70**, 45–67.

40 Lashley, K. S. Thalamo-cortical connections of the rat's brain, *J. comp. Neurol.*, 1941, **75**, 67–121.

41 Lashley, K. S. The problem of cerebral organization in vision, *Biol. Symp.*, 1942, **7**, 301–322.

42 Lashley, K. S. The mechanism of vision: XVII. Autonomy of the visual cortex, *J. genet. Psychol.*, 1942, **60**, 197–221.

43 Lashley, K. S. Studies of cerebral function in learning: XII. Loss of the maze habit after occipital lesions in blind rats, *J. comp. Neurol.*, 1943, **79**, 431–462.

44 Lashley, K. S. Studies of cerebral function in learning: XIII. Apparent absence of transcortical association in maze learning, *J. comp. Neurol.*, 1944, **80**, 257–281.

45 Lashley, K. S. The mechanism of vision: XVIII. Effects of destroying the visual "associative areas" of the monkey, *Genet. Psychol. Monogr.*, 1948, **37**, 107–166.

46 Lashley, K. S. The problem of serial order in behavior, In Jeffress, L. A. (Ed.) *Cerebral mechanisms in behavior.* New York: Wiley, 1951. Pp. 112–136.

47 Lashley, K. S., and McCarthy, D. A. The survival of the maze habit after cerebellar injuries, *J. comp. Psychol.*, 1926, **6**, 423–433.

48 Lashley, K. S., and Wiley, L. E. Studies of cerebral function in learning: IX. Mass action in relation to the number of elements in the problem to be learned, *J. comp. Neurol.*, 1933, **57**, 3–55.

49 Lorente de Nó, R. Studies on the structure of the cerebral cortex: II. Continuation of the study of the Ammonic system, *J. Psychol. Neurol., Lpz.*, 1934, **46**, 113–177.

50 McGeoch, J. A. *The psychology of human learning.* New York: Longmans, Green, 1942.

51 Mettler, F. A. Physiologic effects of bilateral simultaneous removal of Brodmann's cytoarchitectural areas in the human, *Fed. Proc. Amer. Soc. exp. Biol.*, 1949, **8**, 109.

52 Nielsen, J. M. *Agnosia, apraxia, aphasia: their value in cerebral localization.* Los Angeles: Waverly Press, 1936.

53 Poltyrew, S. S., and Zeliony, G. P. Grosshirnrinde und Assoziationsfunktion, *Z. Biol.*, 1930, **90**, 157–160.

54 Smith, K. U. Bilateral integrative action of the cerebral cortex in man in verbal association and sensori-motor coordination, *J. exp. Psychol.*, 1947, **37**, 367–376.

55 Sperry, R. W. Cerebral regulation of motor coordination in monkeys following multiple transection of sensorimotor cortex, *J. Neurophysiol.*, 1947, **10**, 275–294.

56 Tsang, Yü-Chüan. The function of the visual areas of the cortex of the rat in the learning and retention of the maze, *Comp. Psychol. Monogr.*, 1934, **10**, 1–56.

57 Walker, A. E. *The primate thalamus.* Chicago: Univ. Chicago Press, 1938.

58 Ward, A. A., Jr., Peden, J. K., and Sugar, O. Cortico-cortical connections in the monkey with special reference to Area 6, *J. Neurophysiol.*, 1946, **9**, 453–461.

CEREBRAL ORGANIZATION AND BEHAVIOR

R. W. Sperry

CALIFORNIA INSTITUTE OF TECHNOLOGY

Source *Reprinted from* **Science,** *June 2, 1961,* **133,** *1749–1757, with permission of the author and the American Association for the Advancement of Science. Copyright 1961.*

The control centers of the brain, including the cortical areas, come in matched pairs, right and left mirror mates, with a complete set to each side. Normally, right and left brain halves are in direct communication through a series of commissures, which are defined as fiber systems that cross the midline to form reciprocal cross-connections between corresponding structures on the right and left sides. The largest of these is the great commissure of the cerebral hemispheres, the corpus callosum, the general proportions of which are indicated in Fig. 1, with reference to the rhesus monkey, its relative size in man being somewhat larger.

The corpus callosum is the most massive by far of any single fiber tract in the brain. It was, therefore, cause for some concern that complete surgical section of the corpus callosum in human patients failed to produce any clear-cut functional impairments detectable even with extensive neurological and psychological testing. The discrepancy between the large size, strategic position, and apparent importance of the corpus callosum on the one hand, and the lack of functional disturbance after its section on the other, posed for many years one of the more intriguing and challenging enigmas of brain function.

During the past seven years or so the old "riddle of the corpus callosum" has been largely resolved, in animal studies in which it has been possible at last to demonstrate definite high-level integrating functions for this structure. More important, perhaps, the results have also opened some promising new approaches to the study of cerebral organization, significantly extending the general scope and analytic possibilities of the brain lesion method and related techniques. The following is a generalized survey of some of these developments.

The animal studies from the beginning have confirmed the earlier clinical observations that complete section of the corpus callosum produces surprisingly little disturbance of ordinary behavior. Callosum-sectioned cats and monkeys are virtually indistinguishable from their normal cagemates under most testing and training conditions. This tends to be the case also with further midline sections added, even to the extent of including all the structures labeled in Fig. 1, plus the cerebellum.

Except for causing partial loss of vision, these midline cuts leave nearly all the sensory inflow, motor outflow, and other brain-stem relations intact, and they leave most of the internal organization of each hemisphere undisturbed. Aside from manifesting an initial tremor and unsteadiness when the cerebellum is bisected, monkeys recovered from such midline surgery show no disabling paralysis, ataxia, or spasticity. There is no forced circling, nor are there other asymmetries. The animals are not overly hyperactive or lethargic. Visceral and other homeostatic functions continue as before. The monkeys remain alert and curious and retain fair-to-good muscular

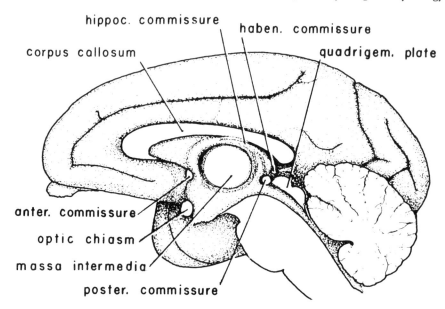

FIGURE 1   *Midline structures divided in surgical bisection of mammalian brain.*

coordination. They perceive, learn, and remember much as normal animals do.

However, if one studies such a "split-brain" monkey more carefully, under special training and testing conditions where the inflow of sensory information to the divided hemispheres can be separately restricted and controlled, one finds that each of the divided hemispheres now has its independent mental sphere or cognitive system—that is, its own independent perceptual, learning, memory, and other mental processes. It is as if each of the separated hemispheres is unaware of what is experienced in the other, as if neither has any direct memory of anything that has gone on in the other subsequent to the midline surgery. In these respects it is as if the animals had two separate brains.

FUNCTIONS OF THE CORPUS CALLOSUM

Although there were indications in the earlier literature on the corpus callosum that this might be the case—indications that now can be picked out, in retrospect—the first convincing demonstration came from the experiments of Ronald Myers on the role of the corpus callosum in interocular transfer in the cat (1, 2). In brief, he found that with both the optic chiasm and the corpus callosum sectioned (see Fig. 2), a cat is unable to perform with one eye visual pattern discriminations learned with the other eye. When obliged to use the second eye such a cat behaved normally except that it appeared to have a complete amnesia for the visual training experienced with the first eye. It learned to respond, with the second eye, to a given stimulus in a manner exactly the reverse of that in which it

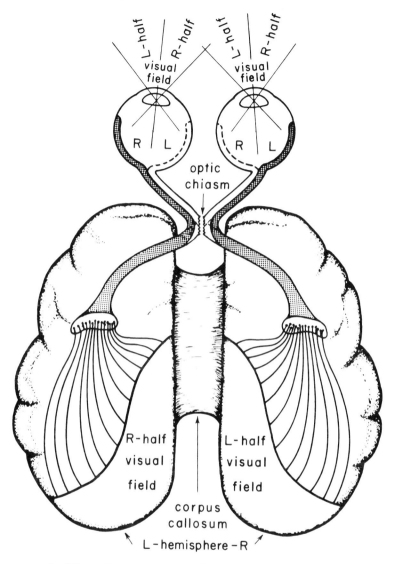

FIGURE 2   *Effect of sectioning crossed fibers in optic chiasm. Half-field*
overlap from contralateral eye is eliminated; this restricts visual inflow to
the homolateral hemisphere.

had been trained to respond with the first eye, and learned the two responses with equal ease.

In controls in which only the chiasm is cut and the callosum is left
intact, discriminations learned with the first eye are readily performed
with the second. If the corpus callosum is not cut until after training
with the first eye is completed, the learning again transfers, and thereafter
the learned discrimination can be performed with either eye (*2*). If, after
training with the corpus callosum intact, the cortex on the directly trained
side is ablated; one still gets transfer of the habit to the second eye (*3*).

In other words, the corpus callosum is shown to be instrumental in laying down a second set of memory traces, or engrams, in the contralateral hemisphere—a mirror-image duplicate or weak carbon copy of the engram on the directly trained side, perhaps, to judge from the symmetry of reciprocal cross-connections in the callosal fiber pattern. These experiments were carried out in apparatus of the type shown in Fig. 3 [Omitted in reprinting. (Ed.)] developed earlier for testing and quantifying refined pattern discrimination in the cat.

Because the memory trace or engram has always been extremely elusive and difficult to pin down or localize by the brain-lesion method, this evidence that it could be confined to one hemisphere by cutting the corpus callosum was not to be accepted without question. Might it merely be, for example, that with chiasm and callosum both sectioned, the hemisphere on the seeing side is more dominant than usual and drains the attention and learning processes off to that side? In partial answer, we find that very large cortical ablations, such as that shown in Fig. 4, that markedly depress

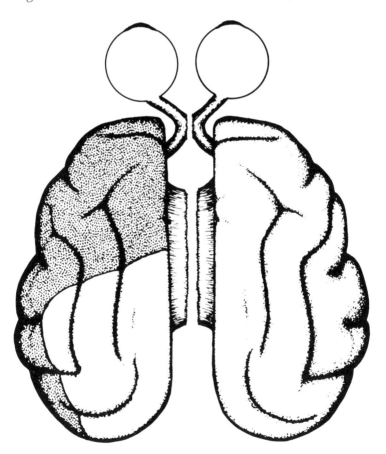

FIGURE 4 *Extent of the extravisual cortex ablated from the seeing hemisphere of a split-brain cat (4).*

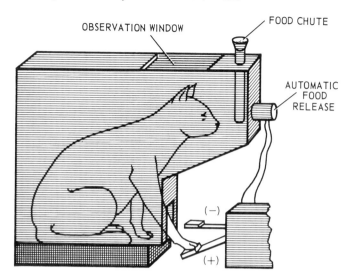

FIGURE 5   *Simplified diagram of the pedal-pressing apparatus for training in tactile discrimination.*

pattern vision on the same side, still do not force into the contralateral hemisphere the learning and memory of pattern discriminations performed through the homolateral eye (4, 5). Also, when we compared the learning curves for the first and second eye on a statistical basis, there was no evidence that learning with the second eye was benefited by the previous experience with the first (6).

In a pedal-pressing apparatus, developed largely by Stamm (see Fig. 5), we were able to demonstrate that the same kind of functional independence prevails in the separated hemispheres with respect to somesthetic learning and memory involving touch and pressure on the surface of the forepaw (7). Not only sensory discriminations of the kind illustrated in Fig. 5 but also the simple motor patterns acquired in learning to operate the pedals smoothly were transferred to the second paw in normal cats but were not transferred in the callosum-sectioned subjects. Again, statistical comparison of the learning curves for the first and second paws indicated complete absence of any transfer of learning from one to the other hemisphere. Learning a reverse response with the second paw proceeded as easily in these subjects as relearning the original response. Further, the learning of reversed or diametrically opposed discriminations by right and left paws was carried out simultaneously by the split-brain cats when right and left limbs were alternated every few trials during the training, and still with no apparent interference between the conflicting habits (8).

The findings with respect to visual learning and memory have been confirmed in the main for the monkey as well, with extension to discrimination of colored and three-dimensional objects (9–11). Because the monkey is much less inclined than the cat to be cooperative about wearing an

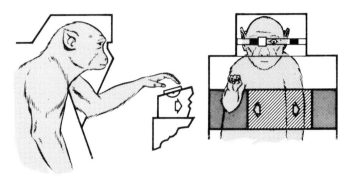

FIGURE 6 *Profile and front-view outline sketches of a training box for controlling eye-use and eye-hand associations in a monkey.*

eye patch, a training box was devised like that sketched roughly in Fig. 6, which has one viewing slot accessible only to the left eye and another accessible only to the right eye, each of which can be opened or closed from trial to trial. A sliding arm panel controls the use of the arms and permits the pairing of either eye with either hand from trial to trial.

This has the advantage over the use of an eye patch for monocular testing and training in that one can easily switch from one eye to the other, giving a few trials to the right eye, then a few to the left, and so on. If this is done while the monkey is learning reversed discriminations with the separate eyes, one can show that while one hemisphere is in the process of learning, for example, to avoid crosses and select circles, the other hemisphere can be learning to do exactly the reverse. The learning curves for the two conflicting habits then rise concurrently in parallel in the two hemispheres with no apparent interference. The normal brain does not of course operate in this way—nor does that of controls with only the optic chiasm cut, nor even that of controls with section of chiasm plus anterior commissure plus the anterior half of the corpus callosum.

Without going further into studies dealing with the properties of the callosum, it may be said that several different functions for this structure are now recognized. First, and perhaps most significant, is that of the laying down of duplicate engrams in the contralateral hemisphere, as out-lined above. In this the callosum serves to keep each hemisphere up to date on what's new in the other; it tends to equate the two hemispheres for those new organizational properties added through learning. It can also be shown that where learning has been deliberately restricted by experimental procedure to one hemisphere, with the corpus callosum left intact, the callosum can then be utilized by the uneducated hemisphere to tap the engram systems of the trained side (3). The callosum also aids in certain types of bilateral sensory-sensory and sensory-motor integra-tion, as for example in visual use of either hand across the vertical midline of the visual field (8, 12, 13). A general excitatory tonic effect can also be demonstrated in the unilateral blindness of one or two weeks' duration produced by section of the callosum in animals with a surgically isolated visual cortex (8). Qualifications of the above properties and special problems relate to the development of language and its lateralized dominance in the human brain, about which little can be said at present. With further analysis it may prove that some of these diverse functions derive from basically the same mechanism.

SIMULTANEOUS LEARNING PROCESSES

After it had been found that the split-brain monkey is able to learn reverse discriminations concurrently with the separated hemispheres (10, 11), the question arose as to whether the two hemispheres could learn their reverse tasks simultaneously. Instead of alternating between right and left eye during the training, what happens if both eyes are left open and each trial feeds conflicting information back through the two eyes at the same time? In other words, does the split-brain animal, in order to learn, have to attend to the information entering one hemisphere at a time? Or does it have two separate attention processes, both able to operate simultaneously, handling the diverse sets of information and filing them in two separate memory systems capable of independent recall?

The question has been answered in part by Trevarthen (13), with an apparatus incorporating polarized light filters to make the two stimulus objects to be discriminated appear simultaneously different to the two eyes. As explained in Fig. 7, what looks to one hemisphere, for example, to be a circle on the left and a cross on the right is made to look the reverse to the other hemisphere. While one hemisphere observes that the pushing of circles but not crosses is rewarded, the other eye and brain discover, by the same process, the converse—that is, that the pushing of crosses is rewarded and not circles. Any kind of projectable two-dimensional figure, design, or picture may be used, with or without color. Learning is allowed to proceed with both eyes open until the learning curve reaches the 90-percent level. The eyes are then tested individually to find out if the learning has occurred in one or in both hemispheres, and to what degree.

Although the results vary, as expected, Trevarthen finds that during the time required for the dominant hemisphere to learn its problem, the other also, in the majority of cases, has been learning its own reverse problem in part or in full. In some instances, both hemispheres fully learn their separate problems simultaneously. In other words, in approximately the length of time and number of trials required by an ordinary-brained monkey to learn one discrimination problem, these altered, twin-brain monkeys are able to master two such problems. This raises some questions with regard to learning theory and the role in learning of attention, motivation, mental and motor set, and the like. Are all such components of the learning mechanism doubled in these brains, or are some perhaps bifurcate in form, with a common brain-stem element and qualitatively different

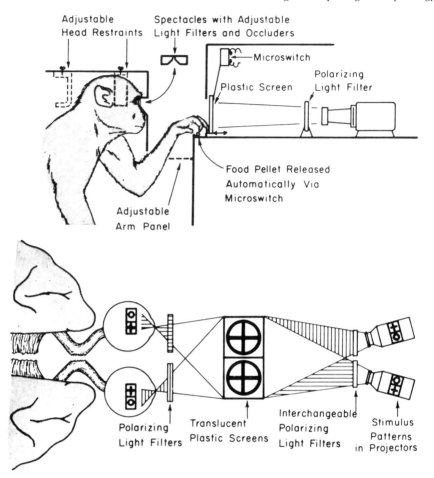

FIGURE 7   *Profile and schematic diagram of apparatus for testing perceptual con-flict in a split-brain monkey (13).*

cerebral prongs? The implications are intriguing and suggest further varia-tions on the initial experiment.

The question of mental conflict is frequently raised in this connection: What happens when one hemisphere has been trained to do one thing and the other trained to do just the opposite, and the animal is given a free choice to perform either or both? With two separate volitional sys-tems inside the same skull, each wanting its own way and each, by training, wanting the opposite of the other, does each of these thinking entities try to decide for itself?

When such a test is run—by rotating one of the eye filters 90° for exam-ple—one sees little evidence of internal conflict, apart from, perhaps, a little hesitance (14). By and large, the monkey starts selecting circles con-sistently or crosses consistently, and it may shift from one to a series of the other, thereby telling us which hemisphere is being used at the moment. These shifts are controllable in part by forcing the use of one or the other hand, which then tends to bring into play the contralateral hemisphere, though this latter correlation is not fixed or rigorous. Apparently when a hemisphere once gains the ascendancy, the lower centers tend to throw their full allegiance to this side. Anything coming down from the other hemisphere that is incompatible or out of line with the going activity of the dominant control is automatically inhibited. This is just another example of the general rule that the patterning of excitation in the central nervous system is an either-or kind of thing. Either one unified pattern or another prevails; seldom is there a confused mixture.

The split-brain cat or monkey is thus in many respects an animal with two separate brains that may be used either together or in alternation. With all pairs of major suprasegmental controls bisected, there is no way for the higher-level integration of one hemisphere to reach and influence that of the other except indirectly through the lower brain stem outflow (Fig. 8). By the time the data processing has reached this stage it already is in such form that any recurrent feedback into the opposite hemisphere carries little of the original content.

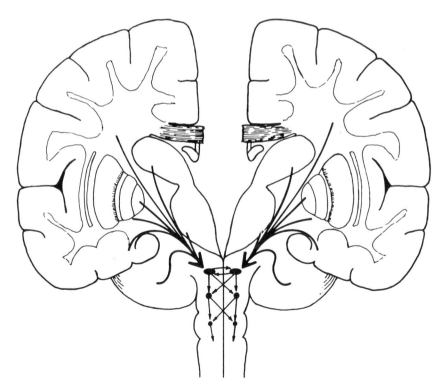

FIGURE 8 *Schematic diagram to aid in visualizing hegemony of the hemispheres of the split brain over lower centers.*

BILATERAL HEGEMONY

Each of the twin half brains with its full complement of control centers has much bilateral hegemony over the brain stem and spinal cord and is thus capable, to a large extent, of taking over and governing the total behavior of the body. The cat especially, but also the monkey and even man, with one hemisphere gone manages to get along fairly well, and most central nervous functions are retained. With both hemispheres present, in the split condition, even though one be strongly dominant or in exclusive control of the going higher-level activities, the other presumably continues to contribute much to generalized, background function. Under most ordinary conditions the higher activities also are bound to have much in common. Only in special training and testing circumstances does the double mental control become apparent. The simultaneous use of the two divided hemispheres presents little problem so long as there is unity in the lower centers. Given lower-level harmony, it doesn't matter, as seen above, whether the higher centers function similarly or in direct contradiction.

There is much yet to be learned in following up studies, like the foregoing, that deal directly with the functional properties of the bisected brain, split to different levels and with various incomplete patterns and combinations of commissurotomy. The split brain may also be used to advantage as a basic preparation for attacking other kinds of questions not directly related to problems of commissure function. With the brain bisected, it becomes possible to direct one's ablations, tests, and other analytic procedures to a single one of the hemispheres, leaving the "spare" hemisphere for the use of the animal. In addition to the obvious benefit to the animal over the usual bilateral invasion, there are a number of significant technical advantages in working on the half brain instead of the whole brain. It is important to remember in this connection that the half brain is, in a sense, pretty much a whole brain in that it contains a complete set of cerebral integrating centers and all their interrelations. That is, practically the entire pattern and most of the problems of cerebral organization are there for the unraveling within the half brain.

ADVANTAGES FOR EXPERIMENTATION

One obvious advantage of the split-brain preparation lies in the factor of built-in controls within the spare hemisphere, controls for all sorts of experiments ranging from short-term studies on innate organization to studies on the long-term effects of early experience on adult behavior. These controls are not only of the homozygous, identical-twin, type but are equated also for almost all experientially derived organization implanted up to the time of splitting. The control hemisphere is fairly well balanced for additions thereafter, also, except for performances that have been deliberately lateralized. These contralateral cerebral controls are thus of a quality almost impossible to obtain by using different animals.

More important is the possibility of extending the surgical analysis within the experimental hemisphere of the split brain far beyond what was possible when the lesions had to be made bilaterally. It has been a long-standing rule in brain-lesion studies of learning and memory that the cortical lesions must be made on both sides to obtain a genuine loss. Unilateral removals are not critical, ordinarily because the functions involved can be handled by the remaining integrating center on the opposite side.

With the split-brain approach it becomes possible to investigate structures like the caudate nucleus, the primary motor cortex, and others, the bilateral ablation of which produces incapacitating or other secondary undesirable effects that act to obscure or confuse possible contributions in other activities. Each brain center tends to be involved in a whole spectrum of different functions. In many cases only the basic impairments can be inferred after bilateral removals, the others being hidden or untestable in the presence of the former.

For the same reasons, with the split-brain approach much larger cortical ablations can be made, even to the extreme of removing most of the cortex and saving only isolated functional remnants—the converse of the usual procedure. We isolated the visual cortex of the cat in this way (see Fig. 9) [Omitted in reprinting. (Ed.)] and found that the primary visual cortex, without aid from other cortical areas, is incapable of sustaining visual functions beyond a bare minimum. A next step is to go back and restore in other animals different portions of the cortex removed in these subjects to determine the respective contributions of each portion to visual learning and memory.

A very different result followed similar surgical isolation of the frontal cortex that includes the somatic sensory and motor areas. In this case the isolated remnant was found to be capable of mediating excellent learning and memory of new somesthetic discrimination habits performed in the pedal-pressing apparatus shown in Fig. 5 (15). The ever-elusive engrams or memory traces for these new habits would seem to have been at least cornered within the local cortical area illustrated in Fig. 10 [Omitted in reprinting. (Ed.)]. It should be possible to further localize the engram by paring away additional parts of the remaining cortical remnant and also by adding deep electrolytic lesions to test the functional contributions of various subcortical centers that remain undegenerated. This somatic island preparation thus furnishes a promising means of determining the critical minimum cerebral apparatus essential for discrimination learning and memory in the mammalian brain. With one hemisphere preserved intact to maintain background and lower-level activity, it becomes feasible, in the experimental hemisphere, to undertake almost complete surgical dissection and analysis as far as function is concerned. About the only limitations that remain are those imposed by surgical technique, particularly that relating to the preservation of circulation.

To further assure, in these studies of somesthetic discrimination habits, that the habits were not being learned and mediated by the contralateral somatic cortex, a complementary removal of the corresponding area was made on the opposite side. The feasibility of thus adding complementary lesion patterns in the intact hemisphere of the split brain offers further possibilities for the analysis of functional relationships—possibilities not available, of course, where the removals have to be made bilaterally.

There are other promising angles in investigations of this "somatic island preparation." For example, it is possible to test the proven pedal-pressing learning capacity of this cortical area with visual or auditory instead of tactile stimuli—in other words, to answer the questions: Could such a cat learn to press a pedal that activates the correct one of two different tone patterns, or the correct one of two different visual patterns? If not, could it then do so if an isolated patch of auditory or visual cortex were left on the same side as the somatic island? If not, again, what kind of inter- and intra-hemispheric bridges and connections are needed to satisfy the learning and memory requirements?

VISUOMOTOR COORDINATION

Figure 11 illustrates a type of complementary lesion preparation we have been using, with a number of variations, to determine the neural pathways used in visuomotor coordination. The experimental question here was: Can visual information that is processed in one hemisphere serve as a guide for limb responses for which the cortical centers lie in the opposite hemisphere and are surgically separated from the visual inflow?

Cats, so prepared, and also monkeys that have undergone similar surgery, are able to use vision to direct the homolateral forelimb and to aim it with near-normal accuracy at both stationary and moving objects (16). Presumably the speed and accuracy might be shown to be somewhat below that in control animals using the other limb, governed from the same hemisphere, if sufficiently delicate tests were available. However, the performance is still there and not markedly impaired. Where the visuomotor guidance depends on unilaterally learned visual discriminations in split-brain cats and monkeys, either forelimb can still be used without difficulty both during learning and in retention tests (11, 17). The neural pathways for these volitional eye-hand coordinations have yet to be determined.

Somewhat in contradiction to the observations that the split-brain monkey or cat readily pairs either eye with either "hand" is a more recent report (12) that visuomotor coordination is markedly disrupted under these conditions, to the extent even that prolonged relearning is required, much like that demanded after unilateral removal of the precentral motor cortex. This observation, though yet unexplained, may be a reflection of particular testing conditions that unduly facilitate the use of the visuomotor system for the contralateral limb.

In any case, the expected preference for the favored arm—that is, for the arm governed from the hemisphere that receives the visual inflow—is found and can be demonstrated in more delicate testing conditions such as those obtainable in the training apparatus described above (Figs. 6 and 7), where the monkey is able to use either arm with either eye. This arm preference is easily overcome, however, in a matter of hours in most cases, and may be lacking from the start in animals in which the homolateral arm is strongly dominant, either naturally or as a result of experience in a given testing situation. Trevarthen (13) describes distinct differences in the learning curves obtained in pairing the homolateral and contralateral arms with a given eye that indicate basic differences in the neural mechanisms for the two combinations. With the homolateral arm, the reaction time tends to be longer, and the learning slower and more erratic and unstable. The effect is enhanced in monkeys with deeper splits that include the cerebellum.

Surgical preparations similar to that illustrated in Fig. 11 have been

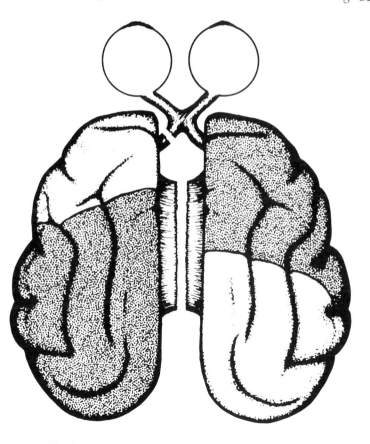

FIGURE 11   Basic complementary lesion pattern used with variations for analyzing conditioned response learning and visuomotor coordination.

used for study of the old and still puzzling problem of the neural pathways involved in the conditioned response. In this case a visual signal is used as the conditioning stimulus to establish a conditioned flexion of the forelimb, the cortical centers for which have been left in the opposite hemisphere. Efforts are now under way to eliminate successively the remaining undegenerated thalamic, midbrain, and other subcortical centers until the critical associations and pathways for the conditioned reflex are delineated (*18*). At the present stage of this program the conditioned forelimb flexion in response to a flashing light signal has been found to survive the following: section of left optic tract; ablation of left occipital (visual) cortex; near-total removal of neocortex from the right hemisphere; midline section of corpus callosum plus the anterior, posterior, hippocampal, and habenular commissures; and midline section of the massa intermedia and the quadrigeminal plate—produced stepwise in the same animal.

Another application of the split-brain approach is indicated in Fig. 12. The behavior under analysis in this case is a kind of sensory-sensory association in which the monkey is trained to perform a discrimination problem that requires in each trial an association of visual plus tactile stimuli. By controlling the hand and the eye used, and thereby the cortical receptor centers involved, it is possible to test intra- and interhemispheric integration with and without different parts of the corpus callosum and then with various types of separating cuts and ablations, to analyze the kind of neural mechanism and associations that mediate this type of perceptual integration.

It was something of a surprise to find that the split-brain monkey was still able to perform the visuotactile integration with the tactile stimuli presumably restricted to the hemisphere opposite that of the visual inflow. In addition to making the animal use the proper hand, the somesthetic cortex was ablated on the side of the visual inflow. We first used color-plus-weight (largely proprioceptive) discriminations (*10, 11*) and are now repeating the study with black-and-white patterns and cutaneous rough-smooth stimuli. In the latter study the monkey is required to pull the rougher of two levers when they are presented behind one visual pattern, and the smoother of the two when they are similarly presented in back of another visual pattern, the two visual patterns being black and white and equated for brightness. This latter performance ability is retained even after additional midline sections have been made (see Fig. 12) that include the habenular and posterior commissures, the massa intermedia, and the quadrigeminal plate, in addition to the corpus callosum and the anterior and hippocampal commissures. The removal of the arm area of the tactile cortex on the side of the visual input (Fig. 12) abolishes performance with the affected hand for several weeks but fails to disrupt performance with the hand governed from the opposite hemisphere. This puzzling result is under further investigation, along with similar cross-integration effects that have appeared recently in studies of visuo-visual conditional discriminations. The surgical analysis promises to be easier in the latter because

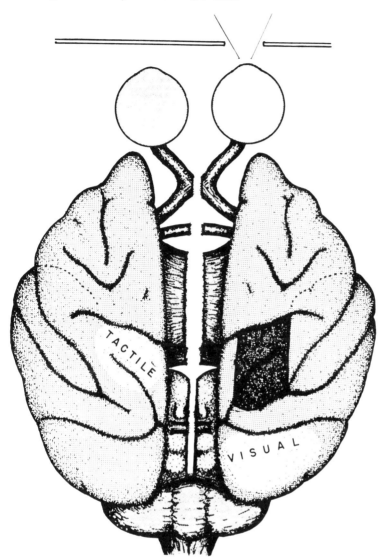

FIGURE 12   *Stylized representation of monkey-brain hemispheres and under-lying midline structures, split through the quadrigeminal plate to the level of the trochlear nerve (11), as prepared for a study of visuotactile integration.*

the input pathways for vision are less diffuse and more easily confined than are those for touch.

APPLICATION TO OLD PROBLEMS

A simple application of the split-brain approach to an old problem is illustrated in Fig. 13. It has been known for many years that bilateral

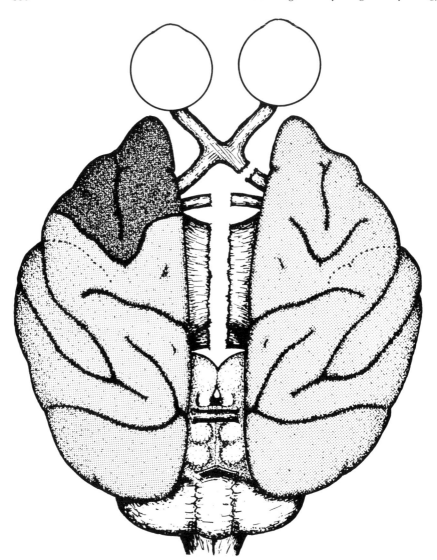

FIGURE 13   *A split brain, as prepared for a study of prefrontal lobe syndrome* (18).

but not unilateral removal of the prefrontal lobes impairs the performance of delayed response in the rhesus monkey. Whether this impairment is indicative of a genuine function of this portion of the brain has been uncertain, in part because the bilateral removals tend to produce also hypermotility and distractibility. It has been found that the impairment, unaccompanied by hyperactivity and distractibility is produced by unilateral lesion in the split-brain animal (5, 19). The unilateral approach thus yields new information regarding the nature of the syndrome and its intrahemispheric involvement; also it permits further analysis through partial removals of the corpus callosum in combination with complementary lesion patterns—procedures not feasible with bilateral ablation.

The split-brain approach has been applied also to the classic Klüver-Bucy temporal lobe syndrome and some of its subsequent fractionations (20). Bilateral ablation of the temporal lobes in monkeys produces impairments in visual perception, a change in temperament in the direction of tameness, hypersexuality, and certain oral and "stimulus bound" tendencies. Observations to date show that most features of the syndrome are demonstrable after unilateral ablation in split preparations (21–23), and the results bring additional insight regarding the underlying neural mechanism. Similarly, a great many of the older brain-lesion studies can be repeated to advantage in the bisected brain, with a gain in information and the possibility of advancing the analysis.

TRANSFER ACROSS THE MIDPLANE

With the growing application of brain bisection to a wide variety of problems, it becomes increasingly important to have background information about the functional properties of the split brain in all its various forms—that is, with the midline sections carried to different levels and with different patterns of commissurotomy and ablation. Particularly critical are questions relating to the leakage or transfer of various functions across the midplane. In this connection, observations bearing on the intermanual transfer of learning (10, 24) have not been entirely consistent in primates. In our own experience, section of the cerebral commissures may lead to failure of intermanual transfer, but this is not true in all cases nor under all conditions. We have seen intermanual transfer of tactile discriminations in chiasm-callosum-sectioned monkeys that were already experienced in using either hand with either eye and had been trained with pairs of objects that were left in sight because they were distinguishable only by touch, not by vision, the one being harder or heavier or looser than its mate, and this being discernible only upon palpation. Also, we find that an ablation of the somato-sensory arm cortex roughly like that shown in Fig. 12 will induce transfer in split-brain monkeys that had failed to exhibit transfer prior to the cortical ablation (25). The interpretation of this latter finding is complicated at present by the fact that when the monkeys are trained to reverse the discrimination response with the second hand, this reversal training consistently fails to transfer back again to the first hand.

Certain types of visual discrimination learning also have been found to be subject to interocular transfer after section of all forebrain commissures plus the optic chiasm. This has been shown for obvious brightness discriminations in cats, whereas the more difficult near-threshold discriminations fail to transfer (26). Interocular transfer of easy color and brightness discriminations and possibility of very simple pattern discriminations occurs similarly in the monkey, according to Trevarthen (14). All of these transferable aspects of visual learning may be elements of visual inflow or learning that cross at the midbrain level. Extension of the tests for color, brightness, and simple pattern to several monkeys having deeper midline sections that include the posterior commissure and rostral half of the quadrigeminal plate (see Fig. 1), plus the cerebellum in one case, show so far a lack of memory transfer for all except simple intensity discriminations.

Evidence is still sketchy regarding the extent to which the divided hemispheres can function independently with respect to emotion. Incidental observations made in the course of training and testing suggest that milder aspects of emotional attitude and temperament, like stubbornness and sulkiness, can be confined to one side (10, 11). By employing deliberate procedures for inducing experimental neurosis, it might thus be possible to make one of the separated hemispheres "neurotic" and leave the other normal. The "taming effect" of unilateral deep temporal lobe ablation is much enhanced and lateralized in the split-brain monkey, according to Downer (21) and others (23). Such animals act normally fearful, or ferocious when using the eye connected to the intact hemisphere, but promptly become more tame, placid, and generally less "touchy" when the lesion hemisphere is made dominant by switching the visual occluder to the other eye. The placement of complementary lesions in right and left hemispheres that produce opposed emotional effects has yet to be explored.

EXPERIMENTAL POSSIBILITIES

By the use of positive and negative reinforcement through implanted electrodes under remote control, the development of different or opposed preferences in right and left brain could presumably be extended to animate objects and social relationships, with some interesting consequences. The so-called *encephale isolée* and *cerveau isolé* preparations of Bremer and others (27) have found considerable use in physiology, and it should not be too difficult to go further and, by adding hemisections of the brain stem to the midline surgery, prepare isolated half brains of different forms and with different kinds and degrees of isolation that would offer significant advantages over the separated whole brain. The isolated half brain could be studied over a long period in the animal in vivo, in the brain's natural habitat, under normal biochemical conditions, and after recovery from the prolonged depression of surgical cerebral shock. To what extent might such long-isolated (or partially isolated) half brains regain wake-sleep states and consciousness and be capable of learning, remembering, feeling emotion, and the like? Where behavioral output is excluded, electrophysiological indications of some of these capabilities could be obtained with implanted electrodes and conditioning techniques.

By combining various ablations and transections like those described above with more localized lesions produced in subcortical nuclei with the stereotaxic apparatus, it is possible today, with methods now available, to attain a fairly extensive surgical dissection of the mammalian brain and to set up a large variety of combinations and permutations of cerebral centers and connecting pathways in animal subjects for long-term functional testing and analysis. Combine with this the analytic potentialities of the chronically implanted electrode for recording, stimulating, and self-stimulating in free-moving, unanesthetized animals, plus the new automated training and programming techniques, along with other technological advances, and those of us working in brain research find ourselves today, as never before, surrounded by seemingly endless possibilities just waiting to be explored (28).

REFERENCES AND NOTES

1 R. E. Myers, *J. Comp. and Physiol. Psychol.* **48**, 470 (1955); ———, *Brain* **79**, 358 (1956); ——— and R. W. Sperry, *Anat. Record* **115**, 351 (1953).

2 R. E. Myers, "CIOMS Conference on Brain Mechanisms and Learning," in press.

3 ——— and R. W. Sperry, *A.M.A. Arch. Neurol. Psychiat.* **80**, 298 (1958).

4 R. W. Sperry, R. E. Myers, A. M. Schrier, *Quart. J. Exptl. Psychiat.* **12**, 65 (1960).

5 R. W. Sperry, in *Biological and Biochemical Bases of Behavior*, H. R. Harlow and C. N. Woolsey, Eds. (Univ. of Wisconsin Press, Madison, 1958).

6 R. W. Sperry, J. S. Stamm, N. Miner, *J. Comp. and Physiol. Psychol.* **49**, 529 (1956).

7 J. S. Stamm and R. W. Sperry, *ibid.* **50**, 138 (1957).

8 R. W. Sperry, unpublished.

9 J. L. C. Downer, *Federation Proc.* **17**, 37 (1958).

10 R. W. Sperry, *Anat. Record* **131**, 297 (1958).

11 ———, *Transactions of the Macy Conference on Central Nervous System and Behavior* (1958).

12 J. L. C. Downer, *Brain* **82**, 251 (1959).

13 C. B. Trevarthen, *Am. Psychologist* **15**, 485 (1960).

14 ———, unpublished.

15 R. W. Sperry, *J. Neurophysiol.* **22**, 78 (1959).

16 R. E. Myers, R. W. Sperry, N. Miner, *J. Comp. and Physiol. Psychol.* **48**, 50 (1955).

17 A. M. Schrier and R. W. Sperry, *Science* **129**, 1275 (1959).

18 T. Voneida, unpublished.

19 M. Glickstein, H. Arora, R. W. Sperry, *Physiologist* **3**, 66 (1960).

20 H. Klüver, in *Ciba Foundation Symposium on the Neurological Basis of Behavior* (1958), p. 175.

21 J. L. C. Downer, unpublished.

22 G. Ettlinger, *Brain* **82**, 232 (1959); M. Mishkin, *Am. Psychologist* **13**, 414 (1958).

23 J. Steiner and J. S. Bossom, unpublished.

24 F. Ebner and R. E. Myers, *Federation Proc.* **19**, 292 (1960); M. Glickstein and R. W. Sperry, *Am. Psychologist* **14**, 385 (1959); R. E. Myers, *Federation Proc.* **19**, 289 (1960); M. Glickstein and R. W. Sperry, *J. Comp. and Physiol. Psychol.* **53**, 322 (1960).

25 M. Glickstein and R. W. Sperry, *Am. Psychologist* **15**, 485 (1960).

26 T. Meikle, Jr., and J. A. Sechzer, *Science* **132**, 734 (1960); T. Meikle, Jr., *ibid.* **132**, 1496 (1960).

27 F. Bremer, J. Brihaye, G. André-Balisaux, *Arch. suisses neurol. et psychiat.* **78**, 31 (1956).
28 This article is based on a talk given at the Federation Meetings in Chicago for the C. J. Herrick symposium on the physiology of learning, 19 April 1960. A more specialized version is being published in *Federation Proceedings*. Original work discussed has been supported by the National Science Foundation, the National Institutes of Health, and the F. P. Hixon Fund of the California Institute of Technology. Special acknowledgement is made to Harbans Arora, who has performed nearly all our monkey-brain surgery during the past 18 months, and to Lois MacBird who has carried the major responsibility for training, medication, and general laboratory assistance.

LOCALIZATION OF A MEMORY TRACE IN ONE CORTICAL HEMISPHERE AND TRANSFER TO THE OTHER HEMISPHERE

I. Steele Russell and S. Ochs

INDIANA UNIVERSITY SCHOOL OF MEDICINE

Source *Reprinted from* **Brain**, *1963,* **86**, *37–54, with permission of the authors and Macmillan & Co., Ltd.*

The localization of an engram to one cortical hemisphere has recently become possible. With an engram localized in one hemisphere the functional importance of the connecting tracts, in particular the corpus callosum, in transferring the engram to the other side could then be studied. Earlier reports that complete sections of the corpus callosum could be produced in man without any definite functional impairment (Akalaitis, 1943; Bridgman and Smith, 1945; and Smith, 1951) led to questions of the functional significance, if any, of the corpus callosum. The work of Myers (1956), Sperry *et al.* (1956) and Downer (1959) on interocular transfer in split-brain animals has revealed that when visual or tactile stimulation is restricted to one hemisphere during the training of a visual or tactile discrimination, then such learning is localized to that hemisphere alone. If the presence of the learned discrimination is tested for with sensory inputs restricted to the other hemisphere then the animals have to completely relearn the discrimination, indicating the presence of the engram in the "trained" hemisphere. If, however, the callosum is left intact the visual discrimination is bilaterally represented (Myers, 1958) indicating the role of the callosum in the transfer of the engram between the two hemispheres.

The split-brain preparation has proved to be an important technique in demonstrating the existence of such engrams, and the work of Sperry (1961) indicates how this method can be used to dissect the structural relationships involved. Surgical isolation, while a valuable technique, does however, have limitations with regard to analysing the conditions under which interhemispheric transfer of an engram occurs. For this purpose a method is required that permits a study of the influence of an established trace in one hemisphere upon the formation of an engram in the other hemisphere when the interhemispheric connexions are intact.

Bures (1959) has demonstrated the feasibility of using spreading depression (SD) as a technique of functional ablation, whereby definite regions of the brain (one cortical hemisphere) can be temporarily excluded from a conditioning procedure without any irreversible surgical lesions. Bures *et al.* (1958) showed that bilateral SD abolished the performance of conditioned behavior for a time period roughly coincident to the duration of the depression of the electro-physiological activity of the cortex. A period of approximately three to four hours of cortical depression took place with application of 25 per cent KCl to one hemisphere. While bilateral SD is continuously present in unrestrained and unanaesthetized rats, their normal posture or mobility is not affected (Buresova, 1956).

Spreading depression first investigated by Leão (1944) is a reversible

[1] This work was supported by PHS grants B1993-C2 and M4815 from the U.S. Public Health Service.

temporary process, readily initiated by direct mechanical, chemical or electrical stimulation of the cortex. It is a propagated depression of cortical activity (EEG, DCR, etc.) that spreads in all directions throughout the cortex. A review of this phenomenon was given by Marshall (1959) and a more recent one is in press (Ochs). Buresova *et al.* (1958) have demonstrated that topical application of KCl to one hemisphere will result in the elaboration of SD in that hemisphere alone. With high concentrations of KCl (25 per cent) a series of SD waves is evoked, such that the electrical responses of the cortex can be depressed for hours (Bures, 1959). A chronic technique was developed (Russell and Ochs, 1960), permitting daily initiation of SD by means of KCl in the unanaesthetized animal over a period of many days. This technique made possible a study of the retention of a memory trace localized to one hemisphere over a period of two weeks and the conditions under which the trace would transfer to the untrained hemisphere (Russell and Ochs, 1961).

MATERIALS AND METHODS

The 35 male rats used were between 90 and 120 days old and weighed approximately 300 grammes at the start of the experiment. They were anaesthetized with pentobarbital and trephine openings 2.5 mm. in diameter were made in the skull of each hemisphere. Care was taken to leave the dura intact to minimize damage of brain tissue. Small plastic cups with a 2 mm. diameter hole at the base fitted into the trephine holes and were cemented into place with acrylic resin which bound them to 6 jeweller's screws inserted in the skull (fig. 1, Plate I). [Fig. 1 and Plate I omitted in reprinting. (Ed.)] A close fitting plunger for the cup was used to minimize dehydration of the dura throughout the duration of the experiment. The skin was sutured around the cups and procaine penicillin administered i.m. after surgery.

The rats were trained in a single conditioning chamber and enclosed in a sound shielded and air ventilated ice chest. The dimensions of the inside chamber were 20 cm. in length, by 13 cm. wide and 17 cm. deep. The animals were trained to press a bar that was situated 3 cm. above floor level, in the centre of one of the end walls of the chamber. This lever consisted of a 7 mm. aluminum bar 3 cm. in length, mounted on a Switchcraft switch and designed to operate by means of a break circuit (Verhave, 1958). The food pan was situated at floor level to the left of the bar. A Davis pellet feeder was used to dispense 45 mg. food pellets as reinforcement. A small light was mounted 2 cm. above the bar and arranged such that it would flash briefly whenever the feeder was operated.

The general programming equipment consisted of automatic tape timers and standard relay circuitry that determined the reinforcement contingencies and the duration of experimental sessions. A Gerbrands' cumulative recorder was used in some cases to monitor the animals' responding during the conditioning, and in all cases Sodeco counters were employed to record the response totals.

All animals were exposed to a food deprivation schedule and gentling procedure for two to four days after implantation. All animals were deprived of food for twenty-two hours and allowed food *ad lib.* for one hour after training. On the day following the operation the operant level of the animals' bar-pressing was determined (the measure of the basal level of responding before conditioning). Each animal was placed in the conditioning chamber for two daily one-hour sessions and the number of spontaneous responses recorded. During this phase the animals pressed the bar with the feeder inactivated, thus being exposed to only the visual and auditory stimuli associated with the operation of the apparatus. No reinforcement was given for responding.

Following the operant level sessions, on the next two days the animals were placed in the apparatus for magazine training. During these sessions they were automatically given 120 pellets randomly distributed over the one-hour session. Any bar press was also reinforced. Before each session the plug over one hemisphere was removed, and a cotton pledget soaked in 25 per cent KCl was applied to the dura via the hole at the base of the cup. After a delay of from 5 to 15 minutes, the animal would be placed in the conditioning chamber. At the termination of the experimental session the pledget was removed and the dura thoroughly washed with mammalian Ringer's solution. The choice of hemisphere was randomly determined for each animal, however, the hemisphere depressed during magazine training was subsequently depressed on all training days of the experiment.

Due to the high concentration of KCl employed in eliciting SD many animals became lethargic or suffered convulsive seizures indicating brain damage. Those animals were all discarded from the present report.

RESULTS

Unilateral learning

In group 1 the animals were on a continuous reinforcement schedule during training days and extinction during test days, while one hemisphere was functional and the other depressed (*see* Table I). Thus, on training days each response the animal made would be reinforced, whereas on test days no matter how many responses were made by the animal no reinforcement was obtained. During training days the animals were run in the apparatus with the same hemisphere depressed as during magazine training. Sessions 5, 6, 8, 9, 10 and 12 were training days; and sessions 7, 11 and 13 were test days. On test sessions 7 and 11 the hemisphere that had been functional during training was depressed, whereas on test session 13 the untrained hemisphere was depressed.

All animals conditioned readily within the first few days of training, despite the fact that only one hemisphere was functional. Usually by the second day of training a fairly stable rate of responding had been achieved, which throughout subsequent training days showed a slight but consistent increase in rate. Table I presents the individual scores that the animals made on all training and test sessions. The two initial days of operant level scores represent the basal level of responding, where the pre-conditioned response rate is on the average 10 responses per hour. Within two days of training, learning is indicated by the rapid increase in response rate to about 100 per hour. Disregarding the interspersed test days for the moment, the response rate is seen to be augmented slightly to 140 responses per hour over the next four days of training. During all training days the animals were exposed to the conditioning procedure with always the same hemisphere depressed, the other functional. They conditioned easily and showed the same type of incremental performance as would normal animals with both hemispheres functional.

For all animals considered, the amount of conditioning was measured in terms of the resistance to extinction shown during standard one-hour test periods. This measure of conditioned behaviour was used as an index of the learning which had taken place because of the obvious advantage that no further conditioning could occur while the animal was being tested for retention.

On the first two test days (sessions 7 and 11) the animals were given an extinction test for retention of learning; the untrained cortical hemisphere was now functional. Clearly when the *trained* cortex was depressed it can be seen that the extinction score is down to the basal pre-conditioned level on both test days, indicating that the *untrained* cortex has been effectively isolated from the conditioning procedure (it had not learned while

Table I. Unilateral Learning

Sessions	R26	R28	R32	R33	R34		Procedure
1	6	8	6	8	4		*Operant level*
2	8	11	10	11	4		
3			*Magazine Training*				
4							
5	46	47	76	31	59		*Conditioning*
6	82	82	148	90	101		*(FR1)*
							Trained Cortex Functional
7	3	10	4	6	4		*Extinction*
							Untrained Cortex Functional
8	99	71	116	101	116		*Conditioning*
9	116	73	110	148	146		*(FR1)*
10	126	131	148		194		Trained Cortex Functional
11	2	0	12		14		Untrained Cortex Functional
							Conditioning
12	89	102	170		227		*(FR1)*
							Trained Cortex Functional
13	47	180	282		177		*Extinction*
							Trained Cortex Functional

depressed). Had this cortex been involved during conditioning it should have shown some signs of retention of learning in terms of the extinction scores. On the last day of testing (session 13), when the animals were given a retention test with the trained cortex functional, the high scores revealed that this hemisphere retained the engram. Not only are the extinction scores obtained with the trained cortex functional above basal level, but they are comparable to the amount of responding made during reinforcement. This difference in extinction scores shows that the trained hemisphere has retained the habit and the other hemisphere has not. The presence of SD in the untrained cortical hemisphere during training prevented it from sharing in the learning which took place in the functional hemisphere during conditioning.

Hemisphere dominance during conditioning

It is possible that one cortical hemisphere is dominant in learning, i.e. that a learning engram is established in only one hemisphere under normal conditions. Two groups of animals were run as controls for this possibility. One group (Table IIa) was conditioned to a simple continuous reinforcement schedule, where each response was reinforced (FR1), for two or three days before testing. The other group (Table IIb) was trained to a more complex reinforcement schedule, where every 25th response received reinforcement (FR25), for seven to ten days before implanting the cup assembly and before any testing. All animals in both groups were trained with both hemispheres functional during conditioning.

The animals in group 2a (see Table IIa) were given two days of continuous reinforcement before testing. After two days of testing under extinction conditions a further day of training intervened before the next two test days which were followed by a final day of training. All training days exposed the animals to the FR1 schedule with both hemispheres functional. On the first test day (session 7) the right hemisphere was depressed and the left hemisphere was depressed on the following test day (session 8). Both hemispheres were depressed on the next day test (session 10) and both were functional on the last such day (session 11). The same procedure was adhered to for the animals in group 2b with the exception that they received five days of training, on a reinforcement schedule where every 25th response was rewarded, before testing. All such training days utilized this schedule. All tests days consisted of the standard one hour of extinction.

On the first test after training the animals in both groups were given an extinction test with one hemisphere depressed, the same procedure being repeated on the following day with the opposite hemisphere depressed. Both groups gave extinction scores that indicated that there was no impairment in retention of learning when one hemisphere was depressed. As would be expected the FR25 group of animals shows a greater resistance to extinction. There is no evidence to support the hypoth-

Table IIa. Bilateral Representation of Simple Learning under Normal Conditions

Sessions	R98	R103	R106	R107	R108	Procedure
1	4	3	1	6	5	*Operant level*
2	3	6	4	1	8	
3		*Magazine Training*				
4						
5	93	100	280	190	166	*Conditioning* (FR1)
6	107	171	183	209	182	Both Cortices Functional
7	70	53	42	104	105	Right Cortex Depressed
8	68	37	54	98	121	Left Cortex Depressed
9	133	195	191	210	192	*Conditioning* (FR1)
						Both Cortices Functional
						Extinction
10	6	0	3	1	0	Both Cortices Depressed
11	96	54	116	216	186	Both Cortices Functional
						Conditioning (FR1)
12	—	182	284	102	—	Both Cortices Functional

esis that learning occurs unilaterally in a "dominant" hemisphere, by virtue of the fact that there is no difference between the extinction scores of either hemisphere. Both a simple and a more complex conditioned performance appear therefore to be normally bilaterally represented, which is in accord with Sperry's suggestions (1961) that a learning engram is typically in duplicate form, one copy in each hemisphere.

These results in groups 2a and 2b also serve as control for the possibility that the operant performance is a function of the animal's hand preference. From Bures' work on hand performance in rats (1960) it is possible to consider learning as normally unilateral in the "dominant" hemisphere that controls the animal's hand preference. In fact from cursory observation of the animals this would appear unlikely. Bar-pressing was typically

Table IIb. Bilateral Representation of Complex Learning Under Normal Conditions

Sessions	R82	R83	R86	R87	R96	Procedure
1	13	3	40	1	10	*Operant level*
2	10	6	25	7	3	
3		*Magazine Training*				
4						
5	320	334	510	382	146	*Conditioning* (FR25)
6	1,168	714	627	2,158	123	Both Cortices Functional
7	1,948	969	820	2,392	594	
8	2,867	1,527	423	1,325	1,381	
9	2,845	2,374	461	1,972	1,637	
						Extinction
10	307	193	335	426	156	Right Cortex Depressed
11	193	262	184	377	135	Left Cortex Depressed
						Conditioning (FR25)
12	3,165	2,507	462	2,671	1,525	Both Cortices Functional
13	50	1	4	0	6	Both Cortices Depressed
14	501	473	124	395	504	Both Cortices Functional
						Conditioning (FR25)
15	2,895	3,040	621	2,335	1,471	Both Cortices Functional

achieved by the animal operating the bar with the head assembly. In general, it should be noted that bar-pressing is very rarely a discrete response made with one paw, but typically the animal will operate the bar in a variety of ways, such as with the mouth or hitting the bar with its flank.

After a further day's training with both hemispheres functional, the animals were tested for retention with bilateral SD present. The extinction scores for both groups under bilateral SD are indistinguishable from the operant level scores, showing no retention of learning. When both hemispheres are functional in the next extinction test, scores were the same as those obtained with unilateral SD tests. The lack of any retention of learning found with bilateral SD is to be expected, and confirms Bures' earlier observations (1959). These results also give no evidence of disturbance in the retention of a bilaterally learned habit when only one cortex is functional as compared with both cortices functional.

Relative performance of a unilateral learning trace

The animals in group 3 were trained on a half-minute variable interval reinforcement schedule (VI½). This schedule programmed reinforcements such that the animals' responding would be reinforced at irregular time intervals, being on the average every half minute. This enabled a more exact test of the results of group 1, in that a more complex habit is used and the functional independence between hemispheres could be studied over a more prolonged time period.

Table III. Relative Performance of a Unilateral Engram

Sessions	R43	R44	R45	R49	R50	R52
1	12	30	20	22	7	32
2	36	36	16	59	1	17
3			*Magazine Training*			
4						
5	40	140	182	57	217	44
6	253	659	1,044	315	710	191
7	24	18	0	9	24	0
8	762	646	896	412	1,627	902
9	1,089	1,326	1,091	524	1,463	801
10	18	9	4	74	18	24
11	No run	No run	284	390	362	No run
12	1,653	1,272	1,022	508	1,643	669
13	1,771	1,616	1,027	No run	1,830	1,563
14	72	No run	15	—	19	62
15	337	241	No run	—	186	185
16	905	—	954	—	1,656	2,229
17	1,131	—	1,276	—	1,763	2,237

The animals in group 3 were exposed to a continuous reinforcement schedule for the initial day of training, and then on all subsequent days of training they were switched to a VI½ reinforcement schedule. On all test days they would be under extinction conditions. During training days the same hemisphere was depressed as during all previous days. The exact sequence according to which hemisphere was depressed during test days is given in Table III. From Table III it can be seen that these animals conditioned just as readily as those in the first group, showing that there is no difficulty in establishing a unilateral engram with SD using this more complex conditioning schedule. The animals in this group were initially given one day of FR1 (session 5) and then on the second training day they were moved to the VI½ schedule. During the next training days (sessions 8, 9, 12, 13, 16, 17) it can be seen that the response rate increased rapidly to an asymptote of around 1,400 responses per hour. This performance is typical for a VI schedule, in that animals settle on a constant high rate of responding which is maintained continuously throughout the entire experimental session (Ferster and Skinner, 1957).

Tests were made on these animals to investigate the possibility that there might be a passive or spontaneous transfer of the engram to the untrained hemisphere over a prolonged period of time. Considering the extinction scores on the test days it is seen that on the days when the trained cortex is depressed the amount of responding is the same as the basal level, indicating no retention of conditioning in the untrained cortex. The extinction scores that were made when the trained cortex was functional were high, almost 300 responses. The extinction scores for the VI½ group (Table III) are much greater than those of the FR1 group (Table

Procedure
Operant level

Conditioning (VI½)
Trained Cortex Functional
Extinction
Untrained Cortex Functional
Conditioned (VI½)
Trained Cortex Functional
Extinction
Untrained Cortex Functional
Trained Cortex Functional
Conditioning (VI½)
Trained Cortex Functional
Extinction
Untrained Cortex Functional
Trained Cortex Functional
Conditioning (VI½)
Trained Cortex Functional

I) which is congruent with the fact that aperiodic schedules of reinforcement generate a greater resistance to extinction than do periodic schedules. All animals retained their unilateral learning over a prolonged time period. In 3 animals, however, there was an appreciable increase above basal level in the extinction scores of the untrained cortex after two weeks. This increment at the end of prolonged test was not, however, comparable to the scores of the trained hemisphere. As it was not possible to follow animals through further testing, because of changes produced by the KCl (e.g. fibrin growth across the trephine holes) no interpretation of this upward trend noted in the extinction scores of the untrained hemisphere is made. The results do indicate that the learning trace remains unilateral for at least ten days before this eventuality arises.

It appears clear then that the cortex which is not depressed by SD during training is the cortex that learns and retains the habit and is able to mediate the conditioned performance. The changes that are established in the trained hemisphere are capable of maintaining the conditioned performance even without reinforcement, as can be seen from the extinction scores. A complete loss of conditioned behaviour occurs when the trained hemisphere is depressed by SD, demonstrating the dependency of the learned behavior on this cortical hemisphere.

The effect of SD on such a trace is temporary, as can be seen from Tables I, II and III where in every case the conditioned performance returns completely on the following test days after the depression of the trained hemisphere. There are no indications that SD has had any enduring effect on neurons which mediate the performance, despite the fact that on interspersed days the trained hemisphere was depressed. The absence of any permanent effect of SD is further demonstrated in group 3 where a strong resistance to extinction of the trained cortex was found the day after it was occupied by SD. Clearly the effect of SD on the learning engram is a temporary functional block and confirms a similar lack of permanent effect in the chronic studies of SD by Ochs et al. (1961).

Table IV. Interhemispheric Transfer of an Engram

Sessions	R59	R61	R64	R66	R70	R72	R74	R91	R94
1	7	6	9	10	12	9	4	13	2
2	8	17	10	18	16	3	3	12	0
3				*Magazine Training*					
4									
5	374	265	233	157	261	325	150	174	104
6	0	2	7	12	7	8	10	24	5
7	63	66	83	171	118	150	191	92	109
8	(1)	(1)	(1)	(1)	(1)	(1)	(1)	(1)	(2)
	54	7	54	97	0	141	98	118	ǀ94

Inter-hemispheric transfer of the learning trace

It was possible to demonstrate the same functional independence between the hemispheres when using this technique as was shown with the split-brain preparation where unilateral traces were established after callosal connexions were severed. However, the effect of SD on the hemisphere will last only as long as the waves of SD are present in the cortex and in the procedure utilized in present experiments this would be at the most from four to five hours (Bures, 1959). Consequently, for a considerable portion of the day, the animals had both hemispheres functional. Despite this, and the fact that all inter-hemispheric connexions were intact, the engram in the trained hemisphere did not transfer to the other hemisphere, but remained restricted to the hemisphere in which it was established for a period of two weeks. It would thus appear that the formation of such an engram occurs during the process of conditioning or shortly thereafter, and that once established in one hemisphere it does not spontaneously transfer to the other hemisphere outside the conditioning situation, when SD is no longer present.

The animals in group 4 (Table IV) were used to investigate the conditions under which transfer of the engram could take place. For this group the animals were conditioned according to a FR1 schedule on the single training day allowed (session 5), and extinction conditions were present during all test days. On the first and third test days (sessions 6 and 8) the trained cortex was depressed, while on the second test day (session 7) the untrained cortex was depressed, as it was during training. The procedure on the third test day (session 8) was unique in that, one hour before the extinction test was given, the animals were allowed to make one reinforced response, with both cortical hemispheres functional (2 reinforcements for R94). Immediately after the animals had received the reinforcement to the single response, they were removed from the apparatus

Procedure
Operant level

Conditioning (FR1)
Trained Cortex Functional
Extinction
Untrained Cortex Functional
Trained Cortex Functional
Reinforced Transfer Response
Extinction
Untrained Cortex Functional

and returned to the home cages until time for testing one hour later. The extinction scores of the animals with the untrained hemisphere functional an hour after this single reinforcement (with two exceptions) revealed response rates of the same order as those for the trained cortex. This indicates transfer of the engram to the previously naïve cortex.

The evidence from group 3 had indicated that over periods of up to ten days and more there was no evidence of any passive transfer of the engram. However, transfer of the trace occurred in the group 4 animals after just one reinforced response. It thus appears that the effect of the performance of bar-pressing, the reinforcement, or both, when the two hemispheres are functional is to transfer the trace from the trained to the untrained hemisphere. The important determinant of transfer appeared to be the reinforcement, because as shown in group 5, when the animals were not reinforced in the transfer situation the engram remained unilateral. The same procedure was followed for group 5 (Table V) as for group 4, except that the reinforcement was withheld when the animal was allowed to press the bar with both hemispheres open. For this group one day of training was allowed (session 5) and then the animals were tested for unilateral learning. It can be seen from Table V that the results paralleled those of previous groups in that one hemisphere retains the habit and the other does not. On the third test day each animal was permitted to respond without reinforcement (between 10 to 25 times) with both hemispheres functional. When the animals were tested for transfer with the *trained* cortex depressed one hour later (session 8) the extinction scores of the previously untrained cortex remained at the basal level in contra-distinction to those of group 4 above. Subsequent scores of the trained cortex show the same degree of retention. Clearly no transfer to the naïve side has occurred. This indicates that not only is transfer an active process, but that it occurs under fairly restricted conditions. When

Table V. Failure of Interhemispheric Transfer with Absence of Reinforcement

Sessions	R113	R109	R115	R116	R117		Procedure
1	2	6	17	10	4		Operant level
2	3	1	0	1	8		
3							
4			Magazine Training				
5	164	245	197	178	163		Conditioning (FR1)
							Trained Cortex Functional
							Extinction
6	17	5	8	32	7		Untrained Cortex Functional
7	91	239	277	120	128		Trained Cortex Functional
							Non-reinforced Transfer
8	(15)	(25)	(10)	(25)	(10)		Responses
	3	8	2	21	21		Extinction
							Untrained Cortex Functional
							Extinction
9	136	157	106	83	106		Trained Cortex Functional
10	86	96	53	—	64		Trained Cortex Functional

the animal performs the exact sequence in the chain of events involved in the performance of the conditioned operant with both hemispheres functional, then transfer takes place. Although one such trial is sufficient for transfer, even many trials are ineffective where responses go unreinforced. It would thus appear that some delicate response-stimulation relationship between bar-pressing and reinforcement is requisite for transfer. Once altered by removing the reinforcement stimulation no transfer occurs irrespective of the number of responses made while both sides are not depressed.

DISCUSSION

The results obtained have shown the feasibility of establishing a unilateral learning engram, using SD as a technique of functional ablation. The instrumental learning that was established during conditioning was found to be restricted to the trained hemisphere. The results are similar to those gained with the split-brain preparation (Sperry, 1961) and to Bures' work with conditioning and SD (1960).

In view of the essentially cortical involvement in the propagation of SD, it would appear reasonable to suppose that the brain changes involved in the mechanism of learning engrams is cortical in nature. Myers' work (1956) demonstrating that interhemispheric transfer of learning dependent on visual cues occurs via the corpus callosum further suggests the cortical nature of the engram. Later work by Sperry (1956) indicates that the cortical localization involved in a visual engram is probably diffuse and requires several cortical areas. Sperry (1959) has further shown, however, that some highly restricted sites can contain an engram. Removal of all but a small area of the sensorimotor cortex in cats does not impair conditioned somaesthetic discrimination, nor create retardations in the learning of new discriminations. Further reduction of this cortical remnant abolished conditioned performance. The work of Sperry on somaesthetic localization and the early experiments in Pavlov's laboratory, argue strongly, if not decisively, for a cortical localization of the learning trace. Anrep (1917, 1923) established conditioned salivary reflexes to tactile stimulation of one hind limb, and found response generalization occurred to tactile stimulation of the same areas of the contralateral limb. Bykow and Speransky (1924) found that such generalization did not occur if animals had previously had the callosum sectioned, indicating that learning under these conditions was unilaterally represented in the hemisphere receiving the sensory input. Foursikow (1925) further noted that unilateral decortication abolished bilateral transfer of conditioning, indicative of the cortical involvement.

The present experiment and the work of Bures (1960) added to those results obtained by Sperry and co-workers with the split-brain preparation show that a unilateral cortical engram is possible despite the fact that conditioning would be bilaterally received in the subcortical centres of the brain. These findings would seem to argue against the centrencephalic theories of Penfield (1954) and Gastaut (1958). In their view conditioning takes place at a subcortical level within the reticular substance of the thalamus and the lower centre is visualized as a single unified system rather than being composed of two independent lateral portions. An example of the unified action of the reticular formation was shown by the recent work of Weiss (1961a, b). He showed that while SD was present in one hemisphere a simultaneous short-term desynchronization (arousal reaction) appeared in the contralateral hemisphere. Section of the brain stem at the interpeduncular level as well as pentobarbital narcosis abolished this reaction. This "global" activation of the reticular formation following SD in one hemisphere is probably one of release. His results are of further importance in showing that SD in our experiments probably does not cause a lateralized effect in the reticular formation which could be an alternate site of the engram. It is difficult to see how the centrencephalic theories of conditioning could account for these and other results showing clear lateralization of an engram, if the global nature of the centrencephalic centre remains an essential part of the theory.

The learning engram that was established in one hemisphere remained restricted to that hemisphere even when both cortical hemispheres were functional and all interhemispheric connexions were intact. Animals lived normally and unrestricted in the home cages for periods of up to two weeks without any transfer of the engram to the other hemisphere. It would appear that the trace once established in one part of the brain remains there as a stable neural alteration. One trial was adequate for transfer, providing the same chain of events involved in operant conditioning is maintained during the procedure to effect transfer. Alteration of the situation so that merely the performance of the conditioned response occurs but without the contingent stimulation of reinforcement present prevented transfer despite many such repetitions. The exact nature of such a highly selective set of requirements to effect transfer is at present puzzling. It appears that the conditions required for transfer involve a sequential code or chain of events, and the performance of the response must be followed by the stimulation of reinforcement. This chain of events once activated in the correct sequence is required to trigger the transfer process. Further experimental analysis, however, would be required before theorizing on the precise nature of the mechanism involved in transfer.

Psychologists from the days of the British Associationists have been explicitly concerned with an analysis of the process whereby learning takes place. The traditional view has long favoured an incremental view of the learning process. This position is exemplified by the concept of the strength of associations between ideas, Thorndikes' formulation of the strength of stimulus-response connexions and the contemporary viewpoint that learning is to be considered as a function of the amount of reinforcement. The evidence for this viewpoint is quite indirect in that it was predicated on the characteristics of performance curves representing average response measures of learning groups. Recent evidence presented by Estes (1960) of a series of direct observations on individual cases indicates learning is an all-or-none process. The observations made here on the all-or-none nature of the formation of learning engrams between hemispheres supports the view that learning in this experimental analogue also occurs in an all-or-none fashion. In this case the naïve hemisphere "learns" from the hemisphere containing the engram.

SUMMARY AND CONCLUSIONS

Unilateral localization of a memory trace to one cortical hemisphere and the conditions under which interhemispheric transfer occurs was studied in rats. Spreading cortical depression of Leão was used as a technique of functional ablation, where repeated waves of spreading depression would depress the cortical function of one hemisphere for several hours. During this time the animals were exposed to bar-press training with unilateral cortical function.

1. Testing revealed that conditioning during unilateral spreading depression resulted in the establishment of a memory trace in the functional hemisphere. No such trace was found in the non-functional hemisphere.

2. Animals that learned a simple or a complex conditioned response with bilateral cortical function were tested to see if learning is represented in a dominant hemisphere. With either hemisphere depressed the same degree of retention of learning was shown as compared with retention under bilateral recall conditions. It thus appears that under normal learning conditions a memory trace is bilaterally represented in the brain.

3. A trace lateralized to one hemisphere was found to remain restricted unilaterally over long periods of time up to two weeks or more. No evidence of passive transfer of the memory trace to the untrained hemisphere was found, despite the fact that all interhemispheric connexions were intact.

4. Interhemispheric transfer was found to occur if the animal was allowed to make only one reinforced response with bilateral cortical function. No transfer was, however, found if the animal made several responses in the absence of reinforcement with bilateral cortical function. Thus transfer appeared to be an active process requiring the animal to go through the exact sequence of events involved in the conditioned performance in order to effect transfer.

REFERENCES

Akalaitis, A. J. (1943) J. Neuropath., 2, 226.
Anrep, G. V. (1917) Archives of Biol. Sciences, XX, 4, 262–275.

—————— (1923) *Proc. roy. Soc.*, **B.94**, 404.

Bureš, J. (1959) "Reversible Decortication and Behaviour." Josiah Macy Jr. Foundation. Conference on the Central Nervous System and Behaviour. **2**, 207.

——————, and Burešova, O. (1960) *In* The Moscow Colloquium on electroencephalography of higher nervous activity, edited by H. H. Jasper and G. D. Smirnov. (Electroencephalography and Clinical Neurophysiology—Supp. No. 13)

——————, —————— (1960) *J. comp. physiol. Psychol.*, **53**, 558.

——————, ——————, and Záhorová, A. (1958) *J. comp. physiol. Psychol.*, **51**, 263.

Burešova, O. (1956) *Physiol. bohemslov.*, **5**, 350–358.

——————, Bureš, J., and Beran, J. A. (1958) *Physiol. bohemoslov.*, **7**, 29.

Bykow, K. M., and Speransky, A. D. Abstract in *Zentralblatt für die gesammte Neurologie und Psychiatrie.* Bd. XXXIX (1925).

Downer, J. L. de C. (1959) *Brain*, **82**, 251.

Estes, W. K. (1960) *Psychol. Rev.*, **67**, 207.

Ferster, C. B., and Skinner, B. F. (1957) "Schedules of Reinforcement." New York.

Foursikow, D. S. (1925) *Russ. J. Physiol.*, VIII, 5–6, 231–240.

——————, and Eurman, M. N. (1926) Archives Biol. Sciences, XXV, 4–5.

Gastaut, H. (1958) *In* CIBA Foundation Symposium on the Neurological Basis of Behaviour, edited by G. E. W. Wolstenholme and C. M. O'Connor. London, p. 255.

Leão, A. A. P. (1944) *J. Neurophysiol.*, **7**, 359.

Marshall, W. H. (1959) *Physiol. Rev.*, **39**, 239.

Myers, R. E. (1955) *J. comp. physiol. Psychol.*, **48**, 470.

—————— (1956) *Brain*, **79**, 358.

—————— (1957) *Fed. Proc.*, **16**, 92.

——————, and Sperry, R. W. (1958) *A.M.A. Arch. Neurol. Psychiat.*, **80**, 298.

Ochs, S. (—) *Int. Rev. Neurobiol.*, in press.

——————, Hunt, K., and Booker, H. (1961) *Amer. J. Physiol.*, **200**, 1211.

Penfield, W. (1954) *Brain*, **77**, 1.

Russell, I. S., and Ochs, S. (1960) *Physiologist*, **3**, 3.

——————, —————— (1961) *Science*, **133**, 1077.

Smith, K. U. (1951) *Science*, **114**, 117.

Sperry, R. W. (1955) "Psychological Plasticity and Brain Circuit Theory." *In* Biological and Biochemical Bases of Behaviour. Symposium on interdisciplinary research. Univ. of Wisconsin Press.

—————— (1959) *J. Neurophysiol.*, **22**, 78.

—————— (1961) *Science*, **133**, 1749.

——————, Stamm, J. S., and Miner, N. (1956) *J. comp. physiol. Psychol.*, **49**, 529.

Verhave, T. (1958) *J. exp. Anal. Behav.*, **1**, 1.

Weiss, T. (1961*a*) *Physiol. bohemoslov.*, **10**, 2, 109.

—————— (1961*b*) *Physiol. bohemoslov.*, **10**, 1, 27.

THE PERMANENT RECORD
OF THE STREAM
OF CONSCIOUSNESS

Wilder Penfield

MC GILL UNIVERSITY AND
MONTREAL NEUROLOGICAL INSTITUTE

Editor's Note   *This is one of the earlier (and briefer)
reports by Penfield on the remarkable results which
he has obtained from a very large number of stimulation
experiments on brains of waking humans.*

*Source   Reprinted from **Proceedings of the 14th International Congress of Psychologists**, with the permission
of the author and the publisher, North-Holland
Publishing Company.*

While considering how I might fortify my position before this Congress, composed as it is of leading psychologists from all the world, I took from my book shelves the two volumes of Psychology by William James (1). I blew off the dust that had lain upon them, I fear, since my undergraduate days at Princeton and read his classical chapter on The Stream of Thought.

Consciousness, he said, is a personal phenomenon. It deals with external objects, some of which are constant, and it chooses among them. But consciousness is never the same in successive moments of time. It is a stream forever flowing, forever changing.

It has fallen to my lot, during explorations of the cortex, to demonstrate a mechanism in the human brain which preserves the record of the stream of thought. When it becomes necessary to operate under local anesthesia and to stimulate the surface of one of the temporal lobes, it happens occasionally that small parts of that record are activated, bringing back a period of past experience with a startling degree of vividness and detail. The patient then re-views the sights and sounds and thinking of a previous period of time.

CORTICAL EXPLORATION

During the past twenty years of neurosurgical practice it has been necessary to expose the cerebral cortex under local anesthesia in a succession of patients. The reason for operation was that they were afflicted by recurring attacks of focal epilepsy. Surgical excision of an abnormal area of cortex in which epileptogenic discharges arise may relieve such patients of their attacks in about fifty percent of cases.

But before excisions are carried out, it is our custom to explore the exposed cortex, applying a gentle electrical current to it from place to place. It is possible, thus, at times, to reproduce the beginning of a patient's attack in the form of a sensory aura or movement and, thus, to verify the position of the epileptogenic focus. Furthermore, stimulation is used to localize the functional areas of the cortex after which the excision can be carried out with a minimal sacrifice of function.

This practice made it possible to map out, in great detail, the motor representation in the cortex of man and the sensory areas—somatic, visual, auditory, etc. As years passed the supplementary motor area was demonstrated, hidden away in the sagittal fissure, and the second somatic sensory area within the fissure of Sylvius.

Two major areas of the human cortex remained, the anterior half of the frontal lobes and the enormously in-folded temporal cortex.[1]

From time to time over the years, stimulation has produced an astonishing result. Instead of movement or sensation, application of the electrode has caused the patient to report a psychical effect.[2]

In each case the location of stimulus was charted and a description immediately dictated to a secretary who sat in the "viewing stand" for the purpose. In such dictation the surgeon has always used the patient's own words as far as possible.

Positive psychical responses were obtained only from the previously unclaimed cortex of the temporal lobes and only then when that cortex had been rendered more responsive by long continued pre-operative epileptic conditioning. The responses, however, might bear no relationship to the content of the patient's seizures and they were produced without setting up epileptic after-discharge. Sensitization of the cortex, so that it reveals its function with greater ease when stimulated, is the common result of the presence of local epileptogenic process in other areas of cortex as well as in the temporal lobes. The stimulating electrode may imitate the effect of a local epileptic discharge but it does other things as well.

GENERAL STIMULATION RESPONSES AND THE MEANING OF CORTICAL LOCALIZATION

It was in 1870 that Fritsch and Hitzig applied an electrical current to a certain area of the cerebral cortex of a lightly anesthetized dog and produced movement in the opposite limbs. Previous to that time, the brain was considered to be the organ of the mind functioning somehow as a whole, although it is true that Hughlings Jackson had suggested some degree of localization and Broca had claimed a localized representation for speech.

The work of Fritsch and Hitzig, followed quickly by Ferrier, prepared the way for the great experimentalists to study the cerebral cortex. I refer to Sherrington and Pavlov and their pupils, but I should also mention many others, Luciani, Dusser de Barenne, Graham Brown, Adrian, Bard, Woolsey, Vogt, Lashley, to name only a few.

What can we say today about localization of function in the cerebral cortex of man? And in what sense can any function be said to have a

[1] A relatively small part of the first temporal convolution, the transverse gyrus of Heschl, was clearly devoted to auditory sensation and, perhaps adjacent to it, was some representation of labyrinthine sensation. The sense of smell has been given an ever smaller foothold in the region of the uncus. Otherwise the temporal cortex, which has enlarged so greatly in man, as compared with other mammals, represented a vast and unclaimed territory.

[2] It may be said at once that the word psychical is used in its original meaning, as Hughlings Jackson used it, to denote the more complicated mental phenomena made possible by final neuronal integration within the brain.

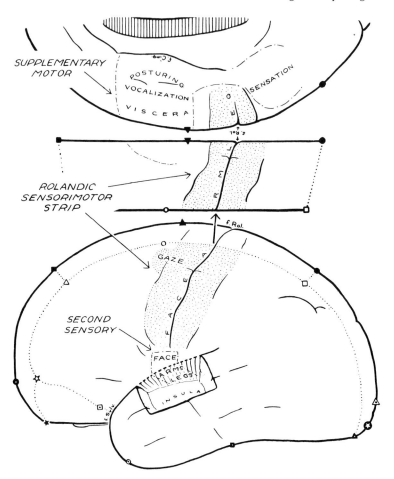

FIGURE 1 *Somatic sensory and motor areas of the human cerebral cortex.
As judged by the results of stimulation all three somatic areas (Rolandic,
Supplementary, Second) are to some extent both motor and sensory. (From
Penfield and Jasper, 1954.)*

localization? These questions have been discussed exhaustively elsewhere
(2, 3, 4) with references to literature. But a few words of interpretation
may be useful here.

Stimulation of the motor cortex of conscious men produces movement
(Fig. 1) but the patient is always aware of the fact that he has not willed
these movements. These movements are gross and uncomplicated with
certain striking exceptions. The exceptions are motor performances which
have a localization of mechanism elsewhere in the central nervous system,
mechanisms which can be activated from a distance by the cortical stimulation. I refer to vocalization mastication, swallowing, conjugate eye
movements.

Stimulation of sensory areas causes the patient to experience only the
elements of sensation. In the somatic area it is tingling, numbness, sense

of movement of some part of the body; in the visual area, lights, shadows, colored forms usually moving; in the auditory area, a buzzing, humming, knocking or ringing sound.

Sensation (Fig. 2) can not be said to be located in the cortex any more than it is in the peripheral receptor. Sensory areas of the cerebral cortex are way-stations in the current of afferent neuronal impulses. These impulses originate in the peripheral sense-organs and travel inward and upward to the cortex with ganglionic interruption in subcortical nuclei. From the cortex they pass inward again to the higher brain stem where the afferent stream from one field or body-half can join the others.[3] The most important, and the final, reorganization of sensory material must take place in the circuits of the higher brain stem rather than in the cerebral cortex.

The motor pathway, on the other hand, which subserves voluntary discriminative movement originates in a central region between the hemispheres and passes out to the motor cortex of each hemisphere. After its

[3] Interference with this portion of the brain produces unconsciousness (5).

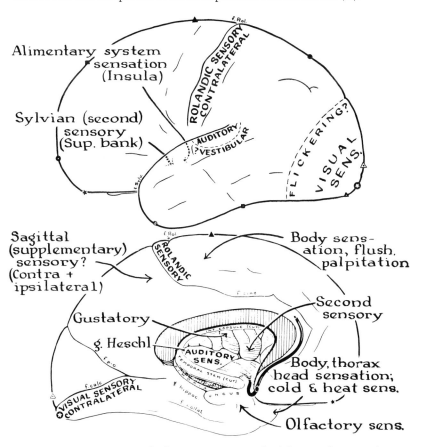

FIGURE 2 *Sensory areas of the human cortex as judged by stimulation exploration in conscious patients. (The sensory area indicated in the anterior temporal region requires verification.)*

ganglionic interruption in the precentral gyrus it descends to medulla and spinal cord and thence to the muscles.

Associative neuronal intercourse from one functional area of the cortex to another is of comparatively little importance. Integration of the function of the separate areas of the cortex by a subcortical centrencephalic system is of great importance.

It is the purpose of this address to discuss the ganglionic organization of an experiential recording mechanism, and to point out that there is some sort of representation of this mechanism in the temporal cortex. As time passes others will, no doubt, elucidate the nature of the role of the temporal cortex in this mechanism.

CASE EXAMPLES

CASE T. S.   T. S. was a young man of 19 years. He had temporal lobe seizures that were sometimes precipitated by listening to music. He was fond of jazz and also symphonic music.

At the beginning of each attack he experienced what he called a "flash-back."[4]

He explained that this usually had to do with himself and his past but was "much more distinct" than anything he could summon to his memory.

At the time of operation, stimulation of a point on the anterior part of the first temporal convolution on the right caused him to say, "I feel as though I were in the bathroom at school." Five minutes later, after negative stimulations elsewhere, the electrode was reapplied near the same point. The patient then said something about "street corner." The surgeon asked him, "where," and he replied, "South Bend, Indiana, corner of Jacob and Washington." When asked to explain, he said he seemed to be looking at himself—at a younger age.

When the stimulation was repeated the response was quite different. This time he said, "that music, from 'Guys and Dolls.'" When asked which song in the play he referred to, he could not name it. "I was listening to it," he said. "It was an orchestration" . . .

Such results have been produced many times and we have used every practicable control and verification. The following case may be reported in greater detail.

CASE M. M.   The patient M. M. was a woman of 26 years who was afflicted by recurring cerebral seizures. The first manifestation of each attack was a sudden "feeling—as though I had lived through this all before." At times there was also a feeling of fear. On other occasions she experienced what she called a flash-back not unlike those just described in the case of T. S.

---

[4] Flash-back is an expression used by those familiar with moving picture techniques to describe the presentation of a scene that has occurred in the earlier history of one of the characters of the play.

The initial feeling of familiarity she described as applying to the whole of any experience she might be having at the moment. On the other hand, the flash-backs were experiences from her earlier life. They came suddenly while she retained awareness of her actual surroundings. She gave the following example: Without warning she seemed to be sitting in the railroad station of a small town, which might be Vanceburg, Kentucky, or perhaps Garrison. "It is winter and the wind is blowing outside and I am waiting for a train." This was apparently an experience from her earlier life but it was one she had "forgotten."

These minor seizures (psychical seizures) were often followed by automatism, periods of irresponsible behaviour of which she would have no memory. During these periods she might fall or walk about in a confused state, speaking unrelated and disjointed words and sentences.

Thus, in summary, the localized epileptic discharges in the right temporal lobe of this young woman were causing her to experience, from time to time: (1) a sense of false familiarity (déjà vu), (2) a feeling of fear, (3) reproductions of previous experience.—The first was an illusion, the second an emotion, the third an hallucination. These are all to be considered psychical phenomena, any one of which the operator might hope to reproduce by stimulation.

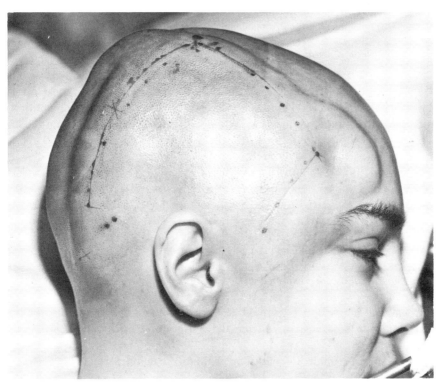

FIGURE 3 *Prepared for operation. Incision marked on scalp after injection of nupercaine. Case M. M.*

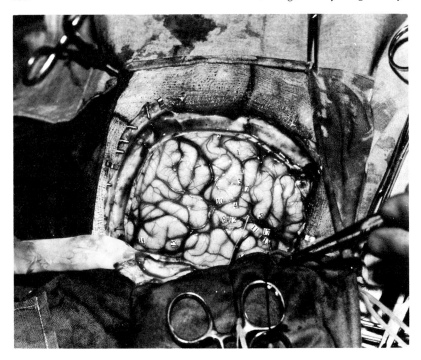

FIGURE 4   *Photograph of brain after craniotomy. The paper tickets dropped on the cortex show points where stimulation produced positive responses, sensory, motor or psychical. Case M. M.*

Osteoplastic craniotomy (Figs. 3 and 4) carried out under local anesthesia disclosed atrophy and sclerosis of the first temporal convolution, and the uncus and hippocampus as well. Electrographic recordings taken directly from the cortex by my associate, Dr. Herbert Jasper, showed spontaneous "spike" discharges from this area.

Electrical stimulation was carried out (Square wave generator, 60 cycles, 2 millisecond pulses). She was ordinarily warned by the operator each time the electrode was applied. But, as usual, at intervals the warning was given with no stimulus and at other times, stimulation without warning. This serves to eliminate with certainty false or imaginary responses.

Sensory and motor responses

A current of two volts proved to be the minimum threshold strength that would produce responses from the sensory and motor areas. See Figs. 4 and 5.

Stimulation at point 2—sensation in thumb and index finger. She called it "quivering," "tingling."

3—"Same feeling on the left side of my tongue."

7—Movement of the tongue.

4—"Yes, a feeling at the back of my throat like nausea."

8—She said, "No." Then she said, "Yes, I suddenly can not hear." This is obviously, the border of auditory sensory cortex.

The foregoing responses were motor and sensory in character much like those obtained routinely. They serve only to identify the Rolandic sensory and motor cortex and Heschl's auditory gyrus, a part of the first temporal convolution buried within the fissure of Sylvius.

Psychical responses

The following effects are psychical. The strength of current was increased from 2 to 3 volts.

11—"I heard something familiar, I do not know what it was."

11—(repeated without warning)—"Yes, Sir, I think I heard a mother calling her little boy somewhere. It seemed to be something that happened

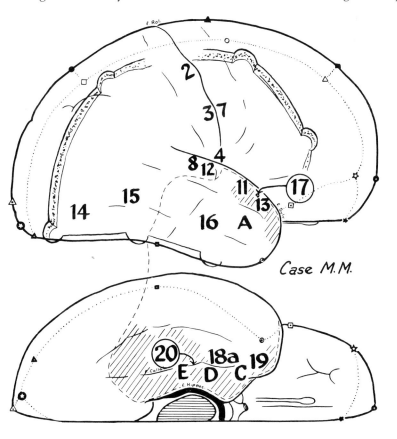

FIGURE 5 *Diagram of the operation. Broken line shows extent of removal of temporal lobe in treatment of the focal epilepsy and the shading indicates sclerosis and atrophy due to arterial compression associated with herniation of the hippocampus through the incisura of the tentorium, at the time of birth (incisural sclerosis).*

years ago." When asked to explain, she said, "It was somebody in the neighbourhood where I live." She added that it seemed that she herself "was somewhere close enough to hear."

Warning without stimulation—"Nothing."

11 repeated—"Yes, I hear the same familiar sounds, it seems to be a woman calling, the same lady." That was not in the neighbourhood. It seemed to be at the lumber yard." Then she added reflectively, "I've never been around the lumber yard much."

This was an incident of childhood which she could never have recalled without the aid of the stimulating electrode. Actually she could not "remember" it but she knew at once, with no suggestion from us, that she must have experienced it sometime. The same incident was evoked again by another stimulation at approximately the same point. Then at a different point, 12, she had another experience but of a similar character. The ticket 12 was displaced before its position was recorded.

12—"Yes. I heard voices down along the river somewhere—a man's voice and a woman's voice calling."

When she was asked how she could tell that the calling had been "along the river," she said, "I think I saw the river." When asked what river it was, she said, "I don't know. It seems to be one I was visiting when I was a child."

Warning without stimulation—"Nothing."

Three minutes later without any warning stimulation was carried out again, probably near 13. While the electrode was held in place, she exclaimed: "Yes, I hear voices. It is late at night, around the carnival somewhere—some sort of travelling circus." Then, after removal of the electrode: "I just saw lots of big wagons that they use to haul animals in."

These simple re-enactments of experience had auditory and visual elements in them.

Eleven minutes later, stimulation was carried out without warning at a point just posterior to 11—"I seemed to hear little voices then," she said, "the voices of people calling from building to building somewhere—I do not know where it is but it is very familiar to me. I can not see the buildings now but they seem to be run-down buildings."

14 (just posterior to 15)—This stimulation caused her to say: "The whole operation now seems familiar."

Warning without stimulation—"Nothing."

15—"Just a tiny flash of familiarity and a feeling that I knew everything that was going to happen in the near future." Then she added, "as though I had been through all this before and thought I knew exactly what you were going to do next."

At point 17, an electrode, covered with an insulating coat except at its tip, was inserted to different depths and the current switched on so as to stimulate in various buried portions of the first temporal convolution and uncus.

17c (1 cm deep)—"Oh, I had the same very, very familiar memory, in an office somewhere. I could see the desks. I was there and someone was calling to me, a man leaning on a desk with a pencil in his hand."

Warning without stimulation—"Nothing."

11 (forty minutes after first stimulation of this point)—"I had a flash of familiar memory. I do not know what it was."

13 (repeated three times)—"Nothing."

11 (after four minutes)—"Nothing."

Conditions seemed to have changed and stimulation now would summon no experiences.

The plan of surgical excision had now been formulated. Accordingly the second and third temporal convolutions were removed, exposing the first temporal convolution and the uncus and hippocampal gyrus deep within the temporal fossa.

Stimulation near uncus or just lateral to it, at 18a—"I had a little memory—a scene in a play—they were talking and I could see it.—It was just seeing it in my memory."

Stimulation at a point nearby—"I feel very close to an attack—I think I am going to have one—a familiar memory."

20 (Stimulation of the lateral aspect of the hippocampal gyrus)—"Oh, it hurts and that feeling of familiarity—a familiar memory—the place where I hang my coat up, where I go to work."

The patient M. M., described in this case, was a good witness, self-critical, understanding and tolerant. I have reported the features which are of psychological interest throughout the whole procedure of exploration and cortical excision, a three-hour period. But little reference is made to the pathological, surgical and electrocorticographic details.

A zone of abnormality due to birth compression was found (shown by cross hatching in Fig. 5). It was obvious that years of epileptic discharge arising in this zone had sensitized the temporal cortex so that stimulation could produce psychical responses. Stimulations elsewhere in the lobe were without positive effect even when a small increase was made in voltage.

The psychical hallucinations, thus produced, were experiences from this patient's past, not particularly important ones, and not ones that she could voluntarily remember with anything like the clarity of the hallucination. Yet she accepted them as part of her own past and she confessed that she was present in them. They brought to her the strong sense of familiarity that means recognition.

CASE N. C. (Figs. 6 and 7). This patient had seemed to be asleep on the operating table, but when the second temporal convolution on the left side was stimulated at point 19, she spoke as follows: "I had a dream, I had a book under my arm. I was talking to a man. The man was trying to reassure me not to worry about the book."

At 20, one cm distant, she said: "Mother is talking to me." Ten minutes later, point 20 was stimulated again and she laughed aloud. When asked to explain she said: "Well, it is kind of a long story but I will tell you."

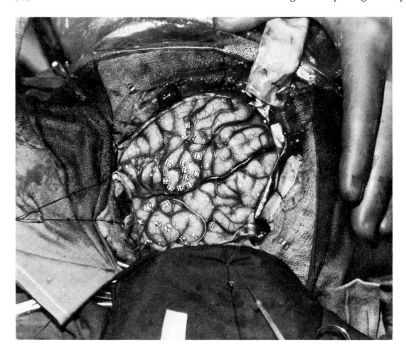

Left hemisphere exposed at operation. Case N. C.

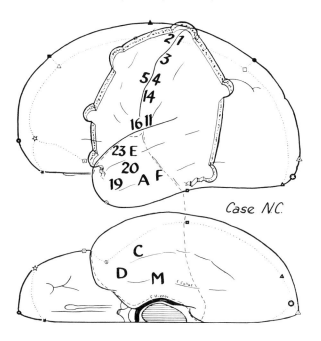

Diagram of operation. Case N. C.

The stimulating electrode was then withdrawn. It seemed the occurrence took place at her home in Richmond, Washington. She said to her mother, "Don't forget the fabulous feeling." Her mother "mocked" her, she said, and she concluded the story, "I took my arm and brought it down on the plate and broke it all to pieces."

Stimulation was repeated at point 20 (Fig. 7) without warning. While the electrode was kept in place the patient spoke quietly: "Yes, another experience, a different experience, a true experience. This man Mr. Meerburger, he, oh well, he drinks . . . The electrode was withdrawn and the patient continued to explain her experience. I said, 'hmm, he is back,' meaning Mr. Meerburger's little boy, and the lady said, 'What is the matter,' etc. etc. etc." This was an experience she did remember.

At 23 on the first temporal convolution, stimulation caused her to hear music. Six times at intervals, stimulation was carried out here. She heard first a "baby song" and later, what she called "The War March of the Priests."

On one occasion following stimulation which had been carried out with no warning, she said, "Yes. I was trying to identify the song." The surgeon asked her if she would like to have him stimulate again and she said, "yes." After the electrode was reapplied and while it was held in place she was quiet for a time. Then she began to hum and she hummed an air quite accurately. Finally she said, "Yes, it is the War March of The Priests." It was obvious that she had been accompanying the music with her humming.

Four minutes later, as a final test, she was asked to report just as soon as she heard music. After considerable delay the electrode was applied again at 23. Instantly she said, "There." It was the "War March" again. She explained that it was an orchestra playing each time, without any voice. She added that she had a phonograph record at home with the "Hallelujah Chorus" on one side and the "War March" on the other.

CASE R. M. During stimulation of the superior surface of the left temporal lobe within the fissure of Sylvius, R. M. said: "A guy coming through the fence at the baseball game, I see the whole thing." Afterward he said, "I just happened to watch those two teams play when the fellow came through the fence . . . That would be like the beginning of an attack, anything might come up." He went on to explain that such scenes from his past came to him suddenly at the beginning of a seizure, when he was thinking of something else, things he had forgotten all about.

One more example may be described. In this case the hallucination had to do with thoughts. It is difficult to discover whether in such cases the thought is divorced from any visual or auditory content or not.

CASE A. D. This patient had temporal lobe seizures introduced by having what he called two thoughts simultaneously.

Stimulation in the first temporal convolution caused him to say, "My thoughts bounced together and I was mixed up for a second."

When the stimulation was repeated, he said, "The same two thoughts came together." After the electrode was withdrawn he explained that one of the thoughts was concerned with what was happening at the present time and the second thought was different but he could not recall it clearly.

When the same area was stimulated after an interval of time he said, "This is it." When asked whether he had had a memory, he said, "No. It is the thought that crosses." But he could not explain and gave up the effort.

DISCUSSION

The foregoing examples demonstrate the nature of evidence upon which this discussion must be based. I have published other cases elsewhere and shall draw on our total experience in this argument.

Psychical responses

From the patient's point of view there is a great difference between psychical responses and sensory responses to stimulation. When a sensory area is stimulated the patient never seems to feel an object. He does not hear words or music, nor see a person or building. In sensory responses there are no recollections of the past and the subject himself is usually clear that the sensation is not an ordinary experience at all.

What we have referred to as psychical responses, on the other hand, include many different elements of thought, made up of auditory, visual, somatic and labyrinthine information, as well as interpretations, perceptions, comparisons, emotions.

Under the heading of psychical, there are two types of response. One is a reproduction of past experience and the other is a sudden alteration in interpretation of present experience. Thus the psychical responses to stimulation, taken together, may be divided into two groups:

1. *Experiential.* This has to do with the past and includes past events and past interpretation.

2. *Interpretative.* This has to do with the present.

Experimental responses

When these flash-backs, these short reproductions of past experience, occurred as epileptic phenomena, Jackson called them dreamy states. They are the same when produced by stimulation—drawn from the patient's past experience. Let me use the words of the patient M. M. again: "I had a little memory—a scene from a play—they were talking and I could see it," and again, "Oh, familiar memory, in an office somewhere. I could see the desks. I was there and someone was calling to me, a man leaning on a desk with a pencil in his hand."

All the detail of those things to which she had paid attention are still there. Perhaps the pencil in his hand had seemed important, but other images that must have reached her retina during the original experience are now lost for they were ignored originally. Throughout all of these evoked experiences she continued to be aware of the fact that she was actually in the operating room.

It is clear that a flash-back response is usually completely experiential, including events and also the patient's interpretation. The patient feels the attendant emotion and understands the original meaning.

Interpretive responses

As an example of interpretive responses, take again the case of M. M. When the electrode was applied to another area of the temporal lobe it produced a sudden sense of familiarity which she referred at once to her present experience. She felt the operation had happened before and that she even knew what the surgeon was about to do. This occurred independently of any recollection of the past.

When such interpretations have been described by temporal lobe epileptics, clinicians have long called them "déjà vu" phenomena. They are disturbances of the present process of interpretation. They are illusions, but these illusions take different forms. There may be a false sense of familiarity as already described; or, on the contrary, everything may seem strange or absurd. The relationship of the individual to his environment may seem to be altered. The distance from things seen or heard may seem to be increased or decreased. The patient may say he is far away from himself or from the world.

Allied to these altered interpretations is the production of emotions not justified by the experience. Fear is the commonest emotion produced by stimulation. It was reported as an epileptic aura 22 times out of 271 cases of temporal lobe epilepsy and was produced by stimulation 9 times.

All of these are interpretive responses. They correspond with the judgments which a normal individual is making constantly as he compares present experience with past experience. If a decision is to be made as to whether present experience is familiar or appropriate or menacing, the record of past experience must be available and the new record must be somehow classified with similar old records for the purposes of comparison.

Localization

Both types of response, experiential and interpretive, argue for the existence of a permanent ganglionic recording of the stream of consciousness. The record of that stream must be preserved in a specialized mechanism. Otherwise experiential responses to an electrode applied locally would be impossible. It seems likely also that appropriate parts of this same record are somehow utilized when recurring judgments are made in regard to familiarity and meaning of each new experience.

These psychical responses were produced by stimulation of the temporal cortex, chiefly on the superior and lateral surfaces of both lobes and probably extending a little way into the parietal lobe (Fig. 8). None resulted from stimulation of other lobes. It seems fair to conclude, therefore, that these areas of cortex have a particular relationship to the formation of a record of experience and the preservation of that record. If this conclusion is correct, another important advance has been made in the evolution of our knowledge of cerebral localization.

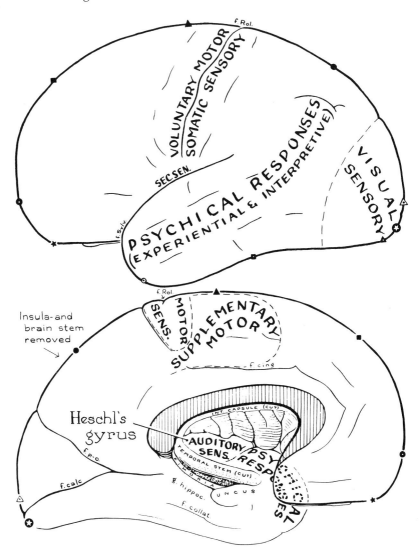

FIGURE 8 *Area of cortex from which psychical responses are obtained. They may be experiential, recalling the experience of some past interval of time, or they may be interpretive and alter the patient's interpretation of present experience. The major sensory and motor areas are also indicated.*

Doubling of conscious experience

When stimulation produced an experiential response during operative exploration, the patient usually recognized that this was something out of his own past. At the same time he may have been acutely aware of the fact that he was lying upon the operating table. Thus he was able to contemplate and to talk about this doubling of awareness and to recognize it as a strange paradox.

A young man (J. T.) who had recently come from his home in South Africa cried out when the superior surface of his right temporal lobe was being stimulated: "Yes, Doctor, yes, Doctor! Now I hear people laughing—my friends—in South Africa." After stimulation was over he could discuss that double awareness and express his astonishment, for it had seemed to him that he was with his cousins at their home where he and the two young ladies were laughing together. He did not remember what they were laughing at. Doubtless he would have discovered that also, if the strip of experience had happened to begin earlier, or if the surgeon had continued the stimulation a little longer.

This was an experience from his earlier life. It had faded from his recollective memory, but the ganglionic pattern which must have been formed during that experience was still intact and available to the stimulating electrode. It was at least as clear to him as it would have been had he closed his eyes and ears 30 seconds after the event and rehearsed the whole scene "from memory." Sight and sound and personal interpretation, all were re-created for him.

It is significant, however, that during the re-creation of that past experience he was not impelled to speak to his cousins. Instead he spoke to the "Doctor" in the operating room. Herein may lie an important distinction between this form of hallucination and the hallucinations of a patient during a toxic delirium or a psychotic state. In my experience (and relying only on my own memory!) no patient has ever addressed himself to a person who was part of a past experience, unless perhaps it was when he had passed into a state of automatism.[5]

As J. T. lay on the operating table two sets of ganglionic recordings were available to him for his conscious consideration, one that had been laid down during an interval of time that belonged to the past, and another that was being laid down during an equal interval of time in what we may call the present. He was evidently able to distinguish between the present experience and the past and so he addressed himself in astonishment to one of the actors in the present experience.

In the recording which he was then making of the present experience, he was including the experience that came to him from the past, together

[5] During automatism patients sometimes talk about unrelated matters, which might suggest that they were addressing someone, but they never describe hallucinations and there is complete subsequent amnesia.

with the sensory information of his present environment in the operating room, and the results of his reasoning in regard to the two recordings.

When such states occurred in an epileptic attack, Hughlings Jackson spoke of a doubling of consciousness. But there is an important difference in the two experiences. Although the sensory elements may be as realistic in one as in the other, the interpretation in the flash-back was all finished while the interpretation of both experiences had to be made and recorded as a part of the present experience!

When we discussed the matter, the patient and I, during the period of convalescence which followed removal of a large portion of his right temporal lobe, he recalled the whole affair and also his own surprise that he should hear his friends so far away and laugh with them while he faced such a serious situation here in Montreal.

One might suggest that, while the right temporal lobe under the influence of stimulation was engaged in the reproduction of the experience from the past, the left temporal lobe was being employed by the patient in the formation of the recording of the whole present experience. Such a suggestion is, of course, no more than a surmise. But that he did make a new record of both experiences somewhere is certain.

There are two elements in the experiential record, first, the sensory material of which the subject was originally aware and, second, the interpretation of the sensory material with a conclusion as to its significance. As already pointed out, in order to make the second, or interpretive, element possible, there must be comparison with past experience so that a conclusion may be drawn as to familiarity, strangeness, distance, danger, advantage, and necessity for action. It seems likely that under normal conditions the actual recording of the stream of consciousness may be utilized for the purposes of comparison long after it has been lost to voluntary recall.

Tempo of action

I conclude that the interval of time involved in the past experience is the same as the time required for its subsequent re-enactment. The action or thought in the re-enactment progresses at the same speed as during the original experience. I make this conclusion about speed from consideration of the following evidence:

The patient N. C., whose case has been described, listened to an orchestra while the electrode was applied. When she hummed the air, accompanying thus the music, the tempo of her humming was the tempo that would be expected of an orchestra.

Let me give another similar example.

D. F. (ref. 3, p. 128) was an intelligent young woman, a secretary and amateur musician. After the anterior end of her right temporal lobe had been amputated, the cut surface of the gray matter was stimulated at a point on the superior surface of the lobe. The stimulus caused her to say that she heard an orchestra playing and she asserted that we had turned on a phonograph. When she hummed the tune, Miss Phoebe Stanley, the operating nurse, recognizing the song, supplied the words of the lyric. The tempo of the patient's humming was certainly the tempo that would be expected of an orchestra playing that air.

And so, since the music is reproduced at a normal tempo regardless of the number of electrical impulses per second which may be varied from 30 to 100, I would conclude that the rate of movement in the re-created experience is the same as that of the original occurrence.

Further, and more important, verification of this conclusion is to be found in the fact that no patient has suggested that the people who walked or spoke or called during the hallucination did so at an unusual or unexpected rate of speed.

The patient's interpretation of an experiential response

Some patients call the response a dream. Others state that it is a flashback from their own life history. All agree that it is more vivid than anything that they could recall voluntarily.

G. F. (ref. 3, p. 137) was caused to hear her small son, Frank, speaking in the yard outside her own kitchen, and she heard the "neighbourhood sounds" as well. Ten days after operation she was asked if this was a memory. "Oh, no," she replied. "It seemed more real than that." Then she added: "Of course, I have heard Frankie like that many, many times, thousands of times."

This response to stimulation was a single experience. Her memory of such occasions was a generalization. Without the aid of the electrode, she could not recall any one of the specific instances nor hear the honking of automobiles that might mean danger to Frankie, or cries of other children or the barking of dogs that would have made up the "neighbourhood sounds" on each occasion.

The patients have never looked upon an experiential response as a remembering. Instead of that it is a hearing—and seeing—again, a living-through moments of past time. Do you remember Dickens' Christmas Carol, and how Old Scrooge seemed to re-live certain boyhood experiences under the strange spell of the "Spirit of Christmas Past?" It seems to be a little like that.

D. F. listened to an orchestra in the operating room but did not recall where she had heard it "that way." It was a song she had never learned to sing or play. Perhaps she had been oblivious of her surroundings while she listened to the orchestra in that previous period of time. T. S. heard music and seemed to be in the theatre where he had heard it. A. Br. heard the singing of a Christmas song in her church at home in Holland. She seemed to be there in the church and was moved again by the beauty of the occasion just as she had been on that Christmas Eve some years before.

Contents of the record

The nature of the contents of the record of the stream of consciousness may be guessed from the words of the patients that I have quoted tonight and of patients included in previous publications. It may be surmised also, by any clinician, from critical study of the content of the temporal lobe seizures which Hughlings Jackson called dreamy states. It may be guessed from the fact that when you meet a friend after many years you detect the little changes in him in a way that proves you had not lost the detail of original experiences. It may well be that seeing him renders details of the original record available for comparison, details which were lost to voluntary recollection.

The recording has strong visual and auditory components but always it is an unfolding of sight and sound and also, though rarely, of sense of position. The experience goes forward. There are no still pictures.

Curiously enough, no patient has yet reported pain or taste or smell during an experiential response. These sensations, without recollection of previous experience, were elicited by the electrode only from sensory areas. They were considered by the patient to be no more than present sensations, not elements in a past experience. It should be said, however, that the failure to get a response of any particular type has little statistical value, for the total number of patients from whom psychical responses have been elicited is, after all, small.[6]

One might seek to discover whether reasoning, which is divorced from awareness of sensory phenomena, finds any place in the cortical record. It is difficult for me to explore this possibility which involves certain questions of philosophical analysis. But it may be pointed out that patients do sometimes speak of unexpected thoughts coming into mind as a warning of the onset of a focal seizure. They usually report that this confuses them so that the account they give of the matter is not clear.

An example was presented above (Case A. D.) of the production of two thoughts by temporal stimulation. The patient said that one thought had to do with what was going on at the present time and the second thought was different, but the effect upon him was confusion and inability to explain. It might seem that two lines of reasoning or thinking could not co-exist without interference and that, if thoughts were really re-activated, they confused the patient's present effort to rationalize.

However that may be, it seems clear that the final interpretation and the understanding of any experience are recorded with the experience.

---

[6] My associate Dr. Sean Mullan informs me that there have been 87 cases of temporal lobe epilepsy in which electrical exploration was carried out during the past three years. In only 22 of them did stimulation produce echoes of past experience. We have explored the cortex in 271 temporal lobe cases in all, which suggests that not over 60 patients had experiential responses. In no case where the epileptogenic focus was located in central or frontal regions have there been such responses.

This interpretation and understanding may be considered the end result or the conclusion of rationalization. Certainly, at the times of re-activation, the patient has no difficulty in perceiving his former understanding of a situation along with the objective aspects of the situation itself.

Memory contrasted with the record

It is clear that each successive recording is somehow classified and compared with previous recordings so that, little by little, each separate song is "learned" and becomes a unit in the memory, and all the familiar things in man's life undergo the same change. A poem or an elocution may be "committed to memory." But memory, as we ordinarily think of it, is something more, and a great deal less, than any recording, unless that recording was made unusually vivid by fear or joy or special meaning. Then perhaps the detail of an original experience and the patient's memory of it might be identical.

The psychical responses of the "flash-back" variety were, for the most part, quite unimportant moments in the patient's life: standing on a street corner, hearing a mother call her child, taking a part in a conversation, listening to a little boy as he played in the yard. If these unimportant minutes of time were preserved in the ganglionic recordings of these patients, why should it be thought that any experience in the stream of consciousness drops out?

The evidence suggests that nothing is lost, that the record of each man's experience is complete. The time taken up by deep sleep or coma must drop out and it must be left an open question as to whether or not the time taken up by reasoning is included in the record.

CONCLUSION

In conclusion it is evident that the brain of every man contains an unchanging ganglionic record of successive experience. The psychical responses which have been produced by electrical stimulation, during craniotomy and cortical exploration, demonstrate that this record embraces and retains the elements that once were incorporated in his stream of thought.

Simply expressed, the conditions which bring about these psychical responses, both experiential and interpretive, are these: The stimulating electrode, delivering for example 60 impulses per second, is applied to a point on the temporal cortex of a man who is fully awake. The ganglion cells of the cortex are hyper-irritable and ready to react because, for years, small electral discharges have been playing over the cortical blanket day and night from a neighboring epileptogenic focus.

Thousands of these conditioned ganglion cells may well be reached directly by the stimulating current and they have neuronal connections that pass through the gray matter that covers the temporal lobe and also inward to the central integrating circuits of the brain stem. But instead of mass activity, a selective and highly patterned ganglionic action results.

Let me describe what seems to happen by means of a parable: Among the millions and millions of nerve cells that clothe certain parts of the temporal lobe on each side, there runs a thread. It is the thread of time, the thread that has run through each succeeding wakeful hour of the individual's past life. Think of this thread, if you like, as a pathway through an unending sequence of nerve cells, nerve fibers and synapses. It is a pathway which can be followed again because of the continuing facilitation that has been created in the cell contacts.

When, by chance, the neurosurgeon's electrode activates some portion of that thread, there is a response as though that thread were a wire recorder, or a strip of cinematographic film, on which are registered all those things of which the individual was once aware, the things he selected for his attention in that interval of time. Absent from it are the sensory impulses he ignored, the talk he did not heed.

Time's strip of film runs forward, never backward, even when resurrected from the past. It seems to proceed again at time's own unchanged pace. It would seem, once one section of the strip has come alive, that a functional all-or-nothing principle steps in so as to protect the other portions of the film from activation by the electric current. As long as the electrode is held in place, the experience of a former day goes forward. There is no holding it still, no turning it back. When the electrode is withdrawn it stops as suddenly as it began.[7]

We have found a way of activating the anatomical record of the stream of consciousness. It is evident, therefore, that the ganglionic mechanism which preserves man's experiential record is either present, in duplicate, in the temporal cortex of each hemisphere, where stimulation produces these responses; or it is located in duplicate in the hippocampal zones of each side where direct stimulation does not produce the responses; or, finally, it is located more centrally in the brain where the closest functional connection is maintained with the stimulable zones of the temporal lobes.[*]

---

[7] A particular strip can sometimes be repeated by interrupting the stimulation and then reapplying it at the same or a nearby point, for the threshold of evocation of that particular response is lowered for a time by the first stimulus. Graham Brown and Sherrington (6) described local facilitation and intensification of motor responses by repeated stimulation at a single point in the anthropoid cortex, and we have found the same to be true for man in motor and sensory areas of the cortex (2).

[*] This point should perhaps be stressed more strongly. A great deal of caution is required in interpreting these results, however dramatic and suggestive they may be. Not only is it perfectly possible that the "record" may be stored somewhere else—it has been estimated that there is a more or less direct path from any point in the brain to any other point—but there are other problems as well. The "flashbacks" which the subjects produce have not been convincingly demonstrated to be true memories, but may just possibly represent new creations. The fact that these effects are obtained only in epileptic patients must also be borne in mind. (Ed.)

However that may be, and whatever the mechanism involved, it is certain that in the temporal cortex lie the keys of activation of the record.

During any given period of waking time each individual forms a record of the stream of consciousness. The record is the final expression, and the outcome, of the action of central integration of nerve impulses. The formation of this record is subject to the selecting and limiting influences of attention. As the record is formed, it includes the elements of consciousness. Possibly, like a film, its contents are projected on the screen of man's awareness before it is replaced by subsequent experience. Thus it might seem that the record of the stream of consciousness is more than a record. It represents one of the final stages in the neuronal integration which makes consciousness what it is.

Probably no man can, by voluntary effort, completely re-activate any portion of the record of the stream of thought. Except for a few seconds or minutes after the event, he seems to have no voluntary mechanism that rivals the electrode. Memory, as ordinarily conceived, is quite a different phenomenon. It seems likely, however, that the original record continues to be available in some sort of way for the purposes of the comparison and interpretation of each new experience, as long as a man may live and keep his wits.

The stream of consciousness flows inexorably onward, as described in the words of William James. But, unlike a river, it leaves behind it a permanent record that seems to be complete for the waking moments of a man's life, a record that runs, no doubt, like a thread along a pathway of ganglionic and synaptic facilitations in the brain. This pathway is located partly or wholly in the temporal lobes.

There is hope in all this that physiology and psychology, and philosophy too, may be drawn more closely together and that, with the opening of a new chapter of understanding of the localization of function within the human brain, some light may yet be thrown upon the mind of man.

BIBLIOGRAPHY

1 James, W., The Principles of Psychology, 1910, Holt & Co., New York.
2 Penfield, W. and T. Rasmussen, 1950, The Cerebral Cortex of Man, Macmillan, New York.
3 Penfield, W. and H. Jasper, 1954, Epilepsy and the Functional Anatomy of ·the Human Brain, Little Brown, Boston.
4 Penfield, W., 1954, Mechanisms of Voluntary Movement, Brain, 77: 1–17.
5 Penfield, W., The Cerebral Cortex and Consciousness. Arch. Neurol. & Psychiat. 40, 1938, 417–442. Also in French, Année Psychol. 39, 1938, 1.
6 Graham Brown, T. and C. Sherrington, On the Instability of a Cortical Point. Proc. Roy. Soc., London, s.B. 85: 250–277.

LOSS OF RECENT MEMORY AFTER BILATERAL HIPPOCAMPAL LESIONS

William Beecher Scoville and Brenda Milner

HARTFORD HOSPITAL, MC GILL UNIVERSITY, AND THE MONTREAL NEUROLOGICAL INSTITUTE, CANADA

Source   Reprinted from the **Journal of Neurology, Neurosurgery and Psychiatry**, 1957, **20**, (11), 11–19, with permission of the authors and the British Medical Association.

In 1954 Scoville described a grave loss of recent memory which he had observed as a sequel to bilateral medial temporal-lobe resection in one psychotic patient and one patient with intractable seizures. In both cases the operations had been radical ones, undertaken only when more conservative forms of treatment had failed. The removals extended posteriorly along the mesial surface of the temporal lobes for a distance of approximately 8 cm. from the temporal tips and probably destroyed the anterior two-thirds of the hippocampus and hippocampal gyrus bilaterally, as well as the uncus and amygdala. The unexpected and persistent memory deficit which resulted seemed to us to merit further investigation. We have therefore carried out formal memory and intelligence testing of these two patients and also of eight other patients who had undergone similar, but less radical, bilateral medial temporal lobe resections.[1] The present paper gives the results of these studies which point to the importance of the hippocampal complex for normal memory function. Whenever the hippocampus and hippocampal gyrus were damaged bilaterally in these operations some memory deficit was found, but not otherwise. We have chosen to report these findings in full, partly for their theoretical significance, and partly as a warning to others of the risk to memory involved in bilateral surgical lesions of the hippocampal region.

OPERATIONS

During the past seven years in an effort to preserve the overall personality in psychosurgery some 300 fractional lobotomies have been performed, largely on seriously ill schizophrenic patients who had failed to respond to other forms of treatment. The aim in these fractional procedures was to secure as far as possible any beneficial effects a complete frontal lobotomy might have, while at the same time avoiding its undesirable side-effects. And it was in fact found that undercutting limited to the orbital surfaces of both frontal lobes has an appreciable therapeutic effect in psychosis and yet does not cause any new personality deficit to appear (Scoville, Wilk, and Pepe, 1951). In view of the known close relationship between the posterior orbital and mesial temporal cortices (MacLean, 1952; Pribram and Kruger, 1954), it was hoped that still greater psychiatric benefit might be obtained by extending the orbital undercutting so as to destroy parts of the mesial temporal cortex bilaterally. Accordingly, in 30 severely deteriorated cases, such partial temporal-lobe resections were carried out, either with or without orbital undercutting. The surgical pro-

[1] These further psychological examinations by one of the authors, B. M., were made possible through the interest of Dr. Wilder Penfield.

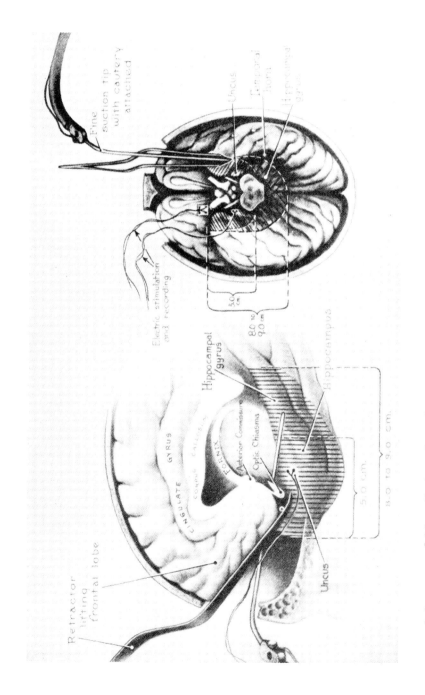

FIGURE 1 *Area removed bilaterally from the medical temporal lobes demonstrating 5 cm. as well as 8 cm. removals through supra-orbital trephines.*

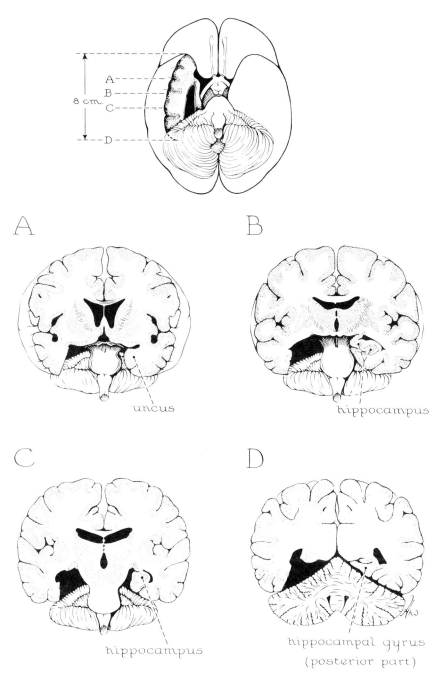

FIGURE 2 *Diagrammatic cross-sections of human brain illustrating extent of attempted bilateral medial temporal lobe resection in the radical operation. (For diagrammatic purposes the resection has been shown on one side only.)*

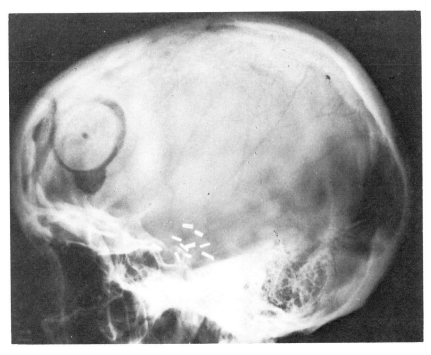

FIGURE 3 *Post-operative skull radiograph with silver clip markers outlining extent of bilateral resections limited to the uncus and amygdala.*

cedure has been described elsewhere (Scoville, Dunsmore, Liberson, Henry, and Pepe, 1953) and is illustrated anatomically in Figs. 1 to 4. All the removals have been bilateral, extending for varying distances along the mesial surface of the temporal lobes. Five were limited to the uncus and underlying amygdaloid nucleus; all others encroached also upon the anterior hippocampus, the excisions being carried back 5 cm. or more after bisecting the tips of the temporal lobes, with the temporal horn constituting the lateral edge of resection. In one case only in this psychotic group all tissue mesial to the temporal horns for a distance of at least 8 cm. posterior to the temporal tips was destroyed, a removal which presumably included the anterior two-thirds of the hippocampal complex bilaterally.

An equally radical bilateral medial temporal-lobe resection was carried out in one young man (H. M.) with a long history of major and minor seizures uncontrollable by maximum medication of various forms, and showing diffuse electro-encephalographic abnormality. This frankly experimental operation was considered justifiable because the patient was totally incapacitated by his seizures and these had proven refractory to a medical approach. It was suggested because of the known epileptogenic qualities of the uncus and hippocampal complex and because of the relative absence of post-operative seizures in our temporal-lobe resections as compared with fractional lobotomies in other areas. The operation was carried out with

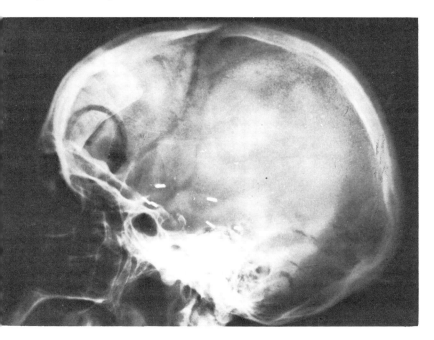

FIGURE 4   *Post-operative skull radiograph with silver clip markers outlining the extent of the bilateral resections including the anterior hippocampal complex (approximately 6 cm. posterior to the tip of the anterior temporal fossa).*

the understanding and approval of the patient and his family, in the hope of lessening his seizures to some extent. At operation the medial surfaces of both temporal lobes were exposed and recordings were taken from both surface and depth electrodes before any tissue was removed; but again no discrete epileptogenic focus was found. Bilateral resection was then carried out, extending posteriorly for a distance of 8 cm. from the temporal tips.

RESULTS

The psychiatric findings bearing upon the treatment of schizophrenia have already been reported (Scoville and others, 1953). Briefly, it was found that bilateral resections limited to the medial portions of the temporal lobes were without significant therapeutic effect in psychosis, although individual patients (including the one with the most radical removal) did in fact show some improvement. There have been no gross changes in personality. This is particularly clear in the case of the epileptic, nonpsychotic patient whose present cheerful placidity does not differ appreciably from his pre-operative status and who, in the opinion of his family, has shown no personality change. Neurological changes in the group have also been minimal. The incidence and severity of seizures in the epileptic patient were sharply reduced for the first year after operation, and although he is once again having both major and minor attacks, these attacks no longer leave him stuporous, as they formerly did. It has therefore been possible to reduce his medication considerably. As far as general intelligence is concerned, the epileptic patient has actually improved slightly since operation, possibly because he is less drowsy than before. The psychotic patient were for the most part too disturbed before operation for finer testing of higher mental functions to be carried out, but certainly there is no indication of any general intellectual impairment resulting from the operation in those patients for whom the appropriate test data are available.

There has been one striking and totally unexpected behavioural result a grave loss of recent memory in those cases in which the medial temporal lobe resection was so extensive as to involve the major portion of the hippocampal complex bilaterally. The psychotic patient having the most radical excision (extending 8 cm. from the tips of the temporal lobes bilaterally) has shown a profound post-operative memory disturbance, but unfortunately this was not recognized at the time because of her disturbed emotional state. In the non-psychotic patient the loss was immediately apparent. After operation this young man could no longer recognize the hospital staff nor find his way to the bathroom, and he seemed to recall nothing of the day-to-day events of his hospital life. There was also a partial retrograde amnesia, inasmuch as he did not remember the death of a favourite uncle three years previously, nor anything of the period in hospital, yet could recall some trivial events that had occurred just before his admission to the hospital. His early memories were apparently vivid and intact.

This patient's memory defect has persisted without improvement to the present time, and numerous illustrations of its severity could be given. Ten months ago the family moved from their old house to a new one a few blocks away on the same street; he still has not learned the new address, though remembering the old one perfectly, nor can he be trusted to find his way home alone. Moreover, he does not know where objects in continual use are kept; for example, his mother still has to tell him where to find the lawn mower, even though he may have been using it only the day before. She also states that he will do the same jigsaw puzzles day after day without showing any practice effect and that he will read the same magazines over and over again without finding their contents familiar. This patient has even eaten luncheon in front of one of us (B. M.) without being able to name, a mere half-hour later, a single item of food he had eaten; in fact, he could not remember having eaten luncheon at all. Yet to a casual observer this man seems like a relatively normal individual, since his understanding and reasoning are undiminished.

The discovery of severe memory defect in these two patients led us to study further all patients in the temporal-lobe series who were sufficiently cooperative to permit formal psychological testing. The operation sample included, in addition to the two radical resections, one bilateral removal of the uncus, extending 4 cm. posterior to the temporal tips, and six bilateral medial temporal-lobe resections in which the removal was carried back 5 or 6 cm. to include also a portion of the anterior hippocampus; in three of these six cases the temporal-lobe resection was combined with orbital undercutting. One unilateral case was also studied in which right inferior

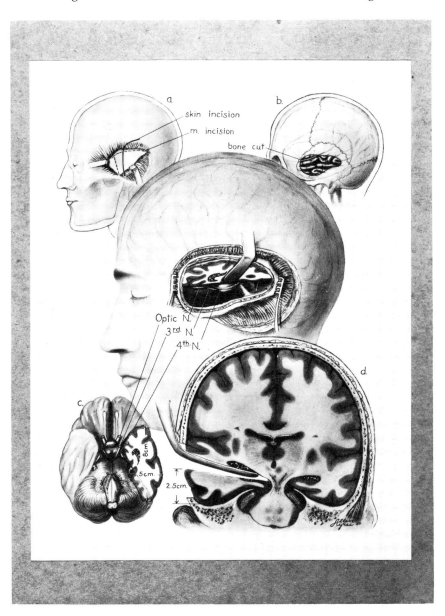

FIGURE 5 *Unilateral inferior horizontal temporal lobectomy extending a distance of 8 cm. posterior to the tip of the anterior temporal fossa. This operation is performed for incisural herination of the temporal lobes (Case 10).*

temporal lobectomy and hippocampectomy had been carried out for the relief of incisural herniation due to malignant oedema (Fig. 5). We found some memory impairment in all the bilateral cases in which the removal was carried far enough posteriorly to damage the hippocampus and hippocampal gyrus, but in only one of these six additional cases (D.C.) did the memory loss equal in severity that seen in the two most radical excisions. The case with bilateral excision of the uncus (in which the removal can have involved only the amygdaloid and peri-amygdaloid areas) showed excellent memory function. The unilateral operation, extensive as it was, has caused no lasting memory impairment, though some disturbance of recent memory was noted in the early post-operative period (Scoville, 1954); we now attribute this deficit to temporary interference with the functioning of the hippocampal zone of the opposite hemisphere by contralateral pressure.

The histories and individual test results for these 10 cases are reported below, and the Table summarizes the principal findings. For purposes of

Table 1. Classification of Cases

Cases	Age at Time of Follow-up (yr.)	Sex	Diagnosis	Operation
Group I: Severe Memory Defect				
Case 1, H. M.	29	M	Epilepsy	Medial temporal
Case 2, D. C.	47	M	Paranoid schizophrenia	Medial temporal and orbital undercutting
Case 3, M. B.	55	F	Manic-depressive psychosis	Medial temporal
Group II: Moderate Memory Defect				
Case 4, A. Z.	35	F	Paranoid schizophrenia	Medial temporal
Case 5, M. R.	40	F	Paranoid schizophrenia	Medial temporal and orbital undercutting
Case 6, A. R.	38	F	Hebephrenic schizophrenia	Medial temporal and orbital undercutting
Case 7, C. G.	44	F	Schizophrenia	Medial temporal
Case 8, A. L.	31	M	Schizophrenia	Medial temporal
Group III: No Memory Defect				
Case 9, I. S.	54	F	Paranoid schizophrenia	Uncectomy
Case 10, E. G.	55	F	Incisural herniation	Inferior temporal lobectomy

comparison the cases have been divided into three groups representing different degrees of memory impairment.

GROUP I: SEVERE MEMORY DEFECT

In this category are those patients who since operation appear to forget the incidents of their daily life as fast as they occur. It is interesting that all these patients were able to retain a three-figure number or a pair of unrelated words for several minutes, if care was taken not to distract them in the interval. However, they forgot the instant attention was diverted to a new topic. Since in normal life the focus of attention is constantly changing, such individuals show an apparently complete anterograde amnesia. This severe defect was observed in the two patients having the most radical bilateral medial temporal-lobe excisions (with the posterior limit of removal approximately 8 cm. from the temporal tips) and in one

Bi- or Uni- Lateral	Approximate Extent of Removal along Medial Temporal Lobes (cm.)	Time between Operation and Testing (mth.)	Wechsler Scale	
			Intelli- gence Quotient	Memory Quotient
B	8	20	112	67
B	5.5	21	122	70
B	8	28	78	60
B	5	40	96	84
B	5	39	123	81
B	4.5	47	Incomplete	
B	5.5	41	Incomplete	
B	6	38	Incomplete	
B	4	53	122	125
U-Rt.	9	16	93	90

other case, a bilateral 5.5 cm. medial temporal excision. These three cases will now be described.

Case 1, H. M. This 29-year-old motor winder, a high school graduate, had had minor seizures since the age of 10 and major seizures since the age of 16. The small attacks lasted about 40 seconds, during which he would be unresponsive, opening his mouth, closing his eyes, and crossing both arms and legs; but he believed that he could "half hear what was going on". The major seizures occurred without warning and with no lateralizing sign. They were generalized convulsions, with tongue-biting, urinary incontinence, and loss of consciousness followed by prolonged somnolence. Despite heavy and varied anticonvulsant medication the major attacks had increased in frequency and severity through the years until the patient was quite unable to work.

The aetiology of this patient's attacks is not clear. He was knocked down by a bicycle at the age of 9 and was unconscious for five minutes afterwards, sustaining a laceration of the left supra-orbital region. Later radiological studies, however, including two pneumoencephalograms, have been completely normal, and the physical examination has always been negative.

Electro-encephalographic studies have consistently failed to show any localized epileptogenic area. In the examination of August 17, 1953, Dr. T. W. Liberson described diffuse slow activity with a dominant frequency of 6 to 8 per second. A short clinical attack was said to be accompanied by generalized 2 to 3 per second spike-and-wave discharge with a slight asymmetry in the central leads (flattening on the left).

Despite the absence of any localizing sign, operation was considered justifiable for the reasons given above. On September 1, 1953, bilateral medial temporal-lobe resection was carried out, extending posteriorly for a distance of 8 cm. from the midpoints of the tips of the temporal lobes, with the temporal horns constituting the lateral edges of resection.

After operation the patient was drowsy for a few days, but his subsequent recovery was uneventful apart from the grave memory loss already described. There has been no neurological deficit. An electro-encephalogram taken one year after operation showed increased spike-and-wave activity which was maximal over the frontal areas and bilaterally synchronous. He continues to have seizures, but these are less incapacitating than before.

Psychological Examination. This was performed on April 26, 1955. The memory defect was immediately apparent. The patient gave the date as March, 1953, and his age as 27. Just before coming into the examining room he had been talking to Dr. Karl Pribram, yet he had no recollection of this at all and denied that anyone had spoken to him. In conversation, he reverted constantly to boyhood events and seemed scarcely to realize that he had had an operation.

On formal testing the contrast between his good general intelligence and his defective memory was most striking. On the Wechsler-Bellevue Intelligence Scale he achieved a full-scale I.Q. rating of 112, which compares favourably with the pre-operative rating of 104 reported by Dr. Liselotte Fischer in August, 1953, the improvement in arithmetic being particularly striking. An extensive test battery failed to reveal any deficits in perception, abstract thinking, or reasoning ability, and his motivation remained excellent throughout.

On the Wechsler Memory Scale (Wechsler, 1945) his immediate recall of stories and drawings fell far below the average level and on the "associate _earning" subtest of this scale he obtained zero scores for the hard word associa- ions, low scores for the easy associations, and failed to improve with repeated _ractice. These findings are reflected in the low memory quotient of 67. More- _ver, on all tests we found that once he had turned to a new task the nature _f the preceding one could no longer be recalled, nor the test recognized if _epeated.

In summary, this patient appears to have a complete loss of memory for _vents subsequent to bilateral medial temporal-lobe resection 19 months before, _together with a partial retrograde amnesia for the three years leading up to _his operation; but early memories are seemingly normal and there is no impair- _ment of personality or general intelligence.

Case 2, D. C. This 47-year-old doctor was a paranoid schizophrenic with a _four-year history of violent, combative behaviour. Before his illness he had been _practising medicine in Chicago, but he had always shown paranoid trends and for _this reason had had difficulty completing his medical training. His breakdown _followed the loss of a lawsuit in 1950, at which time he made a homicidal _attack on his wife which led to his admission to hospital. Since then both insulin _ind electro-shock therapy had been tried without benefit and the prognosis _was considered extremely poor. On May 13, 1954, at the request of Dr. Frederick _Gibbs and Dr. John Kendrick, a bilateral medial temporal-lobe resection com- _bined with orbital undercutting was carried out at Manteno State Hospital (W. _B. S., with the assistance of Dr. John Kendrick). The posterior limit of the _removal was 5 cm. from the sphenoid ridge, or roughly 5.5 cm. from the tips _of the temporal lobes, with the inferior horns of the ventricles forming the _lateral edges of resection. Recording from depth electrodes at the time of opera- _tion showed spiking from the medial temporal regions bilaterally with some _spread to the orbital surfaces of both frontal lobes, but after the removal had _been completed a normal electro-encephalographic record was obtained from _the borders of the excision.

Post-operative recovery was uneventful and there has been no neurological _deficit. Since operation the patient has been outwardly friendly and tractable _with no return of his former aggressive behaviour, although the paranoid thought _content persists; he is considered markedly improved. But he too shows a pro- _found memory disturbance. At Manteno State Hospital he was described as _"confused," because since the operation he had been unable to find his way _to bed and seemed no longer to recognize the hospital staff. However, no psycho- _logical examination was made there, and on November 29, 1955, he was trans- _ferred to Galesburg State Research Institute where he was interviewed by one _of us (B. M.) on January 12, 1956.

Psychological Findings. This patient presented exactly the same pattern of _memory loss as H. M. He was courteous and cooperative throughout the examina- _tion, and the full-scale Wechsler I.Q. rating of 122 showed him to be still _of superior intellect. Yet he had no idea where he was, explaining that naturally _the surroundings were quite unfamiliar because he had only arrived there for _the first time the night before. (In fact, he had been there six weeks.) He _was unable to learn either the name of the hospital or the name of the examiner, _despite being told them repeatedly. Each time he received the information as _something new, and a moment later would deny having heard it. At the ex- _aminer's request he drew a dog and an elephant, yet half an hour later did _not even recognize them as his own drawings. On the formal tests of the Wechsler

Memory Scale his immediate recall of stories and drawings was poor, and the memory quotient of 70 is in sharp contrast to the high I.Q. level. As with H. M., once a new task was introduced there was total amnesia for the preceding one; in his own words, the change of topic confused him. This man did not know that he had had a brain operation and did not recall being at Mantenc State Hospital, although he had spent six months there before the operation as well as six months post-operatively. Yet he could give minute details of his early life and medical training (accurately, as far as we could tell).

Case 3, M. B. This 55-year-old manic depressive woman, a former clerical worker, was admitted to Connecticut State Hospital on December 27, 1951 at which time she was described as anxious, irritable, argumentative, and restless but well-orientated in all spheres. Her recent memory was normal, in that she knew how long she had been living in Connecticut and could give the date of her hospital admission and the exact times of various clinic appointments. On December 18, 1952, a radical bilateral medial temporal-lobe resection was carried out, with the posterior limit of removal 8 cm. from the temporal tips. Post-operatively she was stuporous and confused for one week, but then recovered rapidly and without neurological deficit. She has become neater and more even-tempered and is held to be greatly improved. However, psychological testing by Mr. I. Borganz in November, 1953, revealed a grave impairment of recent memory; she gave the year as 1950 and appeared to recall nothing of the events of the last three years. Yet her verbal intelligence proved to be normal.

She was examined briefly by B. M. in April, 1955, at which time she showed a global loss of recent memory similar to that of H. M. and D. C. She had been brought to the examining room from another building, but had already forgotten this; nor could she describe any other part of the hospital although she had been living there continuously for nearly three and a half years. On the Wechsler Memory Scale her immediate recall of stories and drawings was inaccurate and fragmentary, and delayed recall was impossible for her even with prompting; when the material was presented again she failed to recognize it. Her conversation centred around her early life and she was unable to give any information about the years of her hospital stay. Vocabulary, attention span, and comprehension were normal, thus confirming Mr. Borganz' findings.

GROUP II: MODERATELY SEVERE MEMORY DEFECT

In this second category are those patients who can be shown to retain some impression of new places and events, although they are unable to learn such arbitrary new associations as people's names and cannot be depended upon to carry out commissions. Subjectively, these patients complain of memory difficulty, and objectively, on formal tests, they do very poorly irrespective of the type of material to be memorized. The five remaining patients with bilateral medial temporal-lobe removals extending 5 or 6 cm. posteriorly from the temporal tips make up this group. Only two of these patients were well enough to permit thorough testing, but in all five cases enough data were obtained to establish that the patient did have a memory defect and that it was not of the gross type seen in Group I. The individual cases are reported below.

Case 4, A. Z. This 35-year-old woman, a paranoid schizophrenic, had been in Connecticut State Hospital for three years and extensive electro-shock therapy had been tried without lasting benefit. She was described as tense, assaultative, and sexually preoccupied. On November 29, 1951, bilateral medial temporal-lobe resection was carried out under local anaesthesia, the posterior limit of the removal being approximately 5 cm. from the tips of the temporal lobes. During subpial resection of the right hippocampal cortex the surgeon inadvertently went through the arachnoid and injured by suction a portion of the right peduncle, geniculate, or hypothalamic region with immediate development of deep coma. The injury was visualized by extra-arachnoid inspection. Post-operatively the patient remained in stupor for 72 hours and exhibited a left spastic hemiplegia, contracted fixed pupils, strabismus, and lateral nystagmus of the right eye; vital signs remained constant and within normal limits. She slowly recovered the use of the left arm and leg and her lethargy gradually disappeared. By the seventh post-operative day she could walk without support and pupillary responses had returned to normal. The only residual neurological deficit has been a left homonymous hemianopia. Of particular interest was the dramatic post-operative improvement in her psychotic state with an early complete remission of her delusions, anxiety, and paranoid behaviour. At the same time she showed a retrograde amnesia for the entire period of her illness.

This patient was discharged from the hospital nine months after operation and is now able to earn her living as a domestic worker. However, she complains that her memory is poor, and psychological examination (April 27, 1955) three and a half years post-operatively confirms this. But the deficit is less striking than in the three cases reported above. This patient, for example, was able to give the address of the house where she worked although she had been there only two days, and she could even describe the furnishings in some detail although she had not yet learned the name of her employer. She was also able to give an accurate, though sketchy, description of a doctor who had spoken to her briefly that morning and whom she had never seen before. However, she could recall very little of the conversation.

Formal testing at this time showed her intelligence to lie within the average range with no impairment of attention or concentration. The Wechsler-Bellevue I.Q. rating was 96. On the Wechsler Memory Scale her immediate recall of stories was normal, but passing from one story to the next was enough to make her unable to recall the first one, though a few fragments could be recovered with judicious prompting. She showed the same rapid forgetting on the "visual retention" subtest, indicating that the memory impairment was not specific to verbal material. Finally, she was conspicuously unsuccessful on the "associate learning" subtest, failing to master a single unfamiliar word association. This examination as a whole provides clear evidence of an impairment of recent memory.

Case 5, M. R. This 40-year-old woman, a paranoid schizophrenic with superimposed alcoholism, had been a patient at Norwich State Hospital for 11 years, receiving extensive electro-shock therapy. Bilateral medial temporal-lobe resection combined with orbital undercutting was carried out on January 17, 1952, the posterior extent of removal being roughly 5 cm. from the temporal tips. The patient has shown complete remission of psychotic symptoms and was discharged from the hospital on September 16, 1954, to the care of her family.

Psychological Examination. This was performed on April 29, 1955. Tests, showed this woman to be of superior intelligence, with a full-scale I.Q. rating of 123 on the Wechsler Scale. However, she complained of poor memory, adding that she could remember faces and "the things that are important," but that, to her great embarrassment, she forgot many ordinary daily happenings. Upon questioning she gave the year correctly but did not know the month or the day. She knew that she had had an operation in 1952 but did not recognize the surgeon (W. B. S.) nor recall his name. Formal testing revealed the same pattern of memory disturbance as A. Z. had shown, and the memory quotient of 81 compares most unfavourably with the high I.Q. rating. In conversation, she reverted constantly to discussion of her work during the years of depression and showed little knowledge of recent events.

Case 6, A. R. This 38-year-old woman had been in hospital for five years with a diagnosis of hebephrenic-schizophrenia. Before operation she was said to be noisy, combative, and suspicious, and electro-shock therapy had caused only transient improvement in this condition. On May 31, 1951, bilateral medial temporal-lobe resection combined with orbital undercutting was carried out, the posterior limit of removal being slightly less than 5 cm from the bisected tips of the temporal lobes. After operation the patient gradually became quieter and more cooperative and on September 29, 1952, she was discharged to her home. There have been no neurological sequelae.

Psychological Examination. This was performed in April, 1955. Examination revealed a hyperactive woman, too excited and talkative for prolonged testing. She showed a restricted span of attention but scores on verbal intelligence tests were within the dull normal range. Moreover, she appeared to recall some recent happenings quite well. Thus, she knew that her daughter had caught a 7 o'clock train to New York City that morning to buy a dress for a wedding the following Saturday. She could also describe the clothes worn by the secretary who had shown her into the office. However, on formal testing some impairment of recent memory was seen, although unlike the other patients in this group she did succeed on some of the difficult items of the "association learning" test. As with A. Z. and M. R., the deficit appeared most clearly on tests of delayed recall after a brief interval filled with some other activity. Thus, on the "logical memory" test she gave an adequate version of each story immediately after hearing it, but passing from one story to the next caused her to forget the first almost completely; similar results were obtained for the recall of drawings. We conclude that this patient has a memory impairment identical in type to that of the other patients in this group, but somewhat milder. It is interesting that she had a relatively small excision.

Case 7, C. G. This 44-year-old schizophrenic woman had been in the hospital for 20 years without showing any improvement in her psychosis. On November 19, 1951, bilateral medial temporal-lobe resection was carried out under local anaesthesia, the posterior limit of removal being 5.5 cm. from the tips of the temporal lobes. There was temporary loss of consciousness during the resection but the patient was fully conscious at the end of the procedure and post-operative recovery was uneventful. There has been no neurological deficit. She is considered to be in better contact than before but more forgetful.

This patient was examined at Norwich State Hospital in April, 1955, and although she was too distractible for prolonged testing, it was possible to show that she remembered some recent events. For example, she knew that she had been working in the hospital beauty parlour for the past week and that she had been washing towels that morning. Yet formal memory testing revealed the same deficit as that shown by A. Z and M. R., though less extensive data were obtained in this case.

Case 8, A. L. This 31-year-old schizophrenic man had been a patient at Norwich State Hospital since October, 1950. He had first become ill in August, 1950, demonstrating a catatonic type of schizophrenia with auditory and visual hallucinations. On January 31, 1952, bilateral medial temporal-lobe resection combined with orbital undercutting was carried out, the removal extending posteriorly for a distance of 6 cm. along the mesial surface of the temporal lobes. Recovery was uneventful and no neurological deficit ensued. The patient has been more tractable since the operation but he is still subject to delusions and hallucinations. He is said to have a memory defect. When interviewed by B. M. in April, 1955, he was found to be too out of contact for extensive formal testing. However, he was able to recall the examiner's name and place of origin 10 minutes after hearing them for the first time, and this despite the fact that the interval had been occupied with other tasks. He could also recognize objects which had been shown to him earlier in the interview, selecting them correctly from others which he had not seen before. But his immediate recall of drawings and stories was faulty and these were forgotten completely once his attention was directed to a new topic.

In this patient we stress the negative findings: despite his evident psychosis he did not show the severe memory loss typical of the patients in Group 1. Yet the brief psychological examination and the hospital record both indicate some impairment of recent memory, though no reliable quantitative studies could be made.

GROUP III: NO PERSISTENT MEMORY DEFECT

Case 9, I. S. This 54-year-old woman had a 20-year history of paranoid schizophrenia, with auditory hallucinations and marked emotional lability. She had attempted suicide on several occasions. On November 16, 1950, six months after admission to a state hospital, a bilateral medial temporal lobectomy was carried out under local anaesthesia with sectioning of the tips of the temporal lobes and subpial suction removal of the medial portion, extending back 4 cm. to include the uncus and amygdala. Thus this was a conservative bilateral removal, sparing the hippocampal region. The operation was complicated by accidental damage to the midbrain from the electrocautery, causing the patient to give a convulsive twitch which was followed by coma and extensive rigidity. After operation she was somnolent for a time with continuing rigidity, more marked on the left side than on the right. Vital signs were normal. She required traction to prevent flexure spasm contractures. There was slow improvement over the ensuing two months, with some residual clumsiness and spasticity of gait. For a time the patient's mental state was worse than before operation, but within three months she had improved markedly, with increased gentleness, diminished auditory hallucinations, and no depression. She ultimately showed the best result of all the cases in this series and was discharged from the hospital five months after operation.

This patient was re-examined on May 11, 1956. She shows a complete remission of her former psychotic behaviour and is living at home with her husband

and leading a normal social life. Her hallucinations have ceased. Upon neurological examination she shows some 25% residual deficit, manifested chiefly by spastic
incoordination of gait and similar but less marked incoordination of the arms.
The deep leg reflexes are increased to near clonus, but there is no Babinski
sign. Arm reflexes are moderately increased and abdominal reflexes absent. Smell
is completely lost but all other sense modalities are intact and other cranial
nerves normal.

Psychological Findings. The patient was examined psychologically in April,
1955. From the standpoint of memory, this patient presents a complete contrast
to the cases reported above, obtaining excellent scores for both immediate and
delayed recall of stories, drawings, and word associations, and describing accurately episodes from the relatively early post-operative period. The memory quotient of 125 is consistent with the I.Q. level of 122, and both would be classed
as superior. This is so despite prolonged psychosis, intensive electro-shock therapy, and brain-stem damage of undetermined extent.

Case 10, E. C. This 55-year-old woman developed malignant oedema after
removal of a huge, saddle-type meningioma from the right sphenoid ridge; the
pupils were dilated, she lost consciousness, and vital signs began to fail. A
diagnosis of incisural hippocampal herniation was made, and, as a life-saving
measure, unilateral nondominant inferior temporal lobectomy was carried out,
with deliberate resection of the hippocampus and hippocampal gyrus to a distance
of 9 cm. from the tip of the temporal lobe. (The operative procedure is illustrated
in Fig. 5). Vital signs improved immediately and consciousness gradually returned, but for a few weeks the patient showed a disturbance of recent memory
resembling that seen in our bilateral cases. However, follow-up studies in April,
1955, 16 months after operation, showed no residual memory loss. Both immediate
and delayed recall were normal and the memory quotient of 90 was completely
consistent with the I.Q. level of 93. Neurological examination at this time showed
a left homonymous visual field defect with macular sparing but no other deficit.

DISCUSSION

The findings in these 10 cases point to the importance of the hippocampal
region for normal memory function. All patients in this series having bilateral medial temporal-lobe resections extensive enough to damage portions
of the hippocampus and hippocampal gyrus bilaterally have shown a clear
and persistent disturbance of recent memory, and in the two most radical
excisions (in which the posterior limit of removal was at least 8 cm. from
the temporal tips) the deficit has been particularly severe, with no improvement in the two or more years which have elapsed since operation. These
observations suggest a positive relationship between the extent of destruction
to the hippocampal complex specifically and the degree of memory impairment. The correlation is not perfect, since D. C., who had only a 5.5
cm. removal, showed as much deficit as did the two cases of most radical
excision. Moreover, in the absence of necropsy material we cannot be sure
of the exact area removed.

In all these hippocampal resections the uncus and amygdala have also of course been destroyed. Nevertheless the importance of the amygdaloid and periamygdaloid region for memory mechanisms is open to question, considering the total lack of memory impairment in the bilateral uncectomy case (I. S.), in which a 4 cm. medial-temporal lobe removal was made. But not enough is known of the effects of lesions restricted to the hippocampal area itself to permit assessment of the relative contributions of these two regions. This is a question on which selective ablation studies in animals could well shed important light, but unfortunately the crucial experiments have yet to be done (Jasper, Gloor, and Milner, 1956).

The role of the hippocampus specifically has been discussed in some clinical studies. Glees and Griffith (1952) put forward the view that bilateral destruction of the hippocampus in man causes recent-memory loss and mental confusion, citing in support of this a somewhat unconvincing case of Grünthal (1947) and also a case of their own in which the hippocampus, the hippocampal and fusiform gyri and 75% of the fornix fibers had been destroyed bilaterally by vascular lesion, but in which the rest of the brain appeared normal at necropsy. Interestingly enough, the amygdaloid nuclei were found to be intact as were the mamillary bodies. This patient showed marked anterograde and retrograde amnesia.

More recently Milner and Penfield (1955) have described a memory loss similar in all respects to that shown by our patients, in two cases of unilateral partial temporal lobectomy in the dominant hemisphere. In one case the removal was carried out in two stages separated by a five-year interval, and the memory loss followed the second operation only at which time the uncus, hippocampus, and hippocampal gyrus alone were excised. Although these authors had carried out careful psychological testing in over 90 other cases of similar unilateral operations only in these two cases was a general memory loss found. To account for the unusual deficit, they have assumed that there was in each case a pre-operatively unsuspected, but more or less completely destructive lesion of the hippocampal area of the opposite hemisphere. The unilateral operation would then deprive the patient of hippocampal function bilaterally, thus causing memory loss. The present study provides strong support for this interpretation.

Memory loss after partial bilateral temporal lobectomy has been reported by Petit-Dutaillis, Christophe, Pertuiset, Dreyfus-Brisac, and Blanc (1954) but in their patient the deficit was a transient one, a finding which led these authors to question the primary importance of the temporal lobes for memory function. However, their temporal lobe removals were complementary to ours in that they destroyed the lateral neocortex bilaterally but spared the hippocampal gyrus on the right and the uncus and hippocampus on the left. It therefore seems likely that the memory loss was due to temporary interference with the functioning of the hippocampal system, which later recovered.

We have stated that the loss seen in patients with bilateral hippocampal lesions is curiously specific to the domain of recent memory; neither in our cases nor in those of Milner and Penfield was there any deterioration in intellect or personality as a result of hippocampal resection. It appears important to emphasize this, since Terzian and Dalle Ore (1955) have described gross behavioural changes (affecting memory, perception, and sexual behaviour) after bilateral temporal lobectomy in man; they consider these changes comparable to Klüver and Bucy's (1939) findings after radical bilateral temporal lobectomy in the monkey. But Terzian and Ore included not only the uncal and hippocampal areas, but also the lateral temporal cortex in their bilateral removal. In contrast to the grossly deteriorated picture they describe, we find that bilateral resections limited to the mesial temporal region cause no perceptual disturbance, even on visual tests known to be sensitive to unilateral lesions of the temporal neocortex (Milner, 1954).

The findings reported herein have led us to attribute a special importance to the anterior hippocampus and hippocampal gyrus in the retention of new experience. But the hippocampus has a strong and orderly projection to the mamillary bodies (Simpson, 1952), and as early as 1928 Gamper claimed that lesions of the mamillary bodies were commonly found in amnesic states of the Korsakoff type. Moreover, Williams and Pennybacker (1954) have carried out careful psychological studies of 180 patients with verified intracranial lesions and find that a specific deficit in recent memory is most likely to occur when the lesion involves the mamillary region. It is possible, then that when we have two interrelated structures (hippocampus and mamillary bodies) damage to either can cause memory loss, a point which has been emphasized by Jasper and others (1956). In view of these findings it is interesting that sectioning the fornix bilaterally, and thereby interrupting the descending fibres from the hippocampus, appears to have little effect on behaviour (Dott, 1938; Garcia Bengochea, De la Torre, Esquivel, Vieta, and Fernandez, 1954), though a transient memory deficit is sometimes seen (Garcia Bengochea, 1955).

To conclude, the observations reported herein demonstrate the deleterious effect of bilateral surgical lesions of the hippocampus and hippocampal gyrus on recent memory. The relationship between this region and the overlying neocortex in the temporal lobe needs further elucidation, as does its relationship to deeper-lying structures.

SUMMARY

Bilateral medial temporal-lobe resection in man results in a persistent impairment of recent memory whenever the removal is carried far enough posteriorly to damage portions of the anterior hippocampus and hippocampal gyrus. This conclusion is based on formal psychological testing of nine cases (eight psychotic and one epileptic) carried out from one and one-half to four years after operation.

The degree of memory loss appears to depend on the extent of hippocampal removal. In two cases in which bilateral resection was carried to a distance of 8 cm. posterior to the temporal tips the loss was particularly severe.

Removal of only the uncus and amygdala bilaterally does not appear to cause memory impairment.

A case of unilateral inferior temporal lobectomy with radical posterior extension to include the major portion of the hippocampus and hippocampal gyrus showed no lasting memory loss. This is consistent with Milner and Penfield's negative findings in a long series of unilateral removals for temporal-lobe epilepsy.

The memory loss in these cases of medial temporal-lobe excision involved both anterograde and some retrograde amnesia, but left early memories and technical skills intact. There was no deterioration in personality or general intelligence, and no complex perceptual disturbance such as is seen after a more complete bilateral temporal lobectomy.

It is concluded that the anterior hippocampus and hippocampal gyrus, either separately or together, are critically concerned in the retention of current experience. It is not known whether the amygdala plays any part in this mechanism, since the hippocampal complex has not been removed alone, but always together with uncus and amygdala.

REFERENCES

Dott, N. M. (1938). In Clark, W. E., Le Gros, Beattie, J., Riddoch, G., and Dott, N. M. *The Hypothalamus: Morphological, Functional, Clinical and Surgical Aspects.* Oliver and Boyd, Edinburgh.

Gamper, E. (1928). *Dtsch. Z. Nervenheilk.,* **102**, 122.

Garcia Bengochea, F. (1955). Personal Communication.

——, De La Torre, O., Esquivel, O., Vieta, R., and Fernandez, C. (1954). *Trans. Amer. neurol. Ass.,* **79**, 176.

Glees, P., and Griffith, H. B. (1952). *Mschr. Psychiat. Neurol.,* **123**, 193.

Grünthal, E. (1947). *Ibid,* **113**, 1.

Jasper, H., Gloor, P., and Milner, B. (1956). *Ann. Rev. Physiol.,* **18**, 359.

Klüver, H., and Bucy, P. C. (1939). *Arch. Neurol. Psychiat.* (*Chicago*), **42**, 979.

MacLean, P. D. (1952). *Electroenceph. clin. Neurophysiol.,* **4**, 407.

Milner, B. (1954). *Psychol. Bull.,* **51**, 42.

——, and Penfield, W. (1955). *Trans. Amer. neurol. Ass.,* **80**, 42.

Petit-Dutaillis, D., Christophe, J., Pertuiset, B., Dreyfus-Brisac, C., and Blanc, C. (1954). *Rev. neurol.* (*Paris*), **91**, 129.

Pribram, K. H., and Kruger, L. (1954). *Ann. N.Y. Acad. Sci.,* **58**, 109.

Scoville, W. B. (1954). *J. Neurosurg.,* **11**, 64.

——, Dunsmore, R. H., Liberson, W. T., Henry, C. E., and Pepe, A. (1953). *Res. Publ. Ass. nerv. ment. Dis.,* **31**, 347.

——, Wilk, E. K., and Pepe, A. J. (1951). *Amer. J. Psychiat.,* **107**, 730.

Simpson, D. A. (1952). *Journal of Neurology, Neurosurgery and Psychiatry,* **15**, 79.

Terzian, H., and Dalle Ore, G. (1955). *Neurology,* **5**, 373.

Wechsler, D. (1945). *J. Psychol.,* **19**, 87.

Williams, M., and Pennybacker, J. (1954). *Journal of Neurology, Neurosurgery and Psychiatry,* **17**, 115.

HIPPOCAMPECTOMY AND
BEHAVIOR SEQUENCES

Daniel P. Kimble and Karl H. Pribram

STANFORD UNIVERSITY

Source *Reprinted from* **Science,** *March 1963,* **139,**
824–825, with permission of the authors and the American Association for the Advancement of Science. Copyright 1963.

Abstract   Four monkeys with bilateral hippocampal lesions were trained to respond sequentially to visual stimuli, presented with an automated discrimination apparatus. Two different sequential tasks were presented. The experimental animals were significantly inferior on both problems to six control animals. Since no impairment appeared on simple visual discriminations presented with intertrial intervals from 5 seconds to 6 minutes, simple sensory deficits and "short-term" memory impairments appear unlikely. The results strengthen the interpretation that bilateral hippocampal lesions interfere with the acquisition of those behaviors which involve the execution of sequential responses.

Experiments which involve limbic system lesions have generally been relevant to one of two apparently separate hypotheses concerning the functions of the limbic system in behavior. Milner and Penfield (*1*), Scoville (*2*), and Walker (*3*) have reported that hippocampal damage in humans results in serious "short-term" memory deficits. The other major hypothesis stems from Klüver and Bucy's work on the "temporal lobe syndrome" (*4*) coupled with Papez' idea that the limbic system is critically involved in emotional behaviors (*5*).

The majority of limbic lesions reported above have included damage to the amygdala as well as the hippocampus. Conclusions concerning the functions of the hippocampus per se are therefore difficult. It has been suggested by Pribram that a common element running through these studies is that limbic system lesions in fact disrupt the execution of complex sequences of action (*6*). The hippocampus (Ammon's horn) was selected as the limbic system structure to be ablated. The purpose of this experiment was to test directly the effect of bilateral hippocampal damage on behavior sequences.

The apparatus used was an automated discrimination apparatus (DADTA) (*7*). This machine can present 1 to 12 different stimuli on 2.5- by 1.5-inch Lucite panels. The subject makes his choice by depressing these panels. The presentation of the stimulus patterns and reinforcements are pre-programmed and responses recorded for processing by a general-purpose computer. For this experiment, the stimuli were presented in random positions across the 16 possible panels. Reinforcement consisted of one peanut kernel.

The subjects were ten experimentally naive, immature rhesus monkeys, six females and four males. After initial familiarization with the apparatus, all subjects were trained to discriminate a numeral "6" from a "4" to a 90-percent criterion of 45 correct out of 50 responses. Matched pairs were then formed among eight of the monkeys on the basis of their performance on the initial discrimination.

All animals were retrained to criterion 2 weeks after the initial acquisition. One member of each of the four matched pairs then received a one-stage bilateral hippocampal ablation. Two additional animals were given control lesions to the hippocampal gyrus, but with the hippocampus itself spared. These lesions were approximately the same size as the hippocampal lesions.

Anatomical reconstructions of the brains of monkeys previously operated in the same manner as in the present study have been published elsewhere (8). The surgical procedures are outlined in the same publication. The subjects in the present study are currently being used in further experiments.

Two weeks postoperatively, the subjects were retrained to the 90-percent criterion on the "6"-"4" discrimination. The sequential problems were then presented to the subjects. In the first of these, which we have termed the "self-ordered" sequence, the subjects were required to press two numeral "1"s which were displayed randomly among the 16 possible panels. Both panels had to be pressed in order to obtain the reinforcement. This could be done in either order, but repetitive pressing of the same stimulus was counted as an error. We have used the term "self-ordered" because once a panel is selected, the sequence is determined and the other panel must then be selected in order to obtain the peanut. Subjects were given 50 trials per day until they had either reached a criterion of 10 consecutive correct responses or had completed 1200 trials.

The other sequential task we have called the "externally ordered" sequence. In this situation, the subjects were required to depress a numeral "1" and then a numeral "5," in that order. All other sequences of responding were counted as errors. The stimuli were again displayed in random positions. All monkeys were given 50 trials per day until they reached a criterion of ten consecutive correct responses or until they had completed 3000 trials. If a monkey had not reached criterion after 1200 trials, added feedback was instituted: the houselight within the experimental box blinked off for $\frac{1}{2}$ second after each response. In both problems, the intertrial interval was 6 seconds.

Although the animals with lesions of the hippocampus demonstrated a slight transient impairment of the preoperative learned discrimination, all experimental subjects showed great retention, and no significant difference occurred between the groups ($t = <1$).

On the "self-ordered" sequence, however, three of the four hippocampal animals showed no indication of learning, failing to reach criterion in 1200 trials. One hippocampal subject did reach criterion in 130 trials, which is within the normal range. With regard to the control groups, separate analysis revealed no significant differences between the operated and unoperated, and they were combined into a single group. The average number of trials to criterion for this control group was 298. The difference between this performance and that of the subjects with hippocampal lesion is significant as $<.05$ (Fisher's exact probability test).

The subjects with hippocampal lesions also demonstrated a significant deficit on the "externally ordered" sequential problem. All of the contro subjects learned the problem in an average of 1216 trials, while the average for subjects with hippocampal lesions was 1897. The difference between the two groups was significant at $<.01$. Moreover, no hippocampal subject reached criterion before the added feedback light was instituted, as did three of the six control animals. The added feedback improved the performance of all animals.

The performance of the hippocampectomized subjects was further analyzed to determine if simple response perseveration could account for their inferior performance in the sequential tasks. One could be led to this conclusion from the results of the "self-ordered" task, where this was the only possible type of error. The data from the "externally ordered" task, however, do not support a perseveration hypothesis. Perseveratory errors (responding to the same panel) either within or across trials were not significantly more prominent in either group. Individual monkeys in both groups did on occasion display stretches of perseveratory behavior, but no consistent result obtained. It is of course possible that a breakdown of sequential responding could be manifested as perseveration in some situations (as in the "self-ordered" task), but it appears that this is only one of possible alternative behaviors.

Following completion of the two sequential tasks, two of the previously unoperated control monkeys received bilateral hippocampectomies. All animals were then retrained to criterion on both problems 2 weeks after these operations. For these retention tests, the "self-ordered" sequence was tested first, followed by the "externally ordered" task.

The retention results were rather ambiguous. Clear differences occurred between the two newly hippocampectomized subjects and the other monkeys. On the "self-ordered" problem, these two animals took 160 and 346 trials to re-reach criterion. In contrast, the other four hippocampectomized subjects retrained in an average of 48 trials. However, this result was reversed for the "externally ordered" sequence. The two "retention" hippocampectomized subjects retrained in only 73 and 33 trials, as compared with an average of 147 for the other hippocampectomized subjects and 168 trials for the control subjects. A deficit in retention occurred in the "self-ordered" task, while on the "externally ordered" problem, these same subjects retrained in fewer trials than the other animals. One possible explanation for this result is that the hippocampectomized "retention" subjects benefited from the extra practice on the first task, this benefit showing up on the second task.

Following these retention tests, the "short-term" memory hypothesis was investigated. All subjects were trained to a criterion of ten consecutive correct choices on each of four different visual discriminations. The DADTA apparatus was again used to present the four different pairs of numerals which served as stimuli. One of the stimuli of each pair was consistently reinforced, and the position of the two stimuli was varied randomly across the 16 panels.

On these four problems, each discrimination was presented with a differ-

Table 1. Number of trials (and errors) to criterion for subjects with the hippocampus resected and for control subjects, on the "self-ordered" and "externally ordered" sequence tasks and discrimination tasks with varying intertrial intervals

	Trials to Criterion (Errors)	
	Resected Subjects ($N = 4$)	Control Subjects ($N = 6$)
Task		
Ordered sequences		
"Self"	932* (574)	298 (133)
"External"	1897† (1476)	1216 (728)
Discrimination trial spacing		
5 seconds	108 (38)	100 (39)
30 seconds	66 (23)	76 (22)
3 minutes	42 (18)	49 (21)
6 minutes	27 (7)	26 (6)

* Three of four did not reach criterion in 1200 trials.

† One of four did not reach criterion in 3000 trials.

ent intertrial interval (5 seconds, 30 seconds, 3 minutes, 6 minutes). The order of the presentation of the four tasks was balanced.

It was assumed that if any short-term memory impairment occurred, it would be more apparent on the discriminations with the longer intertrial intervals. No impairment occurred among the hippocampectomized animals on any of the discriminations. Both groups took, on the average, fewer trials to criterion on the problems with longer intertrial intervals. Since the order of presentation of the problems was balanced, transfer effects from one discrimination to another cannot be a factor in this result. It is of course possible that the discriminations were easier at the longer intertrial intervals, although there was no a priori reason to suspect this. Table 1 summarizes the data of this experiment with regard to "self-ordered," "externally ordered," and varying intertrial interval discriminations.

Our conclusion is that bilateral hippocampal lesions interfere selectively with the acquisition of behaviors which involve the execution of sequential responses. We found no indication of "short-term" memory deficits with two-choice visual discriminations over intertrial intervals up to 6 minutes. This result is similar to that of Orbach et al. (9), who found no retardation of learning a simple visual discrimination in widely separated trials by monkeys with primarily amygdala and hippocampal lesions.

No emotional changes were noted in these animals, although further tests utilizing the galvanic skin response are in progress to investigate this possibility (10).

REFERENCES AND NOTES

1 B. Milner and W. Penfield, *Trans. Am. Neurol. Assoc.* **80**, 42 (1955).
2 W. B. Scoville, *J. Neurosurg.* **11**, 64 (1954).
3 A. E. Walker, *A.M.A. Arch. Neurol. Psychiat.* **78**, 543 (1957).
4 H. Klüver and P. C. Bucy, *J. Psychol.* **5**, 33 (1938).
5 J. W. Papez, *A.M.A. Arch. Neurol. Psychiat.* **38**, 725 (1937).
6 K. H. Pribram, *Ann. Rev. Psychol.* **11**, 1 (1960).
7 ———, K. W. Gardner, G. L. Pressman, M. Bagshaw, *Psychol. Repts.* **11**, 247 (1962).
8 K. H. Pribram and L. Weiskrantz, *J. Comp. Physiol. Psychol.* **50**, 74 (1957).
9 J. Orbach, B. Milner, T. Rasmussen, *Arch. Neurol.* **3**, 230 (1960).
10 Supported by grants from the U.S. Public Health Service (MF-17,131; MY-3732-C2) and the Department of the Army (MD-2073). A preliminary report was presented at the American Psychological Association meetings in St. Louis, Mo. on 5 September 1962.

Learning and Memory:

Formation and Nature of the Trace

CONDITIONED REFLEXES ESTABLISHED BY COUPLING ELECTRICAL EXCITATION OF TWO CORTICAL AREAS

R. W. Doty

UNIVERSITY OF ROCHESTER

C. Giurgea

UNION CHIMIQUE-CHEMISCHE BEDRIJVEN

Source *Reprinted from **Brain Mechanisms and Learning**, A. Fessard, R. W. Gerard, J. Konorsky, and J. F. Delafresnaye, Eds., 1961, 133–147, with permission of the authors and Blackwell Scientific Publications.*

Is the mere coincidence of action of two stimuli sufficient to form a learned association between them, or is some motivational factor also required? This has been a persistent question in psychology (and psychiatry) and is of major importance in any attempt to solve the riddle of the neural mechanisms subserving learning. Human experience is too complex to provide an answer despite the long history of "associationism" as a science. In animal experimentation, on the other hand, it has been difficult to demonstrate learning or establish conditioned reflexes when motivation or "drive reduction" have been unequivocally absent.

The pertinent evidence has been reviewed elsewhere (Giurgea, 1953a). The experiments of Loucks (1935), however, are of special interest since they are the direct antecedents of our own. In several dogs Loucks stimulated the "motor" cortex through permanently implanted electrodes effecting a movement of one of the animal's limbs. With each animal on as many as 600 occasions over several days he preceded the motor stimulation with an auditory conditional stimulus (CS). The CS never came to evoke the movement with which it was so thoroughly paired, nor any other movements. A food reward was then introduced to follow the CS and the induced movement. Within a few trials the animal began moving to the CS. Loucks drew the justifiable conclusion from these experiments that the motivational element was essential to the formation of conditioned reflexes and these results have had a wide and well-deserved influence on psychological theory since that time.

Loucks's position was apparently confirmed by Masserman (1943) who failed to obtain any signs of conditioning when stimulation of the hypothalamus was used as US. However, Brogden and Gantt (1942) were able to produce movements by presenting a CS alone after repeated pairing of CS and stimulation of the cerebellum. In some animals the "conditioned response" (CR) so elicited was very similar to the movement induced by cerebellar stimulation. Motivation seemed to be absent here. In 1951, while working in the laboratories of P. S. Kupalov seeking further confirmation of the hypothesis of "shortened conditioned reflexes," it was discovered that conditioned reflexes could readily be formed by pairing stimuli at two cortical points (Giurgea, 1953a, b). Stimulation of occipital cortex which is initially without apparent effect ultimately produces movement highly similar to that elicited by the stimulation of the sigmoid gyrus with which it is paired. This direct contradiction of the results of Loucks seems best explained by differences in the timing of presentation of stimuli.

[1] New research reported here was supported by grants to R. W. Doty from the Foundations' Fund for Research in Psychiatry and the National Institutes of Neurological Diseases and Blindness (B-1068), and by a travel grant to C. Giurgea from the Academy of the Rumanian Peoples Republic.

In all his experiments Loucks (1935) used intertrial intervals of 2 minutes or less, usually 30–60 seconds, whereas an intertrial interval of 3–5 minutes was used in our experiments. If the intertrial interval is reduced to 2 minutes even after such CRs have been established, the CRs disappear in the majority of dogs tested so far (Giurgea, 1953a, b), although the unconditioned response (UR) is unaffected.

Continuing these studies, it has been shown that formation of CRs by cortical stimulation is not dependent upon sensory endings in the meninges since the CR may be readily established after destruction of the Gasserian ganglion (Raiciulescu, Giurgea and Savescu, 1956). A CR established to stimulation of parietal-occipital cortex as CS was also elicited by a tonal or photic CS (Giurgea and Raiciulescu, 1957). In two animals with total, histologically confirmed section of the corpus callosum CRs were established even though CS and US were applied to different hemispheres (Raiciulescu and Giurgea, 1957; Giurgea, Raiciulescu and Marcovici, 1957). The electrical activity recorded from the US area does not appear to be changed by this conditioning procedure and is within normal limits of low voltage, fast activity very shortly after the US is applied (Giurgea and Raiciulescu, 1959). In none of these experiments does the behaviours of the dogs indicate even the slightest element of motivation. This impression has now been confirmed objectively in the experiments reported below.

TECHNIQUE

The experiments at Michigan have so far been performed on four dogs, two cats and two cynomolgous monkeys. The dogs are restrained easily by placing their legs through plastic loops (e.g. Fig. 1). [Figures have been omitted in reprinting. (Ed.)] Cats are held by placing their heads through a heavy plastic stock leaving their limbs free. Monkeys are kept permanently seated in a Lilly-type chair (Mason, 1958). All animals are adapted to restraint prior to electrode implantation. During the experiment the animals are isolated and observed through a "one-way" glass.

The cortex is stimulated through platinum electrodes, usually resting on the pial surface or just beneath it although in some dogs the thickness of the skull made such adjustment difficult. Two of four electrodes are carried in 7 mm. diameter plastic buttons which are held in trephine holes by means of screws (Doty, Rutledge and Larsen, 1956). Flexible 0.5 mm. diameter polyethylene insulated wires connect the electrodes to an 18 or 34 contact receptacle permanently secured to the skull by stainless steel posts (Doty, 1959).

Stimulation consists of 1 msec. rectangular current pulses at a frequency of 50/sec. and is monitored on a cathode-ray oscilloscope with a long-persistence screen. Great care is taken to keep the stimulating circuits and the animals isolated from ground and to avoid any other possibility of stimulation outside that intended.

Prior to pairing CS and US the effects of stimulation are observed for each electrode pair. It is advantageous to have several pairs of electrodes in "motor" cortical areas so that the chances are increased for procuring a relatively simple movement to serve as an UR. By means of automatic and silent control the CS is presented for 3–4 seconds and is slightly over-lapped by the US of 1–1.5 seconds duration. Six to ten combinations of CS and US are made daily.

After study of CS-US coupling is complete, the animals are trained in the same experimental chamber to press a lever to obtain food. The lever is then connected to administer cortical stimulation with each press.

RESULTS

DOG ALPHA   All stimulation in the "motor" cortical regions produced stiff, complex and unnatural movements. That finally chosen as an UR was a lifting and extension of the right hind leg, a slight lifting and curling of the tail, and a rotation of the head to the midline and down (Fig. 1). The US was 1.8 mA. applied just posterior to the left postcrucial sulcus. The CS of 1.1 mA. was applied to the left posterior suprasylvian gyrus. It elicited no response for the first forty-two CS-US pairings. The CS current was then increased to 2.2 mA. and elicited an opening of the eyes and turning of the head to the right, a response judged to be inherent to stimulation of this area. It was still obtained, when, later in the experi-ment, the CS was again reduced to 1.0 mA. The first distinct CR was seen on the thirtieth post-operative day after 108 CS-US pairings. It was a turning of the head to the midline and down, a movement similar to the head movement seen to the US and in opposition to that inherently evoked by the CS. Movement of the leg or tail was never elicited by the CS. This CR subsequently occurred up to 100 per cent of the time in some sessions and had a threshold of about 0.3 mA. It could also be elicited by 0.4 mA. applied to a second pair of electrodes about 2 mm. distant from the original CS pair.

The same CR was evoked by a CS of 3/seconds clicks after one session (eight trials) combining this CS with the UR. A second UR was coupled with 9/seconds clicks as CS. This at first produced the previous CR which gradually became modified to a sidewise oscillation of the head with nose pointing down. This new "CR," however, had nothing in common with the second UR.

It was very difficult to teach this dog to eat in the experimental situation. Once trained, however, the animal pressed the lever repeatedly despite accompanying CS or US stimulation which in the case of the US produced violent movements. In contrast, if the side of the cage was tapped gently each time the lever was pressed, two or three taps abolished all pressing for the rest of the session.

DOG BETA   A US of 2.0 mA. at the right postcruciate gyrus produced a brisk, well-integrated flexion of the left hind leg as its only apparent effect. The CS at the right marginal gyrus gave no overt sign at intensities up to 2.2 mA. The first sign of movement to this CS occurred during the sixth session, forty-fifth pairing. The slight tossing of the head and indefinite movements such as stepping or shifting posture seen then subsequently became very common. On the sixty-sixth pairing two 10-cm. flexions of the left hind leg, held for about 1 second each, were seen as the only movement to the CS. This was the first CR. This type of CR occurred seventy-four times in 171 subsequent CS presentations (including extinction) and had a threshold of 0.95 mA. It was not extinguished by eighty-four presentations of the CS alone at 2–3 minute intervals for eleven sessions. These CRs were also obtained to stimulation of the right posterior ectosylvian gyrus indicating some generalization had occurred.

Technical difficulties prevented testing this dog in the lever-pressing situation. However, the animal was extraordinarily sensitive and yelped violently even when grasped gently by the scruff of the neck. Yet there was no evidence of pain or emotion during the training sessions, and the animal ran each day to the experimental room and jumped into the enclosure to be harnessed.

DOG GAMMA   Stimulation at 0.4 mA. 1.5 mm. above the right pyramid in the field H_1 of Forel was used as US. It produced a forceful extension of the neck and rotation of the head over the right shoulder, wider opening of the eyes, flaring of the nostrils and occasionally a lifting of the right lip (Fig. 2) [omitted in reprinting]. This response was elicited sixty-eight times in ten sessions with no particular alteration in the animal's behaviour. Pairing of the US with a CS of 3/second clicks was then begun. A CR of turning the head up and 130° right was elicited by the CS on the sixteenth trial and similar CRs occurred on forty-eight of ninety-six subsequent presentations. The CS also evoked great agitation, whining and yelping. Both the CRs and this agitation to the CS were extinguished in three sessions totalling twenty-two presentations of the CS alone.

Lever-pressing behaviour was little altered by coupling with stimulation of the postcruciate gyrus producing a hind-leg left. It was slowed greatly by the click CS or other sounds, and abolished immediately by the US.

DOG EPSILON   Stimulation at right or left postcruciate gyri produced well co-ordinated, maximal flexions of left or right forelegs respectively. Stimulation of left posterior ectosylvian gyrus with 1.8 mA. or right mid-marginal gyrus with 1.6 mA. produced no response when tested initially. Stimulation at the latter points was then used as CS and at the former as US. For convenience the prefix "R" or "L" will be used to designate to which hemisphere the stimulus was applied, e.g. L-CS with R-US means CS applied to left posterior ectosylvian gyrus, US to right post cruciate.

For the first forty pairings of R-CS with R-US there was no response to the R-CS. During the next few sessions the R-CS frequently elicited a lowering of the head and flexion of the right foreleg as shown in Fig. 3 [omitted in reprinting] i.e. the limb opposite that in which the UR was induced. The first left foreleg CR occurred on the eighty-first presentation of R-CS and in the next 113 trials occurred fifty-eight times. These CRs were discrete, 4–20 cm. elevations of the left foreleg held for several seconds and frequently returned to the floor prior to the UR. The threshold for CR elicitation was 0.5–0.7 mA. Other movements, not so specific, occurred regularly, so that movement now occurred 95 per cent of the time to this CS.

L-CS was now paired four times with R-US, and except for the first presentation produced flexions of the right foreleg (again opposite to the UR) each time. Two sessions later differentiation was begun and continued for twelve sessions with results as shown in Table I. Obviously no differentiation occurred under these conditions; CRs were maintained to stimulation of either area though the percentage of occurrence to R-CS may have declined.

It is characteristic of these animals (Giurgea, 1953 a, b) that just prior to the appearance of the first CRs and frequently thereafter, movements of the affected limb occur sporadically during the intertrial period. This phenomenon was observed in Dogs *Beta* and *Epsilon*. These movements might possibly arise from some "irritative" process consequent to the repeated presentation of the US, but the following experiments show this is not the case. Using the usual timing and parameters, the L-US alone was presented 100 times in twelve sessions producing a forceful right foreleg flexion each time. No spontaneous lifts of this limb occurred in this period. Another 150 presentations were then given in which L-US preceded L-CS by irregular intervals. Initially L-CS still gave some left foreleg CRs or other movements, but these reactions were extinguished by this procedure since for the last seventy presentations there was no response whatever to L-CS. Orthodox temporal relations for L-CS and L-US were then used. At first this restored the nonspecific movements, then left foreleg CRs and ultimately right foreleg CRs occurred about 50 percent of the time to L-CS at a threshold of 0.7 mA.

The R-CS was then presented for the first time in 79 days. The left foreleg was lifted 15 cm., flexing at the wrist, and was held so for about 5 seconds. Ultimately it was possible to obtain right leg flexions to L-CS and left leg flexions to R-CS.

Table I. Initial Failure of Differentiation in Dog Epsilon

Stimulus Location	Total Differentiation Trials	LFL CRs	RFL "CRs"
R-CS, R-US	50	11	7
L-CS, no US	44	14	5

Coupling L-CS, L-US or R-US with the animal's lever-pressing had no effect, whereas auditory stimuli or R-CS completely abolished pressing. The effect of R-CS had been predictable on the basis of behaviour changes seen as soon as the use of R-CS was resumed (after the hiatus described above). Since more than 5 months had then elapsed from time of electrode implantation it seems likely trigeminal fibres had grown into this medial electrode location.

MONKEY 1   The CS of 1.0 mA. applied to the left occipital pole consistently produced movement of the eyes, and sometimes the head down and to the right. At any time during this stimulation, however, the eyes might be moved elsewhere if attention was so directed. The 0.2 mA. US (300/second) in the left precentral cortex produced a smooth, vigorous flexion of the right forearm and contraction of the muscles on the right side of the neck and face causing the mouth to open (Fig. 4) [omitted in reprinting]. Coupling of the CS and US was begun 2 weeks after surgery and continued for 4 weeks, 200 trials in twenty-four sessions. In these 200 trials the right arm made random movements during the CS eleven times. Obviously there was no conditioning. During the next 25 weeks the animal was used sporadically for testing various lever-pressing procedures with fruit juice rewards.

Coupling of CS and US was then resumed. The effects of these stimuli were still exactly as they had been 7 months earlier. Using a two-minute intertrial interval for the first fifty-one trials in five sessions there was no sign of conditioning. A four-minute interval was then used for trials 52 to 84. The first CR was seen on the sixty-seventh pairing. The right arm was flexed to the level of the restraining collar, then extended along its lower surface with fingers fluttering as though seeking an object. In the next forty-seven trials a movement similar to this occurred to the CS thirty-one times. At the threshold current of 0.55 mA. or during the later phases of subsequent extinction sessions the movement was more likely to be a simple flexion very similar to that evoked by the US. Even when the movement was vigorous, it often terminated prior to the US. In ninety-one presentations of the CS given in five sessions without the US this CR was elicited fifty-six times. One-minute intervals were frequently employed. In two sessions after repeated presentations of the CS without the US, the CR was absent for five or more consecutive trials. The head and eye movements evoked by the CS were still present during this period of extinction. On several occasions it was noted, however, that the eyes closed at the onset of the CS and the animal appeared to drowse even though the eyes could be seen moving beneath the lids.

Stimulation with an electrode pair within 2–3 mm. of those used as CS gave no eye movements if the polarity of the stimulus was negative for the electrode separated from the others by a small sulcus. None the less the CR was evoked from this pair with this polarity three times in six stimulations, never using the US. Stimulation in the right posterior parietal lobe elicited eye and head movements which were almost the exact counterpart of those elicited by the CS save they were to the left. No CRs were elicited by this stimulation in nine attempts during two sessions.

With four-minute intervals and the same US there was no CR to an auditory CS despite 110 pairings in nine sessions. After this, giving the auditory CS simultaneously with the CS to the occipital pole often produced "external inhibition" of the CR to the latter stimulus. Seventeen tests with the auditory CS alone (plus the US) elicited no CRs even though the tests were given randomly throughout twenty-four presentations in which simultaneous auditory and cortical CS (plus US) was used.

The effect of coupling various stimuli with lever-pressing was then studied. On July 11th the animal pressed the lever forty-one times in a five-minute period and with each press received a US of 0.4 mA. (double the intensity used routinely) which produced violent movements, and often convulsive after-discharges, with each press. There was no hesitation whatever in lever-pressing behaviour beyond that attributable to the physical handicap consequent to the induced movement (e.g. Fig. 5). Coupling with cortical CS was similarly without effect. On the following day, as seen in Fig. 5 [omitted in reprinting], a novel clicking stimulus completely disrupted the behavior when coupled with each lever-press.

The animal was then taught in sessions of twenty trials per day to press a lever to avoid a shock to its tail. The first response to a tonal CS occurred on the thirty-third trial and a criterion of twelve avoidances in twenty CS presentations was reached in 128 trials. Generalization to 20/sec. and 5/sec. clicks as CS was immediate. The cortical CS, however, produced the former CR, a flexion of the right hand towards the chin rather than the extension to press the lever at the level of the abdomen. After twenty-five combinations of this cortical CS with the tail-shock, the animal began making lever presses to avoid this US. It took more than 100 trials, however, before the former CR was fully extinguished under these conditions. The threshold for the shock-avoidance response to cortical CS was 0.2 mA. which is significantly less than the 0.55 mA. threshold at the same electrodes for the flexion CR established without motivational context.

MONKEY 2   The CS and US elicited responses very similar to those seen in *Monkey 1* save that the seizure threshold was much lower in this animal and the UR was frequently followed by a few clonic movements. The animal struggled almost continuously in the experimental situation (even when being given fruit juice) and no CRs were ever observed. Using three-minute intervals ninety-one couplings were administered in twelve sessions. Then after a hiatus of 25 weeks another 116 combinations were given with two-minute intervals in three sessions and eighty-five combinations at four-minute intervals in four sessions. Finally, 265 couplings were given automatically at four-minute intervals in two overnight sessions, but still without indication of conditioning.

The animal was then conditioned to avoid a shock to the tail by pressing a lever. The first CR to a tonal CS required 105 trials and 238 trials to attain twelve avoidances in twenty CS presentations. Generalization to other auditory conditional stimuli was immediate and complete. The cortical CS was then employed. For 300 combinations of this CS with the tail-shock US there was, judging by the animal's general behaviour and visually observed respiration, no anticipation whatever of the impending shock during a four-second CS. Yet on every presentation the CS was patently effective since the eyes moved persistently down and to the right during each stimulation. The first CRs occurred after the CS was increased to 1.2 mA. The threshold was ultimately determined to be 0.6 mA. for the elicitation of this CR.

CAT 425   Conditioning with cortical stimulation was likewise a failure in this animal; but so too was conditioning using an auditory CS and foot-shock as US. The animal was also seizure-prone. A total of 345 pairings of a right middle ectosylvian gyrus CS with right ansate gyrus US produced no CRs, and 420 pairings of a tonal CS with foot-shock US was almost equally ineffective although a few CRs were seen.

CAT 489   This animal has been thoroughly studied by Allan Minster. The CS applied to right middle ectosylvian gyrus usually elicited no overt response initially at the currents used. At higher currents the animal looked up and to the left. The US in the right ansate area produced an abrupt turn of the head to the left and flexion of the left foreleg. The first CR occurred on the thirty-ninth pairing, fifth session. These CRs, however, never became consistent from one session to the next. In 100 trials after the first CR there were a total of only thirty-two and fifteen of these were made in three of the fifteen sessions. At first, the CR was a vigorous lifting and extension of the left foreleg, but after the seventy-second pairing the right foreleg executed this same movement to the CS more often than did the left. The threshold for CR elicitation by stimulation of middle ectosylvian gyrus was probably about 0.8 mA. Stimulation of the right posterior ectosylvian gyrus at 0.35 mA. yielded seven right and one left foreleg CRs in eleven presentations. To date, ninety-seven pairings of the right ansate US with a CS applied to left middle suprasylvian gyrus produced only four leg lifts that could equivocally be called CRs, yet the current for this suprasylvian CS has been kept high enough that head movements initially seen to this stimulation still occurred frequently.

Ten-channel EEG records taken for each trial in this cat have not yielded much new information. Confirming Giurgea and Raiciulescu (1959) there is rarely any electrical abnormality even in the immediate vicinity of the electrodes following either CS or US. No changes characteristic of the conditioned state could be detected and it could not be predicted from the electrical record whether a CR would or would not occur. The CS in middle or posterior ectosylvian gyrus usually produced immediate electrocortical arousal whereas slower patterns frequently persisted through most of the middle suprasylvian CS. The arousal produced by CS and US, however, was minimal since 8–12 sec. rhythms returned often within 1–2 seconds after stimulus cessation.

INTERPRETATION OF RESULTS

There can be no question that conditioned reflexes can be established with cortical stimulation as US. To the thirty dogs successfully conditioned in this manner in the laboratory in Bucharest and the cats observed by Nikolayeva (1957) can be added the animals of this study extending the phenomenon to the monkey and to a wide variety of cortical electrode placements. The vagaries in the appearance of this phenomenon undoubtedly arise not only from its complexity but from ignorance of its nature and the procedures most favourable for its induction. Such problems are not unknown in the study of more usual types of conditioning.

With equal assurance one can state that, in the usual sense of the word, there is no motivation involved in the formation of CRs by coupling cortical stimulations. The animals tested so far have remained entirely insouciant to self-administered cortical stimulation of near convulsive strength inducing violent movement, yet were profoundly inhibited by moderate and innocuous auditory stimuli. There is little reason to expect the cortical stimulation might be rewarding, and there was nothing in our observations to suggest this. On the other hand where motivational factors were expected as with the possible meningeal involvement (*Dog Epsilon*) or in the field of Forel (*Dog Gamma*), the method readily confirmed this impression. It is of some interest that in *Dog Gamma* the presence of this aversive factor did not preclude some form of motor conditioning.

Besides the direct evidence gained from coupling the cortical CS and US with lever-pressing there is equally convincing circumstantial evidence for the absence of motivation in these conditioning procedures. The extreme brevity of electrocortical arousal following the CS-US combination in *Cat 489*, or *Monkey 1* closing its eyes to doze with onset of the CS, is scarcely expected from motivational stimuli. Nor are these CR movements purposeful; rather they are physiological absurdities. They seldom prepare the animal posturally for the ensuing UR and more often than not the CR is terminated before the UR begins. Watching *Monkey 1* day after day raise its arm to stimulation of its "visual" cortex one could not escape the feeling that his nonsensical yet persistent movement was somehow analogous to the compulsive movements of neurotic humans.

The work of Segundo and his colleagues, reported at this meeting and elsewhere (Segundo, Roig and Sommer-Smith, 1959), in which a tonal CS evokes movements similar to those elicited by electrical stimulation of centre median or the mesencephalic reticular formation as US, provide excellent confirmation of our observations—movements produced by central stimulation can be conditioned. Masserman's failure to obtain such results from hypothalamic stimulation (Masserman, 1943) stands in sharp contrast to the results with *Dog Gamma* and the work of Segundo *et al.* Obviously the hypothalamus must be carefully re-examined in this regard. The US in the experiments of Segundo *et al.* probably produced motivational effects in some of their animals, but in others it appears less clear. In any event it would be difficult to ascribe some "biological significance" or appropriateness to the movements induced by the CS. It is equally difficult to find a motivational basis for the "backwards" type of conditioning linking the US with the CS as analysed by Asratyan in this volume.

Since CRs can be established without a motivational factor, there is more hope that the basic phenomena of learning can be sought in neural systems sufficiently simple for meaningful analysis, perhaps with purely electrophysiological techniques. The temporal factor appears to be critical and the experiments with *Dog gamma* and especially *Dog Epsilon* show the conditioned state is not established by the repeated, randomized excitation of US and CS systems.

Several observations support Sperry's hypothesis (1955) that the significant alteration is to be sought in the effector system. In motivated conditioning an alteration in excitability specific to the limb being conditioned can be observed some time before any CRs appear (Doty and Rutledge, 1959). In the present and earlier experiments (Giurgea, 1953a, b) movements similar to the CR, never seen previously in the animal's behaviour, often appeared spontaneously at about the same time the CRs were first noted. The threshold of the neural heirarchy controlling the complex CR thus seems to have been lowered. The frequent generalization of these CRs to other stimuli supports this view and in *Dog Epsilon* and *Cat 489* it was observed that convulsions induced accidentally by high-current CS began with remarkably prolonged CRs.

Some animals seem to have inherently low thresholds for particular movement complexes so that stimulation at widely separated points within the nervous system will evoke the same response. For instance in *Cat 523* stimulation in sensorimotor cortex, posterior ectosylvian and middle suprasylvian gyri, and the caudate nucleus produced an abrupt turning of the head which was highly similar for the different stimulus points. Stimulation in middle ectosylvian gyrus, ventral anterior and ventral posterolateral nuclei did not produce this effect but a convulsion elicited from middle ectosylvian gyrus began with prolonged turning of the head 180° to the rear. In *Cat 365* flexion and, at higher currents, attack movements of the foreleg could be elicited by stimulation in the anterior portion of the caudate nucleus, septal region, ventral hippocampus, and periaqueductal grey. This motor response was not correlated with the motivational effects of this stimulation since caudate and septal stimulation increased lever-pressing, periaqueductal stimulation was avoided and hippocampal stimulation was "neutral." Stimulation of the median forebrain bundle, pyriform area and habenula which produced aversive effects in this animal did not elicit the foreleg attack movement.

The data are too limited to know whether electrodes in these areas in any cat would give these responses. The impression is gained, however, that they would not and that somehow a particular type of movement has in a given individual come to be "prepotent" over others. The stimu-

lating electrodes may thus be revealing the existence of "individually acquired reflexes" (Beritoff, 1924) established through the animal's own
activities. At least they are not different from the individually acquired
reflexes deliberately given the animal by the stimulating electrodes during
the course of our experiments. However, the relation, if any, between these
phenomena must, as so many questions raised by these experiments, await
further experimental analysis.

GROUP DISCUSSION

Segundo. I shall first comment on the finding that motor cortical stimulation
is relatively "indifferent." It agrees with other observations, for excitation of
this region in the sleeping monkey produced no arousal unless a generalized
seizure occurred and, under the latter conditions, one should doubt whether
wakefulness derived from stimulation itself or from proprioceptive "feed back"
resulting from clonic movements. The same "indifference" was shown by the
visual area: when the animal was awake, excitation with few volts produced
investigation movements directed towards the contralateral field; when the animal
was asleep, stimulation of up to 80 volts produced no effect. A different result
occurred when excitation was applied to temporal pole, cingular cortex or hippocampus: with low voltages, animals were immediately aroused, both behaviourally
and electroencephalographically (Segundo, Arana and French, 1955). Therefore,
and as far as we can infer from the influence of animal brain stimulation upon
sleeping state or tendency to excite itself, certain areas are "indifferent" and
others are not.

Dr Doty mentioned that stimulation of subcortical structures may be conditioned. In our laboratory, brief tones have been reinforced by direct excitation
of mesencephalic reticular formation, centre median, basolateral amygdala or
head of caudate nucleus and learned responses to tones have eventually appeared.
In some cases (centre median, mesencephalic reticular formation, certain amygdaloid or caudate placements) conditioned effects were practically identical to
the absolute responses. In other cases, responses from different points in caudate
or amygdala, could not be conditioned *in toto;* some of their components, however, could and consequently conditioned responses were similar to a part of
the absolute response. In a third group of animals (also caudate or amygdala)
the conditioned reaction, though consistent, was completely different to the
absolute effect. This variable relationship has been found in other tyes of conditioning and, therefore, though difficult to interpret here, is not altogether surprising (Hilgard and Marquis, 1940).

To summarize we can say that stimulation effects of certain areas of the
brain can be conditioned. The latter term seems justified in the sense that the
process has many features (technique, effects, inhibitions) of classical conditioning. These studies may help to understand the physiology of learning and that
of tested nuclei (Roig, Segundo, Sommer-Smith and Galeano, 1959; Segundo,
Roig and Sommer-Smith, 1959).

Chow. In your monkey work, do you worry about whether your stimulus
would activate the pain sensation in your animal?

Doty. We are very much aware that the factor of meningeal stimulation must be considered. Dr Rutledge and I have shown that stimulation of the dura mater of the saggital sinus in the cat can serve as a conditional stimulus and is undoubtedly also a nocuous stimulation. However, I feel satisfied that, as outlined in the text, this factor can be detected by the self-stimulation procedure employed and was present only as stated. In addition, Dr Girugea has established these responses in dogs after destruction of the Gasserian ganglion.

Hernández-Peón. The conditioned response obtained by Dr Doty using cortical stimuli as conditioned and unconditioned stimuli provides a method for testing definitely whether there might be some cortico-cortical connections in some cases of conditioning. And I wonder whether he has done transcortical cutting isolating the respective cortical areas and testing whether these conditioned responses persist after the transection or not.

Doty. I think the experiments of Girugea and his colleagues showing these conditional reflexes to be established after callosal section when the conditional stimulus and unconditioned stimulus are in different hemispheres, indicate that a subcortical pathway is likely to be involved in the production of this phenomenon. Perhaps pertinent also are experiments which Dr Rutledge and I have been doing using electrical stimulation of marginal gyrus in the cat as conditional stimulus and shock to the foreleg as unconditioned stimulus. If the stimulated cortical zone is circumsected so that most of the pathways available for intracortical elaboration of the excitation are severed, conditioned reflexes still occur to the cortical conditional stimulus. If, on the other hand, the stimulated cortical zone is undercut for a total length of more than about 8 mm. the conditioned reflexes are lost. They often return, however, after about a month of training. The critical factors are not fully determined in the reappearance of conditional reflexes after this undercutting of the stimulated cortex, but it may be that "U" fibres are necessary. It is also not certain whether that mere passage of time is sufficient or whether it is the retraining which is critical.

Konorski. Did you try to extinguish these reflexes that you have established and how did you obtain the extinction?

Doty. Dr Giurgea taught me a lot about extinction. Apparently it is extremely difficult to bring about a total extinction of a salivary conditioned reflex. Those "temporary connections" are surprisingly permanent. Hence a technique of "acute" extinction is used wherein the conditional stimulus is presented as one might expect without the unconditioned stimulus, but also at much shorter time intervals than employed during the establishment of the conditioned state. I objected that this alteration of procedure would not yield a proper comparison so we tried extinguishing by rather long intervals between conditioned stimulus presentations. In *Dog Beta* we got no extinction in eighty-five presentations. Hence in *Monkey 1* shown in the film, we used shorter intervals of 1–2 minutes and on the two occasions produced "acute" extinction in which the conditioned reflexes were totally absent to the conditional stimulus and in five or more consecutive presentations of the conditioned stimulus, although the animal remained alert. Giurgea has also published extinction data on some of his dogs. Our *Dog Gamma* in which an aversive factor, was present in the unconditioned stimulus showed rapid extinction.

Anokhin. Much of the recently gathered data points to the possibility of obtaining "conditioned responses" by an association between the most distinct points of the brain. In fact, this trend of thought covers also some of the better-known conditioned reflexes, as the one induced by training with sound and light.

Yet a question comes reasonably to our mind: what aspect of the activity of the brain, taken as a whole, do such facts reveal? Dr Doty's interesting experiments may be taken as instances of the brain tissue's ability to act as a specialized substratum, and to establish instant links between any two stimuli which affect it simultaneously.

Our team considers that such aptitude proves the capacity of the nervous tissue to unite any separate elements during stimulation. This capacity is the basic physiological ground of any spontaneous conditioned response. But if we assume at the start that conditioned responses are a physiological function of the animal, we must consider them as the outcome of a complex physiological system, leading necessarily to an adaptation process which involves the organism as a whole.

Dr Doty tells us that he finds it difficult to draw objectively a difference between the leg-lifting response which he has induced, and the one obtained in the classical Pavlovian test by direct application of an electric shock to the animal's paw. Yet to us, the difference seems considerable. In Pavlov's test, the subject draws away the paws from the source of stimulation, thus displaying an adaptative behaviour, which terminates in a reverse afferent drive, in our sense of the word, indicating that the animal has avoided the impact of the electric current. Besides, Dr Doty in his experiment shows the movement of limbs as the mechanical effect of a stimulation which, after having been subject to association, is now conveyed outwards onto the motor system. This proves admirably the capacity of the brain tissue to register any sequence of induced stimuli.

I wish, in concluding, to draw your attention to one important factor, which is of particular relevance, to Dr Hernández-Peón's remark on the possibility of showing pure cortico-cortical connections. Our laboratory has shown that the most insignificant stimuli, as well as lesions of the cortical tissue will instantly involve subcortical formations, and possibly, reticular ones. This is why, by the very nature of the process, no subsequent effects of stimulation can be *only* cortical.

Doty. In reply to Dr Anokhin—I think we must simply adopt the mechanistic, objective approach which Pavlov used so successfully. If I form a conditioned reflex by using an avoidable, painful, "biologically significant" stimulus to a forepaw so that the animal lifts it when a tonal conditional stimulus is sounded, and for the other paw proceed as Giurgea and I have done so that the other paw is lifted when the "auditory analyser" is stimulated directly at the cortex, you would be unable to tell me simply by looking at the animal's behaviour, which conditioned reflex was which. True, by careful analysis I suspect you would find great differences in the autonomic nervous system responses to the stimuli employed, at least during some stages of the training. But their absence in the latter case only proves them to be an unnecessary complication in the process of establishing the neural alteration responsible for the change in effect of the conditional stimulus. Both tone and direct electrical stimulation of the "auditory analyser" are initially without effect on somatic musculature save possibly for an "orientation reflex" which is soon lost. Both become effective on the same motor apparatus in approximately the same number of trials. Both states are subject to the laws of conditioning, i.e. there is no apparent backward conditioning, there can be external inhibition, they can be extinguished. Why then call them different states or infer for them different mechanisms?

We have shown that if the ventral roots are crushed and an animal immobilized with bulbocapnine, it can still be conditioned to make conditioned reflexes with its hind leg even though the leg has never moved during conditioning. Thus we can show proprioceptive feedback from the unconditioned reflex to be unnecessary for the formation of conditioned reflexes. This does not say, that such factors are not normally present; only that they need not be. Such experimental simplification of the situation certainly does not alter significantly the process we desire to elucidate, nor change its name. In similar vein the elimination of motivational factors must not be construed to infer qualitatively different processes to be operative in "cortical-cortical" conditioning as compared to the more usual procedures which involve such unknowns as "biological purpose" or unanalysable emotional and subjective factors.

REFERENCES

Doty, R. W., Rutledge, L. T. and Larsen, R. M. (1956) Conditioned responses established to electrical stimulation of cat cerebral cortex. *J. Neurophysiol.* **19**, 401–15.

Giurgea, C., Raiciulescu, N. and Marcovici, G. (1957) Reflex condition—at interhemisferic prin excitarea directa corticala dupa sectionarea corpului calos. Studiu anatomo-histologic. *Revista Fiziol. Norm. Patol.* **4**, 408–14.

Doty, R. W. and Rutledge, L. T. (1959) Conditioned reflexes elicited by stimulation of partially isolated cerebral cortex. *Fed. Proc.* **18**, 37.

Beck, E. C. and Doty, R. W. (1957) Conditioned flexion reflexes acquired during combined catalepsy and de-efferentation. *J. comp. Physiol. Psychol.* **50**, 211–16.

ELECTROPHYSIOLOGICAL CORRELATES OF A CONDITIONED RESPONSE IN CATS

Robert Galambos, Guy Sheatz, and Vernon G. Vernier

WALTER REED ARMY MEDICAL CENTER

Editor's Note   *Attention is called to the relation between this finding and the ones reported in the papers by Galambos and by Hernández-Peón et al.*

Source   *Reprinted from* Science, *March 2, 1955,* **123,** *376–377, with permission of the authors and the American Association for the Advancement of Science. Copyright 1955.*

The search for neurophysiological correlates for psychological phenomena such as learning and emotion has a long history that cannot profitably be treated here. This report presents a brief account of some electric changes that are observable in the brain when animals are conditioned and extinguished to an auditory stimulus.

The animals under study lived in a box measuring 0.5 by 1.0 by 0.5 m that contained a loud-speaker through which clicks (at constant intensity) were delivered at a rate of 1 click/3 sec along with noise generated by a thermionic noise generator. The noise intensity was adjusted at the outset so that it was sufficient to mask most ambient sounds. Recording from brain structures was achieved through electrodes of the Delgado type that were implanted stereotaxically at sterile operation some weeks or months prior to the testing; as many as 14 separate brain locations were thus made available for study in each animal. To date, ten cats with implantations in or on auditory and visual cortex, cochlear nucleus, hippocampus, caudate nucleus, septal area, and amygdala have been examined in the conditioning process. The electrodes were directly connected through a plug to the amplifiers of a Grass EEG machine and thereafter, alternately or simultaneously, to inkwriters and a cathode-ray oscilloscope. The cats also wore a harness bearing two metal brushes, each making contact with one side of the thorax; the output of a Grass stimulator could be delivered to these brushes, and thus shocks could be applied, at will, across the chest of the animal.

The plan and results of the experiments are as follows. The animals were placed in the box for periods of many days or weeks, clicks being delivered continuously day and night throughout. From time to time their electrodes were connected to the recording devices, and the activity evoked by the clicks was visualized. The report (*1*) that under such conditions the response at the cochlear nucleus becomes, with time, much reduced in size ("habituation," "adaptation") was readily confirmed; in addition, we found that responses evoked in various other brain loci diminished in a similar manner. Responses so attenuated in the cochlear nucleus can be seen in the left column of Fig. 1.

After an animal had been in the box for hours or days, the tracings from its brain showed small, absent, or irregular evoked potentials caused by the clicks, and consistent behavior toward the stimuli was absent. At this point single strong shocks were given across the chest contiguously with randomly selected clicks. After these shocks had been discontinued—perhaps some 10 or 20 having been given—the behavior in response to the click stimuli was noticeably different. The animals crouched, appeared alert, and most of them twitched, snarled, or otherwise responded to many individual clicks. When exhibiting this behavior, the animals were con-

COCHLEAR NUCLEUS

EXTINGUISHED CONDITIONED

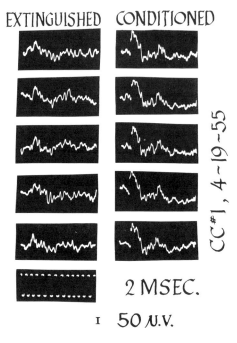

2 MSEC.

I 50 Л.V.

FIGURE 1 *Cochlear nucleus responses to successive identical click stimuli before ("extinguished") and after ("conditioned") application of three shocks to a cat. The increase in response magnitude after shocks as noted here has been observed eight times in this animal, two of them previous to the instance given here.*

sidered to have been "conditioned" to the auditory stimulus; records from the cochlear nucleus of such an animal are shown in the right column of Fig. 1. As the click continued without shock reinforcement, both motor and electric responses tended to disappear (motor long before electric), and the "extinguished" condition invariably returned after hours or days. In most of our animals, the cycle of conditioning and extinction thus defined has been repeated many times.

In view of the motor behavior accompanying the conditioned state, the possibility that the responses recorded are somehow generated by muscle activity or its consequences must obviously be ruled out. Although such considerations can hardly be held to apply to the phenomenon shown in Fig. 1, where the entire event is substantially completed within some 15 msec after the application of the stimulus, it must seriously be considered as a possibility for responses that have longer latency and duration.

Of all our attempts to settle this point, the experiments of the sort illustrated in Fig. 2 are perhaps the most conclusive. The upper record shows the extinguished record from an animal that had previously been conditioned and extinguished five times. The lower record, made about 1 hour after the upper one, shows evoked responses regularly in the stations along the classical auditory pathway (cochlear nucleus and auditory cortex) as well as in at least two of the electrodes in the hippocampus. Between the times at which the upper and lower records were made, the animal had received conditioning shocks and, additionally, gallamine triethiodide (Flaxedil, Lederle) 4 mg/kg intravenously in two divided doses within 1 minute. This dosage was sufficient to cause apparent complete muscular paralysis, and artificial respiration via an endotracheal tube was required. The only muscle activity noted was constriction of the iris as an object was brought close to the eye of the animal. Pupillary dilatation was also observed coincident with the conditioning shocks or with clicks alone immediately after shock. Certainly there was no movement of the animal that could account for the responses shown in the lower half of Fig. 2, during the recording of which, of course, only clicks were being applied at the times indicated in the top trace. It may parenthetically be stated here that, in extinguished animals that have been immobilized by Flaxedil, applied shocks promptly change the records of responses to those typical of the conditioned state.

From the data, only some of which have been presented here, the following general statements appear to be justified. When cats with indwelling electrodes are subjected to a relatively simple auditory conditioning technique, changes in electric activity of the brain apparently related to condi-

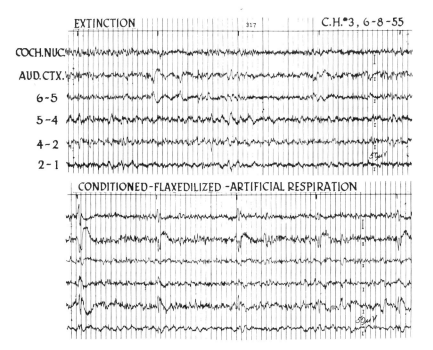

FIGURE 2 *EEG responses to identical clicks (indicated by artifact in upper trace) before (top records) and after a shock had been delivered for a time with each click. Bipolar recording from cochlear nucleus (second trace), monopolar from auditory cortex. The bottom four traces are derived from a hippocampal array (as yet not histologically verified) inserted in a dorsoventral line, the active tips being 2 mm apart with No. 1 the deepest. The animal had received Flaxedil prior to the bottom recording and thus exhibited no motor activity whatever.*

tioning and extinction can be reliably recorded. Evoked auditory responses are larger and are seen more frequently and in more numerous locations when a given animal is in the conditioned as opposed to the extinguished state. Such changes occur near the origin of the classical auditory pathway (cochlear nucleus) as well as at its termination (auditory cortex), in portions of such limbic system structures as the hippocampus and septal area and in the head of the caudate nucleus.

REFERENCE

1 R. Hernández-Peón and H. Scherrer, *Federation Proc.* **14, 71** (1955).

EFFECT OF ANODAL POLARIZATION
ON THE FIRING PATTERN
OF SINGLE CORTICAL CELLS

Frank Morrell

UNIVERSITY OF MINNESOTA

.

Source   Reprinted from the Annals of the New York
Academy of Sciences, *1961,* **92,** *860–876, with permission
of the author and* The New York Academy of Sciences.

In 1953, at the Nineteenth International Physiological Congress, V. S. Rusinov (1953) presented the results of a remarkable series of experiments. Rusinov observed that a constant current, low-level (2 to 10 μAmp.) anodal stimulus applied to the motor region for the fore- or hindlimb of the rabbit cerebral cortex produced a so-called "dominant focus of excitation." The anodal current did not in itself produce movement, but when a sensory stimulus such as a tone or a light was administered during the current flow a discrete movement corresponding to the polarized region was noted. The level of polarization was apparently quite critical since either increase or decrease of current flow prevented a motor response to the interpolated sensory stimulus. Rusinov felt that the connection so formed between two "analyzers," the motor and auditory, for example, demonstrated that extracellular current fields exerting an electronic influence on cell populations played a definite role in the normal connecting function of brain. Because of some technical misunderstandings, an attempt a few years later by Morrell and Naquet (1955) to confirm these findings met with failure. However, in 1958, an opportunity was provided to visit the Soviet Union to attend the Moscow Colloquium on Electroencephalography of Higher Nervous Activity. At that time, Rusinov and his associate, A. Sokolova, hospitably received my associates and me in their laboratory and spent an entire day demonstrating all the details of this experiment. As a result of that experience it was possible to confirm the "dominant focus" experiment in our own laboratory. As a modest repayment for the hospitality of Soviet scientists we take special pleasure in introducing this paper with our own confirmation of the Rusinov experiment and with some further observations obtained by means of microelectrode recording.

METHOD

Experiments were performed on 12 adult rabbits and 4 cats. An initial operation was performed with sterile technique under light barbiturate anesthesia. Recording electrodes contained in a polyethylene sheet were inserted over the dural surface through bilateral posterior burrholes to the positions indicated in the diagram of Figure 1. [Figures 1–5 have been omitted in reprinting (Ed.)] Bilateral anterior bone flaps were turned to expose the motor cortex of both hemispheres. A bipolar stimulating electrode was used to define the cortical areas that, when stimulated, produced movement of the contralateral fore- and hindlimbs of the animal.

[1] The work described in this article was supported in part by Grant B2616 from the National Institute of Neurological Diseases and Blindness, Public Health Service, Bethesda, Md.

This was an easy procedure in the cat, but was much more difficult in the rabbit, in which most stimulated points gave rise to movements of mastication. In particular, discrete movements of the hindlimb were rarely observed. With sufficient diligence, however, points were found that gave predominant movements of one or the other hindlimb, although some bilaterality of response was always evident. A nylon plug containing two apertures was threaded into the bone flap so that it rested over the motor point for contralateral forelimb movement. This was usually in the right hemisphere. In four animals similar plugs were inserted over the corresponding forelimb area in the left hemisphere and over the hindlimb area of the left hemisphere. The bone flaps were then replaced with wire sutures, and the animals were allowed to recuperate for a period of several months, by which time healing of the bony defect was largely complete.

The experiment itself was performed without anesthesia; the animal was restrained in a device that permitted fairly rigid fixation of the head but free movement of the extremities. Needle electrodes were inserted into each limb for electromyographic recording. Anodal* polarization was introduced through a glass capillary electrode filled with saline-soaked cotton and inserted through one of the apertures in the nylon plug. The current source was a constant-current stimulator that provided continuous monitoring of the current flow and was usually set to deliver about 10 μAmp. Current return was affected by a connection to the mouth bar of the animal. Peripheral sensory signals were provided by an audio generator and a flickering or continuous light source. In later experiments, a tungsten microelectrode (Hubel, 1957) with a tip diameter of about 5 μ was inserted into the other aperture of the nylon plug for single-unit recording. This electrode was connected through a cathode follower and short time-constant amplifier to a conventional oscilloscope. The cortical recording leads were connected to an electroencephalograph. Substitution of the peripheral sensory stimulus by electrical shocks delivered directly to the cortex as well as several operative procedures will be described later.

RESULTS

BEHAVIORAL DATA Application of the low-level polarizing current produced no motor or other behavioral changes in the animal, nor were there any EEG changes even when the current was maintained for many hours. A tone or light administered in the absence of polarizing current was also ineffective in eliciting motor responses, although EEG changes in the form of desynchronization or evoked potentials were usually seen. When an acoustic signal (in this case a 200-cps tone, the onset of which is indicated by the upward deflection on the signal channel and cessation by the downward deflection) was applied against a background of maintained anodal polarization of the cortical region giving rise to right hind-

* An anode is the positive pole in a direct current circuit. (Ed.)

limb movement, a definite movement was seen that was maximal in the appropriate limb.

If the polarizing current was discontinued, application of the sound continued to produce a motor response for about 20 to 30 min., after which the effect gradually diminished and disappeared. Figure 1 [omitted in reprinting] illustrates the lack of motor response to the tone one hour after cessation of polarization. Note, however, that the behaviorally inert tone still gave rise to evoked potentials at the "on" and the "off" that were even more pronounced than those seen at the beginning of the experiment or when the sound elicited a behavioral response. In our experience the evoked potential was more often augmented when there was no behavioral response than when such response occurred. It was thus negatively correlated with the formation of temporary connections as defined by this technique. In fact, the evoked potentials tended to wax and wane in a more or less random fashion from trial to trial, the amplitude seeming to depend more upon the characteristics of the background rhythm than upon any particular phase of the conditioning procedure.

Occasionally these animals showed signs of spontaneous drowsiness or light sleep, as judged by behavioral criteria such as pupillary miosis and by the appearance of slow waves and spindling in the electroencephalogram. During drowsy intervals there was a marked increase in the latency of the motor response to tone. Figure 2 [omitted in reprinting] demonstrates a control tracing (a) in which the tone was presented before polarization. The background activity had the moderate voltage rhythmic appearance of the waking animal. There was no motor response. The polarizing current was then turned on and motor responses to the acoustic signal were elicited. One hour later the animal became spontaneously drowsy and, although polarization remained constant, increased response latency was observed beginning with a small movement at $2\frac{1}{2}$ sec. and a larger more definite one after the cessation of tone, or a small movement at 5 sec. and no movement at all in the next trial. Again an augmented evoked potential was observed when the behavioral response failed.

In addition to the phasic motor response to the sensory signal, low-voltage "tonic" muscle potentials were noted throughout the period of polarization in the limb corresponding to the cortical region involved. This was best seen when the polarizing electrode was shifted successively from the area for left forelimb to the contralateral homotopic point for right forelimb movement and, finally, to the cortical region corresponding to right hindlimb movement (Figures 3a, b, c) [omitted in reprinting]. In Figure 3a, the muscle potentials appear most prominently in the left forelimb, with some spillover to the right side. In Figure 3b the action potentials appear in both right-sided limbs, but more prominently in the forelimb electrodes. Finally, in Figure 3c, electrodes in the right hindlimb show maximum activity with some associated movement of the contralateral hindlimb. If one examines each of these records in the sections before application of tone and after its cessation, the tonic muscular activity may be seen to shift in location along with the shift of the phasic movement. Forty to 60 min. must be allowed to elapse between the termination of current flow in one area and the beginning of polarization in the next, otherwise overlapping effects will be noted. It seems unlikely that such changes in the routing of the temporary connection could be explained if the effect of the anodal current were simply to provide another sensory cue by stimulation of trigeminal nerve endings. Indeed, subsequent experiments in which trigeminal neurectomy was performed after the manner of Doty *et al.* (1956) have clearly ruled out such a possibility.

One of our underlying assumptions had been that the effect of anodal current was simply to sensitize or lower the threshold of a particular region so that any sensory input to the central nervous system would trigger those particular cell populations. Indeed during polarization any transitory event such as a handclap, extraneous noise, a puff of air to the animal's face, entrance of the experimenter into the recording cage, or a tone or light stimulus, would trigger the appropriate behavioral response. An attempt to demonstrate differential conditioning by frequently presenting a tone and rarely or intermittently presenting a light stimulus during polarization was without success. In Figure 4 [omitted in reprinting] the light (differential stimulus) and the tone (conditional stimulus) are shown to produce no motor effect before polarization. During polarization the tone and the light were equally effective in eliciting a motor response, despite the fact that the tone had been presented 30 times and the light only twice in the course of a three-hour experiment.

It may be recalled that we had previously noted, as had Rusinov (1953) before us, that the effect of anodal current outlasted the period of actual polarization by about 20 min. This is an extraordinary length of time for neurophysiological events, and I am completely unable to explain it in biophysical terms. Nevertheless the investigation of some of the properties of this interval has proved particularly fruitful.

The experiment of Figure 4 was discontinued and the animal allowed to rest for about five hours. At the end of that time, anodal polarization was reinstituted, and the tone previously used as a conditional signal was found to elicit the same motor response. The light (differential stimulus) was not presented at all. Polarization was then discontinued and, during the next 20 min., there were five presentations of tone and five of the light. In each of the five trials with tone, and in none of the five trials with light was a motor response observed. When this result was found to be reproducible in all of the animals, it was assumed, for the first time, that the experiment might have some validity as a model of neural learning. Since an environmental signal that had been presented to the animal during polarization was found to continue to elicit a characteristic behavioral response in the 20 min. following cessation of polarization, while another signal that had not been paired with the anodal current was ineffective in this regard, one must conclude that differential conditioning had been established. The cell systems acted upon by the polarizing current exhibited at least some of the attributes of short-term memory.

RESULTS OF SINGLE-UNIT ANALYSIS Since there was a disappointing paucity of electroencephalographic change during the procedures previously outlined, microelectrode studies were undertaken in order to provide some information about the behavior of single elements in the polarized region. A microelectrode was inserted through the second aperture of the nylon plug by means of a calibrated hydraulic microdrive. Prior to polarization, a randomly firing unit was unaltered by administration of a tone of 200 cps (Figure 6a). The onset and cessation of tone are indicated respectively by the two upward deflections in the second channel of the oscilloscope. During the passage of anodal current, individual cells were affected by the same tonal stimulus (Figures 6b, c, and d). Three distinct response patterns were found. Some cells showed a single burst of high-frequency discharge following the onset of the acoustic signal (Figure 6b), others showed an abrupt cessation of discharge (Figure 6c), and a third group exhibited bursts of high-frequency spikes at the "on" and at the "off" of the stimulus (Figure 6d). Of the 210 cells sampled, 82 were of the first type, 70 of the second, 31 of the third, and 27 cells were unresponsive. Thus the great majority of cells within the polarized region were active, and the commonest change observed was an increase in discharge frequency. Most of these cells were continuously recorded for 30 to 90 min., during which time the response pattern to the same stimulus remained true to type. For the sake of brevity and simplicity, the remaining discussion will deal only with cells that showed a response pattern of the first type.

Using the experimental procedure illustrated in Figures 4 and 5, a differential response of single units could also be demonstrated. During polarization a positive tone (Figure 7a) and a negative tone (Figure 7b) were equally effective in eliciting high-frequency bursts. Twenty min. after discontinuing polarization the positive tone (Figure 7c) continued to elicit unit discharge, while the negative tone (Figure 7d) failed to do so. Forty min. after cessation of the anodal current, neither the positive tone (Figure 7e) nor the negative signal (Figure 7f) produced any change in unit-discharge frequency.

Doty and Rutledge (1959) have demonstrated that an electrical stimulation of the cortex could serve as the conditional stimulus for establishment of a motor-conditioned response. They found definite evidence of transfer when an electrical stimulus was used to elicit a conditioned response previously elaborated to a peripheral signal, as well as when a peripheral signal was used to elicit a response previously elaborated to direct cortical stimulation. Doty and Giurgea (1959) also demonstrated that conditioned responses could be obtained when the conditional signal was an electrical shock to one hemisphere and the unconditional signal an electrical shock to another hemisphere. Their observations provide a useful tool for analysis

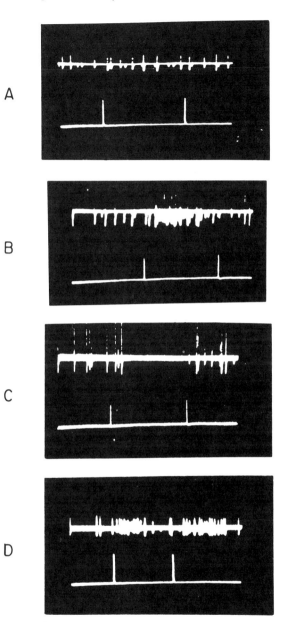

FIGURE 6 *Patterns of response in single units to an acoustic stimulus. Duration of the tone of 200 cps is indicated by the two upward deflections in the second channel of the oscilloscope. Before polarization (a) there was no effect on the discharge frequence of a unit in motor cortex. During polarization responses to sound appeared, either in the form of a single high frequency burst (b), a sudden cessation of firing (c), or high-frequency bursts at the "on" and at the "off" of the tone (d). Calibration: 5 mv and 1 sec.*

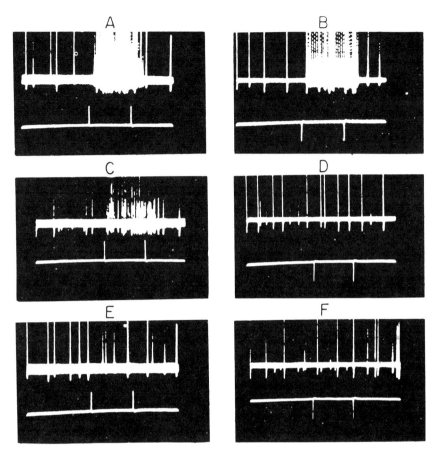

FIGURE 7 *"Generalization and differentiation" in single-unit responses. During the passage of anodal current (a and b) the positive tone (a) and a single presentation of the negative tone (b) were equally effective in provoking high-frequency bursts. Twenty min. after cessation of current flow (c and d) the positive tone (c) continued to elicit the response, while the negative tone (d) did not. Forty min. after discontinuing polarization (e and f) neither signal produced any change in unit-discharge frequency. Calibration: 2mv and 500 msec.*

of the essential anatomical substrates of the conditioned response, since the pathways involved may be more precisely determined and much abbreviated.

The animals of this series were subjected to an acute experiment involving wide exposure of the cortical surface of both hemispheres under ether anesthesia. The ether was allowed to dissipate and the animals were immobilized with Flaxedil and artificially ventilated. The polarizing electrode was applied to the motor cortex as before, and the microelectrode inserted directly beneath it. Since a behavioral response was impossible, we were concerned here only with the manifestation of a temporary connection as expressed by the conditioning of a single-unit discharge. One bipolar stimluating electrode was placed on the cortical surface ipsilateral to the microelectrode placement, at a distance of 1 to 2 cm. A second stimulating electrode was placed on the opposite hemisphere. The stimulating electrodes delivered a 100-msec. burst of 100-per-second pulses, 4 to 8 v in magnitude. The onset of the ipsilateral burst is indicated by an upward deflection of the signal channel, and its cessation by a downward deflection. Reverse directions signify the contralateral stimulating electrode (Figures 8 and 9). Prior to polarization (Figure 8a), the ipsilateral shock did not provoke a change in unit-discharge frequency. The anodal current was

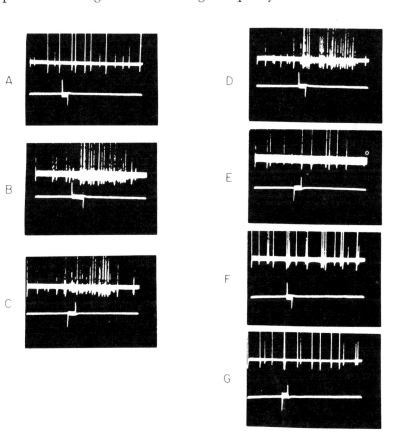

FIGURE 8 *Substitution of cortical electrical stimulus for the peripheral sensory signal. The ispilateral (positive) cortical stimulus is signified by an upward, followed by downward, deflection on the second channel of the oscilloscope. The contralateral (negative) cortical stimulus is signified by reverse deflections. Both stimuli are 100-msec. trains of 100-per-second pulses, 4 to 8 v in magnitude. Before polarization (a) the positive stimulus elicted no change in unit discharge. During polarization (b and c) both positive and negative signals were effective. Twenty min. after cessation of current flow (d and e) the positive signal was effective (d), whereas the negative signal was not (e). Forty min. after termination of current flow (f and g) neither signal was effective. Calibration: 2 mv and 1 sec.*

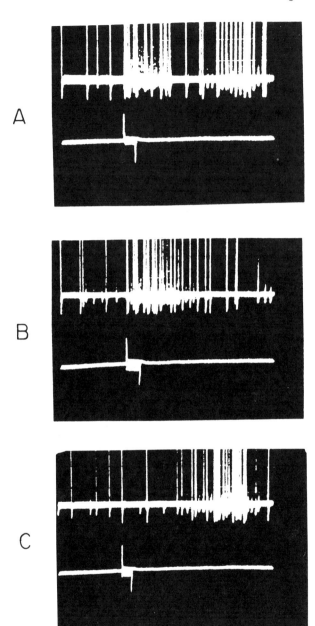

FIGURE 9 *Separation of the two phases of the unit re-*
sponse to cortical stimulation. In the intact brain the bi-
phasic response to cortical shock is shown (a). A subpial
circumsection of the area containing the polarizing and
microelectrodes that severed all transcortical connections,
but left subcortical connections intact (b), eliminated the
long-latency response but preserved the short-latency one.
Undercutting (c) without circumsection eliminated the
short-latency, but preserved the long-latency response.
Calibration: 2 mv and 1 sec.

then applied (Figures 8b and c), and the ipsilateral shock effectively elicited an increase in unit-discharge frequency (Figure 8b). This was presented repeatedly over a 30-min. period. A single test shock at the contralateral cortical electrode was also effective during the time of polarization (Figure 8c). Twenty min. after discontinuing the anodal current (Figures 8d and e), the ipsilateral shock was effective (d), while the contralateral (e) was not. Forty min. later (Figures 8f and g), neither stimulus provoked a change in unit responses.

If one examines Figure 8d carefully, it is apparent that there are two components to the unit response pattern. The components were separated more clearly when the distance between the stimulating electrode and the recording microelectrode was increased. The initial event seemed to have a short fixed latency independent of the position of the stimulating electrode. The second component had a longer and more variable latency and, when the distance between the stimulating and recording electrodes was short, the two components merged and were indistinguishable. The two components were not just "on" and "off" responses to the stimulus. Each was conducted through a separate anatomical pathway. The two components of the response seen in Figure 9a could be dissected apart by a subpial circumsection of the area containing the polarizing and microelectrodes that severed all transcortical connections but left the subcortical connections intact. The result of that procedure is shown in Figure 9b, where only the short latency initial response is evident. Undercutting of the same region that sectioned the subcortical projections but left the transcortical pathways intact (Figure 9c), abolished the short latency response but still allowed the late response to appear. A precise measurement of these latencies was difficult since we were dealing with a change in rate (the delta f of Fessard, 1960) rather than with a potential having a clearly defined onset. Judging the latency with the unaided eye at best could be only an approximation. The use of data processing computers, which were not available to us, would have made this task much easier. Yet even with these reservations, a fairly good linear relationship could be established (Figure 10) between the distance separating the stimulating and recording electrodes and the latency of the late response. It should be noted that the absolute values vary considerably from animal to animal and with change in the general state of any given animal. The measurements recorded in Figure 10 were all made within the space of a few minutes from a cat in which the state of the cortex appeared to be fairly good, as judged by electroencephalographic tracing.

DISCUSSION

If one takes an anthropomorphic view of the nerve cell in this situation, it is clear the temporal relationship of these two components of the response to a single stimulus could serve to provide the cell with information con-

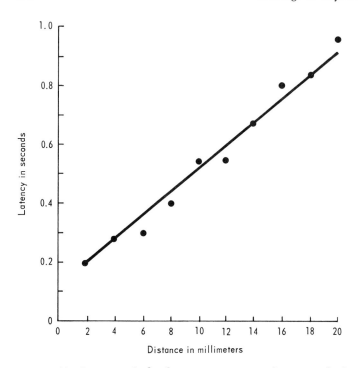

FIGURE 10 *Latency of the late response in undercut cerebral cortex as a function of the distance between stimulating and recording electrodes.*

cerning the source of the stimulus. The early response had a latency of the order of a few milleseconds and was propagated via a subcortical pathway. The constancy of the latency, regardless of the cortical area stimulated, suggests perhaps that a common neuronal pool was activated. Future research employing selective subcortical coagulation and/or recording may, of course, permit fractionation of the early response still further, that is, there may be more than one subcortical component. In any event, the demonstration of at least two synaptic pathways impinging upon a single cellular element might enable the cell to compare a new pattern of afferent input with previously established patterns of synaptic engagement. Arrangements such as they might provide a basis for the phase-comparator mechanisms suggested by Adey *et al.* (1960), or for the frequency comparison suggested by Brazier (1960) and by John and Killam (1960). Certainly the complexity of organization observed in this simplest of temporary connections renders any hypothesis based upon simple linear links from sensory to motor centers untenable. Furthermore, it is quite evident that the recording of the all-or-none discharge of single cells provides only a fragmentary glimpse into the integrative processes that may be going on in the graded response tissue of the dendritic tree.

The role of the anodal current in making these observations possible is still obscure. The mechanism would appear to be electrical, however,

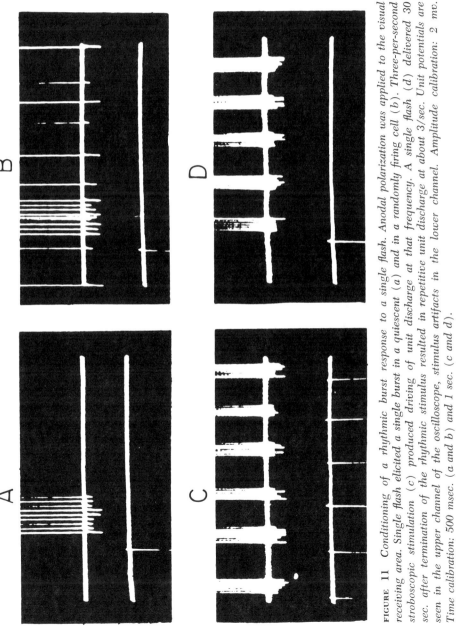

FIGURE 11 *Conditioning of a rhythmic burst response to a single flash. Anodal polarization was applied to the visual receiving area. Single flash elicited a single burst in a quiescent (a) and in a randomly firing cell (b). Three-per-second stroboscopic stimulation (c) produced driving of unit discharge at that frequency. A single flash (d) delivered 30 sec. after termination of the rhythmic stimulus resulted in repetitive unit discharge at about 3/sec. Unit potentials are seen in the upper channel of the oscilloscope, stimulus artifacts in the lower channel. Amplitude calibration: 2 mv. Time calibration: 500 msec. (a and b) and 1 sec. (c and d).*

rather than one of chemical injury, since the effect is abolished by momentary reversal of current flow. The constant current may mimic the steady potential fields of normal cortex. While such fields may not be discrete enough to carry coded information (Eccles, 1958), they may provide the means for establishing the intercellular synchrony considered by Livanov (1960) to be an essential stage in the developing conditioned reaction. In addition to lowering the threshold of the involved cells (Burns, 1954, 1955), the anodal current appears to confer upon these cell populations the property of retaining, at least for a short period of time, a representation of a stimulus imposed during the polarization. Indeed this may be demonstrated even more graphically if one shifts the polarizing electrode to the visual cortex and studies the effect of single or rhythmic stroboscopic stimulation. Figure 11a illustrates the burst response to a single flash of a relatively quiescent cell in the visual cortex. A randomly firing cell (Figure 11b) also exhibited a single burst to a single flash. The maintained anodal polarization made it extraordinarily easy to drive a single unit in burst responses at a 3/sec. flash frequency (Figure 11c). If such driving was continued for a few minutes and then stopped, a single flash delivered

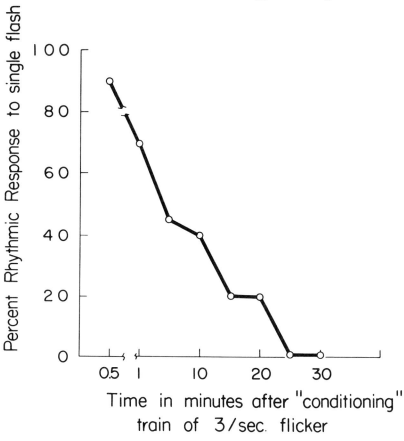

Time in minutes after "conditioning" train of 3/sec. flicker

FIGURE   12

30 sec. later almost always elicited burst responses at the frequency of the original rhythmic flicker. Single flashes delivered at intervals longer than 30 sec. were less and less likely to provoke such rhythmic response, but occasional rhythmic responses to single flash were noted as long as 20 min. after the rhythmic stimulation was discontinued [see Fig. 12]. This seems a particularly clear illustration of the capacity of polarized cells to retain some representation of an imposed stimulus pattern for a relatively long period of time. The order of magnitude of this time interval is itself significant. It correlates well with the data of Duncan (1948) on the abolition of a learned response in rats consequent to massive electro-shock delivered at various intervals following the training session. It also correlates with clinical experience on the duration of amnesia produced by electroconvulsive therapy and with the amnesia secondary to cerebral concussion. Brazier (1960) has previously pointed out that the enduring neural changes that are the basis of long-term memory of the sort not abolished by sleep, by concussion, or by electroshock probably will not be found by electrophysiological measurements. However the synaptic changes that underlie short-term memory and are sensitive to the effects of anesthesia, sleep, and concussion may very well be discerned by the probing instruments of the electrophysiologist when he discovers how and where to look for them. I have presented here the very small and tentative beginnings of such a search. The "dominant focus" of Rusinov has provided an intriguing tool for this investigation.

ACKNOWLEDGMENT

Sincere appreciation is expressed for the help of Paul Naitoh in the early phases of this work.

REFERENCES

Adey, W. R., C. W. Dunlop & C. E. Hendrix. 1960. Hippocampal slow waves. Arch. Neurol. 3: 74–90.
Brazier, M. A. B. 1960. Long-persisting electrical traces in the brain of man and their possible relationship to higher nervous activity. The Moscow Colloquium on Electroencephalography of Higher Nervous Activity. H. H. Jasper and G. D. Smirnov, Eds. EEG Clin. Neurophysiol. Suppl. 13: 347–358.
Burns, B. D. 1954. The production of after-bursts in isolated unanesthetized cerebral cortex. J. Physiol. 125: 427–446.
Burns, B. D. 1955. The mechanism of after-bursts in cerebral cortex. J. Physiol. 127: 168–188.
Doty, R. W. & C. Giurgea. In Symposium on Brain Mechanisms and Learning, Montevideo, August, 1959. Blackwell Scientific Publ. Oxford, England. In press.
Doty, R. W., L. T. Rutledge & R. M. Larsen. 1956. Conditioned reflexes established to electrical stimulation of cat cerebral cortex. J. Neurophysiol. 19: 401–415.
Doty, R. W. & L. T. Rutledge. 1959. "Generalization" between cortically and peripherally applied stimuli eliciting conditioned reflexes. J. Neurophysiol. 22: 428–435.

Duncan, C. P.   1948.   The retroactive effect of electroshock on learning in rats. J.
    Comp. Physiol. Psychol. **42**: 32–44.

Eccles, J. C.   1958.   The behavior of nerve cells. *In* The Neurological Basis of Be-
    havior. G. E. W. Wolstenholme and C. M. O'Connor, Eds. Little, Brown. Boston,
    Mass.

Fessard, A.   1960.   Le conditionnement consideré à l'échelle du neurone. The Moscow
    Colloquium on Electroencephalography of Higher Nervous Activity. H. H. Jasper
    and G. D. Smirnov, Eds. EEG Clin. Neurophysiol. Suppl. **13**: 157–184.

Hubel, D. H.   1957.   Tungsten microelectrode for recording from single units. Science.
    125: 549–550.

John, E. R. & K. F. Killam.   1960.   Studies of electrical activity of brain during
    differential conditioning in cats. *In* Recent Advances in Biological Psychiatry. J.
    Wortis, Ed. Grune and Stratton. New York, N.Y.

Livanov, M. N.   1960.   Concerning the establishment of temporary connections. The
    Moscow Colloquium of Electroencephalography of Higher Nervous Activity. H.
    H. Jasper and G. D. Smirnov, Eds. EEG Clin. Neurophysiol. Suppl. **13**: 185–198.

Rusinov, V. S.   1953.   An electrophysiological analysis of the connecting function
    in the cerebral cortex in the presence of a dominant region area. Abstr. Communica-
    tions XIX Internat. Physiol. Congr. Montreal. : 719–720.

SHORT-TERM RETROGRADE AMNESIA IN RATS

Stephan L. Chorover and
Peter H. Schiller

MASSACHUSETTS INSTITUTE OF TECHNOLOGY

Editor's Note   *The effect of electroconvulsive shock (ECS) on previously learned behavior has had a rather controversial experimental history. Initially it was believed that ECS could produce amnesia for things learned up to 30 minutes or longer before its occurrence. However, as of this writing, it appears that such long-term effects may be due to other functions of the ECS than retrograde amnesia as such. However, Chorover and Schiller, and Quartermain, Paolino, and Miller (A brief gradient of retrograde amnesia independent of situational change, Science, 1965, 149, 1116–1118) have presented evidence that there is a true amnestic effect for events happening within a very short period prior to the ECS. The results reported here have to do with this short-term phenomenon.*

Source   *Reprinted from the Journal of Comparative and Physiological Psychology, 1965, 59, (1), 73–78, with permission of the authors and the American Psychological Association.*

Abstract. Retroactive effects of electroconvulsive shock (ECS) were studied in 477 male hooded rats which received ECS 0.5–60.0 sec. after single passive avoidance training trials. As in previous studies, impairment in retention was inversely related to duration of ECS-delay interval. However, unlike earlier studies, impairment was observed only at relatively short (0.5–10.0 sec.) ECS-delays. Impairment is attributed to brief RA and not to aversive effects of ECS which were shown to develop only after repeated ECS treatments. The results are discussed in terms of both the consolidation hypothesis and alternative "conflict" and "competing-response" hypotheses of ECS effects.

Electroconvulsive shock (ECS) tends to impair performance of learned responses in rats. The magnitude of the impairment is generally found to vary inversely with the time interval between learning and the ECS treatment. Considerable controversy still surrounds the question of whether such impairments are due to retroactive "memory interference" (retrograde amnesia—RA) (Duncan, 1949; Hudspeth, McGaugh, & Thompson, 1964; Leukel, 1957; Thompson & Dean, 1955) or to other disruptive effects such as conflict (Coons & Miller, 1960) or competing conditioned responses (Lewis & Adams, 1963) produced by ECS.

In general, experiments in which repeated convulsive treatments have been employed tend to support the "conflict" or "competing-response" hypotheses, while the results of "one-trial learning" studies (Chorover, 1964; Hudspeth et al., 1964) suggest that ECS may actually produce RA (perhaps by interfering with some hypothetical "consolidation" processes involved in the permanent encoding of "memory traces").

In the present study we attempted to show: (*a*) That it is possible to clearly identify amnestic effects of ECS in a one-trial passive avoidance learning situation; (*b*) that, under the conditions employed, the duration of ECS-induced RA is considerably briefer than previously reported and; (*c*) that aversive effects of ECS, which can also be identified, are experimentally dissociable from the amnestic ones. Our results provide a possible basis for resolving some of the apparent contradictions between the RA hypothesis on the one hand and the conflict or competing response views on the other.

METHOD

SUBJECTS

Four hundred and seventy-seven male hooded rats of the Long-Evans strain were used in the experiment. They were obtained in several lots from a commer-

[1] Supported in part by the Rockefeller Foundation and by the National Institute of Mental Health Grants No. M-5673 and MG-07923-01. We are indebted to Anne Marie DeLuca for assistance in various phases of this research.

cial supplier (Research Animals, Incorporated, Pittsburgh, Pennsylvania) at about 60 days of age. At the time of the experiment Ss were 75–100 days old. Throughout their time in the laboratory they were housed in pairs in standard wire-mesh cages (17.5 × 17.5 × 24 cm.) and provided with ad-lib access to food (Purina laboratory chow) and water.

APPARATUS

The apparatus employed was patterned after one first described by Jarvik and Essman (1960). Our version of the apparatus consists of a 40-cm. square compartment with walls 30 cm. high, made of polyvinyl chloride sheet, and a floor of stainless-steel rods (³⁄₃₂ in. diameter) placed 1.25 cm. apart. The grid floor is connected to a source of dc voltage (a Grass S-4 stimulator) through a grid-scrambler so that foot shocks (10 pulses/sec; 0.75 ma.) may be delivered when S's feet touch two or more of the grid rods. Located in the center of the compartment is a 13-cm. square insulated platform 5.5 cm. high.

PROCEDURE

The normal response of most Ss when placed upon the raised platform was to step down rather rapidly onto the grid floor and explore the test compartment. The time required to perform this step-down response was our measure of the aversive properties of the test situation. In order to obtain adequate control information and base-line performance levels, each S was first allowed a 5-day (one trial per day) period of habituation to the apparatus as follows: At the start of each trial, S was placed in the center of the raised platform, and the time taken to step down (more precisely, the time required to place both forepaws on the grid) was recorded. Ten seconds after stepping down S was removed from the compartment and returned to its home cage. On Day 3, several hours after the usual habituation trial, two small snap connectors ("Starlet-Dot fasteners"—manufactured by United-Car Corporation, Cambridge 39, Massachusetts) were set in Ss' pinnae under brief ether anesthesia. On all subsequent trials, wires for administering ECS were attached to the ear snaps just prior to placing S on the raised platform.

Differential treatments were begun on Day 5 and were repeated on the 2 following days. The last test trial was run on Day 8. Animals were matched on the basis of step-down latencies (SDL) obtained on Days 1–4 and were assigned randomly to three main groups and two additional control groups as shown in Table 1. To test for the aversive properties of the foot shock, the first group (FS, $N = 102$) was divided into four subgroups which, upon stepping from the raised platform, received foot shocks lasting 0.5, 1, 2, or 4 sec. The second group (FS-ECS, $N = 242$) was treated exactly like the first, but in addition to the FS these Ss received ECS in the apparatus. The ECS was produced by passing 35–50 ma. ac between the ear snaps for 0.2 sec. Different subgroups of the FS-ECS group received the convulsive treatment 0.5, 2, 5, 10, or 30 sec. after termination of the foot shock. The purpose of the third group was to assay the effects of ECS itself upon the step-down performance. This group (ECS; $N = 111$) did not receive foot shock, but did receive ECS in the apparatus. Different subgroups received the convulsive treatments at delay intervals equal to those of comparable Ss in the FS-ECS group (i.e., 0.5–30 sec.). One additional ECS subgroup ($N = 10$) received the convulsive treatment after a delay of 60 sec. Two additional groups were foot-shock controls patterned after a treatment devised by Duncan (1945). The first group (D_1, $N = 6$) received no FS; these Ss were removed from the apparatus 10 sec. after stepping down; 20 sec. later, after being placed in a large white plastic basin, they were given 35–50 ma. shock to the hindlegs. The second group (D_2, $N = 6$) received a 2-sec. foot shock followed in 30 sec. by the hindleg shock.

On Days 6, 7, and 8 the same procedure was followed: wires were attached to the ear snaps, S was placed on the platform, and the step-down latency was recorded. After stepping down, FS and/or ECS were given as described above. The maximum latency score was 30; Ss which avoided (i.e., remained on the platform; beyond 30 sec. were gently pushed off in order to equalize the total number of foot shocks and ECS treatments given to all Ss.

Skewness in the distribution of latency scores dictated use of nonparametric statistical analysis. Therefore, within each group, central tendency was calculated in terms of median step-down latency (mdn. SDL) and performance of individual Ss was compared by means of a series of Mann-Whitney U tests (intergroup comparisons) and sign tests (intragroup, day-by-day comparisons).

RESULTS

On the trial prior to implantation of the ear snaps (Day 3), the overall median step-down latency was 1.5 sec; on the following trial (Day 4) it was 1.51 sec. This indicates that neither the brief operation performed on Day 3, nor attachment of wires to the ear snaps on Day 4 affected Ss performance during the habituation phase of the experiment.

The posttreatment results are expressed in terms of the mdn. SDL for each subgroup and the percentage of Ss avoiding for at least 20 sec. The effects of single treatments (data for Day 6 only) are presented first (Table 1 and Figure 1), followed by results after three repeated treatments (data for Days 6, 7, and 8 combined).

Effects of Single Treatments

1. *Effects of a single foot shock* (FS). On Day 5 all Ss dismounted from the raised platform within 4 sec. (mdn. SDL = 1.6 sec.). Animals which received FS upon stepping down on Day 5 showed an increased tendency to remain on the platform on Day 6. The overall mdn. SDL for Ss in the FS groups rose to 30 sec. ($p < .001$). Avoidance of the grid floor varied slightly as a direct function of FS duration (Figure 1).

2. *Effects of a single ECS treatment*. After receiving a single convulsive treatment on Day 5, most Ss in the ECS groups showed no increased tendency to remain on the platform on the following day (Table 1).

3. *Effects of a single FS-ECS treatment*. The interactions between FS duration and ECS-delay interval are summarized in Table 1 and in the central portion of Figure 1. After a single FS-ECS treatment, avoidance of the grid increased as a function of duration of the ECS-delay interval. As FS duration was increased, the tendency to avoid the grid also increased.

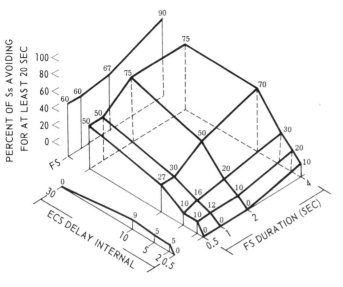

FIGURE 1 *Effects of a single treatment upon percentage of Ss avoiding for at least 20 sec. on first posttreatment day (Day 6). (Isometric orthographic projection in center depicts passive avoidance performance of FS-ECS groups as a joint function of FS duration—0.5-4 sec.—and ECS-delay interval—0.5-30 sec. Values on curve in left foreground are for Ss which received ECS only. Values on curve in left background are for Ss which received FS only. Numerals on the curves indicate actual percentage values at each data point.)*

Table 1. *Median Step-down Latency on First Posttreatment Trial (Day 6) as a Function of Foot-shock Duration and ECS-Delay Interval*

ECS delay (sec.)	Foot-shock duration (in sec.)								ECS only		N^a
	0.5		1		2		4				
	N	Mdn. SDL	N	Mdn. SDL	N	Mdn. SDL	N	Mdn. SDL	N	Mdn. SD	
0.5	10	2.25	10	2.75	10	4.55	10	6.50	30	1.55	70
2	10	3.25	17	1.50	10	5.50	10	5.75	20	1.00	67
5	10	3.00	19	2.00	10	9.75	10	15.00	20	1.50	69
10	11	9.50	20	9.00	10	18.00	10	26.80	22	1.25	73
30	10	18.50	10	20.00	24	30.00	11	30.00	19	4.00	74
FS only	10	27.50	20	29.75	62	30.00	10	30.00	—		102[b]
N	61		96		126		61		111	1.50	455

[a] Three subgroups which do not appear in the table make the total $N = 477$: Group D_1 ($N = 6$) received hindleg shock only (mdn. SDL = 17.00); Group D_2 ($N = 6$) received 2-sec. FS plus hindleg shock (mdn. SDL = 30.00); 10 Ss received ECS at 60-sec. delay (mdn. SDL = 1.50).

[b] Mdn. SDL = 30.00.

Footshock duration was, however, a weaker determinant of the increased avoidance. With ECS-delay intervals of 5 sec. or more, the FS-ECS groups began to show significantly increased avoidance of the grid. Step-down latencies approaching control (FS) levels were obtained when the ECS-delay interval was increased to 10 sec. Finally, at the 30-sec. delay interval, performance of the FS-ECS groups was indistinguishable from that of FS controls.

Effects of Three Repeated Treatments

1. *Effects of repeated foot shocks* (FS). Figure 2 shows that repetition of the FS treatments produced relatively little overall change in the level of avoidance performance. The mdn. SDL of 30 sec., attained after a single FS, was maintained throughout the subsequent trials.

2. *Effects of repeated ECS treatments.* Although avoidance did not increase following a single ECS treatment (Figure 2), daily repetition of the convulsions for 3 successive days produced a progressive increase in Ss' tendency to remain on the platform. The mdn. SDL for all ECS groups on Days 6, 7, and 8 was 1.5, 3.5, and 10.3, respectively. Thus, by the end of the 3-day test period, overall avoidance performance of the ECS groups was approaching (but did not yet equal) that of the FS groups. It must be emphasized that all of the ECS-delay subgroups did not contribute equally to this result. On the contrary, marked differences in SDL were observed as a function of the duration of the ECS-delay interval. Thus, it can be seen from Figure 3 that avoidance was least at the shortest (0.5 sec.) delay interval, increased significantly ($p < 0.001$) up to 10 sec.

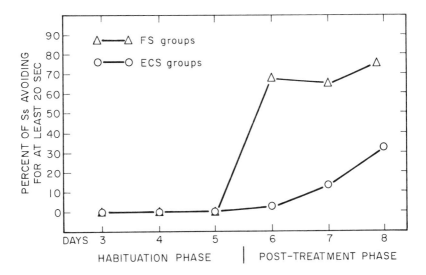

FIGURE 2 *Development of avoidance performance on Days 6, 7, and 8 by Ss which received FS and ECS on treatment Days 5, 6, and 7. (Numbers in parentheses indicate number of Ss at each data point.)*

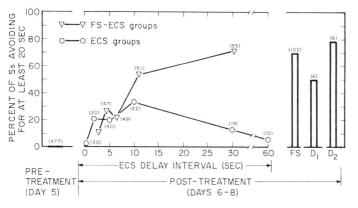

FIGURE 3 *Overall avoidance performance of FS-ECS, ECS, and control groups. (Central portion of the figure compares performance of FS-ECS and ECS groups as a function of the delay of posttrial ECS administration. Numbers in parentheses indicate the number of Ss in each group. Each point is based upon overall step-down latencies on Days 6, 7, and 8. Vertical bars at the right indicate performance of groups which received FS only—FS, hindleg shock only—D₁—or, FS plus hindleg shock—D₂.)*

and then declined; Ss which received the ECS treatments at 30- and 60-sec. delay intervals avoided the grid significantly less than those in the 10-sec. delay subgroup ($p < 0.001$).

3. *Effects of repeated FS-ECS treatments.* Duration of FS initially exerted a considerable influence upon the degree of avoidance by the FS-ECS

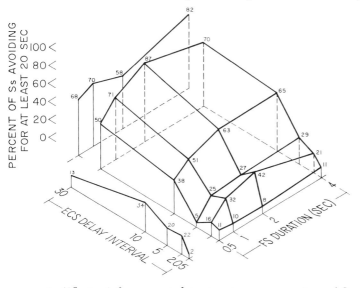

FIGURE 4 *Effects of three repeated treatments upon percentage of Ss avoiding for at least 20 sec. (Each data point reflects overall performance on Days 6, 7, and 8. Details of the figure are otherwise the same as for Figure 1.)*

groups (Figure 1). However, when the overall data for each FS-ECS sub-group were combined for 3 successive days (Figure 4) the latency differences originally observed as a function of FS duration tended to disappear. By contrast, after three trials (Figure 4) as after a single trial (Figure 1), avoidance continued to be a negatively accelerated, increasing function of the ECS-delay interval. As shown in Figure 3, the percentage of trials on which FS-ECS Ss avoided for at least 20 sec. was markedly increased when the ECS-delay interval was 10 sec or longer. Another important result shown in Figure 3 is that the avoidance performance of FS-ECS and ECS groups was equivalent at ECS-delay intervals less than 10 sec.

DISCUSSION

The results are in agreement with the general observations that (a) retention test performance may be impaired by one or more ECS treatments given shortly after avoidance training trials and (b) the degree of ECS-induced interference varies inversely with the duration of time elapsed between training and ECS. However, we have found no evidence to support the idea that ECS produces RA for events preceding the convulsion by several hours or even minutes. On the contrary, Ss in the present situation clearly retained a previously acquired passive avoidance response when ECS was administered as little as 10 sec. after training.

Aversive effects of ECS (without accompanying FS) did not seem to develop after a single convulsion but did become increasingly prominent with repeated ECS treatments (Figure 2). Two specific lines of evidence indicate that the aversive effects were dissociable from the amnestic ones and could not (in the present case at least) be invoked to account for the latter:

1. In the experimental situation, aversive stimuli which evoke fear or competing response should cause the animal to abandon its normal step-down response and to "freeze" on the raised platform. This is precisely the effect produced by the noxious foot shock and by the hindleg shock (Figure 3). It is clear from Figure 2, however, that this was not the effect of a single ECS although repetition of the ECS treatments increased the probability that a "freezing" response would occur.

2. According to generally accepted principles of conditioning, the influence of a reinforcer (including punishment) may be expected to decline as the delay of reinforcement increases (Kamin, 1959; Kimble, 1961). Therefore, if ECS has aversive properties, its maximum effect upon step-down performance should appear at the shortest ECS-delay intervals and its disruptive influence should decline as the ECS-delay interval is lengthened. This was not the case in the present experiment. On the contrary (see Figure 3) the aversive effects of ECS, which were least at very short-delay intervals, increased up to about 10 sec. and then declined again. The decline in avoidance observed when ECS was administered at rela-

tively long ECS-delay intervals (i.e., 10–60 sec.) may be adequately accounted for in terms of a temporal-delay-of-punishment gradient (Kamin, 1959), but this notion does not explain why ECS groups showed a gradual increase in avoidance up to 10 sec. In order to account for this increase, we must compare performance of the ECS and FS-ECS groups during ECS-delay intervals up to 10 sec. and consider the relationship of our data to the memory interference hypothesis.

The FS-ECS curve in Figure 3 clearly shows that, although Ss were able to retain the avoidance response when the ECS-delay interval exceeded 10 sec., retention declined as the delay of ECS administration was reduced below 10 sec. If we assume (a) that ECS produces RA lasting up to 10 sec. and (b) that ECS has aversive effects which may become associated with antecedent stimuli in accordance with principles of classical conditioning, it becomes possible to account for the increased avoidance of ECS subgroups as the ECS-delay interval is increased up to 10 sec: Since successful conditioning presumably requires that S "remember" the CS, it is only when delay interval is increased up to 10 sec. (i.e., to the apparent "limits" of the RA) that it becomes possible for the aversive consequences of the ECS to be conditioned to antecedent stimuli in the test situation.

In summary, by proposing that ECS induces a brief RA, we are able to account for (a) the failure of ECS, in the present study, to interfere with retention of a passive avoidance response learned 10–30 sec. prior to ECS and (b) the comparable effects of ECS and FS-ECS at very short ECS-delay intervals (i.e., the apparent failure of the aversive effects of both FS and ECS to produce avoidance of the grid when ECS is given within the first few seconds after a trial).

Although our results appear to support a "brief RA" hypothesis of ECS effects, two important questions remain unanswered. First, how can we account for the apparent contradictions between our results and those of other workers who have reported that impaired retention of different passive avoidance tasks may be produced at much greater ECS-delay intervals (Bures and Buresova, 1963, Heriot and Coleman, 1962, Weissman, 1963)? Second, assuming that ECS produces RA which, irrespective of whether it is "brief" or "prolonged," appears to be a true *amnesia* (i.e. loss or absence of memory), is it valid to attribute this effect to interference with "memory trace consolidation?"

REFERENCES

Bureš, J., & Burešová, O. Cortical spreading depression as a memory disturbing factor. *J. comp. physiol. Psychol.*, 1963, **56**, 268–272.

Chorover, S. L. Rapid memory consolidation: Effects of electroconvulsive shock upon retention in the rat. In D. P. Kimble (Ed.), *Learning, remembering and forgetting*. Vol. 1. *The anatomy of learning*. Washington, D. C.: American Institute Biological Sciences, 1964.

Coons, E. E., & Miller, N. E. Conflict versus consolidation of memory traces to explain "retrograde amnesia" produced by ECS. *J. comp. physiol. Psychol.*, 1960, **53**, 524–531.

Duncan, C. P. The effect of electroshock convulsions on the maze habit in the white rat. *J. exp. Psychol.*, 1945, **35**, 267–278.

Duncan, C. P. The retroactive effect of electroshock on learning. *J. comp. physiol. Psychol.*, 1949, **42**, 32–44.

Heriot, J. T., & Coleman, P. D. The effect of electroconvulsive shock on retention of a modified "one-trial" conditioned avoidance. *J. comp. physiol. Psychol.*, 1962, **55**, 1082–1084.

Hudspeth, W. J., McGaugh, J. L., & Thomson, C. W. Aversive and amnesic effects of electroconvulsive shock. *J. comp. physiol. Psychol.*, 1964, **57**, 61–64.

Jarvik, M. E., & Essman, W. B. A simple one-trial learning situation for mice. *Psychol. Rep.*, 1960, **6**, 290.

Kamin, L. J. The delay of punishment gradient. *J. comp. physiol. Psychol.*, 1959, **52**, 434–437.

Kimble, G. A. *Hilgard and Marquis' conditioning and learning.* (2nd ed.) New York: Appleton-Century-Crofts, 1961.

Leukel, F. A comparison of the effects of ECS and anesthesia on acquisition of the maze habit. *J. comp. physiol. Psychol.*, 1957, **50**, 300–306.

Lewis, D. J., & Adams, H. E. Retrograde amnesia from conditioned competing responses. *Science*, 1963, **141**, 516–517.

Thompson, R., & Dean, W. A further study of the retroactive effect of ECS. *J. comp. physiol. Psychol.*, 1955, **48**, 488–491.

Weissman, A. Effect of electroconvulsive shock intensity and seizure pattern on retrograde amnesia in rats. *J. comp. physiol. Psychol.*, 1963, **56**, 806–810.

DRUG FACILITATION
OF LATENT LEARNING

William H. Westbrook

UNIVERSITY OF CALIFORNIA, BERKELEY

James L. McGaugh

UNIVERSITY OF CALIFORNIA, IRVINE

Editor's Note *McGaugh and his collaborators have conducted a series of experiments, referred to in the early
parts of this reading, on the effects of drugs which
appear to facilitate learning. These studies may be
thought of as the counterpart of reading 31; they are
experiments in which memory is **improved** by enhanced
central nervous system function as compared to memory decrements through central nervous system interference. The study reprinted here is perhaps the most
convincing of the series by McGaugh and his collaborators.*

Source *Reprinted from **Psychopharmacologia** (Berl.),
1964, **5**, 440–446, with permission of the authors and
Springer-Verlag.*

A number of recent investigations have shown that, in rats, learning is facilitated by injections of several compounds, including picrotoxin, strychnine, and the strychnine-like compound 1-5-diphenyl-3-7-diazadamantan-9-01 (1757 I.S.)[1] (Kelemen and Bovet, 1961; McGaugh and Petrinovich, 1959; McGaugh *et al.*, 1961; Petrinovich, 1963). These findings have been interpreted as indicating that the drugs improve performance by enhancing memory storage or consolidation. This interpretation is strengthened by evidence that retention is facilitated by injections of CNS stimulants if the injections are administered within a few minutes *after* the training trials (Breen and McGaugh, 1961; McGaugh, Westbrook, and Thomson, 1962; McGaugh *et al.*, 1962; Paré, 1961; Stratton and Petrinovich, 1963). Although these latter findings provide strong support for a view that the drugs used improve performance by enhancing memory storage, an alternative possibility that the post-training injections are rewarding has not as yet been excluded. If the improvement found with post-trial injections is due to a rewarding effect in place of, or in addition to, an effect on memory storage, rats given only drug injections and no other reward following each training trial in a maze should show improvement in performance from trial to trial. If the drug acts only to enhance memory storage, however, the subjects should learn more, in comparison with control subjects, about the features and plan of the maze but should not improve in performance until a relevant reward (e.g. food or water) is given at the end of the trial. Further, following the introduction of the reward the performance of the subjects previously given posttrial drug injections should be superior to controls: that is, they should exhibit greater latent learning. To test these interpretations the present study investigated the effect of post-trial injections of the CNS stimulant 1757 I.S. on learning under rewarded or non-rewarded followed by rewarded ("latent learning") conditions. The "latent learning" training procedure was similar to those used by Blodgett (1929) and Tolman and Honzik (1930). Longo *et al.*, (1959) reported that 1757 I.S. affects CNS activity in a manner highly similar to that of strychnine. The dose used in the present study has been found to facilitate learning in several previous studies (cited above), and is comparable to the doses of strychnine and picrotoxin previously found to influence learning.

[1] In previous publications this compound was termed 5-7-diphenyl-1-3-diazadamantan-6-01 (1757 I.S.).

METHOD

Subjects

Forty-eight rats, 24 males and 24 females, from the S_1 strain and 48 rats, 24 males and 24 females, from the S_3 strain were used in this study. Twelve additional subjects (8 S_1 males, 2 S_1 females, I S_3 male, and 1 S_3 female) were eliminated for failure to complete all stages of training. All subjects were between 70 and 85 days of age at the beginning of the experiment. The S_1 and S_3 strains are decendents of the Tryon maze-bright and maze-dull strains maintained at the University of California at Berkeley. The subjects used in this study were all reared in the animal laboratory at San Jose State College.

Apparatus

A 6 unit alley U maze was used (see Fig. 1) [omitted in reprinting]. Each main unit of the maze was 10 cm wide, 12.7 cm high, and 50.8 cm long. The 2 arms extending forward from each main unit were 10 cm wide, 12.7 cm high and 17 cm long. A 25.4 cm starting-alley connected the starting-box to the first main unit. The goal-box was connected directly to the correct arm of the last unit. The walls and floor of the maze were painted a dull medium grey. Units were separated by guillotine doors. The doors in both arms of each unit were raised at the beginning of each trial to prevent any differential visual cues for the two arms. The incorrect arms were blocked by a false door placed behind the guillotine door. Guillotine doors were also placed between the starting-box and the starting-alley, the starting-alley and the first unit, and the last unit and the goal-box. Two narrow white lines were painted on the floor of each unit 5 cm from the sides of the entrance to the unit. The correct alleys were, in sequence, L R L R R L. Mirrors suspended from a wooden frame over the maze provided a clear view of each unit. The maze was situated in a partitioned section of a large room and was centered under a large covered light which provided adequate illumination in all units.

Procedure

The subjects were first placed on a 22 hour food and water deprivation schedule for 5 days. Each subject was allowed access to water for two hours daily and was given sufficient wet mash to maintain body weight at 85 percent of the subjects weight on the second day. This schedule was maintained throughout the experiment.

Following the adaptation period, the subjects were divided into four groups, each consisting of twenty-four subjects: 6 males and 6 females of each strain.

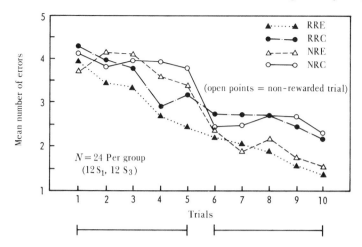

FIGURE 2 *Mean daily errors made by subjects in the four experimental (drug and reward) conditions.*

All subjects were given one trial per day for ten days in the maze. Errors were recorded whenever a subject's head crossed the white line in front of a blind alley. Two of the groups were given wet mash in the goal-box and were allowed one minute of eating after each trial. These two groups will be referred to as Reward-Reward Experimental (RRE) and Reward-Reward Control (RRC). The subjects in the other two groups were also deprived of food and water but received no reward in the goal-box for the first four trials. On the fifth and succeeding trials they were rewarded with wet mash. Thus each subject in these latter groups had five trials with *no* prior reward and five trials *with* prior reward. These two groups will be referred to as Non-reward-Reward Experimental (NRE) and Non-reward Control (NRC).

Table 1. Means and Standard Deviations (in parentheses) of Initial Errors Made by Subjects in Each Subgroup on Trials 2–5 (prior to reward introduction) and Trials 6–10 (after reward introduction)

		Groups			
Strain	*Sex*	*Trials 2–5*			
		RRC	RRE	NRC	NRE
S_1	♂	14.5 (4.3)	13.0 (1.5)	15.2 (1.2)	14.8 (1.9)
	♀	13.3 (1.8)	11.0 (1.7)	15.7 (2.7)	17.7 (1.1)
S_3	♂	13.8 (1.9)	13.7 (2.4)	15.0 (2.1)	16.7 (2.5)
	♀	15.3 (2.0)	12.7 (2.3)	17.5 (3.0)	15.8 (1.6)
Combined mean		14.2	12.6	15.8	15.5

All subjects were given an intraperitoneal injection immediately after each daily trial. Subjects in the experimental groups in each reward condition (RRE and NRE) received 1.0 ml/kg of a 1.0 mg/ml solution of 1757 I.S. after each of the first five trials. Following each of the last five trials, they received 1.0 ml/kg of a citrate buffer control solution. Subjects in the two control groups (RRC and NRC) received the control solution after each trial.

RESULTS

The means and standard deviations of errors made by subjects in each subgroup on trials 2–5 and trials 6–10 are shown in the Table. Fig. 2 shows the mean errors made by subjects in each of the four experimental groups (ignoring strain and sex) on each trial. Only initial errors were used because of the variability of repetitive errors during the non-rewarded trials. As can be seen, the RRE subjects made fewer errors than the RRC subjects throughout the training. An analysis of variance of errors made by subjects in these groups on trials 2–10 indicated a significant drug effect ($F = 13.9$, $df = 1/40$, $p < .005$) but no significant strain or sex differences and no significant interactions.

During the first 5 trials the mean errors of the two rewarded groups decreased while those of the non-rewarded subjects remained fairly constant. An analysis of variance of the errors of all subgroups on trials 2–5 indicated a significant drug effect ($F = 3.95$, $df = 1/80$, $p < .05$), a significant strain effect ($F = 4.29$, $df = 1/80$, $p < .05$) and a highly significant reward effect ($F = 20.01$, $df = 1/80$, $p < .005$). Fisher t tests indicated that on trials 2–5 the mean of the RRE subjects was significantly lower than that of the RRC subjects ($t = 2.29$, $df = 46$, $p < .05$), but the means of groups NRE and NRC did not differ significantly ($t = 0.5$). Sign tests

Groups			
Trials 6–10			
RRC	RRE	NRC	NRE
12.3 (4.0)	11.7 (2.1)	13.8 (1.7)	9.0 (2.2)
12.7 (3.4)	8.7 (2.1)	14.7 (2.9)	11.8 (2.4)
12.3 (2.6)	9.2 (2.7)	12.2 (2.0)	9.0 (3.2)
15.7 (3.2)	8.7 (2.5)	12.2 (2.3)	11.0 (2.1)
13.2	9.5	13.2	10.2

indicated that in these latter groups, the performance of subjects on trial 5 was not significantly different ($p > .05$) from that of trial 1. These analyses indicate that the drug effect on performance on the first 5 trials was limited to the rewarded subjects.

Following the introduction of reward and termination of the drug injections all subjects were treated alike. As Fig. 2 and the Table show, however, on trials 6–10 the means of groups RRE and NRE were lower than those of groups RRC and NRC. An analysis of variance of the errors made on trials 6–10 indicated a significant drug effect ($F = 32.11$, $df = 1/80$, $p < .005$). The effect of condition of prior reward was insignificant ($F < 1$). The effect of the drug depended upon the sex and prior reward of the subjects ($F = 5.59$, $df = 1/80$, $p < .025$); in groups RRC and NRC male subjects made fewer errors than female subjects while females were superior in group RRE and males superior in group NRE. No other main effect (strain and sex) or interaction approached significance. Fisher t tests indicated that on trials 6–10 group RRE made significantly fewer errors than group RRC ($t = 3.45$, $df = 46$, $p < .01$) and that group NRE made significantly fewer errors than group NRC ($t = 3.90$, $df = 46$, $p < .01$). Sign tests indicated that both non-rewarded groups improved significantly ($p < .01$) between trials 5 and 6 (i.e., following the introduction of reward).

DISCUSSION

The findings indicate that posttrial injections of 1757 I.S. facilitate latent learning as well as conventional (rewarded) maze learning. The performance of the consistently rewarded groups was similar to that of comparable groups in previous posttrial injection studies which have used different tasks and testing procedures (McGaugh, Westbrook, and Thomson, 1962).

The results of the subjects which received 5 trials prior to reward introduction provide additional evidence bearing on the question of the basis of the faciliating effect of 1757 I.S. on maze performance. During the non-rewarded trials the performance of the control subjects was similar to that of the subjects receiving posttrial injections of 1757 I.S.; there was no evidence of improvement in maze performance in either group. This finding is evidence against the interpretation that the drug-control difference in performance is due either to a rewarding effect of the drug or a punishing effect of the control solution. Further evidence against these latter interpretations is provided by subjects' performance on the last 5 trials when all subjects received food reward and posttrial control injections. If the drug affects performance only because it is rewarding, all groups would be expected to perform alike on the last few trials. This was clearly not the case. On the last trials the subjects previously injected with 1757 I.S. made significantly fewer errors than subjects that had received only the control solution. Further, the performance of subjects on the last five trials was not significantly influenced by the presence or absence of reward on the earlier trials: the mean errors of the two 1757 I.S. groups were similar and the mean errors of the two control groups were identical.

In general, the effects of condition of reward and drug were similar for males and females of the two strains. The only exceptions to this were a strain difference in errors made during the early trials and a drug by sex by condition of prior reward interaction in the later trials. The significance of these effects is obscure.

The findings of this study, as well as those of other recent studies using other CNS stimulants are most consistent with the hypothesis that posttrial injections of CNS stimulants improve learning by facilitating memory storage. Since facilitation has been found with a variety of tasks and drugs it seems likely that the facilitation is due to a common excitatory effect of the agents on the CNS. An understanding of the process or processes underlying drug facilitation of learning will require additional knowledge of the common CNS effects of the effective compounds.

SUMMARY

Male and female rats of the S_1 and S_3 strains (descendants of the Tryon strains) were injected with either 1.0 mg/kg of 1757 I.S. (1-5-diphenyl-3-7-diazadamantan-9-01) or a control solution immediately after each daily trial in a 6-unit alley U maze. One half of the rats received a food reward in the goal box and one half was not rewarded. The non-rewarded drug and control rats did not improve in performance. Both of the rewarded groups improved, and the 1757 I.S.-injected rats made significantly fewer errors than the controls. The drug injections were then discontinued and all rats were given 5 rewarded trials (one per day), each followed by a control injection. On the last 5 trials the mean errors of the rats previously given posttrial 1757 I.S. injections were significantly lower than those of the controls. Further, performance on the last 5 trials was not influenced by the reward condition on the first 5 trials. These results were interpreted as providing further support for the hypothesis that 1757 I.S. improves learning by enhancing memory storage processes.[2]

REFERENCES

Blodgett, H. C.: The effect of introduction of reward upon the maze performance of rats. Univ. Calif. Publ. Psychol. 4, 113–134 (1929).

[2] This study was conducted in the Psychology Department Animal Laboratory of San Jose State College and was supported by Research Grants MY-3541 and MH 07015 from the National Institute of Mental Health, United States Public Health Service. We would like to express our appreciation to Professor Daniel Bovet for providing the 1757 I.S.

Breen, R. A., and J. L. McGaugh: Facilitation of maze learning with posttrial injections of picrotoxin. J. comp. physiol. Psychol. **54**, 498–501 (1961).

Kelemen, K., and D. Bovet: Effect of drugs upon the defensive behavior of rats. Acta physiol. Acad. Sci. hung. **19**, 143–154 (1961).

Longo, V. G., B. Silvestrini, and D. Bovet: An investigation of convulsant properties of the 5–7 diphenyl-1-3-diazadamantan-6-01 (1757 I.S.). J. Pharmacol. exp. Ther. **126**, 41–49 (1959).

McGaugh, J. L., and L. Petrinovich: The effect of strychnine sulphate on maze learning. Amer. J. Psychol. **72**, 99–102 (1959).

———, C. W. Thomson, W. H. Westbrook, and W. J. Hudspeth: A further study of learning facilitation with strychnine sulphate. Psychopharmacologia (Berl.) **3**, 352–360 (1962).

———, W. H. Westbrook, and G. S. Burt: Strain differences in the facilitative effects of 5-7-diphenyl-1-3-diazadamantan-6-01 (1757 I.S.) on maze learning. J. comp. physiol. Psychol. **54**, 502–505 (1961).

———, ———, C. W. Thomson: Facilitation of maze learning with posttrial injections of 5-7-diphenyl-1-3-diazadamantan-6-01 (1757 I.S.). J. comp. physiol. Psychol. **55**, 710–713 (1962).

Paré, W.: The effect of caffeine and seconal on a visual discrimination task. J. comp. physiol. Psychol. **54**, 506–509 (1961).

Petrinovich, L.: Facilitation of successive discrimination learning by strychnine sulphate. Psychopharmacologia (Berl.) **4**, 103–113 (1963).

Stratton, Lois O., and L. Petrinovich: Post-trial injections of an anti-cholinesterase drug on maze learning in two strains of rats. Psychopharmacologia (Berl.) **5**, 47–54 (1963).

Tolman, E. C., and C. H. Honzik: Introduction and removal of reward and maze performance in rats. Univ. Calif. Publ. Pyschol. **4**, 257–275 (1930).

GLIAL RNA CHANGES
DURING A LEARNING
EXPERIMENT IN RATS

H. Hydén and E. Egyházi

UNIVERSITY OF GOTEBORG, SWEDEN

Editor's Note Ribonucleic acid (RNA) is the giant molecule which carries information from the genes to the protein-manufacturing machinery of the cell. The RNA molecule is made up of sequences of the four bases, adenine, guanine, cytosine, and uracil, the order of which determines the "coding" of the protein molecules for the manufacture of which it serves as a template. In the experiments reported here, Hydén and Eghyázi demonstrate a change in this coding of the RNA in glial cells surrounding a special kind of large neuron in the nucleus which receives information from the inner ear. Changes in coding—base ratio—appear to be associated with learning, while a change only in overall quantity is associated with stimulation without learning. A similar finding with respect to the RNA in the neurons themselves was previously reported by these workers and is described briefly in the introduction to the reading. The reader should be aware that some objections have been raised to the adequacy of the definition of learning used in the present study. The interpretation of these results is also in doubt for other reasons. For example, there is evidence (S. H. Barondes, and M. E. Jarvik. The influence of actinomycin-D on brain RNA synthesis and on memory, Journal of Neurochemistry, 1964, 11, 187–195) that learning can proceed normally in a brain in which new RNA synthesis is almost completely inhibited. Thus, whether new coding of RNA represents the coding of memory, or whether the changes in RNA observed by Hydén and Egyházi are only incidental to other processes cannot be stated as yet.

*Source Reprinted from the **Proceedings of the National Academy of Sciences**, 1963, **49**, 618–624, with permission of the authors and the National Academy of Sciences.*

In a previous study using rats, *nuclear* RNA changes in neurons were found during the establishment of the complex motor and sensory task of learning to balance. In both the learning rats and in two types of controls an increase in the RNA content per nerve cell indicated that the neurons had been stimulated,[1] but only in the learning rats was a net synthesis of nuclear RNA with an increased adenine to uracil ratio found.

Previously it has been shown that the neuron and its neighboring glia are linked in an energetic system and it was suggested that they reacted as a functional unit;[2-4] their biosynthesis of RNA is also linked.[5,6]

In the present study, during the same type of learning experiment in rats and using the neuronal glia of the vestibular Deiters' nerve cells, the base ratio composition of the glial RNA was analyzed by microelectrophoresis. The glial RNA responded with similar, although not identical, base ratio changes as was found in the nuclear RNA of the neurons. On the other hand, in further control experiments, although RNA synthesis increased, RNA with altered base ratio composition was not found, either in reticular nerve cells during learning, or in vestibular nerve cells, when the animals were passively stimulated.

Material and Experimental Setup. The type of learning experiment has been previously described.[1] Fifty-three white rats of the Sprague-Dawley strain weighing 150–160 gm were used. The rats were kept hungry on 4 gm of food daily and had free access to water. They had to learn how to balance on a 1 m long, 1.5 mm thick steel wire, set at 45°, in order to reach their food. Each experiment lasted about eight days. Every day the rats were allowed 45 min of training. It can be seen (Fig. 1) that the rats continued to learn until, by the fifth day, they succeeded in balancing the whole way to the platform. In a group of nine rats, the food was removed from the platform on the eighth day and the experiment prolonged for six days more. The decrement of the curve after food removal shows a decrease in four days below the first day level.

The control consisted of rats of the same litter kept on the same diet as that of the learning animals. Of these, one group was subjected to rotatory stimulation back and forth through 120° horizontally and through 30° vertically.[2] The loss in weight in the learning rats during the 8 days' period was $16 \pm 1.3\%$, and in the controls $15 \pm 1.5\%$, respectively.

Another group of rats was subjected to rotatory stimulation through 120° along a vertical arc. A wheel, 0.7 m in diameter, had a 0.18 m wide pathway made from a wire netting at its periphery. The animals thus had a good foothold when the wheel was moved. During the experiment the wheel was moved from 0 to 180° with the rat placed at the 0° position at the beginning. Each experiment lasted for 30 min with 10 turns/min, and the animal was then killed.

In both the learning and the functional control rats, a significant increase of 70 $\mu\mu$g of RNA per Deiters' nerve cell was observed; this quantitative response of the nerve cells suggested that in both cases the neurons had been stimulated.[1,2]

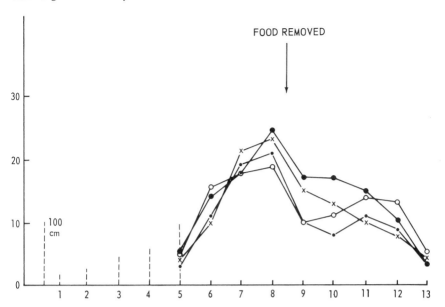

FIGURE 1 *Ordinate: Number of successful trips to the platform during the 45 min allotted each day for food intake. Dotted lines, distance along the wire in centimeters, that the rats were able to balance during the 45 min of training allotted per day. In the examples given, success (100 cm) was obtained on the fifth day. After the eighth day the food was removed from the platform, but the rats were allowed 45 min food-seeking time each day. Slope of curves demonstrates the decreasing frequency and change of behavior.*

In the case of the learning, the rats were *active* but in the functional control experiments *passive*.

The Deiters' nerve cells, as well as corresponding volumes of the surrounding glia, were taken out by microdissection.[7] Approximately 2×10^{-8} g of glia was used for each analysis. The large multipolar nerve cells and samples of the neuronal glia were taken from nucleus giganto-cellularis of the reticular formation, in the oral part of the nucleus, in order to have control from another part of the central nervous system.

The samples were treated with ice-cold 1 N perchloric acid for 5 min, absolute ethanol for 5 min, and chloroform for 5 min. Some samples were taken from 70 μ thick sections through the vestibular nucleus which had been fixed with Carnoy's solution. The tissue was treated with chloroform, ether, ethanol, and hydrated in 0.01 M acetic acid. The amount of RNA per nerve cell was determined by extracting the RNA with a buffered solution of ribonuclease. The RNA in the cell extracts was determined in microdrops with a photographic-photometric method using a radiation at 2.570 Å. Edström *et al.*[8] have demonstrated that this assay of RNA is quantitative down to 20 $\mu\mu$g with a variation coefficient of $\pm 5\%$.

Sampling and analyses of nerve cell nuclei: The modified procedure of Harris[9] allowed simultaneous precipitation of the nuclear RNA and microdissection of the neuronal nuclei. The isolated nerve cells placed on a glass slide were briefly rinsed in cold isotonic NaCl solution, then treated with cold phenol-saturated water from 15 min, followed by cold absolute ethanol for 10 min, and then

Table 1. Composition of Deiters' Nerve Cell and Glial RNA from Control Rats (Base Ratios Expressed as Molar Proportions in Per Cent of the Sum)

	Nerve Cells		Glia		P
	Mean	V	Mean	V	
Adenine	20.5 ± 0.54	5.5	25.3 ± 0.16	1.5	0.001
Guanine	33.7 ± 0.33	2.2	29.0 ± 0.24	1.9	0.001
Cytosine	27.4 ± 0.34	3.0	26.5 ± 0.43	3.7	
Uracil	18.4 ± 0.26	3.1	19.2 ± 0.27	3.1	
No. of animals	5		5		
No. of analyses	50		33		

V = variation coefficient, (S × 100)/mean.

covered by paraffin oil (*pro analysi*). This treatment causes slight contraction of the nuclei just visible at a magnification of 600×. The nucleus from each nerve cell was then removed with a glass needle on a de Fonbrune micromanipulator. Twenty-five nuclei were used for each RNA analysis of base ratios.

The pooled RNA, approximately 700 $\mu\mu$g, extracts from 25 nerve cell nuclei were used for purine-pyrimidine analysis.[10] The purines and pyrimidines were calculated as molar proportions in percentages of the sum. For 500 $\mu\mu$g of RNA the error of the method was ±5%.

RESULTS   *Base ratio composition of glial RNA of the Deiters' nerve cells;* (a) *Control rats:* As is seen from Table 1, the RNA of the glia immediately surrounding the neurons shows higher adenine and lower guanine values compared with that of the nerve cell RNA, with small variability. For the glia the $(A + U)/(G + C)$ ratio is 0.80, $(A + G)/(C + U) = 1.19$, and $A/U = 1.32$. The purine-pyrimidine ratio agrees well with that of the nerve cell which is 1.18.

(b) *Glial RNA in learning experiment:* From Table 2 it can be seen that the adenine value has increased significantly ($P = 0.001$) to give an increased adenine/uracil ratio compared to that of the control glial RNA, from 1.32 ± 0.021 to 1.52 ± 0.037. The ratio $(A + G)/(C + U)$ is 1.33, thus being higher than that of the nerve cell RNA of 1.18. A significant decrease in the cytosine value can also be seen.

(c) *Glial RNA in functional controls with rotatory stimulation:* No significant changes in the glial RNA base ratios occurred as a result of vestibular stimulation when the rats were passive (Table 3).

SOME OTHER CONTROL EXPERIMENTS   (a) *Nuclear RNA of nerve cells belonging to the reticular formation in learning experiment:* The Deiters'

Table 2. Composition of the Glial RNA Surrounding Deiters' Nerve Cells from Control Rats and During Learning

	Controls		Learning		P
	Mean	V	Mean	V	
Adenine	25.3 ± 0.16	1.5	28.3 ± 0.45	3.9	0.001
Guanine	29.0 ± 0.24	1.9	28.8 ± 0.31	2.4	
Cytosine	26.5 ± 0.43	3.7	24.3 ± 0.36	3.7	0.01
Uracil	19.2 ± 0.27	3.1	18.6 ± 0.21	2.8	
No. of animals	5		6		
No. of analyses	33		42		

Table 3. Composition of the Glial RNA Surrounding Deiters' Nerve Cells from Rats Subjected to Vestibular Stimulation for 25 Min/Day and Four Days

	Controls		Vestibular Stimulation	
	Mean	V	Mean	V
Adenine	25.3 ± 0.16	1.5	25.1 ± 0.37	2.9
Guanine	29.0 ± 0.24	1.9	28.6 ± 0.50	3.5
Cytosine	26.5 ± 0.43	3.7	27.4 ± 0.22	1.6
Uracil	19.2 ± 0.27	3.1	18.9 ± 0.20	2.1
No. of animals	5		4	
No. of analyses	33		22	

nerve cells send thin collaterals to the nerve cells of the reticular formation.[11] On the other hand, the reticular formation is not primarily connected with the vestibular peripheral apparatus. An extension of the analyses to the reticular nerve cells would, therefore, at the same time provide a control of possible RNA changes occurring outside of the vestibular lateral area in the brain stem.

The results in Table 4 demonstrate that a moderate increase in the amount of RNA per nerve cell occurred in the reticular nerve cells during the learning period as if they had also been stimulated. The question therefore arose whether nuclear RNA changes similar to those in the Deiters' nerve cells also occurred in the reticular cells.

As is seen from Table 5, no significant changes could be found in the base ratios of the nuclear RNA of the big nerve cells of the reticular formation.

(b) *Nuclear RNA of Deiters' nerve cells after vestibular stimulation:* In the previous paper on RNA in rat learning experiment, control rats were subjected to rotatory stimulation through 120° horizontally and 30° vertically for short times. Although increase in the amount of RNA/cell was found, no base ratio alteration occurred. In this study we have ex-

Table 4. The Amount of RNA/Nerve Cell, the Reticular Formation, of Rats During Learning

	Controls	1st Day	2nd Day	3rd Day	4th Day
μμg RNA/CELL	544 ± 18	515 ± 21	564 ± 24	568 ± 24	590 ± 19

Number of analyses, 107. Number of animals, 11.

Table 5. Composition of Nuclear RNA of Nerve Cells of the Reticular Formation from Control Rats and During Learning

	Controls		Learning	
	Mean	V	Mean	V
Adenine	23.9 ± 1.09	10.0	22.8 ± 0.36	4.2
Guanine	25.3 ± 0.71	6.2	26.2 ± 0.57	5.8
Cytosine	28.9 ± 0.89	6.9	29.7 ± 1.00	8.9
Uracil	21.9 ± 0.36	3.7	21.3 ± 0.55	6.9
No. of nuclei	125		175	
No. of analyses	5		7	
No. of animals	5		7	

tended these functional controls, using a simple rotation along a vertical curve. (See section on *Methods*.) This type of stimulation has been found to induce a 25 to 30 per cent increase of RNA in nerve cells belonging to the vestibular pathway within one hr.[12] We analyzed therefore the nuclear RNA of the Deiters' nerve cells of rats subjected to such stimulation for 30 min.

The analyses of these functional controls showed no significant changes in the nuclear RNA base ratios (Table 6).

(c) *Duration of the nuclear RNA change in learning experiment*: In two series of experiments the rats were returned on the eighth day to their cages and given an adequate amount of food. Twenty-four hours after stopping the experiment, no increased adenine/uracil value could be detected in the nuclear RNA.

DISCUSSION   It seemed pertinent to explore further the question whether the *nuclear* RNA with increased adenine/uracil ratio formed during the learning experiment was specific, or if it reflected a physiological reaction from the neurons, due to increased demands on the neuronal function *per se*. Control experiments presented in our previous paper were therefore extended further.

A significant increase of RNA was found in the big nerve cells of the reticular formation during learning, but no alteration in the nuclear RNA base ratios. In extended functional controls using Deiters' nerve cells and rotatory stimulation, the results were similar. RNA analyses have thus been performed on nerve cells belonging to other parts of the brain than the vestibular nucleus during learning, and on Deiters' nerve cells after vestibular stimulation. In all cases an increase of RNA/cell was found, but no production of nuclear RNA fractions with changed base ratios as was observed in the Deiters' nerve cells, which are involved in establishing the learned behavior. These latter functional controls have therefore excluded the possibility that the nuclear RNA changes observed during learning were due to the increased neural function *per se*.

The synthesis of the nuclear RNA with increased adenine/uracil ratio could not be observed 24 hr after stopping the experiment. This is on the decremental part of curve shown in Figure 1. From this coincidence it cannot be inferred, however, that a correlation has been shown between

Table 6. Composition of the Nuclear RNA of Deiters' Nerve Cells from Rats Subjected to Vestibular Stimulation by Rotation Vertically for 30 Minutes

	Controls		Rotatory Stimulation	
	Mean	V	Mean	V
Adenine	22.9 ± 0.28	2.4	22.9 ± 0.44	4.7
Guanine	25.9 ± 0.59	4.6	24.6 ± 0.53	5.2
Cytosine	29.1 ± 0.48	3.3	29.1 ± 0.64	5.4
Uracil	22.1 ± 0.44	4.0	23.4 ± 0.80	8.4
No. of nuclei	150		225	
No. of analyses	6		9	
No. of animals	4		6	

synthesis of specific nuclear RNA in neurons and a learning process. The decrement of the curve in Figure 1 shows simply a change of behavior. But it is more pertinent that a synthesis of a few thousand RNA molecules with extreme base ratios could occur in the nuclei without being detected by an analytical method with a sensitivity of $3 \cdot 10^{-11}$ gm.

In the present study, the analyses demonstrated a formation of *glial* RNA with a significantly increased adenine/uracil ratio during the learning experiment.

While in the nerve cell of learning rats, the cytoplasmic RNA showed quantitative but no base ratio changes, in the glia the bulk of the RNA showed changed base ratio composition. The explanation is probably that such changes will be obscured at the electrophoretic analysis by the great mass of the ribosomal RNA in the nerve cell (around 750 $\mu\mu$g). The glial RNA, on the other hand, constitutes only ten per cent of the neuronal RNA.

It does not seem surprising that the glial RNA should react at the same time as the neuronal RNA during such a primary physiological process since these two types of cells together compose a functional unit. This relationship has been demonstrated in a series of recent studies. On physiological stimulation there occur inverse chemical changes in the nerve cell and its glia. The amount of RNA, proteins, and respiratory enzyme activities rise in the neuron and decrease in the glia.[2] Kinetic studies revealed a difference in behavior between the two types of cells indicating a neuronal priority of energy utilization over the glia.[3] Inverse changes involving respiratory enzyme activity and anaerobic glycolytic activity gave further information about this mechanism.[13]

During development of the Parkinson syndrome, profound changes in RNA base ratios of the glia were found to precede in time similar changes of the nerve cells in globus pallidus.[14]

Therefore, the changes of the RNA base composition in both the neuron and its glia shown in this study demonstrate that the glia share with their neurons the capacity to house at least part of the chemical substrate utilized in learning. In this connection, it seems appropriate to remember that both neurons and glia are epithelial derivatives of the ectoderm, developing jointly from the primary cells lining the neural tube.

In the previous paper,[1] the evidence that the nuclear RNA fractions produced by the neurons in the learning experiment reflected an increased chromosomal activity was discussed. That gene sites in chromosomes of neurons can be induced to synthesize RNA in an acute learning situation in mammals, is no more surprising than that addition of galactose induces such gene activities in bacteria. The mechanism of learning and recall of stored information is securely anchored in the genome. The learning occurring during a life cycle by "change by use" is probably a superposition on the genetically stable mechanism of the central nervous system reflected in innate behavior. The production of RNA with specific base ratios concomitantly in both neurons and glia in our learning experiments could be considered as reflecting such a mechanism.

It is possible that the glia and the glial RNA constitute the substrate for a short-term memory since the folded membranes of the glia would be well suited for very rapid processes. The neuron and its mass of RNA could then house the substrate of long-term memory.

Previously, experiments were reported where interference with biosynthesis of brain RNA impaired learning in rats.[15] Recently, suppression of protein production by puromycin has been found to impair the ability of rats to remember learned behavior.[16]

SUMMARY Purine-pyrimidine analyses were carried out on *glial* RNA immediately surrounding Deiters' neurons from rats subjected to a learning experiment during which complicated motor and sensory behavior was established. The adenine/uracil ratio of the glial RNA increased significantly while the cytosine decreased.

Nuclear RNA had previously been found to be formed in Deiters' nerve cells during such learning experiments. Several types of control experiments were performed to exclude the possibility that the formation of RNA with highly specific base ratios was due to demands on neural function *per se*. It has been shown that the neuron and the neuronal glia compose a functional unit and the significance of the RNA glia-neuron changes in learning is discussed. It is suggested that the learning during the life cycle by "change by use" involves a utilization of a genetically stable mechanism of the neuron-glia unit and is reflected in the observed RNA changes.*

REFERENCES

1 Hydén, H., and E. Egyházi, these proceedings, 48, 1366 (1962).

2 Hydén, H., and A. Pigon, *J. Neurochem.*, 6, 57 (1960).

3 Hydén, H., and P. Lange, *J. Cell Biol.*, 13, 233 (1962).

4 Hydén, H., *Endeavour*, 21, 144 (1962).

5 Egyházi, E., and H. Hydén, *J. Biophys. Biochem. Cytol.*, 10, 403 (1961).

6 Hydén, H., and E. Egyházi, *J. Cell Biol.*, 15, 37 (1962).

7 Hydén, H., *Nature*, 184, 433 (1959).

8 Edström, J.-E., W. Grampp, and N. Schor, *J. Biophys. Biochem. Cytol.*, 11, 549 (1961).

9 Harris, H., *Proc. Royal Soc.*, B156, 109 (1962).

10 Edström, J.-E., *J. Biophys. Biochem. Cytol.*, 8, 39 (1960).

11 Brodal, A., O. Pompeiano, and F. Walberg, in *The Vestibular Nuclei and their Connections, Anatomy, and Functional Correlations* (London: Oliver and Boyd, 1962).

12 Jarlstedt, J., personal communication, to be published.

13 Hamberger, A., and H. Hydén, *J. Cell Biol.*, 16, 521 (1963).

14 Hydén, H., and G. Gomirato, *Brain*, in press.

15 Dingman, W., and M. B. Sporn, *J. Psychiatr. Res.*, 1, 1 (1961).

16 Flexner, J. B., L. B. Flexner, E. Stellar, G. de la Haba, and R. B. Roberts, *J. Neurochem.*, 9, 595 (1962).

* These studies have been supported by the U.S. Air Force under Grant AF EOAR 62-29, monitored by the European Office, Office of Aerospace Research; by the National Multiple Sclerosis Society, New York, and by the Ollie and Elof Ericsson Foundation. The skilful assistance of Mrs. Margareta Berggren is gratefully acknowledged.

MEMORY IN MICE AS AFFECTED BY INTRACEREBRAL PUROMYCIN

Josefa B. Flexner, Louis B. Flexner, and Eliot Stellar

UNIVERSITY OF PENNSYLVANIA

Source *Reprinted from* Science, *1963,* 141, *57–59, with permission of the authors and the publisher. Copyright 1963 by the American Association for the Advancement of Science.*

Abstract. The antibiotic, puromycm, caused loss of memory of avoidance discrimination learning in mice when injected intracerebrally. Bilateral injections of puromycin involving the hippocampi and adjacent temporal cortices caused loss of short-term memory; consistent loss of longer-term memory required injections involving, in addition, most of the remaining cortices. Spread of the effective memory trace from the temporal-hippocampal areas to wide areas of the cortices appears to require 3 to 6 days, depending upon the individual animal. Recent reversal learning was lost while longer-term initial learning was retained after bilateral injections into the hippocampal-temporal areas.

The suggestion has become increasingly frequent during recent years that nucleic acids or proteins may be concerned with learning and memory. We were led to investigate the effects of the antibiotic, puromycin, on these aspects of behavior by the discovery of Yarmolinsky and de la Haba (*1*) that puromycin produces profound inhibition of protein synthesis in a cell-free system and by the later demonstration that it efficiently suppresses protein synthesis in vivo (*2*). In an earlier paper with de la Haba and Roberts (*3*) we have reported studies on mice which received the maximum amount of puromycin which could be tolerated in a single subcutaneous injection. Although this treatment appeared to suppress the rate of protein synthesis in various parts of the brain to 80 percent of the control value for a period of 6 hours, it was without effect on the learning and retention of simple or discrimination avoidance responses.

The experiments to be reported here have been made with intracerebral injections of puromycin. The amounts injected were smaller than previously used (*3*) so that disorientation of the animal at the time of testing was avoided. With this intracerebral approach, we have found that memory can be consistently destroyed, difference in the effective loci of recent and longer-term memory apparently established, and the time factor concerned in modification of the effective locus determined. Upon recovery, animals were capable of learning again. We cannot now relate these behavioral effects to suppression of protein synthesis, since our biochemical studies are not yet complete.

Adult white mice were trained in a Y-maze with a grid floor through which shock could be applied. The animal was placed in the stem of the Y. To avoid shock the mouse had to move into the correct arm within 5 seconds. If it entered the incorrect arm, it received shock until it moved to the correct arm. Training was continued in one session of about 20 minutes to a criterion of 9 out of 10 correct responses, thus avoiding overtraining. The same procedure was used in testing for memory of the training experience, shock having been given for errors of performance except as noted. In this type of training we have found mice to behave essentially like rats and to retain excellent memory of the training for at least 5 weeks.

Intracerebral injections of puromycin, each injection of a volume of 0.012 ml, were made through small holes in the skull, as previously described (3).

From one to three injections of puromycin were made into each hemisphere, all at a depth of 2 mm from the surface of the skull. Bilateral injections were made through holes placed (i) just above the angle between the caudal sutures of the parietal bones and the origins of the temporal muscles—these are here designated temporal injections; (ii) 2 mm lateral to the sagittal suture and 2 mm rostral to the caudal sutures of the parietal bones—these are here designated ventricular injections; and (iii) 4 mm rostral to these last holes and 1 mm lateral to the sagittal suture—these are here designated frontal injections. At the present time we are dependent upon control injections of a solution of fluorescein (3) to estimate the spread of puromycin; more refined studies, using other techniques, are not yet complete. Animals which received injections of fluorescein were sacrificed 1 hour after the injection.

Results with four of the seven types of injections are shown in Fig. 1. This shows that the area around the caudal rhinal fissure was stained with temporal but spared with ventricular injections. The three types of injection not shown in the figure consisted of combined ventricular and temporal injections, of combined ventricular and frontal injections, and of combined temporal and frontal injections. The distribution of fluorescence in these combined injections was essentially the sum of the individual injections as shown in Fig. 1.

The effects of intracerebral injections of puromycin on memory of the training experience are given in Table 1, which shows the number of animals in which memory was lost, impaired, or retained after puromycin injection. In the legend of the table, the means and standard deviations of the percentage savings in retention are given for the three categories of memory. Percentage savings in retention tests were calculated for both trials and errors by subtracting the number to criterion in the retention test from the number to criterion in the learning experience, dividing by the number in the learning experience, and multiplying by 100. Retention tests were given usually 3 days after puromycin, to allow ample time for recovery of the animal. At the time of testing, any weight loss had commonly been regained and feeding, general locomotor activity, and reactions to the maze were normal.

Our first observations were made on mice trained to criterion on one arm of the maze and injected with puromycin 1 day later (Table 1, "Short-term memory"). After combined bilateral temporal, ventricular, and frontal injections, retention tests showed that memory of the training experience had been completely lost. An effort was then made to localize this effect. Memory was also completely lost with high consistency when puromycin was given in bilateral temporal injections. By contrast, bilateral frontal, ventricular, or combined frontal and ventricular injections were essentially without effect.

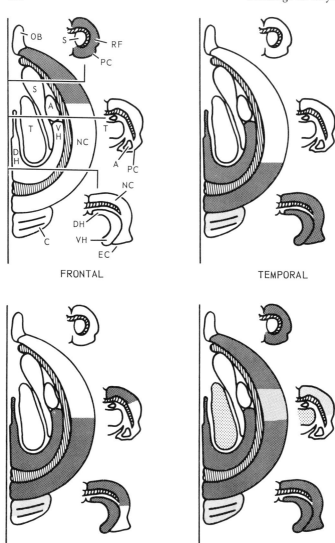

FRONTAL

TEMPORAL

VENTRICULAR

F+T+V

FIGURE 1   *Spread of fluorescein after intracerebral injection. The diagrams at the left indicate structures viewed from the top after removal of a horizontal section of the hemisphere; at the right, cross (frontal) sections of the hemispheres at the level indicated in the diagram for frontal injections. Relative intensity of staining is indicated by relative density of stippling. With all injections there was intense staining, not shown in the diagram, of the corpus callosum (cross hatched). Abbreviations: A, amygdaloid nucleus; C, cerebellum; DH, dorsal hippocampus; EC, entorhinal cortex; NC, neocortex; OB, olfactory bulb; PC, pyriform cortex; RF, rhinal fissure; S, corpus striatum; T, thalamus; VH, ventral hippocampus; F + T + V, frontal + temporal + ventricular injections.*

Table 1. *Effects of different sites of injection of puromycin on short- and longer-term memory. T, V, and F refer, respectively, to temporal, ventricular, and frontal injections, all given bilaterally*

	Puromycin injections		No. of mice in which memory was:		
Site	Days after learning	Milligrams	Lost*	Impaired*	Retained*
		Short-term memory			
T + V + F	1	0.03 to .06	7	0	0
T	1	.09	8	0	0
T	1	.06	14	3	1
V	1	.09	0	0	5
F	1	.09	0	0	5
V + F	1	.09	0	1	2
		Longer-term memory			
T + V + F	18 to 43	0.03 to .06	7	0	0
T	11 to 35	.06 to .09	0	0	7
V	12 to 38	.06 to .09	0	0	3
F	16 to 27	.06 to .09	0	0	3
V + F	28	.06 to .09	0	2	2
V + T	28 to 43	.09	1	1	2
T + F	28	.09	0	0	3

* For the 37 mice with loss of memory, the means and standard deviations for percentages of savings of trials and of errors were respectively 1 ± 3 and 2 ± 6; for the seven mice with impaired memory, 26 ± 29 and 39 ± 12; and for the 33 mice with retention of memory, 90 ± 14 and 90 ± 9. Negative savings in the group with lost memory have been designated zero so that the mean for this group is an overestimation of savings.

The next series of observations was made on mice trained to criterion and injected with puromycin 11 to 43 days later (Table 1, "Longer-term memory"). Only combined, bilateral temporal, ventricular plus frontal injections consistently destroyed memory in these animals. Bilateral temporal or frontal or ventricular injections were without effect. Three combinations of two injections (combined ventricular and temporal, or ventricular and frontal, or temporal and frontal) into each hemisphere were without effect in the majority of animals, even though the total amount of puromycin in all but two of eleven of these was at the maximum level tolerated and twice that amount injected in six of the seven experiments with combined temporal, ventricular, and frontal injections. There was consequently a clear distinction between recent and longer-term memory; recent memory was lost when puromycin was introduced through temporal injections into hippocampi and caudal cortices, including the entorhinal areas, while loss of longer-term memory required puromycin additionally in a substantially greater part of the cortex and possibly in the thalamus also.

How long does it require for this modification of the locus of the effective memory trace? As shown in Table 2, bilateral temporal injections consis-

Table 2. Effect of bilateral temporal injections of puromycin on memory of increasing age. Each injection contained 0.09 mg of puromycin.

Injections: days after learning	No. of mice in which memory was:		
	Lost*	Impaired*	Retained*
2	3	0	0
3	4	0	1
4	0	1	1
5	0	1	2
6	0	0	3

* For the seven mice with loss of memory, the means and standard deviations for percentages of savings of trials and of errors were respectively 1 ± 4 and 0 ± 0; for the seven mice with retention of memory, 85 ± 19 and 93 ± 7. In one mouse with impaired memory the percentages of savings for trials and errors were respectively 38 and 20; for the other, 39 and 55.

tently destroyed memory 2 days after training but were consistently without effect 6 days after training. Results were variable at 3, 4, and 5 days. It consequently appears that the enlarged locus of longer-term memory in the type of learning experience we have used with the mouse becomes completely effective in from 3 to 6 days, depending upon the individual animal.

We proceeded from these observations to experiments in which the animal received reversal learning 3 weeks after its first training in the Y-maze that is, the mouse was first trained, for example, to move from the stem of the Y into its left arm; then 3 weeks later was retrained to move from the stem of the Y into its right arm. Was it possible to destroy memory of reversal learning 24 hours after reversal training, spare the longer-term memory of the initial training experience given 3 weeks earlier, and in consequence have the mouse perform the task for which he was first trained?

To test this possibility bilateral temporal injections were made 24 hours after reversal learning and 3 weeks after initial learning in seven animals. Shock was omitted in the retention trials 3 days after puromycin injection, since there was, within the design of the test, no right or wrong choice. As shown in Table 3, on testing for memory the first choice of all animals was consistent with the first learning experience, as were the large majority of subsequent choices. In view of consistent results with numerous untreated animals on various schedules of learning and reversal learning, only two control animals (Table 3) were used in this series. All these untreated animals, in sharp contrast to the experimental group, made choices consistent with their second, or reversal, learning. Because the experimental animals were able to perform the older position habit efficiently and consistently, this experiment offers strong evidence that the effect of puromycin in destroying a recent habit is not due to disorganization or incapacitation of the animal.

A beginning has been made in testing for the specificity and reversibility of the puromycin effect. Numerous control injections of saline, of subliminal concentrations of puromycin, and of puromycin hydrolyzed at the glycosidic bond were without effect on memory. Most animals treated with effective doses of puromycin were demonstrated to be capable of relearning after loss of memory, though the process of relearning, particularly with high doses of puromycin, often required considerably more trials than in the initial training experience. This aspect of the effects of puromycin will be reported more extensively at a later time.

Although the effective locus of short-term memory clearly appears different from that of longer-term memory we cannot now define the difference with precision. It does appear that the area around the caudal rhinal fissure, likely entorhinal cortex, carries the short-term memory trace, since short-term memory was retained with ventricular injections but lost with temporal injections. The part played by the hippocampus will not become evident until experiments are performed which provide for exposure of the entire

Table 3. Differential effect of bilateral temporal injections of puromycin on recent and longer-term memory. Each injection had a volume of 0.012 ml and contained 0.06 or 0.09 (experiment 71) mg of puromycin. Choices of the arm of the Y-maze by an animal after injection were scored as "1" if consistent with initial learning, and as "2" if consistent with reversal learning. For various reasons trials were continued irregularly beyond the ten originally planned.

Expt. No.	Animal No.	Initial learning: trials to 9/10 criterion	Reversal learning 3 weeks later: trials to 9/10 criterion	Choice of arm of Y-maze*
			Experimental animals	
86	26A	13	22	1,1,1,1,1,1,1,1,1,1,1,1,1,1,1
86	24A	7	10	1,1,2,1,1,1,1,2,1,1,1,1,1,1,1,1,1,1,1,1,1,2,1,1,1
86	25A	8	10	1,1,1,1,2,1,1,1,1,2,1,2,2,1,2
86	22A	9	8	1,2,2,1,1,2,1,2,1,2,1,1,1,1,1,1,1,1,1,1,1
86	23A	13	4	1,1,1,1,1,1,1,1,1,1,1,1,1
71	49	22	9	1,1,2,2,1,1,1,2,1,1,1,1,2,1,1,1,1,1,1,1,1,1,1
86	27A	12	5	1,1,1,1,1,1,1,1,1,2,1
			Control animals	
86	58A	10	14	2,2,2,2,2,2,2,2,2,2,2,2,2,2
86	60A	10	12	2,2,2,2,2,2,2,2,2,2,2,2

* The experimental animals made their choices 3 days after temporal injections of puromycin, which were given 24 hours after reversal learning. The control animals made their choices 4 days after reversal learning, no puromycin being injected. Neither group received shock.

temporal cortex to puromycin while the hippocampus is spared. Similarly, we cannot state whether the locus of longer-term memory is confined to the cortex or whether other parts of the brain, principally the hippocampus, are also involved. It can only be said that our observations are consistent with the evidence and conclusions of others (4), that the hippocampal zone is the site of recent memory and, that an extensive part of the neocortex is concerned with longer-term memory.

It must be emphasized that our results, although apparently clear-cut in important particulars, should be interpreted at this time with caution. We are in the process of obtaining more precise information, for example, on the localization of puromycin after intracerebral injection. Histological studies on the cells of the hippocampus and cortex must be completed. Determinations must be made of the degree of suppression of protein synthesis, and, particularly in view of the negative behavioral results with subcutaneous puromycin (3), the possibility must be kept in mind that loss of memory after intracerebral injection of puromycin may be owing to effects not related to changes in protein synthesis.* Further, it remains to be shown that other learning situations, currently being investigated, and other animals are comparable to the mouse in the training experience we have used (5).

REFERENCES AND NOTES

1 M. B. Yarmolinsky and G. L. de la Haba, *Proc. Natl. Acad. Sci. U.S.* **45**, 1721 (1959).
2 J. Gorski, Y. Aizawa, G. C. Mueller, *Arch. Biochem. Biophys.* **95**, 508 (1961).
3 J. B. Flexner, L. B. Flexner, E. Stellar, G. de la Haba, R. B. Roberts, *J. Neurochem.* **9**, 595 (1962).
4 B. Milner and W. Penfield, *Trans. Am. Neurol. Assoc.* **80**, 42 (1955); W. B. Scoville and B. Milner, *J. Neurol. Neurosurg. Psychiat.* **20**, 11 (1957); L. S. Stepien, J. P. Cordeau, T. Rasmussen, *Brain* **83**, 470 (1960).
5 Supported by grants NB-00514 and MH-03571 from the U.S. Public Health Service. We are indebted to the Lederle Laboratories for our supply of puromycin.

* It should be noted that more recent findings of a lack of effect on memory of other drug treatments which inhibit protein synthesis have led Flexner and Flexner (*Proc. Nat. Acad. Sci. U.S.*, 1966, **55**, 369–374) to suggest that puromycin may influence memory by an effect on messenger RNA rather than protein as such. (Ed.)

Learning and Memory:

Theory and Speculation

THE POSSIBILITY OF A
DUAL TRACE MECHANISM

D. O. Hebb

MC GILL UNIVERSITY

*Source   Reprinted from **The Organization of Behavior,** New York, John Wiley & Sons, Inc., 1949, 60–66, with permission of the author and John Wiley & Sons, Inc.*

The first step in this neural schematizing is a bald assumption about the structural changes that make lasting memory possible. The assumption has repeatedly been made before, in one way or another, and repeatedly found unsatisfactory by the critics of learning theory. I believe it is still necessary. As a result, I must show that in another context, of added anatomical and physiological knowledge, it becomes more defensible and more fertile than in the past.

The assumption, in brief, is that a growth process accompanying synaptic activity makes the synapse more readily traversed. This hypothesis of synaptic resistances, however, is different from earlier ones in the following respects: (1) structural connections are postulated between single cells, but single cells are not effective units of transmission and such connections would be only one factor determining the direction of transmission, (2) no direct sensori-motor connections are supposed to be established in this way, in the adult animal; and (3) an intimate relationship is postulated between reverberatory action and structural changes at the synapse, implying a dual trace mechanism.

Hilgard and Marquis (1940) have shown how a reverberatory, transient trace mechanism might be proposed on the basis of Lorente de Nó's conclusions, that a cell is fired only by the simultaneous activity of two or more afferent fibers, and that internuncial fibers are arranged in closed (potentially self-exciting) circuits. Their diagram is arranged to show how a reverberatory circuit might estabish a sensori-motor connection between receptor cells and the effectors which carry out a conditioned response. There is of course a good deal of psychological evidence which is opposed to such an oversimplified hypothesis, and Hilgard and Marquis do not put weight on it. At the same time, it is important to see that something of the kind is not merely a possible but a necessary inference from certain neurological ideas. To the extent that anatomical and physiological observations establish the possibility of reverberatory after-effects of a sensory event, it is established that such a process would be the physiological basis of a transient "memory" of the stimulus. There may, then, be a memory trace that is wholly a function of a pattern of neural activity, independent of any structural change.

Hilgard and Marquis go on to point out that such a trace would be quite unstable. A reverberatory activity would be subject to the development of refractory states in the cells of the circuit in which it occurs, and external events could readily interrupt it. We have already seen (in Chapter 1) that an "activity" trace can hardly account for the permanence of early learning, but at the same time one may regard reverberatory activity as the explanation of other phenomena.

476

There are memories which are instantaneously established, and as evanescent as they are immediate. In the repetition of digits, for example, an interval of a few seconds is enough to prevent any interference from one series on the next. Also, some memories are both instantaneously established and permanent. To account for the permanence, some structural change seems necessary, but a structural growth presumably would require an appreciable time. If some way can be found of supposing that a reverberatory trace might cooperate with the structural change, and *carry the memory until the growth change is made*, we should be able to recognize the theoretical value of the trace which is an activity only, without having to ascribe all memory to it. The conception of a transient, unstable reverberatory trace is therefore useful, if it is possible to suppose also that some more permanent structural change reinforces it. There is no reason to think that a choice must be made between the two conceptions; there may be traces of both kinds, and memories which are dependent on both.

A NEUROPHYSIOLOGICAL POSTULATE

Let us assume then that the persistence or repetition of a reverberatory activity (or "trace") tends to induce lasting cellular changes that add to its stability. The assumption can be precisely stated as follows: *When an axon of cell A is near enough to excite a cell B and repeatedly or persistently takes part in firing it, some growth process or metabolic change takes place in one or both cells such that A's efficiency, as one of the cells firing B, is increased.*

The most obvious and I believe much the most probable suggestion concerning the way in which one cell could become more capable of firing another is that synaptic knobs develop and increase the area of contact between the afferent axon and efferent soma. ("Soma" refers to dendrites and body, or all of the cell except its axon.) There is certainly no direct evidence that this is so, and the postulated change if it exists may be metabolic, affecting cellular rhythmicity and limen; or there might be both metabolic and structural changes, including a limited neurobiotaxis. There are several considerations, however, that make the growth of synaptic knobs a plausible conception. The assumption stated above can be put more definitely, as follows:

When one cell repeatedly assists in firing another, the axon of the first cell develops synaptic knobs (or enlarges them if they already exist) in contact with the soma of the second cell. This seems to me the most likely mechanism of a lasting effect of reverberatory action, but I wish to make it clear that the subsequent discussion depends only on the more generally stated proposition italicized above.

It is wise to be explicit on another point also. The proposition does not require action at any great distance, and certainly is not the same as Kappers' (Kappers, Huber, and Crosby, 1936) conception of the way in which neurobiotaxis controls axonal and dendritic outgrowth. But my assumption is evidently related to Kappers' ideas, and not inconsistent with them. The theory of neurobiotaxis has been severely criticized, and clearly it does not do all it was once thought to do. On the other hand, neurobiotaxis may still be one factor determining the connections made by neural cells. If so, it would cooperate very neatly with the knob formation postulated above. Criticism has been directed at the idea that neurobiotaxis directs axonal growth throughout its whole course, and that the process sufficiently accounts for all neural connections. The idea is not tenable, particularly in view of such work as that of Weiss (1941b) and Sperry (1943).

But none of this has shown that neurobiotaxis has *no* influence in neural growth; its operation, within ranges of a centimeter or so, is still plausible.

The details of these histological speculations are not important except to show what some of the possibilities of change at the synapse might be and to show that the mechanism of learning discussed in this chapter is not wholly out of touch with what is known about the neural cell. The changed facilitation that constitutes learning might occur in other ways without affecting the rest of the theory. To make it more specific, I have chosen to assume that the growth of synaptic knobs, with or without neurobiotaxis, is the basis of the change of facilitation from one cell on another, and this is not altogether implausible. It has been demonstrated by Arvanitaki (1942) that a contiguity alone will permit the excitation aroused in one cell to be transmitted to another. There are also earlier experiments, reviewed by Arvanitaki, with the same implication. Even more important, perhaps, is Erlanger's (1939) demonstration of impulse transmission across an artificial "synapse," a blocked segment of nerve more than a millimeter in extent. Consequently, in the intact nervous system, an axon that passes close to the dendrites or body of a second cell would be capable of *helping* to fire it, when the second cell is also exposed to other stimulation at the same point. The probability that such closely timed coincidental excitations would occur is not considered for the moment but will be returned to. When the coincidence does occur, and the active fiber, which is merely close to the soma of another cell, adds to a local excitation in it, I assume that the joint action tends to produce a thickening of the fiber—forming a synaptic knob—or adds to a thickening already present.

Lorente de Nó (1938a) has shown that the synaptic knob is usually not a terminal structure (thus the term "end foot" or "end button" is misleading), nor always separated by a stalk from the axon or axon collateral. If it were, of course, some action at a distance would be inevitably suggested, if such connections are formed in learning. The knob instead is often a rather irregular thickening in the unmyelinated part of an axon near its ending, where it is threading its way through a thicket of dendrites and cell bodies. The point in the axon where the thickening occurs does not appear to be determined by the structure of the cell of which it is a part but by something external to the cell and related to the presence of a second cell. The number and size of the knobs formed by one cell in contact with a second cell vary also. In the light of these facts it is not implausible to suppose that the extent of the contact established is a function of joint cellular activity, given propinquity of the two cells.

Also, if a synapse is crossed only by the action of two or more afferent cells, the implication is that the greater the area of contact the greater the likelihood that action in one cell will be *decisive* in firing another.[2] Thus three afferent fibers with extensive knob contact could fire a cell that otherwise might be fired only by four or more fibers; or fired sooner with knobs than without.

In short, it is feasible to assume that synaptic knobs develop with neural activity and represent a lowered synaptic resistance. It is implied that the knobs appear in the course of learning, but this does not give us a means of testing the assumption. There is apparently no good evidence concerning the relative frequency of knobs in infant and adult brains, and the assumption does *not* imply that there should be none in the new-born infant. The learning referred to is learning in a very general sense, which must certainly have begun long before birth.

[2] One point should perhaps be made explicit. Following Lorente de Nó, two afferent cells are considered to be effective at the synapse, when one is not, only because their contacts with the efferent cell are close together so their action summates. When both are active, they create a larger region of *local* disturbance in the efferent soma. The larger the knobs in a given cluster, therefore, the smaller the number that might activate the cell on which they are located. On occasion, a single afferent cell must be effective in transmission. It is worth pointing this out, also, because it might appear to the reader otherwise that there is something mysterious about emphasis on the necessity of activity in two or more cells to activate the synapse. All that has really been shown is that in some circumstances two or more afferent cells are necessary. However, this inevitably implies that an increase in the number of afferent cells simultaneously active must increase the reliability with which the synapse is traversed.

THE PROBLEM OF SERIAL
ORDER IN BEHAVIOR

K. S. Lashley

HARVARD UNIVERSITY AND THE YERKES
LABORATORIES OF PRIMATE BIOLOGY

Source   Reprinted from **Cerebral Mechanisms in Be-**
havior, *L. A. Jeffries, Ed., New York, John Wiley &
Sons, Inc., 1951, Pp 112–136, with permission of the
California Institute of Technology.*

The previous speakers have approached our common problem by considering the properties of the elementary units of which we believe the cerebral structure to be built up. They have considered the kinds of neural integration or behavior which can be anticipated from those properties. The remaining members of the symposium have in their research been concerned chiefly with the analysis of complex behavior, seeking to derive general principles of neural integration from the infinitely complex products of that integration. Our common meeting ground is the faith to which we all subscribe, I believe, that the phenomena of behavior and of mind are ultimately describable in the concepts of the mathematical and physical sciences. In my discussion here, I have deliberately turned to the opposite extreme from the neuron and have chosen as a topic, one aspect of the most complex type of behavior that I know; the logical and orderly arrangement of thought and action. Our discussion so far has dealt chiefly with the conditions of input and of immediate switching in the nervous mechanism, without explicit consideration of what is already going on within the system.

My principal thesis today will be that the input is never into a quiescent or static system, but always into a system which is already actively excited and organized. In the intact organism, behavior is the result of interaction of this background of excitation with input from any designated stimulus. Only when we can state the general characteristics of this background of excitation, can we understand the effects of a given input.

The unpronounceable Cree Indian word "kekawewechetushekamikowanowow" is analyzed by Chamberlain (7) into the verbal root, *tusheka*, "to remain," and the various particles which modify it as follows: *ke(la)-wow*, the first and last syllables, indicating second person plural; *ka*, a prefix of the future tense; *we*, a sort of imperative mode expressing a wish; *weche*, indicating conjunction of subject and object; *mik*, a suffix bringing the verb into agreement with a third person subject and second person object; and *owan*, a suffix indicating that the subject is inanimate and the object animate. A literal translation: "You will I wish together remain he-you it-man you" or, freely, "may it remain with you." This difference in structure between Cree and English illustrates an outstanding characteristic of verbal behavior; the occurrence of predetermined, orderly sequences of action which are unique for each language. In English the adjective precedes, in French it follows the noun which it modifies. In English the movement or action of the subject is expressed as early as possible after the subject; in German the expression of action may be postponed until all qualifying thoughts have been expressed. In a sentence discussing this subject, Pick (20) introduces fifty-five words between the subject and the principal verb. Each Chinese word, and to a lesser extent, each English word, stands as an unchanging unit. In the highly inflective languages, such as Sioux, the form of almost every word in the sentence may be altered, according to some attribute of the subject, as when two objects rather than one or several are discussed.

The study of comparative grammar is not the most direct approach to the physiology of the cerebral cortex, yet Fournié (10) has written, "Speech is the only window through which the physiologist can view the cerebral life." Certainly language presents in a most striking form the integrative functions that are characteristic of the cerebral cortex and that reach their highest development in human thought processes. Temporal integration is not found exclusively in language; the coordination of leg movements in insects, the song of birds, the control of trotting and pacing in a gaited horse, the rat running the maze, the architect designing a house, and the carpenter sawing a board present a problem of sequences of action which cannot be explained in terms of successions of external stimuli.

ASSOCIATIVE CHAIN THEORIES

In spite of the ubiquity of the problem, there have been almost no attempts to develop physiological theories to meet it. In fact, except among a relatively small group of students of aphasia, who have had to face questions of agrammatism, the problem has been largely ignored. It is not even mentioned in recent textbooks on neurophysiology or physiological psychology, nor is there any significant body of experimental studies bearing upon the problem. The spinal animal scarcely exhibits serial activity, so the physiologist may be excused for overlooking the phenomenon. On the other hand, psychologists have been concerned chiefly with the question of whether or not the organizing processes displayed in serial action are conscious, and very little with the organization itself. I have chosen to discuss the problem of temporal integration here, not with the expectation of offering a satisfactory physiological theory to account for it, but because it seems to me to be both the most important and also the most neglected problem of cerebral physiology. Temporally integrated actions do occur even among insects, but they do not reach any degree of complexity until the appearance of the cerebral cortex. They are especially characteristic of human behavior and contribute as much as does any single factor to the superiority of man's intelligence. A clearer formulation of the physiological problems which they raise should be of value, even though a solution of the problems is not yet in sight.

I shall consider first some of the questions raised by the structure of language, then turn to other forms of serial action for indications of the nature of the nervous mechanisms involved.

To the best of my knowledge, the only strictly physiological theory that has been explicitly formulated to account for temporal integration is that which postulates chains of reflexes, in which the performance of each element of the series provides excitation of the next. This conception underlay the "motor theories" of thinking which were advocated by several psychologists early in this century. Watson (26) sought to identify thought with inaudible movements of the vocal organs, linked together in associative chains. The peripheral chain theory of language was developed in greatest detail by Washburn (25). She distinguished what she called "successive movement systems" and, although she drew her examples from memorized series of nonsense syllables, her implication was that such series are typical of all language behavior. She defined a movement system as "a combination of movements so linked together that the stimulus furnished by the actual performance of certain movements is required to bring about other movements." She described speech as a succession of vocal acts in which the kinesthetic impulses from each movement serve as a unique stimulus for the next in the series (25, page 11 ff.). Attempts to confirm these peripheral theories by mechanical (Thorsen, 23) or electrical (Max, 19) recording of muscular tensions have given no valid evidence in support of them. It should be noted that, at the time when the theories were proposed, it was generally believed that conduction in the nervous system is always downstream from sense organ to muscle, and that muscular contraction must always follow promptly on stimulation. The existence of reverberatory circuits which could maintain central activity was scarcely suspected.

The introspective psychology which objected to such peripheral theories did not explicitly formulate an alternative neurological theory, but there is implicit in it a view that verbal thought is a simple chain of central processes in which each element serves to arouse the next by direct association. Titchener, for example, maintained that the meaning of a word (or of an auditory image in his system) consists of the chain of associations which it arouses; that it has no meaning until such a sequence has occurred. From this it must be inferred that he was thinking in terms of a simple associative chain, since no other relating process is suggested.

OBJECTIONS TO THE ASSOCIATIVE CHAIN THEORY

A consideration of the structure of the sentence and of other motor sequences will show, I believe, that such interpretations of temporal organization are untenable and that there are, behind the overtly expressed sequences, a multiplicity of integrative processes which can only be inferred from the final results of their activity. There is an extensive controversial literature dealing with this inferred integrative activity. Pick (20) devotes almost his entire book, *Die agrammatischen Sprachstörungen*, to reviewing discussion of the subject. Most of this literature deals with the question of whether or not the integrative processes are conscious. Much of this is irrelevant to the present topic, but the advocates of so-called imageless thought did present a great deal of material indicative of the complexity of the problem of thought structure. From this, and other evidence which

I shall present, I believe that the production of speech involves the interaction of at least three, possibly four, major neurological systems which
are interrelated but somewhat independently variable.

Let us start the analysis of the process with the enunciation of the word.
Pronunciation of the word "right" consists first of retraction and elevation
of the tongue, expiration of air and activation of the vocal cords; second,
depression of the tongue and jaw; third, elevation of the tongue to touch
the dental ridge, stopping of vocalization, and forceful expiration of air
with depression of the tongue and jaw. These movements have no intrinsic
order of association. Pronunciation of the word "tire" involves the same
motor elements in reverse order. Such movements occur in all permutations.
The order must therefore be imposed upon the motor elements by some
organization other than direct associative connections between them. So,
for the individual movements in writing or typing the word, finger strokes
occur in all sorts of combinations. No single letter invariably follows *g*,
and whether *gh*, *ga*, or *gu* is written depends upon a set for a larger
unit of action, the word.

Words stand in relation to the sentence as letters do to the word; the
words themselves have no intrinsic temporal "valence." The word "right,"
for example, is noun, adjective, adverb, and verb, and has four spellings
and at least ten meanings. In such a sentence as "The mill-wright on my
right thinks it right that some conventional rite should symbolize the right
of every man to write as he pleases," word arrangement is obviously not
due to any direct associations of the word "right" itself with other words,
but to meanings which are determined by some broader relations.

It has been found in studies of memorization of nonsense syllables that
each syllable in the series has associations, not only with adjacent words
in the series, but also with more remote words. The words in the sentence
have, of course, associations with more remote words as well as with adjacent ones. However, the combination of such direct associations will not
account for grammatical structure. The different positions of the word
"right" in the illustrative sentence are determined by the meanings which
the positions in relation to other words denote, but those meanings are
given by other associations than those with the words in the spoken sentence. The word can take its position only when the particular one of
its ten meanings becomes dominant. This dominance is not inherent in
the words themselves.

From such considerations, it is certain that any theory of grammatical
form which ascribes it to direct associative linkage of the words of the
sentence overlooks the essential structure of speech. The individual items
of the temporal series do not in themselves have a temporal "valence"
in their associative connections with other elements. The order is imposed
by some other agent.

This is true not only of language, but of all skilled movements or successions of movement. In the gaits of a horse, trotting, pacing, and single
footing involve essentially the same pattern of muscular contraction in

the individual legs. The gait is imposed by some mechanism in addition to the direct relations of reciprocal innervation among the sensory-motor centers of the legs. The order in which the fingers of the musician fall on the keys or fingerboard is determined by the signature of the composition; this gives a *set* which is not inherent in the association of the individual movements.

THE DETERMINING TENDENCY

What then determines the order? The answer which seems most in accord with common sense is that the intention to act or the idea to be expressed determines the sequence. There are, however, serious difficulties for this solution. There is not much agreement among psychologists concerning the nature of the idea. The structuralist school, under the leadership of Titchener, held that the idea consists of mental images, often the auditory images of words, and the meanings are nothing but sequences of such images. Describing the role of images in his lecturing, Titchener wrote (24), "When there is any difficulty in exposition, a point to be argued *pro* and *con* or a conclusion to be brought out from the convergence of several lines of proof, I hear my own voice speaking just ahead of me." What solution of the lecture problem for the lazy man! He need not think but only listen to his own inner voice; to the chain of associated auditory images. A behaviorist colleague once remarked to me that he had reached a stage where he could arise before an audience, turn his mouth loose, and go to sleep. He believed in the peripheral chain theory of language. (This clearly demonstrates the superiority of behavioristic over introspective psychology. The behaviorist does not even have to listen to his own inner voice.)

Seriously, such positions offer no solution for the problem of temporal integration. Titchener finds his grammar ready made and does not even raise the question of the origin of the succession of images. The chain-reflex theory, while definite, is untenable.

The third view of the nature of the idea was developed by a group known as the "Würzburg School" (see Boring, 4); exponents of imageless thought. It held that some organization precedes any expression that can be discovered by introspective or objective means. Thought is neither muscular contraction nor image, but can only be inferred as a "determining tendency." At most, it is discovered as a vague feeling of pregnancy, of being about to have an idea, a Bewustseinslage. It is not identical with the words which are spoken, for quite frequently no word can be recalled which satisfactorily expresses the thought, and we search a dictionary of synonyms until a word or phrase is found which does seem appropriate.

In his discussion of the relation of thought to speech, Pick (20) accepts this point of view, but he asserts further that the set or the idea does not have a temporal order; that all of its elements are cotemporal. Evidence in support of this conclusion comes, for example, from translation of one language into another which has a different sentence structure. I read a German sentence, pronouncing the German words with no thought of their English equivalents. I then give a free translation in English, without remembering a single word of the German text. Somewhere between the reading and free translation, the German sentence is condensed, the word order reversed, and expanded again into the different temporal order of English. According to Epstein (9), the polyglot shifts readily from one language to another, expressing the same thought in either, without literal translation. The readiness with which the form of expression of an idea can be changed, the facility with which different word orders may be utilized to express the same thought, thus is further evidence that the temporal integration is not inherent in the preliminary organization of the idea.

THE SCHEMA OF ORDER

The remaining alternative is that the mechanism which determines the serial activation of the motor units is relatively independent, both of the motor units and of the thought structure. Supporting evidence for this may be found in the mistakes of order, the slips and interferences which occur in writing and speaking. For some time I have kept records of errors in typing. A frequent error is the misplacing or the doubling of a letter. *These* is typed t-h-s-e-s, *look* as l-o-k-k, *ill* as i-i-l. Sometimes the set to repeat may be displaced by several words. The order is dissociated from the idea. Earlier, in preparing this paper, I wrote the phrase, "maintain central activities." I typed *min,* omitting the *a,* canceled this out and started again; *ama.* The impulse to insert the *a* now dominated the order. I struck out the *a* and completed the phrase, only to find that I had now also dropped the *a* from *activities.* This example suggests something of the complexity of the forces which are at play in the determination of serial order and the way in which conflicting impulses may distort the order, although the primary determining tendency, the idea, remains the same.

The polyglot, who has become proficient in a secondary language, who thinks in it and even dreams in it, may still tend to use the grammatical structure of his native tongue. If, as in French, that tongue applies gender to inanimate things, the English pronouns referring to them may take the gender of the French equivalents, though the French nouns are not thought. The German postponement of the verb or the Magyar use of the past infinitive may be incorporated in the new language. In such cases, the structuring seems to be dissociated both from the content and from the simple associative connections of the words themselves.

The ease with which a new structure may be imposed on words is illustrated by the quickness with which children learn hog Latin. The form which I learned involved transposing the initial sound of each word to the end of the word and adding a long *a*. Thus—at-thay an-may oes-gay own-day e-thay eet-stray. Some children become very facile at such inversions of words, and re-structure new words without hesitation. From such considerations it seems to follow that syntax is not inherent in the words employed or in the idea to be expressed. It is a generalized pattern imposed upon the specific acts as they occur.

"PRIMING" OF EXPRESSIVE UNITS

There are indications that, prior to the internal or overt enunciation of the sentence, an aggregate of word units is partially activated or readied. Evidence for this comes also from "contaminations" of speech and writing. The most frequent typing errors are those of anticipation; the inclusion in the word being typed of some part of a word or word structure which should properly occur later in the sentence. It may be only a letter. Thus I wrote, *wrapid* writing, carrying the *w* from the second word to the first. Not infrequently words are introduced which should occur much later in the sentence, often five or six words in advance.

In oral speech, Spoonerisms illustrate the same kind of contamination. The Spoonerism is most frequently an inversion of subject and object: "Let us always remember that waste makes haste." But it may be only a transposition of parts of the words: "Our queer old dean" for "our dear old queen." The frequency with which such contaminations occur is increased by haste, by distraction, by emotional tension, or by uncertainty and conflict as to the best form of expression. In some types of aphasia the tendency to disordered arrangement of words is greatly increased, and, in extreme cases, the attempt to speak results in a word hash with complete loss of grammatical organization. Professor Spooner, after whom such slips are named, was probably suffering from a mild form of aphasia. In these contaminations, it is as if the aggregate of words were in a state of partial excitation, held in check by the requirements of grammatical structure, but ready to activate the final common path, if the effectiveness of this check is in any way interfered with.

In his *Psychopathology of Everyday Life*, Freud has given numerous examples of similar contaminations of action outside the sphere of language. We do not need to accept his theories of censorship and suppression to account for such slips. They are of the same order as misplacements in typing and represent contaminations of co-existing, determining tendencies to action.

Such contaminations might be ascribed to differences in the relative strength of associative bonds between the elements of the act, and thus not evidence for pre-excitation of the elements or for simultaneous pre-excitation. However, the understanding of speech involves essentially the same problems as the production of speech and definitely demands the postulation of an after-effect or after-discharge of the sensory components for a significant time following stimulation. Thus, in the spoken sentence, "Rapid righting with his uninjured hand saved from loss the contents of the capsized canoe," the associations which give meaning to righting are not activated for at least 3 to 5 seconds after hearing the word. I shall refer later to other evidence for such long after-discharge of sensory excitations. The fact of continued activation or after-discharge of receptive elements and their integration during this activation justifies the assumption of a similar process during motor organization. The processes of comprehension and producton of speech have too much in common to depend on wholly different mechanisms.

INTERNAL AND OVERT SPEECH

One other point with respect to the organization of speech: The earlier literature on aphasia emphasized the distinction of internal and overt speech. The aphemia of Broca and the pure motor aphasia of Wernicke and later writers were held to be a loss of the ability to enunciate without loss of ability to think in words and without paralysis of the organs of speech. The brain insult was assumed to affect only the transition from the thought to the enunciation of the word. We may doubt the existence of instances of such "pure" defects and question the reliability of the early clinical examinations in view of the more careful analyses that have been made since 1917, but the distinction of internal and overt speech is still valid and the transition still unexplained. Watson interpreted internal speech as inaudible movements of the vocal organs, and Jacobsen (15) and Max (19) have given evidence of changes in muscular tonus during verbal thinking or thought of movement. This is far from proving that the motor discharge is essential for the internal formation of words, however.

I once devised an instrument to record small movements of the tongue. Within the limits of its sensitivity, it showed that in silent thinking the tongue usually drops to the back of the mouth and shows no detectable movement. Verbal problems, such as the correct squaring of three-place numbers, could be carried out with no trace of overt movement. If, however, I urged the subject to hurry or if I slapped his face, his tongue came forward and showed movements corresponding to the syllabification of internal speech or of the computation he was performing. This I interpret as indicating that internal speech may be carried out wholly by processes within the nervous system, with some unessential discharge upon the final common path for vocal movements. Facilitation of the motor path, either by increased emotional tension or by "voluntary" reinforcement, increases its excitability until the same central circuits whose activity constitutes internal speech are able to excite the overt movements. This aspect of the language function is irrelevant to the problem of syntax or serial order, but is important as illustrating a further point in the dynamics of the cerebrum. Many activities seem to require for their performance both a specific patterning and also a general facilitation, a rise in dynamic level. There are, I think, indications that hemiplegia and motor aphasia are primarily expressions of a low level of facilitation rather than a loss of specific integrative connections which are involved in the use of language or in the patterning of our movements. A monkey, for example, after ablation of the precentral gyrus may seem unable to use the arm at all, but if emotional excitement is raised above a certain level, the arm is freely used. As soon as the excitement dies down, the arm is again hemiplegic. I have seen something of the same sort in a human hemiplegic. The problem of the availability of memories, which was raised earlier in the discussion here, may find a partial solution in such fluctuations in dynamic level. In many of the organic amnesias the pattern of integration seems to be retained but can be reactivated only by an abnormally intense sensory or central reinforcement.

GENERALITY OF THE PROBLEM OF SYNTAX

I have devoted so much time to discussion of the problem of syntax, not only because language is one of the most important products of human cerebral action, but also because the problems raised by the organization of language seem to me to be characteristic of almost all other cerebral activity. There is a series of hierarchies of organization; the order of vocal movements in pronouncing the word, the order of words in the sentence, the order of sentences in the paragraph, the rational order of paragraphs in a discourse. Not only speech, but all skilled acts seem to involve the same problems of serial ordering, even down to the temporal coordination of muscular contractions in such a movement as reaching and grasping. Analysis of the nervous mechanisms underlying order in the more primitive acts may contribute ultimately to the solution even of the physiology of logic.

It is possible to designate, that is, to point to specific examples of, the phenomena of the syntax of movement that require explanation, although those phenomena cannot be clearly defined. A real definition would be a long step toward solution of the problem. There are at least three sets of events to be accounted for. First, the activation of the expressive elements (the individual words or adaptive acts) which do not contain the temporal relations. Second, the determining tendency, the set, or idea. This masquerades under many names in contemporary psychology, but is, in every case, an inference from the restriction of behavior within definite limits. Third, the syntax of the act, which can be described as an habitual order or mode of relating the expressive elements; a generalized pattern or schema of integration which may be imposed upon a wide range and a wide variety of specific acts. This is the essential problem of serial order;

the existence of generalized schemata of action which determine the sequence of specific acts, acts which in themselves or in their associations seem to have no temporal valence.

I shall turn now to other phenomena of movement which may be more readily phrased in physiological terms and which may suggest some of the mechanisms underlying serial order.

DURATION AND INTENSITY OF NERVOUS DISCHARGE

A consideration of the control of extent and rate of movement supports the view that sensory factors play a minor part in regulating the intensity and duration of nervous discharge; that a series of movements is not a chain of sensory-motor reactions. The theory of control of movement which was dominant at the turn of the century assumed that, after a movement is initiated, it is continued until stopped by sensations of movement and position, which indicate that the limb has reached the desired position. This theory was opposed by a good bit of indirect evidence, such as that accuracy of movement is increased rather than diminished with speed. I had opportunity to study a patient who had a complete anesthesia for movements of the knee joint, as a result of a gunshot wound of the cord (16). In spite of the anesthesia, he was able to control the extent and speed of movements of flexion and extension of the knee quite as accurately as can a normal person.

The performance of very quick movements also indicates their independence of current control. "Whip-snapping" movements of the hand can be regulated accurately in extent, yet the entire movement, from initiation to completion, requires less than the reaction time for tactile or kinesthetic stimulation of the arm, which is about one-eighth of a second, even when no discrimination is involved. Such facts force the conclusion that an effector mechanism can be pre-set or primed to discharge at a given intensity or for a given duration, in independence of any sensory controls.

CENTRAL CONTROL OF MOTOR PATTERNS

This independence of sensory controls is true not only of intensity and duration of contraction of a synergic muscle group but is true also of the initiation and timing of contraction of the different muscles in a complex movement. The hand may describe a circular movement involving coordinated contractions of the muscles of the shoulder, elbow, and wrist in about $\frac{1}{10}$ second, and the stopping of movement at a given position, of course, is only a small fraction of that time. The finger strokes of a musician may reach sixteen per second in passages which call for a definite and changing order of successive finger movements. The succession of movements is too quick even for visual reaction time. In rapid sight reading it is impossible to read the individual notes of an arpeggio. The notes must be seen in groups, and it is actually easier to read chords seen simultaneously and to translate them into temporal sequence than to read successive notes in the arpeggio as usually written.

Sensory control of movement seems to be ruled out in such acts. They require the postulation of some central nervous mechanism which fires with predetermined intensity and duration or activates different muscles in predetermined order. This mechanism might be represented by a chain of effector neurons, linked together by internuncials to produce successive delays in firing. In some systems the order of action may be determined by such a leader or pace-setter. Buddenbrock (6) has shown for the stick insect, and Bethe (3) for a number of animals from the centipede to the dog, that removal of one or more legs results in a spontaneous change in the order of stepping. Thus, for the insects, the normal order is alternate stepping of the first pair of legs with right first, left second, right third leg advancing together. With removal of the left first leg, the right first and left second alternate and the order becomes right first, left third, right third stepping together, with left second and right second advancing together, instead of alternately. These investigators were interested in spontaneity of reorganization, rather than in the mechanism of coordination, and did not propose any theory for the latter. They did show, however, that it is necessary to remove the leg completely to get the change in pattern of movement; sensory impulses from a limb stump would prevent it. Such coordination might be explained, perhaps, by a combination of loss of excitability in the centers of the absent limb, by the excitation of the remaining anterior center as a leader or pace-setter, and the spread of alternate waves of inhibition and excitation from the more anterior to the more posterior limb centers. The spontaneous change in coordination shows, however, that the coordination is not due to the action of predetermined anatomic paths but is the result of the current physiological state of the various limb centers.

Such an hypothesis implies also the assumption of a polarization of conduction along the neuraxis, with the order of excitation determined by the spatial arrangement of the centers of the legs. I see no other possibility of accounting for the facts. The examples of circular movement and of finger coordination, involving temporal integration of movements, seem to call for a similar hypothesis. They might be ascribed to an habitual linkage of the movements through a simple chain of internuncials but for two facts. First, such series are usually reversible at any point or can be started from any point. This would require the assumption of a second set of internuncials habituated to conduct in the opposite direction, and this in turn leads to the further assumption of a polarization of conduction. Second, such patterns of coordinated movement may often be transferred directly to other motor systems than the ones practiced. In such transfer, as to the left hand for writing, an analysis of the movements shows that there is not a reduplication of the muscular patterns on the two sides, but a reproduction of movements in relation to the space coordinates of the body. Try upside-down mirror writing with the left hand and with eyes closed for evidence of this. The associative linkage is not of specific movements but of directions of movement. An analysis of systems of space coordinates suggests mechanisms which may contribute to production of such series of movements in a spatial pattern.

SPACE COORDINATE SYSTEMS

The work of Sherrington, Magnus, and others on postural tonus and reflexes has defined one level of spatial integration rather fully, yet it is doubtful if these studies have revealed the effective neural mechanism. The work has shown that the tonic discharge to every muscle in the postural system is influenced by afferent impulses from every other muscle, toward increased or decreased activity, according to its synergic or antergic action. To these influences are added vestibular and cerebellar effects. Diagrammatically these mutual influences of the muscular system may be represented by separate reflex circuits from each receptor to every muscle, as Sherrington (21, p. 148) has done. But no neuro-anatomist would, I am sure, maintain that such separate circuits or paths exist. What the experiments on posture actually show is a correlation of sensory stimulation and of tonic changes in a network of neurons whose interconnections are still undefined. The reactions isolated experimentally have the characteristics of simple directly conducted reflexes, but their combination results in patterns of movement and posture which have definite relations to the axes of the body and to gravity.

This postural system is based on excitations from proprioceptors. The distance receptors impose an additional set of space coordinates upon the postural system, which in turn continually modifies the coordinates of the distance receptors. The dropped cat rights itself, if either the eyes or the vestibular senses are intact, but not in the absence of both. The direction of movement on the retina imposes a directional orientation on the postural system. Conversely, the gravitational system imposes an orientation on the visual field. Upright objects such as trees or the corners of a room appear upright, at no matter what angle the head is inclined. Derangement of the vestibular system can disturb the distance orientation or the orientation of the receptors, as in the apparent swaying of the vertical as a result of the after-images of motion following hours of rocking in a small boat.

There are other, still more generalized systems of space coordinates. We usually keep track of the compass points or of some more definite index of direction by a temporal summation of the turns made in walking, though not always with success. Finally, there is a still more plastic system in which the concepts of spatial relations can be voluntarily reversed, as when one plays blindfold chess alternately from either side of the board.

Explanation of these activities, these complex interactions, in terms of simple isolated interconnections of all of the sensory and motor elements involved seems quite improbable on anatomic grounds and is ruled out by results of our experiments on sectioning of the spinal cord. Ingebritzen (14) studied rats with double hemisection of the cord; one-half of the cord cut at the second, the other at the fifth cervical segment. In the best case only a small strand of the spinocerebellar tract of one side remained intact. These rats were able to balance in walking, oriented to visual stimuli, scratched with the right or left hind foot according to the side of the face stimulated, were able to run mazes correctly, and even learned to rise on the hind feet and push down a lever with the forepaws in opening a box.

The alternative to the isolated-path theory of the space coordinates is that the various impulses which modify postural tonus are poured into a continuous network of neurons, where their summated action results in a sort of polarization of the entire system. I shall consider later the integrative properties of such a net. For the moment I wish to emphasize only the existence of these systems of space coordinates. Their influences pervade the motor system so that every gross movement of limbs or body is made with reference to the space system. The perceptions from the distance receptors, vision, hearing, and touch are also constantly modified and referred to the same space coordinates. The stimulus is *there,* in a definite place; it has definite relation to the position of the body, and it shifts with respect to the sense organ but not with respect to the general orientation, with changes in body posture.

Memories of objects usually give them position in the space system, and even more abstract concepts may have definite spatial reference. Thus, for many people, the cardinal numbers have definite positions on a spiral or other complicated figure. What, if anything, such space characters can contribute to temporal integration is an open question. They provide a possible basis for some serial actions through interaction of postural and timing mechanisms.

RHYTHMIC ACTION

The simplest of the timing mechanisms are those controlling rhythmic activity. T. Graham Brown (5) first showed by his studies of deafferented preparations that the rhythmic movements of respiration and progression are independent of peripheral stimulation and are maintained by a central nervous mechanism of reciprocal innervation. He suggested that this mechanism of reciprocal innervation, rather than the simple reflex, is the unit of organization of the whole nervous system. He thus foreshadowed, in a way, the conception of reverberatory circuits which is coming to play so large a part in neurological theory today. Holst (13) has recently shown that the rhythmic movement of the dorsal fin of fishes is a compound

of two superimposed rhythms, that of its own innervation and that of
the pectoral fins. These two rhythms are centrally maintained.

Musical rhythms seem to be an elaboration of the same sort of thing.
The time or beat is started and maintained at some definite rate, say 160
per minute. This rate is then imposed upon various activities. The fingers
of the musician fall in multiples of the basic rate. If the leader of a quartet
speeds up the time or retards, all the movements of the players change
in rate accordingly. Not only the time of initiation but also the rate of
movement is affected. The violinist, in a passage requiring the whole bow,
will draw the bow from frog to tip at a uniform rate for the required
number of beats, whether the tempo is fast or slow. With practiced vio-
linists, the rate of movement is extremely accurate and comes out on the
beat at the exact tip of the bow.

Superimposed on this primary rhythm is a secondary one of emphasis,
giving the character of 3/4, 4/4, 6/4, or other time. The mechanism of
these rhythms can be simply conceived as the spread of excitation from
some centers organized for reciprocal innervation; as a combination of
the principles of Brown and of Holst. There are, however, still more complicated rhythms in all music. That of the melodic line is most uniform.
In much music, the melodic progression changes in 2, 4, or some multiple of
4 measures. In improvisation, the performer keeps no count of measures,
yet comes out almost invariably in a resolution to the tonic of the key
after some multiple of eight measures. Here a generalized pattern is impressed on the sequence, but it is a simpler pattern than that of grammatical
structure. It only requires the recurrence of a pattern at certain rhythmic
intervals; a pick-up of a specific pattern after so many timed intervals.

There are, in addition, still less regular rhythms of phrasing and emphasis. Parallels to these can be found in speech. The skilled extemporaneous
speaker rounds his phrases and speaks with a definite though not regular
rhythm.

The rhythms tend to spread to almost every other concurrent activity.
One falls into step with a band, tends to breathe, and even to speak in
time with the rhythm. The all pervasiveness of the rhythmic discharge
is shown by the great difficulty of learning to maintain two rhythms at
once, as in three against four with the two hands. The points to be emphasized here are the widespread effects of a rhythmic discharge indicating
the involvement of almost the entire effector system, the concurrent action
of different rhythmic systems, and the imposition of the rate upon both
the initiation and speed of movement. Consideration of rhythmic activity
and of spatial orientation forces the conclusion, I believe, that there exist
in the nervous organization, elaborate systems of interrelated neurons
capable of imposing certain types of integration upon a large number of
widely spaced effector elements; in the one case transmitting temporally
spaced waves of facilitative excitation to all effector elements; in the other
imparting a directional polarization to both receptor and effector elements.
These systems are in constant action. They form a sort of substratum upon

which other activity is built. They contribute to every perception and to every integrated movement.

INTERACTION OF TEMPORAL AND SPATIAL SYSTEMS

Integration ascribed to the spatial distribution of excitations in the nervous system has been much more intensively studied than the temporal aspects of nervous activity. Theories of integration are based almost exclusively upon space properties, time entering only in theories of facilitation, inhibition, and after-discharge. In cerebral functions, however, it is difficult to distinguish between spatial and temporal functions. The eye is the only organ that gives simultaneous information concerning space in any detail. The shape of an object impressed on the skin can scarcely be detected from simultaneous pressure, but the same shape can readily be distinguished by touch when traced on the skin with a moving point or when explored by tactile scanning. The temporal sequence is readily translated into a spatial concept. Even for vision it might be questioned whether simultaneous stimulation gives rise directly to space concepts. The visual object is generally surveyed by eye movements, and its form is a reconstruction from such a series of excitations. Even with tachistoscopic exposures, the after-discharge permits a temporal survey, and, with visual fixation, shifts of attention provide an effective scanning.

Since memory traces are, we believe, in large part static and persist simultaneously, it must be assumed that they are spatially differentiated. Nevertheless, reproductive memory appears almost invariably as a temporal sequence, either as a succession of words or of acts. Even descriptions of visual imagery (the supposed simultaneous reproductive memory in sensory terms) are generally descriptions of sequences, of temporal reconstructions from very fragmentary and questionable visual elements. Spatial and temporal order thus appear to be almost completely interchangeable in cerebral action. The translation from the spatial distribution of memory traces to temporal sequence seems to be a fundamental aspect of the problem of serial order.

I spoke earlier of the probability of a partial activation or priming of aggregates of words before the sentence is actually formulated from them. There is a great deal of evidence for such preliminary facilitation of patterns of action in studies of reaction time and of word association. Reaction time, in general, is reduced by preliminary warning or by instructions which allow the subject to prepare for the specific act required. In controlled association experiments, the subject is instructed to respond to the stimulus word by a word having a certain type of relation to it, such as the opposite or a part of which the stimulus is the whole; black-white, apple-seed. The result is an attitude or set which causes that particular category to dominate the associative reaction. Whether such preliminary reinforcement is to be ascribed to accumulation of excitatory state, as defined by Sherrington (21), or to some other physiological process, the facts of behavior assure that it is a genuine phenomenon and plays a decisive role in determining the character of the response.

Once the existence of such states of partial activation is recognized, their possible role in temporal integration must be considered. There are indications that one neural system may be held in this state of partial excitation while it is scanned by another. Here is an example. A series of four to six numbers is heard: 3–7–2–9–4. This is within the attention or memory span and is almost certainly not remembered in the sense in which one's telephone number is remembered, for memory of it is immediately wiped out by a succeeding series of numbers. While it is retained in this unstable way, subject to retroactive inhibition, the order of the numbers can be reassorted: 3–7–2–9–4, 3–2–7–9–4, 4–9–2–7–3, and the like. It is as if, in this case, a rhythmic alternation can suppress alternate items, or a direction of arousal can be applied to the partially excited system. Another example which illustrates even more clearly the spatial characteristics of many memory traces is the method of comultiplication, used in rapid mental calculation. In attempts to play a melody backward, we have a further illustration. I find that I can do it only by visualizing the music spatially and then reading it backward. I cannot auditorily transform even "Yankee Doodle" into its inverse without some such process, but it is possible to get a spatial representation of the melody and then to scan the spatial representation. The scanning of a spatial arrangement seems definitely to determine, in such cases, the order of procedure. Two assumptions are implied by this. First, the assumption is that the memory traces are associated, not only with other memory traces, but also with the system of space coordinates. By this I do not mean that the engram has a definite location in the brain; our experiments show conclusively that such is not the case. Rather, when the memory trace is formed it is integrated with directional characters of the space system, which give it position in reference to other associated traces. Second, the assumption is that these space characters of the memory trace can be scanned by some other level of the coordinating system and so transformed into succession.

This is as far as I have been able to go toward a theory of serial order in action. Obviously, it is inadequate. The assumptions concerning spatial representation and temporal representation may even beg the question, since no one can say whether spatial or temporal order is primary. Furthermore, such determining tendencies as the relation of attribute to object, which gives the order of adjective and noun, do not seem to be analyzable into any sort of spatial structure or for that matter, into any consistent relationship. I have tried a number of assumptions concerning the selective mechanism of grammatical form (spatial relations, the relative intensity or prominence of different words in the idea, and so on) but I have never been able to make an hypothesis which was consistent with any large number of sentence structures. Nevertheless, the indications which I have cited, that elements of the sentence are readied or partially activated before the order is imposed upon them in expression, suggest that some scanning mechanism must be at play in regulating their temporal sequence. The real problem, however, is the nature of the selective mechanism by which the particular acts are picked out in this scanning process, and to this problem I have no answer.

Such speculations concerning temporal and spatial systems do little more than illustrate a point of view concerning nervous organization which is, I believe, more consistent both with what is known of the histology and elementary physiology of the brain and also with behavior phenomena than are the more widely current theories of simple associative chains of reactions.

Nearly forty years ago Becher (2, page 243) wrote: "There is no physiological hypothesis which can explain the origin and relations of temporal forms in mental life; indeed, there is no hypothesis which even foreshadows the possibility of such an explanation." The situation is little better today, but I do feel that changing conceptions of the fundamental organization of the nervous system offer more hope for a solution of such problems than did the physiological knowledge available when Becher wrote. However, we are still very far from being able to form an explicit explanation of temporal structure.

THE FUNDAMENTAL MECHANISM OF INTEGRATION

Neurological theory has been dominated by the belief that the neurons of the central nervous system are in an inactive or resting state for the greater part of the time; that they are linked in relatively isolated conditioned reflex arcs and that they are activated only when the particular reactions for which they are specifically associated are called out. Such a view is incompatible both with the widespread effects of stimulation which can be demonstrated by changes in tonus and also with recent evidence from electrical recording of nervous activity. It is now practically certain that all the cells of the cerebrospinal axis are being continually bombarded by nerve impulses from various sources and are firing regularly, probably even during sleep. The nervous activity which they in turn elicit depends upon the current physiological state of the neurons with which they are connected. It is probably not far from the truth to say that every nerve cell of the cerebral cortex is involved in thousands of different reactions. The cortex must be regarded as a great network of reverberatory circuits, constantly active. A new stimulus, reaching such a system, does not excite an isolated reflex path but must produce widespread changes in the pattern of excitation throughout a whole system of already interacting neurons.

The facts of cerebral structure support such a view. The cortex is composed chiefly of neurons with short axons. LeGros Clark (8) has found for the striate area of the monkey that Marchi degeneration extends for only a short distance from a point of injury. In striate area of the rat, I have never been able to trace degeneration beyond three or four cell diameters from the margin of a lesion, and I believe that this lack of long transcortical fibers is true of other areas as well as of the visual cortex. Visual perception reveals close integration of different parts of the striate areas in spite of the absence of long association fibers. In the visual cortex of the rat there are only 19 neurons for each afferent fiber. To produce the animal's visual acuity, all of the afferent fibers must be firing continually. There are approximately 34,000 cell bodies in the lateral geniculate nucleus of the rat, and the minimum number of visual units necessary to produce the visual acuity of the rat is actually above this figure. (The acuity is determined by direct experimental tests.) These figures should be of interest in relation to the numerical values cited by Dr. von Neumann. The number of cells in the visual cortex of the rat is only about 10^6, and in some of my experiments where I have removed the greater part of the visual cortex the capacity for discrimination of visual forms has been retained when no more than 20,000 cells of the visual cortex remain. There is also evidence that no part of the cerebral cortex except the visual areas is essential for visual perception and memory.

In the rat, I have removed, from one or another animal, practically every other part of the isocortex without disturbing visual perception or memory. With monkeys I have removed the supposed visual associative areas without producing any significant loss of visual functions.

These facts lead to the conclusion that the same cells in the visual cortex participate in a great variety of activities. Practically all of the cells of the area must be fired by every visual stimulation, and these same cells must be the ones which retain the visual memories. The conclusion follows that differential responses depend upon the pattern of cells which are excited in combination. The visual cortex is a network of cells of short axon without long interconnections between its parts or with other cortical areas. Its integrative functions are an expression of the properties of such a network.

The same conception must be applied to other cortical areas. There are, of course, long association tracts in the cortex, such as the corpus callosum, the superior longitudinal fasciculus, and the temporo-frontal tracts. Once, 26 years ago, I suggested facetiously that these might be only skeletal structures, since I could find no function for them. No important functions of these tracts have yet been demonstrated. Section of the corpus callosum produces only a slight slowing of reaction time, ipsilateral as well as contralateral (Akelaitis, 1); section of occipito-frontal fibers produces, perhaps, a temporary disturbance of visual attention but no other symptoms. The integrative functions seem to be carried out as well without as with the main associative tracts. The major integrative functions must, therefore be carried out by the network of cells of short axon. The properties of such networks of cells must be analyzed before the mechanisms of the cerebral cortex can be understood. Something can be inferred from the characteristics of excitability of cells and their arrangement in recurrent loops. If, as seems a necessary conclusion from the histology of the striate area, all of the cells of the network are subject to constant excitation and are firing whenever they recover from the refractory state, then mutual interference of circuits will produce complicated patterns throughout the area, patterns which will stabilize in the absence of differential stimulation, as is perhaps indicated by the regularity of the alpha rhythm. Any new afferent impulses reaching the area can only produce a reorganization of the existing pattern. What happens at any particular point in the system, as at an efferent neuron, is the statistical outcome of the interaction of myriads of neurons, not of the transmission of impulses over a restricted path, of which that efferent cell forms a link. It is possible to isolate parts of the system by operative means or by anesthetics and so to get a one-to-one relation of stimulus locus and responding muscles, from which the reflex mechanism has been inferred. As Goldstein (12) has pointed out, however, the parts isolated in the reflex are influenced by a multiplicity of effects in the intact organism of which there is little or no trace in the isolated preparation.

I can best illustrate this conception of nervous action by picturing the brain as the surface of a lake. The prevailing breeze carries small ripples in its direction, the basic polarity of the system. Varying gusts set up crossing systems of waves, which do not destroy the first ripples, but modify their form, a second level in the system of space coordinates. A tossing log with its own period of submersion sends out periodic bursts of ripples, a temporal rhythm. The bow wave of a speeding boat momentarily sweeps over the surface, seems to obliterate the smaller waves yet leaves them unchanged by its passing, the transient effect of a strong stimulus. Wave motion is not an adequate analogy because the medium which conveys the waves is uniform, whereas the nerve cells have their individual characteristics of transmission which at every point may alter the character of the transmitted pattern.

The great number of axon terminations on every nerve cell has not been considered in theories of integration. It implies, of course, that the cell can be fired by impulses from a variety of sources. But it also suggests another possibility, more fruitful for understanding of integrative processes. A nerve impulse arriving over a single axon terminal may not fire the cell but may modify its excitability to impulses from other sources. In an elaborate system of neurons such subthreshold effects might establish a pattern of facilitation which would determine the combination of cells fired by subsequent excitations. The space coordinate system and various types of *set* or priming may be pictured as patterns of subthreshold facilitation pervading the network of neurons which is activated by the more specific external stimulus.

Such a view of the mechanism of nervous action certainly does not simplify the problems nor does it as yet provide any clue to the structuring that constitutes the set or determining tendency, or to the nature of such relations as are implied in the attribute-object, opposites, or other abstract concepts. A few relations seem reducible to spatial terms, part-whole, for example, but even for these there is no clear conception of the neural basis of their space properties. These considerations do not, I believe, contradict fundamentally the basic conceptions that have been formulated by Dr. McCulloch. They do, however, indicate a direction of necessary elaboration. The nets active in rhythmic and spatial organization are apparently almost coextensive with the nervous system. The analysis must be extended to the properties of such nets; the way in which they are broken up into reactive patterns in the spread of excitation, to give, for example, directional propagation or its equivalent. I strongly suspect that many phenomena of generalization, both sensory and conceptual, are products, not of simple switching, but of interaction of complex patterns of organization within such systems.

SUMMARY

The problems of the syntax of action are far removed from anything which we can study by direct physiological methods today, yet in attempting to formulate a physiology of the cerebral cortex we cannot ignore them. Serial order is typical of the problems raised by cerebral activity; few, if any, of the problems are simpler or promise easier solution. We can, perhaps, postpone the fatal day when we must face them, by saying that they are too complex for present analysis, but there is danger here of constructing a false picture of those processes that we believe to be simpler. I am coming more and more to the conviction that the rudiments of every human behavioral mechanism will be found far down in the evolutionary scale and also represented even in primitive activities of the nervous system. If there exist, in human cerebral action, processes which seem fundamentally different or inexplicable in terms of our present construct of the elementary physiology of integration, then it is probable that that construct is incomplete or mistaken, even for the levels of behavior to which it is applied.

In spite of its present inadequacy, I feel that the point of view which I have sketched here holds some promise of a better understanding of cerebral integration. Attempts to express cerebral function in terms of the concepts of the reflex arc, or of associated chains of neurons, seem to me doomed to failure because they start with the assumption of a static nervous system. Every bit of evidence available indicates a dynamic, constantly active system, or, rather, a composite of many interacting systems, which I have tried to illustrate at a primitive level by rhythm and the space coordinates. Only when methods of analysis of such systems have been devised will there be progress toward understanding of the physiology of the cerebral cortex.

REFERENCES

1 Akelaitis, A. J. Studies on the corpus callosum. ii. The higher visual functions in each hononymous field following complete section of the corpus callosum. *Arch. Neurol. Psychiat.*, 1941, **45**, 788–796.

2 Becher, E. *Gehirn und Seele*. Heidelberg, 1911.

3 Bethe, A. Plastizität und Zentrenlehre. *Handb. d. norm. u. path. Physiol.*, 1931, **15** (zweite H.), 1175–1220.

4 Boring, E. G. *A history of experimental psychology*. New York: Century Co., 1929.

5 Brown, T. G. On the nature of the fundamental activity of the nervous centers. *J. Physiol.*, 1914, **48**, 18–46.

6 Buddenbrock, W. v. Die Rhythmus der Schreitbewegungen der Stabheuschrecke Dyxippus. *Biol. Centralb.*, 1921, **41**, 41–48.

7 Chamberlain, A. F. Indians, North American. *Enc. Brit.*, 1911, **14**, 452–482.

8 Clark, W. E. LeGros. Observations on the associative fiber system of the visual cortex and the central representation of the retina. *J. Anat. London*, 1941, **75**, 225–236.

9 Epstein, I. *La pensée et la polyglossie*. Paris: Payot et Cie (no date).

10 Fournié. *Essai de psychologie*. Paris, 1887.

11 Fritsch, G., and Hitzig, E. Ueber die elektrische Erregbarkeit des Grosshirns. *Arc. f. Anat. u. Physiol.*, 1870, pp. 300–332.

12 Goldstein, K. *The organism*. Boston: Ginn & Co., 1939.

13 Holst, N. v. Vom Wesen der Ordnung im Zentralnervensystem. *Die Naturwissenschaften*, 1937, **25**, 625–631; 641–647.

14 Ingebritzen, O. C. Coordinating mechanisms of the spinal cord. *Genet. Psychol. Monogr.*, 1933, **13**, 483–555.

15 Jacobsen, E. Electrophysiology of mental activities. *Amer. J. Psychol.*, 1932, **44**, 677–694.

16 Lashley, K. S. The accuracy of movement in the absence of excitation from the moving organ. *Amer. J. Physiol.*, 1917, **43**, 169–194.

17 Lashley, K. S. The mechanism of vision. xvii. Autonomy of the visual cortex. *J. Genet. Psychol.*, 1942, **60**, 197–221.

18 Lashley, K. S. The mechanism of vision. xviii. Effects of destroying the visual "associative areas" in the monkey. *Genet. Psychol. Monogr.*, 1948, **37**, 107–166.

19 Max, L. W. Experimental study of the motor theory of consciousness. IV. *J. Comp. Psychol.*, 1937, **24**, 301–344.

20 Pick, A. *Die agrammatischen Sprachstörungen*. Berlin, 1913.

21 Sherrington, C. S. *The integrative action of the nervous system*. London: Constable, 1906.

22 Sherrington, C. S. Some functional problems attaching to convergence. *Proc. Roy. Soc.*, B, 1929, **105**, 332–362.

23 Thorsen, A. M. The relation of tongue movements to internal speech. *J. Exp. Psychol.*, 1925, **8**, 1–32.

24 Titchener, E. B. *Lectures on the experimental psychology of the thought processes*. New York: The Macmillan Co., 1909.

25 Washburn, M. F. *Movement and mental imagery*. Boston: Houghton Mifflin, 1916.

26 Watson, J. B. Is thinking merely the action of the language mechanisms? *Brit. J. Psychol.*, 1920, **11**, 86–104.

Development

CHEMICAL AND ANATOMICAL PLASTICITY OF BRAIN

Edward L. Bennett, Marian C. Diamond, David Krech, and Mark R. Rosenzweig

UNIVERSITY OF CALIFORNIA, BERKELEY

Editor's Note   *Figures 1 and 3 of the original article have been omitted in reprinting, with minor related alterations in the text.*

Source   *Reprinted from* **Science**, *October 30, 1964,* **146,** *610–619, with permission of the authors and the American Association for the Advancement of Science. Copyright 1964 by the American Association for the Advancement of Science.*

Here it may be asked whether the organs [of the brain] increase by exercise? This may certainly happen in the brain as well as in the muscles: nay, it seems more than probable, because the blood is carried in greater abundance to the parts which are excited, and nutrition is performed by the blood. In order however, to be able to answer this question positively, we ought to observe the same persons when exercised and when not exercised; or at least observe many persons who are, and many others who are not, exercised during all periods of life.—*J. G. Spurzhein*, 1815 (*1*).

I have shown that the brains of domestic rabbits are considerably reduced in bulk, in comparison with those of the wild rabbit or hare; and this may be attributed to their having been closely confined during many generations, so that they have exerted their intellect, instincts, senses and voluntary movements but little.—*Charles Darwin*, 1874 (*2*).

One might suppose that cerebral exercise, since it cannot produce new cells (neural cells do not multiply as do muscular cells) carries further than usual the development of protoplasmic expansions and neural collaterals, forcing the establishment of new and more extended intercortical connections.—*S. Ramón y Cajal*, 1895 (*3*).

The question is not whether neural events change the status of the tissue in which they occur. The only question which may still be debated is: whether such changes as do undoubtedly occur have the permanence and those other properties which we must attribute to memory-traces. According to our present knowledge the primary effect which nerve impulses produce in ganglionic layers is chemical activity . . . —*Wolfgang Köhler*, 1938 (*4*).

Thus, the results of our original experiment and the replication strongly support these two general conclusions: (a) Manipulating the environment of animals during the 80 days after weaning can alter significantly the weight of the cerebral cortex, the total ChE [acetylcholinesterase] activity of the brain, and the cortical/subcortical distributions of the specific activity of ChE and of tissue weight. (b) Similar but much greater alterations in the brains of the animals can be accomplished by a program of genetic selection carried out over a few generations.—*M. R. Rosenzweig, D. Krech, E. L. Bennett,* and *M. C. Diamond*, 1962 (*5*).

As these quotations show, it has long been speculated that the use of the brain might lead to changes in its size, in the interconnections of its cells, and in its chemical composition. Speculation led to research, and in the last century measurements of the size and weight of brains of men were made in an effort to discover differences that might relate to the degree of intellectual attainment. The first results were encouraging, since men of distinction were usually found to have larger brains than those of inferior intellect. Gradually it was realized, however, that men of different stations in life often differed in health and nutrition as well as in intellect, and that the former factors might affect brain weight. There were also striking exceptions to the general relation— idiots with large brains and geniuses with small brains. The hypothesis of an intrinsic relation between brain size and cerebral exercise or ability was therefore generally abandoned. In its place there were suggestions of more subtle factors involving neural interconnections or chemical changes in the brain. The difficulty of working with such factors discouraged research, and the problem largely reverted to the speculative realm.

In spite of their speculative nature, physical or chemical residuals of experience in the brain continued to be incorporated in most physiological theories of learning. It was generally supposed that changes must occur in the brain in order to account for memory—the registration, the storage, and the retrieval of information. No other hypothesis seemed tenable. So certain were the theoreticians about this that they long ago gave names to these hypothesized changes—they called them "memory traces" or "brain engrams." But, unfortunately, the brain physiologists and anatomists were singularly unsuccessful in finding any solid evidence to justify the certainty of their colleagues. In time an alternative hypothesis was developed—the hypothesis that memory might be stored purely in the form of reverberating neural impulses. However, experiments in the late 1940's and early 1950's indicated that electrical shock could disrupt impulses and that low temperature could drastically reduce their number, but that in both of these cases memories formed before the treatment were still available afterwards. The reverberating impulse hypothesis of long-term memory was therefore abandoned, and the residual change hypothesis was revived. In fact most workers had never left it. Now it became even more important to find some evidence for physiological residuals of experience in the brain. Indeed, evidence for *brain plasticity* would seem to be propaedeutic and essential for the sound development of research on many major questions of brain-behavior relations.

We took up the search for responses of the brain to experience about 6 years ago in the context of a larger project dealing with relations of intelligent behavior in animals to brain chemistry. This project was started in 1953 by the two psychologists and the chemist of our group. It could not have begun nor continued without the interest and material support of Melvin Calvin, who has long espoused interdisciplinary research in chemistry and biological sciences. We have also benefited from the counsel of Everett Dempster on research involving genetic selection for brain chemicals. When we found evidence 4 years ago that experience could modify not only the chemistry but also the anatomy of the brain, a neuroanatomist joined the group in order to investigate both gross and microscopic anatomical changes in detail. What we have to report, therefore, is the result of several years of cooperative interdisciplinary effort on one research problem (6).

PREDICTION OF CHEMICAL CHANGE WITH TRAINING

Transmission of neural impulses across the synapses or junctions between neurons requires a chemical step. When the impulse reaches the end of a neuron, it causes the release of a chemical mediator which diffuses across the narrow synaptic gap and combines with receptor sites on the post-synaptic membrane. This alters the post-synaptic potential. If this potential reaches the threshold value, a nerve impulse is initiated. Acetylcholine was the first synaptic transmitter to be studied in the peripheral nervous system, and evidence for its role in the brain has been accumulating steadily. Once acetylcholine is liberated at a synapse, it is rapidly inactivated by the enzyme acetylcholinesterase, so that the synapse is restored to its resting state.

In earlier studies, we had found evidence that the ratio of cerebral acetylcholine concentration to acetylcholinesterase activity is positively related to problem-solving ability in rats (7); that is, the higher the ratio, the better the learning scores. We then hypothesized that differential experience would lead to quantitative changes in this synaptic transmitter system. Specifically, we predicted (8) that enhanced stimulation and training would increase the rate of liberation of acetylcholine, and that this in turn would lead to an increased rate of synthesis of acetylcholinesterase. We did not at the outset intend to look for changes in the size or weight of the brain, because the idea that "cerebral exercise" can increase the size of the brain had been pretty generally abandoned by the 20th century. Indeed, we had completed several experiments and published an article on effects of training on brain chemistry (8) before further examination of the data suggested that there are anatomical changes as well.

DESIGN OF BEHAVIORAL TREATMENTS

In designing an experimental approach to the problem, we followed the second proposal of Spurzheim by varying the amount of experience given to different groups of subjects. We incorporated several features in the design to reduce random variation among subjects and thus to increase the reliability of any results that we might obtain. All comparisons were made among animals alike in lineage, parentage, sex (male) and age, and differing systematically only in amount of experience. To test the generality of the effects, different lines of rats were employed in several of the experiments.

What type of experience might be important in producing measurable cerebral effects could not be foretold, so we combined both informal and formal training. The control animals are kept under colony conditions, housed three in a cage and exposed to ongoing activity in the room, but with no special treatment; this we term our Social Condition (SC). For enhanced experience, animals are given Environmental Complexity and Training (ECT). The ECT animals are housed in groups of 10 to 12 in large cages provided with "toys."

Every day they are placed for 30 minutes in a square field 90 cm on a side where the pattern of barriers is changed daily. In the home cage and in the open field, the rats play and explore as actively as kittens. After some weeks they are also given one or two trials a day in various standardized mazes for sugar pellet rewards. For the third condition—reduced experience—animals are caged singly in a dimly lit and quiet room where they cannot see or touch another animal (although they can hear and smell them); this is the Isolated Condition (IC). Animals in all three conditions have food and water available at all times, and all are weighed on the average of once in 2 weeks. In most of our experiments, animals are kept under the experimental conditions for 80 days and then are killed for analysis of the brain (9).

REMOVAL OF BRAIN SAMPLES AND CHEMICAL ANALYSIS

At the end of the behavioral phase of an experiment, the animals are delivered to the chemists under code numbers that do not reveal their group membership. The animals are killed by decapitation, members of a litter being taken in immediate succession but with randomized order for treatment within litters. In most experiments the brain is then removed and divided by gross dissection into the following five samples: (i) sample of visual cortex, (ii) sample of somesthetic cortex, (iii) remaining dorsal cortex, (iv) ventral cortex and adjacent tissue including corpus callosum, hippocampus, and amygdala, and (v) the remaining brain or subcortex. The first four samples will be referred to collectively as "total cortex."

The visual and somesthetic samples are demarcated with a miniature plastic T-square, as Fig. 2 shows. In defining the regions from which the visual and somesthetic samples were selected, we were guided by earlier ablation and electrophysiological mapping studies of the rat cortex (10). Once these regions are circumscribed, they can be peeled cleanly from the underlying white matter, since in the rat brain there is a clear mechanical gradient between these two kinds of tissue. There is a sharp histological boundary between the cortex and the white matter of the rat—far more distinct than the boundaries in man, cat, or dog. The absence of folds in rat cortex also facilitates stripping off the cortex. As each sample is removed, it is weighed and then frozen on a block of dry ice. About 10 minutes elapse between decapitation and the weighing of the last sample for a rat. The samples are then stored at $-20°$ C until they can be analyzed chemically.

Until the last few years we analyzed acetylcholinesterase activity by

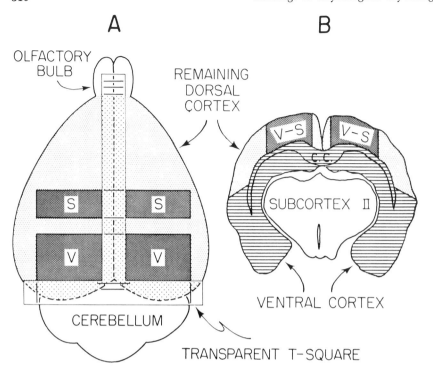

FIGURE 2 *To the left, the dorsal aspect of the rat brain, showing how samples of the visual cortex (V) and of the somesthetic cortex (S) are dissected, guided by a small transparent T-square. To the right, a transverse section of the rat brain. Total cortex is made up of four samples: the V and S sections—telescoped together in this diagram —plus the remaining dorsal cortex, plus the ventral cortex. The rest of the brain— labelled Subcortex II here—includes the olfactory bulbs and the cerebellum.*

means of an automatic titrator or "pH-stat." Recently, we have speeded the analyses without sacrificing reliability by using a colorimetric method adapted from that of Ellman, Courtney, Andres, and Featherstone (*11*).

While reliability of chemical results *within* any experiment is high, there are some variations of absolute values from one experiment to another. We therefore found it prudent, when investigating the effects of new variables, to include our standard groups (ECT and IC) within each experiment. This has led to the replication of the main conditions in many successive experiments. While the replication is costly, the consistency of the results over many experiments provides great assurance about the existence of the effects which we will now describe.

EFFECTS OF EXPERIENCE ON WEIGHT OF BRAIN TISSUE

In seven successive experiments, we have used animals of the Berkeley S_1 line, putting them into the enriched and impoverished environments at weaning (about 25 days of age) and maintaining them there for about

80 days. Three of these experiments also included Social Control (SC) groups, as we will discuss later.

A highly consistent difference between the brains of littermates given enriched or restricted experience occurs in the weight of the cerebral cortex. The left column of data in Table 1 gives the mean weight of total cortex for each group in each of the seven experiments. It also gives the number of pairs in which the cortical weight of the ECT animal surpassed that of its IC littermate and the amount by which the ECT mean exceeded the IC mean, expressed as a percentage of the IC mean. As can be seen from Table 1, a highly consistent set of results was obtained in experiments performed over a 4-year period, sampling a number of different generations of the S_1 line, and with some experiments falling in each season of the year.

Several points should be noted with regard to this greater growth of cortex among the enriched-experience rats.

1. It does not reflect overall growth of the whole brain. As the right-hand column of Table 1 shows, outside of the cortex there is actually a slight decrease in weight of the brain of enriched-experience animals (1.2 percent, $p < .05$).

2. It does not reflect an increase in body weight. The enriched-experience animals end the experiment weighing about 7 percent *less* than their rather inactive isolated littermates. If we had calculated the results in terms of brain weight per unit of body weight rather than in terms of absolute brain weight, the relative difference between groups would have been much larger.

3. It does not occur equally throughout the cortex. Instead, as Table 2 shows, there is a pronounced regional distribution, the mean difference being greatest in the visual region (6.2 percent, $p < .001$) and least in the somesthetic region of the cortex (2.7 percent, $p < .05$).

4. It can be measured in other terms than wet weight of tissue, and completely comparable results are obtained. In two further experiments, we sectioned the brains for anatomical measurement instead of consuming them in chemical analysis (12). The depth of the cortex was measured from the pial surface down to the underlying white matter, using an optical micrometer. Figure 3 shows the location of lines along which we measured the depth. Subcortical landmarks were used to locate comparable cortical regions to be measured in each animal. In the visual region, the cortex of enriched-experience rats was 6.2 percent thicker than that of their littermates ($p < .001$), while in the somesthetic region the difference was only 3.8 percent thicker ($p < .01$). The anatomists making these measurements did not, of course, know which experimental treatment any animal had received.

5. Finally, the increases in weight and depth of the cortex with experience do not mean that absolute weight of cortex can be used as a correlate of experience or ability. The absolute weight of the cortex is determined not only by experience but also by other factors such as heredity. For

Table 1. Brain weights of littermate S_1 rats exposed to environmental complexity and training (ECT) or isolation condition (IC) from 25 to 105 days of age; seven replication experiments

Experiment: Termination date, N (pairs)	Statistic	Weight (mg)	
		Total cortex	Rest of brain
May 1960, 11	ECT $\bar{X}$	663	894
	IC $\bar{X}$	626	896
	ECT > IC*	9/11	5/11
	% Diff.†	5.8	−0.1
Oct. 1960, 11	ECT $\bar{X}$	682	971
	IC $\bar{X}$	645	992
	ECT > IC*	9/11	5/11
	% Diff.†	5.8	−2.1
Dec. 1961, 11	ECT $\bar{X}$	702	912
	IC $\bar{X}$	672	922
	ECT > IC*	9/11	5/11
	% Diff.†	4.4	−1.1
Mar. 1962, 10	ECT $\bar{X}$	705	916
	IC $\bar{X}$	673	923
	ECT > IC*	9/10	5/10
	% Diff.†	4.8	−0.7
June 1962, 12	ECT $\bar{X}$	740	977
	IC $\bar{X}$	708	988
	ECT > IC*	10/12	5/12
	% Diff.†	4.5	−1.1
Dec. 1962, 12	ECT $\bar{X}$	710	980
	IC $\bar{X}$	688	982
	ECT > IC*	9/12	6/12
	% Diff.†	3.2	−0.2
July 1963, 10	ECT $\bar{X}$	694	912
	IC $\bar{X}$	667	942
	ECT > IC*	7/10	2/10
	% Diff.†	3.9	−3.2
1960–1963, 77	ECT $\bar{X}$	700	939
	IC $\bar{X}$	669	951
	ECT > IC*	62/77	33/77
	% Diff.†	4.6	−1.2
	p‡	< .001	< .05

* Number of littermate pairs in which the ECT value exceeds the IC value.   † Percentage by which the ECT mean exceeds the IC mean.   ‡ Probability values were determined by analyses of variance.

Table 2. Weights of brain regions from 77 littermate pairs of S₁ rats in ECT and IC conditions (seven experiments combined)

| | Weight (mg) | | | | | | |
| | Cortex | | | | | | |
Statistic	Visual sample	Somes-thetic sample	Remain-ing dorsal	Ventral	Total	Rest of brain	Total brain
ECT $\bar{X}$	63.0	48.7	282	306	700	939	1639
IC $\bar{X}$	59.3	47.4	268	294	669	951	1620
ECT > IC*	57/77	48/77	57/77	51/77	62/77	33/77	51/77
% Diff.†	6.2	2.7	5.2	4.0	4.6	−1.2	1.2
p‡	<.001	<.05	<.001	<.01	<.001	<.05	<.05

* Number of littermate pairs in which the ECT value exceeds the IC value.   † Percentage by which the ECT mean exceeds the IC mean.   ‡ Probability values were determined by analyses of variance.

example, the Berkeley S₃ line [descendents of Tryon's maze-dull line (13)] has about one-tenth greater weight of cortical tissue than the S₁ line (descendents of Tryon's maze-brights). We have found the S₃ animals to be inferior to the S₁ animals in solving several standardized mazes (7, 14). Within each line, the enriched-experience animals develop significantly heavier cortices than their isolated littermates (15), but the ECT's of the S₁ line nevertheless have lighter cortices than the IC's of the S₃ line. It must be borne in mind that our experiments are all confined to the question, "How does experience transform the brain from what it would have been without that experience?"

EFFECTS OF EXPERIENCE ON ACETYLCHOLINESTERASE ACTIVITY

Activity of acetylcholinesterase (Table 3) was measured in the same seven experiments for which we have just considered the results on brain weight. Total activity of the enzyme was greater for the enriched-experience than for the isolated animals by 2.7 percent in total cortex ($p < .01$) and by 2.1 percent in the rest of the brain ($p < .001$). As was the case with tissue weight, the increase in total activity is greatest in the visual region of the cortex—3.6 percent—and least in the somesthetic region. Note that in each cortical region the relative increase in total acetylcholinesterase activity is less than the increase in tissue weight, as can be seen by comparing Tables 2 and 3. In the rest of the brain, however, the enzymatic activity goes up with enriched experience although weight decreases slightly. (These relations for both cortex and subcortex are shown in Fig. 4.) If enzymatic activity is measured *per unit of tissue weight,*

Table 3. Total acetylcholinesterase activity of brain regions from S₁ rats in ECT and IC conditions (seven experiments combined). Activity is expressed in terms of moles of acetylcholine hydrolyzed per minute under our standard assay conditions

| | Activity (10^{-8} mole/min) | | | | | | |
| | Cortex | | | | | | |
Statistic	Visual sample	Somes- thetic sample	Remain- ing dorsal	Ventral	Total	Rest of brain	Total brain
ECT $\bar{X}$	38.6	36.5	212	344	631	1825	2455
IC $\bar{X}$	37.2	35.8	206	336	614	1787	2401
ECT > IC*	50/76	43/77	48/76	46/76	53/74	50/76	52/73
% Diff.†	3.6	1.8	3.2	2.6	2.7	2.1	2.2
p‡	< .01	N.S.§	< .01	< .10	< .01	< .001	< .001

* Number of littermate pairs in which the ECT value exceeds the IC value.   † Percentage by which the ECT mean exceeds the IC mean.   ‡ Probability values were determined by analyses of variance.   § N.S., not significant.

as is often done, the enriched-experience rats have lower values than the restricted animals in the cerebral cortex but higher values in the rest of the brain. The possible significance of this peculiar pattern of changes will be discussed later.

Protein may provide a better base than wet weight of tissue for measuring enzymatic activity. Total protein was determined in experiments 4, 5, and 6 of Table 1 and was found to vary directly with tissue weight, as Fig. 4 shows; therefore the measures of enzymatic activity were quite comparable whichever base was used. If anything, we have found measures *per unit of protein* to be somewhat more stable, so that the statistical significance of differences tended to be greater for this measure than for activity per unit of weight.

These differences in enzymatic activity are reliable, as is shown both by statistical analyses and by their consistency from replication to replication. The value for total acetylcholinesterase activity is greater for the ECT than for the IC groups in each of the seven experiments for total cortex (53 of 74 littermate pairs) and in six of the seven experiments for the rest of the brain (50 of 76 pairs). The chemists doing the analysis did not know to which group any animal belonged.

There still remain certain questions of validity: Is it certain that the changes we measure reliably are changes of acetylcholinesterase activity and that they occur in brain tissue rather than in the blood content of the brain? Certain possible interpretations that call the validity of our measures into question have been ruled out by further tests that we have made:

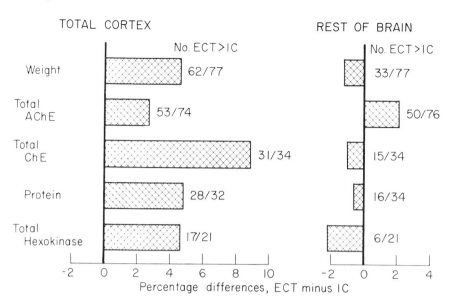

FIGURE 4 *Relative differences between enriched-experience (ECT) and restricted (IC) groups on several cerebral measures. Each difference is expressed as a percentage of the IC value. For each measure, the number of littermate pairs in which the ECT value exceeded the IC value is also given. In the cortex, the ECT-IC difference in acetylcholinesterase is less than that for tissue weight, the difference in cholinesterase is greater, and the difference in protein and hexokinase are almost identical to the weight difference. In the rest of the brain, only acetylcholinesterase is greater for the enriched-experience than for the restricted animals; all other measures show the ECT animals lower than the IC animals, and by roughly equal percentages. The figure is based entirely upon males of the Berkeley S_1 line.*

1. Acetylcholine can be split in the brain not only by the specific enzyme acetylcholinesterase, but also by a less specific enzyme, cholinesterase (16). Since our usual measure includes all enzymatic activity that hydrolyzes acetylcholine, the effects so far reported might be due in whole or in part to changes in cholinesterase rather than acetylcholinesterase activity. In recent experiments with S_1 rats we have explicity investigated this question. The results demonstrate that with our current methods, which employ acetylthiocholine as the substrate, at least 95 percent of the enzymatic activity measured in the rat brain is due to acetylcholinesterase and at least 90 percent of the changes reported here are due to acetylcholinesterase.

2. Our anatomical investigation has shown that the mean diameter of capillaries is greater in the cortices of enriched-experience animals than in those of their littermates (12). Since red blood cells contain acetylcholinesterase and blood serum contains cholinesterase, this raises the possibility that the increases in activities of the two enzymes in the cortex might only reflect increased blood content. We have investigated this possibility and have found that the activities per unit weight of these enzymes

in blood are on the order of one-sixth of the values for cortical tissue. Thus, even if the entire increase in cortical weight were to be attributed to increased blood volume, the enzymes in the blood could not account for the observed changes.

ARE THE EFFECTS DUE TO VARIABLES OTHER THAN ENRICHED EXPERIENCE?

Let us now consider whether it is indeed enriched experience that is responsible for the changes in cerebral weight and acetylcholinesterase activity or whether other aspects of the behavioral conditions may bring about these effects. Three possible alternative explanations have been subjected to experimental tests:

1. Since the animals in the condition of environmental complexity and training receive more handling and are more active than the animals in isolation, can these components alone produce cerebral effects similar to those we have described?

2. May the differences between the groups be attributed chiefly to the isolation to which the restricted animals are subjected?

3. May the cerebral differences be due simply to alterations induced in the rate of early development by differential experience?

These questions will be taken up in turn in the next three sections.

POSSIBLE CEREBRAL EFFECTS OF HANDLING OR DIFFERENTIAL LOCOMOTION

Since handling has been shown to affect both physiological variables and later learning in the rat, we designed an experiment to look for possible cerebral effects of handling. Twenty-four animals were taken from their cages and handled daily, 12 for 30 days and 12 for 60 days, while littermates were never removed from their cages. This treatment started at weaning in order to provide a control for our previous studies. The results yielded no indication of cerebral changes with handling.

To control for differential locomotion, we ran two experiments in each of which some rats had free access to activity wheels while their littermates did not. No consistent differences were found between the active and inactive groups.

Recently, we ran another experiment in which rats of one group were handled daily and also had free access to activity wheels, while their littermates had neither of these forms of stimulation. Again, 80 days of this differential treatment did not produce significant cerebral differences between the groups. It is clear that neither differential handling, nor locomotion, nor the combination of both treatments can produce the cerebral changes we are considering.

IS ISOLATION STRESS THE CAUSE OF OUR EFFECTS?

Isolation has been reported to be stressful for rats, making them so aggressive that they cannot be handled with bare hands, producing caudal dermatitis, and making them much more susceptible to a toxic agent, iso-prenaline (17). It is, therefore, possible that the differences we observed were due primarily to the deleterious effects of isolation stress on the restricted group. We doubt this interpretation for the following two reasons.

First, animals of our lines do not show the obvious signs of isolation stress described above. When isolated for 80 or even 160 days, they can still be picked up with bare hands for their occasional weighings, and they do not develop caudal dermatitis. The adrenals were weighed in some experiments, and those of the isolates were not enlarged. It may be that some strains are stressed severely by isolation while others are not.

Second, evidence comes from the last three of the seven experiments with S_1 rats; in these experiments we also included a colony or Social Control (SC) group in which animals were housed three to a cage. The results permit us to measure the effects of increasing or restricting experience, using the SC condition as a baseline (see Fig. 5). On every measure except weight of subcortex, the ECT group differed significantly from the SC group and differed further from them than did the IC group. Thus

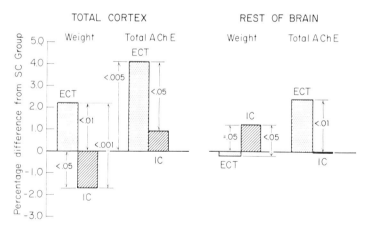

FIGURE 5 *Cerebral values of enriched-environment (ECT) and isolated (IC) groups, given in relation to the baseline of the standard colony (SC) group. In each case, the difference from the SC value is expressed as a percentage of the SC value. Where differences are significant, the p values are shown by the figures on the arrows. Thus, in weight of total cortex, the ECT animals were 2.2 percent heavier than the SC animals (p < .01), and the IC animals were 1.6 percent lighter than SC baseline (p < .05). The data were obtained in three experiments involving 34 sets of male triplets of the S_1 line. The rats were in the differential environment from the age of 25 days to the age of 105 days.*

the bulk of the effects on cerebral weight and acetylcholinesterase activity is due to enriching rather than to restricting the experience of our colony animals (18). Similar findings for older animals will be reported in the next section.

ARE CEREBRAL CHANGES CONFINED TO YOUNG ANIMALS?

The experiments described to this point have all been done with animals put into the differential environments at weaning, when they were about 25 days old, and maintained there until the age of about 105 days. During this period, colony animals show an increase of about 30 percent in total brain weight. To test the possibility that the complex environment and training simply accelerated the development of the normally rapidly growing young brain, we ran two successive experiments with older S_1 rats, employing 12 sets of male triplets in each experiment (19). One animal in each litter was assigned to the ECT condition, one to the SC condition, and one to the isolation condition. The animals were taken from the colony at about 105 days of age, the age at which the younger animals had been killed. At about 70 days rats are sexually mature, and during the 80-day period following 105 days of age, growth of total brain weight of rats in the colony is only about 6 percent—as contrasted with 30 percent in the preceding 80-day period.

The results for older animals, shown in Fig. 6, are seen to be rather similar to those for younger animals (Fig. 5). In Fig. 6, the ECT animals

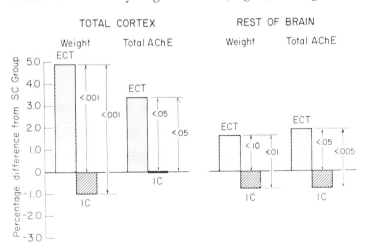

FIGURE 6 *Comparisons among brain values of littermate rats maintained in the ECT, SC, or IC conditions from 105 to 185 days of age. The same conventions are followed as in Fig. 5. Thus, in weight of total cortex, the ECT animals were 4.9 percent heavier than the SC group (p < .001) and the IC animals were 1.0 percent lighter than the SC animals (nonsignificant). The data were obtained in two experiments including 24 sets of male triplets of the S_1 line.*

Table 4. Weights of brain regions from 24 littermate pairs of S₁ rats in ECT and IC conditions from 105 to 185 days of age (two experiments combined)

| | Weight (mg) | | | | | | |
| | Cortex | | | | | | |
Statistic	Visual sample	Somesthetic sample	Remaining dorsal	Ventral	Total	Rest of brain	Total brain
ECT $\bar{X}$	72.6	52.9	280	338	744	1019	1763
IC $\bar{X}$	65.6	51.7	266	319	702	995	1697
ECT > IC*	20.5/24	12/24	17/24	18/24	22/24	17/24	17/24
% Diff.†	10.7	2.3	5.4	6.0	5.9	2.4	3.9
p‡	<.001	N.S.	<.005	<.001	<.001	<.01	<.001

* Number of littermate pairs in which the ECT value exceeds the IC value.   † Percentage by which the ECT mean exceeds the IC mean.   ‡ Probability values were determined by Duncan's new multiple range test, since the analysis of variance included the SC group.

surpass the colony controls significantly on every measure, while the IC animals do not differ significantly from the colony controls on any measure. The regional differentiation of effect among the adults, presented in Tables 4 and 5, is even sharper than that among the young animals (Tables 2 and 3). Among the adults the increases of total acetylcholinesterase approach more nearly the increases of cortical weight than was true among the young animals. At the subcortex, the adult ECT animals gain in tissue weight almost as much as they gain in total acetylcholinesterase activity, whereas the young ECT animals did not gain at all in subcortical weight.

We conclude that the adult brain shows increases in cortical weight and total acetylcholinesterase activity as readily as the young brain. The occurrence of such cerebral effects among adults supports the argument that these effects, rather than being consequences of accelerated early development, are residuals of experience.

EFFECTS ON OTHER CHEMICAL MEASURES

The pattern of change of acetylcholinesterase activity with experience differs from those of the four other chemicals that we have measured so far: cholinesterase, protein, hexokinase, and serotonin.

Cholinesterase activity was determined in the last three experiments completed with S₁ rats, and the results are given in Table 6. Total cholinesterase activity in total cortex was 8.9 percent greater in the ECT than in the IC groups. As Fig. 5 (based on the same animals) indicates, cortical weight was greater by 3.9 percent and total acetylcholinesterase activity by 3.2 percent. Thus, in terms of activity per unit of weight, cholinesterase in-

creased in the cortex while acetylcholinesterase decreased. In the rest of
the brain, however, cholinesterase activity remained essentially unchanged,
while acetylcholinesterase activity rose significantly. The different patterns
of change for tissue weight and total enzymatic activity are presented
graphically in Fig. 4. With total cholinesterase activity, in contrast to the
case for acetylcholinesterase activity, the major differences are found between the isolated and colony groups, rather than between the ECT and
colony groups (see Table 6).

Certain other chemical measures show changes similar to those of tissue
weight. We have already seen that this is true of protein. We have also
measured hexokinase activity in experiment 4 of Table 1 and in one other
experiment. This enzyme is important in the general metabolism of cells
but it does not appear to have a different function in the nervous system
from its function in other organs. Hexokinase activity per unit of weight
did not alter with differential experience in either cortex or subcortex.
A substance that has attracted a good deal of study recently with respect
to brain activity is serotonin, which some investigators believe to be a
central synaptic-transmitter agent. Gordon T. Pryor in our laboratories has
assayed serotonin in S_1 littermates exposed to the ECT or IC conditions.
While Pryor found the usual modifications of cortical weight and of acetylcholinesterase and cholinesterase activities, he was unable to find a significant difference between groups in the concentration of serotonin (see
20).

In summary, when we compare the extreme experiential groups—ECT
versus IC—the results show a clearly differentiated pattern among chemicals in the cortex. Acetylcholinesterase changes less with experience than

Table 5. Total acetylcholinesterase activity of brain regions from S_1 rats in ECT
and IC conditions from 105 to 185 days of age (two experiments combined).
Activity is expressed in moles of acetylcholine hydrolyzed per minute under our
standard assay conditions

	Activity (10^{-8} mole/min)						
	Cortex						
Statistic	Visual sample	Somes-thetic sample	Remain-ing dorsal	Ventral	Total	Rest of brain	Total brain
ECT $\bar{X}$	42.2	37.1	195	361	635	1828	2463
IC $\bar{X}$	38.5	37.0	189	349	614	1779	2392
ECT > IC*	16/24	12/24	15/24	19/24	19/24	19/24	19/24
% Diff.‡	9.6	0.3	2.9	3.4	3.4	2.8	3.0
p‡	<.001	N.S.	N.S.	N.S.	<.05	<.005	<.001

* Number of littermate pairs in which the ECT value exceeds the IC value.   † Percentage by which the ECT mean exceeds the IC mean.   ‡ Probability values were
determined by Duncan's new multiple range test.

Table 6. Total cholinesterase activity of brain regions from 34 sets of triplet S_1 rats in ECT, SC, and IC conditions from 25 to 105 days of age (three experiments combined); activity expressed in moles of butyrylthiocholine hydrolyzed per minute under our standard assay conditions

| | Activity (10^{-8} mole/min) | | | | | | |
| | Cortex | | | | | | |
Statistic	Visual sample	Somesthetic sample	Remaining dorsal	Ventral	Total	Rest of brain	Total brain
ECT $\bar{X}$	2.28	1.82	8.34	8.52	21.0	51.4	72.4
SC $\bar{X}$	2.23	1.76	8.18	8.42	20.6	51.1	71.7
IC $\bar{X}$	2.04	1.65	7.56	8.00	19.3	51.9	71.2
ECT > IC*	26/34	27/34	30/34	23/34	31/34	15/34	20/34
ECT > SC*	18/34	18/34	21/34	18/34	21/34	22/34	21/34
SC > IC*	24/34	23/34	25.5/34	24/34	28/34	13/34	19/34
% Diff., ECT-IC†	11.8	10.3	10.3	6.5	8.9	−1.0	1.7
% Diff., ECT-SC†	2.2	3.4	2.0	1.2	1.8	0.5	0.9
% Diff., SC-IC†	9.3	6.7	8.2	5.2	6.9	−1.5	0.8
p_{ECT-IC}‡	< .001	< .001	< .001	< .005	< .001	N.S.	= .05
p_{ECT-SC}‡	N.S.	< .10	N.S.	N.S.	= .10	N.S.	N.S.
p_{SC-IC}‡	< .01	< .005	< .001	< .05	< .001	N.S.	N.S.

* Number of cases in which the value of the littermate in the first condition exceeded that of the littermate in the second; for example, for the visual sample, the ECT value was greater than the IC value in 26 of the 34 littermate pairs.   † Percentage difference between means in the first and second conditions; for example, for the visual sample, the ECT mean exceeded the IC mean by 11.8 percent.   ‡ Probability values were determined by Duncan's multiple range test after analyses of variance.

does the weight of the tissue; cholinesterase changes more; and the others—protein, hexokinase, and serotonin—vary with tissue weight. The decrease in acetylcholinesterase activity per unit of cortical weight suggests that the growth of cortex with use involves especially elements low in acetylcholinesterase, such as glia, noncholinergic neurons, and blood vessels and blood volume. (Our finding of increased diameter of cortical blood vessels in ECT animals has already been cited.) The increase in cholinesterase activity per unit of cortical weight may be another indication of the growth of glia cells, since these are relatively high in cholinesterase activity. The lack of change in protein, hexokinase, and serotonin per unit of weight indicates that the additionally formed tissue is normal in its chemical endowment as far as these constituents are concerned.

GENERALITY OF EFFECTS OVER LINES

In addition to the S_1 animals, five other lines have been exposed to our standard ECT and IC conditions, and all lines have shown cerebral effects in the same directions but varying in magnitude (5, 8). The S_1 line was one of two lines showing relatively large effects, while the S_3 line was one of those showing relatively small effects. In order to determine the reliability of such genetic differences, we have performed three replications in each of which S_3 groups were run and analyzed simultaneously with S_1 groups. In all three cases, the S_1 animals showed larger effects on all measures than the S_3 animals (15). We conclude that while all lines show cerebral plasticity in response to environmental pressure, some lines are more readily modifiable than others.

BLINDNESS AND LIGHT DEPRIVATION

Further evidence of plasticity of the brain comes from experiments in which animals were blinded or totally deprived of light at about 25 days of age. The experiments continued for about 80 days. In two experiments (21) blinded animals, when compared with sighted littermates kept in the same enriched condition, showed a 5 percent loss in weight of the visual cortex and an 8 percent loss in the superior colliculi (midbrain visual reflex centers). Total acetylcholinesterase activity surprisingly increased by 4 percent in the visual cortex of the blinded rats and decreased by 21 percent in the superior colliculi. In three experiments we have found that deprivation of light in sighted animals produced anatomical and chemical effects similar in direction but generally smaller in magnitude than those following blinding (22). The results of these experiments suggest that modifying the amount of experience in one sensory modality can affect rather specifically the brain regions serving that modality. Further results suggest that impairment of one sensory channel leads to greater use of other modalities and thus to greater cerebral development ("compensation") in the corresponding brain areas. Specifically, if blinded or light-deprived animals are raised in a complex environment, the somesthetic area of the cortex shows increases in weight and total acetylcholinesterase activity, when compared with light-stimulated littermates raised in otherwise comparable environments. Results on this effect of blinding were published in 1963 (21). Since then, we have accumulated further confirmatory results on blinding, and Eleanor Saffran in our laboratories has found similar results in experiments with light deprivation.

SELECTIVE BREEDING

Darwin, as we have seen, offered evidence for brain plasticity through comparison of domestic and wild animals. It seems reasonable to suppose that the cumulative effects of generations of selection could produce large changes in the brain. In fact, a program of selection for cortical acetylcholinesterase carried out by T. H. Roderick in our laboratories has demonstrated relatively large changes in brain chemistry after six generations (23). Two foundation stocks (Castle and Dempster) were used for a simultaneous replication, and lines with both high and low acetylcholinesterase activity were selected from each stock. The Roderick Castle high and low lines differed by 34 percent ($p < .0005$) in acetylcholinesterase activity per unit of cortical weight, and the Roderick Dempster lines differed by 25 percent ($p < .0005$). These differences are several times larger than those that we have been able to produce by differential experience.

POSSIBLE FUNCTIONAL SIGNIFICANCE

We believe it essential now to extend our knowledge of cerebral changes with experience in order to determine what significance they may have for physiological theories of learning and memory. Further characterization of the effects is being pursued both chemically and anatomically. Ribonucleic acids, various brain lipids, the synaptic-transmitter acetylcholine, and other possible neural transmitters and their related enzymes will be assayed to determine whether their concentrations or activities are affected by differential experience. Anatomically, we are extending our measures to include ramification of neuronal processes, vascularization, skull volume and dimensions, the sizes of cell bodies and of nuclei of both glia and neurons, and the ratio of glial to neuronal number. We do not want to overlook the possible participation of glial cells in cerebral changes because of our preoccupation with neural cells.

It may seem premature to attempt to assess the possible functional significance of cerebral modifications already observed while we are still attempting to extend our knowledge of them, but neither we nor our readers can avoid making at least a preliminary assessment.

For purposes of discussion let us consider whether our findings are compatible with the hypothesis that long-term memory storage involves the formation of new synaptic connections among neurons. This was Ramón y Cajal's suggestion in the 1890's. It would appear from a number of considerations that the magnitude and nature of the observed effects are such as to accommodate a substantial increase in synaptic connections. Synaptic sites are known to be especially rich in acetylcholinesterase. An increase in number of functional synapses could, however, very well be many times greater than the concurrent increases in acetylcholinesterase activity and tissue weight. Thus, for example, Eayrs (24) reports that the number of interconnections per cortical neuron in the rat increases by about 400 percent between the ages of 15 and 36 days; meanwhile the cortex, according to data from our animals, is increasing in weight by only about 50 percent and in total acetylcholinesterase activity by only about 100 percent. These relations suggest the possibility that a 5-percent change in total acetylcholinesterase activity may reflect a 20-percent change in the number of synapses. A more direct test of this possibility may come from our attempts to measure neuronal ramifications.

Whatever the cerebral residuals of experience are, it is unlikely that they will involve large changes of either gross anatomy or chemistry. It is characteristic of the brain that its variability is extremely low. Weight of the brain varies less from individual to individual of a species than the weight of almost any other organ, and we have found the coefficients of variation for acetylcholinesterase activity to be almost as small as those for weight (25). Brain values can be modified by genetic selection, as we have seen, and drastic treatments such as thyroidectomy or prolonged undernourishment can alter the brain substantially. Short of such interfering factors, the enzymes and the weight of the brain are kept within tight limits. It can therefore be seen that even modifications that seem small in absolute terms may be large in terms of ordinary variability and may have functional consequences.

CONCLUSIONS

Our observations demonstrate that rats given enriched experience develop, in comparison to restricted littermates, greater weight and thickness of cortical tissue and an increase in total acetylcholinesterase activity of the cortex, the gain in weight being relatively larger than the increase in enzymatic activity. In the rest of the brain, acetylcholinesterase activity also increases, even though tissue weight decreases with enriched experience. These changes have been produced consistently in many replications; they have appeared in each line of rats tested to date, and they are found in adult as well as young animals. Control experiments have demonstrated that these changes cannot be attributed primarily to differential handling or locomotor activity, to isolation stress of restricted animals, or to altering the rate of development of the rapidly growing young brain. In a smaller number of experiments we have also found cholinesterase activity to change more than does tissue weight in the cortex but not in the rest of the brain. Protein, hexokinase activity, and serotonin follow closely the changes in weights of brain regions.

We wish to make clear that finding these changes in the brain consequent upon experience does not prove that they have anything to do with storage of memory. The demonstration of such changes merely helps to establish the fact that the brain is responsive to environmental pressure—a fact demanded by physiological theories of learning and memory. The best present conjecture, based both on the research reported here and on that of others, is that when the final story of the role of the brain in learning and memory is written, it will be written in terms of both chemistry and anatomy.

AN INVITATION

Because we believe that our findings demonstrate the feasibility of research on the effects of experience on the brain, and because we believe that such research offers many challenges and a wide field for investigation, we hope to see it taken up in other laboratories. To this purpose we offer qualified investigators animals from our special lines and complete information about our behavioral, biochemical, and anatomical procedures, either through written descriptions or by direct demonstration.

REFERENCES AND NOTES

1 J. G. Spurzheim, *The Physiognomical System of Drs. Gall and Spurzheim* (Baldwin, Cradock, and Joy, London, ed. 2, 1815), pp. 554–555.
2 C. Darwin, *The Descent of Man* (Rand, McNally, Chicago, ed. 2, 1874), p. 53.
3 S. Ramón y Cajal, *Les Nouvelles Idées sur la Structure du Système Nerveux chez l'Homme et chez les Vertébrés*, edition française revue et augmentée par l'auteur, L. Azoulay, trans. (Reinwald, Paris, 1895), p. 78.
4 W. Köhler, *The Place of Value in a World of Facts* (Liveright, New York, 1938), p. 239.
5 M. R. Rosenzweig, D. Krech, E. L. Bennett, M. C. Diamond, *J. Comp. Physiol. Psychol.* **55**, 429 (1962).
6 The collection and analysis of the data reported in this paper required the aid of chemists, anatomists, statisticians, and behavioral technicians. Among the chemists were Hiromi Morimoto, Marie Hebert, and Barbara Olton; among the anatomists, Fay Law and Helen Rhodes; among the statisticians, Carol Saslow, Bea Markowitz, and Peter Varkonyi; among the behavioral technicians, Frank Harris and Carol Poe. Roberta Robbins has been our secretary. The research has been supported by grants from the U.S. Public Health Service, the National Science Foundation, and the Surgeon General's Office. It has also been aided by the U.S. Atomic Energy Commission.
7 M. R. Rosenzweig, D. Krech, E. L. Bennett, *Psychol. Bull.* **57**, 476 (1960).
8 D. Krech, M. R. Rosenzweig, E. L. Bennett, *J. Comp. Physiol. Psychol.* **53**, 509 (1960).
9 The three conditions are described more fully in several of our reports: (8) and M. R. Rosenzweig, D. Krech. E. L. Bennett, in *Current Trends in Psychological Theory* (Univ. of Pittsburgh Press, Pittsburgh, 1961), p. 87.
10 I. Krechevsky, *J. Comp. Psychol.* **19**, 425 (1935). C. N. Woolsey and D. H. Le Messurier, *Federation Proc.* **7**, 137 (1948); J. P. Zubek, *J. Comp. Physiol. Psychol.* **44**, 339 (1951).
11 The automatic titrator method is described by M. R. Rosenzweig, D. Krech, E. L. Bennett, in a Ciba Foundation Symposium, *Neurological Basis of Behaviour* (Churchill, London, 1958), p. 337. The colorimetric method was adapted from G. L. Ellman, K. D. Courtney, V. N. Andres, Jr., R. M. Featherstone, *Biochem. Pharmacol.* **7**, 88 (1961).
12 M. C. Diamond, D. Krech, M. R. Rosenzweig, *J. Comp. Neurol.* **123**, 111 (1964).
13 R. C. Tryon, *Yearbook Natl. Soc. Stud. Educ.* **39**, part I, 111 (1940).
14 M. R. Rosenzweig, *Kansas Studies in Educ.* **14**, No. 3, 3 (1964).

15 M. R. Rosenzweig, E. L. Bennett, D. Krech, *Federation Proc.* **23**, 255 (1964), abstr.

16 In the past we and other investigators have called both enzymes "cholinesterase," but we are now employing the common terms recognized in the *Report of the Commission on Enzymes,* International Union of Biochemistry (Pergamon, New York, 1961).

17 T. Balazs, J. B. Murphy, H. C. Grice, *J. Pharm. Pharmacol.* **14**, 750 (1962); A. Hatch, T. Balazs, G. S. Wiberg, H. C. Grice, *Science* **142**, 507 (1963).

18 While the cerebral differences in weight and acetylcholinesterase activity occurred principally between the ECT and SC groups, these groups were almost identical in terminal body weights. The IC group, which was close to the SC group in cerebral measures, exceeded the SC group by about one-tenth in body weight.

19 M. R. Rosenzweig, E. L. Bennett, D. Krech, *J. Comp. Physiol. Psychol.* **57**, 438 (1964).

20 G. T. Pryor, unpublished doctoral dissertation (Univ. of Calif., 1964); *Univ. of Calif. Radiation Lab. Rept. No. 1179* (1964).

21 D. Krech, M. R. Rosenzweig, E. L. Bennett, *Arch. Neurol.* **8**, 403 (1963).

22 E. L. Bennett, M. R. Rosenzweig, D. Krech, *Federation Proc.* **23**, 384 (1964), abstr.

23 T. H. Roderick, *Genetics* **45**, 1123 (1960).

24 J. T. Eayrs, in *Structure and Function of the Cerebral Cortex,* D. B. Tower and J. P. Schadé, Eds. (Elsevier, Amsterdam, 1960), p. 43.

25 E. L. Bennett, M. R. Rosenzweig, D. Krech, H. Karlsson, N. Dye, A. Ohlander, *J. Neurochem.* **3**, 144 (1958).

AUTORADIOGRAPHIC EXAMINATION OF THE EFFECTS OF ENRICHED ENVIRONMENT ON THE RATE OF GLIAL MULTIPLICATION IN THE ADULT RAT BRAIN

Joseph Altman and Gopal D. Das

MASSACHUSETTS INSTITUTE OF TECHNOLOGY

Editor's Note   *The technique of autoradiography as used here consists of injecting an animal with a radioactive form of a component chemical which will be incorporated into newly synthesized biochemicals within the animal. Later the tissue to be studied is sectioned and coated with a photographic emulsion. After an exposure period, the whole slide is developed and the regions in which the radioactivity has been incorporated into the tissue are revealed as blackened grains overlying structures which can be visualized by ordinary staining methods.*

Source   Reprinted from Nature, *1964,* 204, *1161–1163, with permission of the authors and Macmillan (Journals) Ltd.*

This pilot experiment was prompted by the results of a recent autoradiographic investigation[1] in which we injected tritiated thymidine into normal adult rats and cats and obtained evidence of the incorporation of this specific DNA precursor by the nuclei of many glia cells. This indicated that glia cells are multiplying in the normal adult brain. Recent electron microscopic and biochemical investigations have suggested that neuroglia form an insulating matrix and a sustaining medium for the neurones embedded in them, and there has been a resurgent interest in the possible role of glia cells in the organization of neural function and behaviour.[2] Is glial multiplication an aspect in the organization and re-organization of brain and behaviour? Since, through their multiplication, neuroglia could modify the electrical and chemical properties of neighbouring neurones, and through their paramount role in myelin formation they could recruit new neurones for newly organized circuits, we undertook to determine if changes occur in the rate of glial multiplication as a consequence of a sustained and radical behavioural manipulation. The procedure utilized in this work was one originally introduced by Hebb[3] in which rats are reared in "impoverished" and "enriched" environments, representing different conditions for the development of behaviour. This procedure was shown to affect the subseqeunt learning ability of animals[4,5] as well as the concentration of cholinesterase in brain structures[6,7] and the size of the cortex.[8,9]

Laboratory-bred, normally raised Long-Evans hooded rats were weaned at the age of 23–26 days. From each litter, half of the males were transferred into isolation cages 10 in. deep, 4 in. wide and 6.5 in. high, covered with opaque material on all sides except the bottom. This represented the "restricted" environment. The other half of the males, and all the females, were put into a large communal cage, 30 in. deep, 45 in. wide and 70 in. high, with a "Plexiglass" front. This latter cage, which represented the "enriched" environment, had three levels. The food trays and water bottles were initially placed at the first level which could be reached by the animals by climbing a metal strip 1 in. wide. The food trays and water bottles were gradually shifted from level to level and their position was changed every second or third day, forcing the animals to climb higher and follow varied routes to changing locations of food and water. Later, some of the metal strips forming the passageways were removed and replaced by less easily negotiable chains, then gaps were left across which the animals had to jump. In addition to this regimen, the animals, from the age of 1.5 months, were made to run 5 days every week in a motor-driven activity wheel 14 in. in diameter, the speed of which was gradually increased from 3 to 8 r.p.m. while the duration of daily running was increased from 15 min to 1 h.

At the age of about 4.5 months 3 restricted and 3 enriched rats, matched as nearly as possible for weight, were injected intraperitoneally on two successive days with 2 mc. of tritiated thymidine (specific activity 6.0 c./mmole, dissolved in 2 ml. of sterile water). After the injections the animals continued to live in their respective environments for 1 week and were then killed by cardiac perfusion with 10 per cent neutral formalin. In a similar manner 3 "restricted" and 3 "enriched" rats were injected with 2.4 mc. of tritiated leucine (specific activity 5.4 c./mmole; dissolved in 2.4 ml. of sterile isotonic saline) and killed after an exchange period of 60 min by cardiac perfusion with neutral formalin. While an attempt was made to match the restricted and enriched animals for weight, the mean body-weight of the 6 enriched rats was 5.2 per cent below the body-weight of the 6 restricted rats. In contrast, the brain-weight of the enriched rats was 9.7 per cent above the brain-weight of the restricted rats ($P < 0.01$). The fixed brains were embedded in "Paraplast" and 6-μ sections were cut serially. The deparaffinized sections from the brains of the thymidine-injected rats were stained with gallocyanin chromalum and all sections were coated in the dark by the dipping technique with NTB-3 nuclear emulsion. The coated slides were exposed for 13 weeks at 5° C and were then developed in the usual manner. In this article we shall deal essentially with autoradiographic results obtained from the animals injected with tritiated thymidine, with occasional references to findings with the animals injected with tritiated leucine.

The glial nuclei incorporating tritiated thymidine are easily recognizable by the overlying reduced silver grains (Fig. 1). Such "labelled" glial cells were identified in varied numbers in all the animals, both in white and grey matter, over the entire neuraxis. However, the frequency of labelled

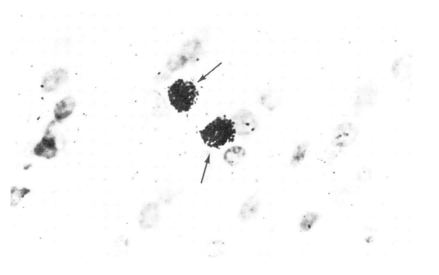

FIGURE 1 *Photomicrograph of a gallocyanin and chromalum stained autoradiogram. Arrows point to labelled glia cells in cortical radiation.*

Table 1. Mean Number of Labelled Glia Cells in Circular Areas 310μ in Diameter in the Brains of Rats reared in Enriched and Impoverished Environments

In all instances the designated structures were scanned in their entirety bilaterally.

Structure	Enriched group	Impover- ished group	% increase in enriched group	t-test P
Neocortex	0.44	0.28	59	<0.001
Amygdala and pyriform cortex	0.38	0.34	12	n.s.
"Dorsal thalamus"	0.28	0.24	17	n.s.
Hypothalamus	0.25	0.25	0	n.s.
Inferior colliculus	0.34	0.28	21	n.s.
Medulla	0.20	0.18	11	n.s.

glial cells varied over different regions. For quantitative evaluation, the number of labelled glial cells in circular areas 310μ in diameter was counted at a high magnification (500 times) over the entire surface of several brain structures. To obtain sufficient samples, some structures with identifiable components were counted as single entities (for example, "dorsal thalamus"). Table 1 gives a summary of the results, showing a significant increase in the number of labelled glial cells over the neocortex in the group of enriched rats. A trend of statistically non-significant increase was also obtained in the rhinencephalon, thalamus, inferior colliculus and medulla, with the exception of the hypothalamus in which the number of labelled cells in the enriched and impoverished animals was identical. Table 2 gives a breakdown for the neocortex at different coronal levels, indicating greater increases in some regions than others. But in all instances the increases were higher in the neocortex than in other structures.

Table 2. Mean Number of Labelled Glia Cells in Circular Areas 310μ in Diameter at Different Coronal Levels in the Neocortex

Coronal sections of neocortex at the level of:	Stereotaxic coordinate (ref. 10)	Enriched group	Impover- ished group	% in- crease in enriched group	t-test P
(a) Inferior colliculus	—	0.37	0.17	118	<0.01
(b) Oculomotor nucleus	A 1.4	0.45	0.34	32	<0.05
(c) Parafascicular nucleus	A 3.0	0.47	0.28	68	<0.10
(d) Posterior mamillary nucleus	A 3.4	0.52	0.31	68	<0.02
(e) Mediodorsal nucleus of thalamus	A 4.6	0.48	0.32	50	<0.01
(f) Paraventricular nucleus of hypothalamus	A 6.2	0.41	0.28	46	<0.10
(g) Caudate nucleus	A 9.4	0.41	0.31	32	<0.20

Table 3. Mean Area of Neocortex at Different Coronal Levels

Coronal sections of neocortex at the level of:	Stereotaxic coordinate (ref. 10)	Enriched group × 10³ square μ	Impover- ished group × 10³ square μ	% increase in enriched group	t-test P
(a) Oculomotor nucleus	A 1.4	537	477	12.58	<0.010
(b) Parafascicular nucleus	A 3.0	596	502	18.73	<0.005
(c) Posterior mamillary nucleus	A 3.4	596	544	9.56	<0.050
(d) Mediodorsal nucleus of thalamus	A 4.6	660	576	14.58	<0.005
(e) Paraventricular nucleus of hypothalamus	A 6.2	675	624	8.17	<0.005
(f) Optic chiasma	A 7.8	661	605	9.26	<0.005

In addition to an increase in labelled cells per unit area in the neocortex of enriched rats, areal measurements at 160 times magnification gave significant increases in the size of the cortex of enriched animals at all coronal levels examined (Table 3). This increase in the area of the cortex should further contribute to the absolute increase in the number of labelled glia cells. A comparison of the mean total number of labelled cells at different cortical levels is given in Table 4, which indicates a pooled increase of 75 per cent in the total number of labelled glia cells in the sampled sections of the cortex of enriched rats. The number of labelled cells given in Table 4 represents cells preparing for multiplication at the time of injection (and possibly some of their daughter cells) in an average section

Table 4. Mean Total Number of Labelled Glia Cells at Different Coronal Levels of the Neocortex

Coronal sections of neocortex at level of:	Stereotaxic coordinate (ref. 10)	Enriched group	Impover- ished group	% in- crease in enriched group	t-test P
(a) Inferior colliculus	—	57.5	23.8	142	<0.10
(b) Oculomotor nucleus	A 1.4	68.8	39.7	73	<0.001
(c) Parafascicular nucleus	A 3.0	79.7	38.8	105	<0.05
(d) Posterior mamillary nucleus	A 3.4	76.5	43.8	75	<0.005
(e) Mediodorsal nucleus of thalamus	A 4.6	83.5	47.2	69	<0.005
(f) Paraventricular nucleus of hypothalamus	A 6.2	68.5	41.3	65	<0.10
(g) Caudate nucleus	A 9.4	68.8	53.7	28	<0.30
Neocortex as a whole	—	71.9	41.2	75	<0.001

of the cortex with a nominal thickness of $1-2\mu$, which is the range of penetration of the electrons emitted by tritium into the emulsion.

We did not attempt a breakdown of the type of neuroglia cells labelled in the cortex, but it was clear from our results that the great increase in labelled cells in the cortex of enriched animals was to be attributed largely to cells situated in the cortical radiation and corpus callosum rather than the grey matter of the cortex. This observation can be interpreted in at least two ways. First, the increased labelling of cells in these fibrous structures may be a regional phenomenon, perhaps reflecting the proliferation of interfascicular glia cells. An alternative interpretation is that the labelled cells in these tracts are undifferentiated cells which are in the process of migration to undetermined cortical sites. This latter possibility was suggested by earlier histological observations of the presence of an ependymal and sub-ependymal germinal matrix in adult rats in the dorsal and lateral walls of the lateral ventricle[11-13], a finding which was confirmed more recently in colchicine-treated animals[14] and in animals injected with tritiated thymidine[15-18]. According to recent autoradiographic evidence from our laboratory (unpublished), the cells of the sub-ependymal layer of the dorsal and lateral walls of the anterior lateral ventricle are in a rapid process of turnover in young as well as adult rats. At this site the majority of labelled cells in the adult rat disappear after survival for 2 weeks, whence the labelled cells migrate to as yet undetermined sites along the cortical radiation over the wall of the caudate nucleus. Since the animals in this investigation were permitted to survive for 1 week only after injection of tritiated thymidine, the cells produced along the wall of the lateral ventricle may have been caught in their migration along the cortical tracts. If this hypothesis were correct, we could expect a more rapid depletion of labelled cells in the wall of the lateral ventricle in the enriched than in the impoverished animals. Accordingly, we counted the number of labelled cells in the dorso-lateral wall of the lateral ventricle and in the adjacent portion of the cortical radiation which is characteristically studded with dark-staining nuclei (the presumed path of migration). Supporting the hypothesis, we found a smaller proportion of labelled cells in this germinal region in the enriched animals (15.6 per cent) than in the impoverished animals (21.1 per cent), though the difference between the two groups was not statistically significant.

It could be argued that the uptake of labelled thymidine by a larger number of glia cells in the cortex of enriched animals is not due to a higher rate of cellular proliferation but to an increased availability of exogenous chemicals as a consequence of changed circulation or a modified "blood-brain barrier." This possibility is counter-indicated by our finding of an absence of increased uptake of tritiated leucine in the brain of enriched animals. Indeed, paralleling the findings of Krech et al.[6,7], preliminary evaluation of our results indicates a decline in "protein metabolism" per unit area in the cortex of enriched rats. Our findings also confirm the report of these investigators, based on much larger samples, of an increase in the weight and the volume of the cortex in the enriched animals. The increased addition of new glia cells to the cortex might be one of the variables contributing to this increase in cortical volume, but other variables (such as increased outgrowth of neuronal processes and increased vascularization) may also be involved.

In summary, this pilot investigation brought evidence of the addition of a higher number of newly formed glia cells to the cortex of rats reared in an enriched environment than in rats reared in an impoverished milieu. A trend of less pronounced increase in labelled glia cells was also observed in most of the subcortical structures sampled, the hypothalamus excepted. Since the hypothalamus is the only structure in the series which is practically devoid of corticopetal and corticofugal fibres, the increase in the other subcortical structures may be attributed to cortical fibres passing through them. As a final point we stress that those results cannot be interpreted as representing morphological changes produced by learning. The raising of animals in an enriched environment represents a complex of behavioural and related variables, and increased opportunity for learning and for the storage of experience may or may not have been among the factors that produced the demonstrated change.

This investigation was supported by the U.S. Atomic Energy Commission.

REFERENCES

1 Altman, J., *Anat. Rec.*, **145**, 573 (1963).
2 Galambos, R., *Proc. U.S. Nat. Acad. Sci.*, **47**, 129 (1961).
3 Hebb, D., *The Organization of Behaviour*, 298 (Wiley, New York, 1949).
4 Bingham, W. E., and Griffiths, W. J., *J. Comp. Physiol. Psychol.*, **45**, 307 (1952).
5 Forgays, D. G., and Forgays, J. W., *J. Comp. Physiol. Psychol.*, **45**, 322 (1952).
6 Krech, D., Rosenzweig, M. R., and Bennett, E. L., *J. Comp. Physiol. Psychol.*, **53**, 509 (1960).
7 Krech, D., Rosenzweig, M. R., and Bennett, E. L., *J. Comp. Physiol. Psychol.*, **55**, 801 (1962).
8 Rosenzweig, M. R., Krech, D., Bennett, E. L., and Zolman, J. F., *J. Comp. Physiol. Psychol.*, **55**, 1092 (1962).
9 Diamond, M. C., Krech, D., and Rosenzweig, M. R., *J. Comp. Neurol.*, **123**, 111 (1964).
10 De Groot, J., *The Rat Forebrain in Stereotaxic Co-ordinates* (Noord-Hollandische, Amsterdam, 1959).
11 Allen, E., *J. Comp. Neurol.*, **22**, 547 (1912).
12 Jones, O. W., *Arch. Neurol. Psychiat.*, **28**, 1030 (1932).
13 Kershman, J., *Arch. Neurol. Psychiat.*, **40**, 937 (1938).
14 Bryans, W. A., *Anat. Rec.*, **133**, 65 (1959).
15 Messier, B., Leblond, C. P., and Smart, I., *Exp. Cell Res.*, **14**, 224 (1958).
16 Smart, I., *J. Comp. Neurol.*, **116**, 325 (1961).
17 Altman, J., *Anat. Rec.*, **145**, 573 (1963).
18 Altman, J., and Das, G. D., *J. Comp. Neurol.* (in the press).

DIFFERENTIAL MATURATION OF
AN ADRENAL RESPONSE TO
COLD STRESS IN RATS
MANIPULATED IN INFANCY

*Seymour Levine, Morton Alpert,
and George W. Lewis*

OHIO STATE UNIVERSITY

Source *Reprinted from the* **Journal of Comparative
and Physiological Psychology,** *1958,* **51,** *774–777, with
permission of the authors and the American Psychological Association.*

During the past several years there has been a marked resurgence of experimentation related to the effects of prior experience on adult behavior. Investigators have reported differences in adulthood in learning (1, 6, 10), emotionality (4, 6, 7, 16), and physiological resistance to stress (8, 16) as a function of experience during the preweaning and immediately postweaning periods. Although there have been numerous experiments concerning the effects of infantile (preweaning) and early (postweaning) experience on adult behavior, there has been little work concerning the effects of infantile experience on the physiological development of the infant organism.

A review of the experiments concerning infantile experience and subsequent behavior indicates that one of the major differences between Ss manipulated in infancy and nonmanipulated Ss is observed in the relative differences in emotionality of these Ss. Characteristically, rats that are left in the breeding cage and not manipulated in any manner prior to weaning show more responses associated with emotionality (defecation, freezing) in adulthood than Ss that were either shocked or picked up and placed in a small compartment once daily during the first 21 days of life. Since emotional responses are usually made to stressful situations in adulthood, the present study was designed to investigate the maturation of the physiological response of adrenal ascorbic-acid depletion to stress in infant Ss as related to prior manipulation.

Jailer (5) reported that infant rats subjected to cold stress failed to show adrenal ascorbic-acid depletion* prior to 16 days of age, when a 19% depletion was found. Infant animals as young as 4 to 8 days do show ascorbic-acid depletion to injection of ACTH and large doses of epinephrine, and to the surgical trauma of laparotomy (5, 12). One hypothesis offered to account for these results is the lack of development of the hypothalamo-hypophysial system, which appears to be essential in the reaction to certain types of stress (5). Since it has been previously suggested that infantile manipulation modifies later reactivity of the central nervous system under conditions of stress (8), it was hypothesized that manipulation in infancy would affect the rate of development and the intensity of the stress response in the infant organism.

[1] This investigation was supported by Research Grant PHS M-1630 from the National Institute of Mental Health of the National Institutes of Health, U.S. Public Health Service. The authors are indebted to Benjamin Pasamanick, Director of Research, for his assistance throughout this investigation.
* Adrenal ascorbic acid depletion reflects the amount of ascorbic acid used to manufacture steroid hormones in the adrenal cortex, and thus is an indirect measure of the amount of these stress hormones which is produced. (Ed.)

METHOD

SUBJECTS

Two hundred and seventy-eight infant Sprague-Dawley Holtzman albino rats were used as Ss. The Ss came from 31 females bred in this laboratory. The experimental treatments of manipulation and nonmanipulation were assigned alternately to litters as they were born.

PROCEDURE

The Ss were run at 10, 12, 14, and 16 days of age. Half the litters within each age group were manipulated prior to the experimental day. The manipulation procedure was identical to that previously described as handling (6) and consisted of removing the pup from the nest, placing it in a 2½ by 3½ by 6-in. cardboard compartment for 3 min. and then returning it to the breeding cage. This procedure was followed once daily from Day 1 through the day prior to the experimental day for each of the age groups.

At 10, 12, 14, and 16 days approximately half the pups within each litter were randomly assigned to the stress condition. There were thus four groups at each age point: (a) manipulated, nonstressed; (b) manipulated, stressed; (c) nonmanipulated, nonstressed; and (d) nonmanipulated, stressed. The total N for each condition is presented in Table 1.

On the experimental day the nonstressed animals were removed from their cages, killed by cervical spinal separation, and weighed. Their adrenals were removed immediately, weighed on a 25-mg. Roller-Smith balance, and analyzed for ascorbic-acid content. The stressed animals were removed from their cages, placed in small individual stainless-steel compartments, and subjected to a cold stress of 5° C. for 90 min. They were then killed, and their adrenals were removed, weighed, and assayed.

Table 1. Summary Table of t Tests

Group	Condition	N	Depletion (mg. %)	S	t	p
16-Day manipulated	Stressed	15	110.1	13.0	8.47	< .005
	Nonstressed	15				
16-Day nonmanipulated	Stressed	18	68.8	9.1	7.56	< .005
	Nonstressed	17				
14-Day manipulated	Stressed	20	49.7	21.3	2.15	< .025
	Nonstressed	18				
14-Day nonmanipulated	Stressed	19	16.2	13.1	1.24	> .20
	Nonstressed	18				
12-Day manipulated	Stressed	19	47.4	20.0	2.37	< .025
	Nonstressed	20				
12-Day nonmanipulated	Stressed	19	+4.1	18.3	0.22	> .80
	Nonstressed	17				
10-Day manipulated	Stressed	16	+7.1	15.0	0.47	> .60
	Nonstressed	16				
10-Day nonmanipulated	Stressed	15	2.7	14.2	0.19	> .80
	Nonstressed	16				

Adrenal ascorbic acid was assayed by a modification of a micro technique (3). After weighing, the adrenals were placed in a 15-ml. ground-glass stoppered centrifuge tube and thoroughly ground in 2 ml. of 0.5% oxalic acid. Five milliliters of n-amyl alcohol was added to the tube followed by 3 ml. of a 4-mg.% aqueous solution of sodium 2,6-dichlorophenol indophenol dye. The tubes were then thoroughly shaken and centrifuged. The colored alcohol layer was then removed and its optical density determined on the Beckman D U spectrophotometer at a wave length of 546 mμ. The obtained optical density was then converted to micrograms of ascorbic acid by reading it on a standard curve obtained with known quantities of ascorbic acid. The obtained value was expressed as milligrams of ascorbic acid per 100 gm. of adrenal weight, or mg.%. The amount of depletion of ascorbic acid was determined by subtracting the adrenal ascorbic acid present in the stressed Ss from the mean of the nonstressed Ss.

RESULTS

The major findings are presented in Figure 1.

The animals manipulated during infancy evidenced a physiological response to cold stress earlier, and consistently to a greater extent than did the nonmanipulated animals. The manipulated animals first showed

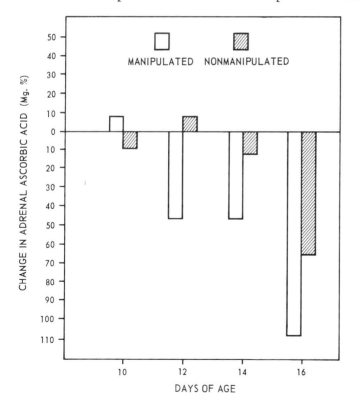

FIGURE 1 *Adrenal ascorbic-acid depletion in manipulated and nonmanipulated infant rats.*

a significant depletion in adrenal ascorbic acid at 12 days of age, whereas
the nonmanipulated animals failed to show significant depletion until 16
days of age. At 10 days, neither group showed significant depletion. At
12 days of age, the nonmanipulated Ss showed no depletion, whereas the
manipulated Ss showed a depletion of 47 mg.%. At 14 days, the nonmanipulated animals evidenced a depletion of 16 mg.% (not significantly different
from zero), while the manipulated animals showed 50 mg.% depletion.
Sixteen-day-old nonmanipulated Ss had an average depletion of 69 mg.%
whereas the manipulated Ss had a depletion of 110 mg.%, a level which
is not normally observed until adulthood (Fig. 1). Table 1 consists of
a summary of t tests between experimental and control groups at the various
age points.

DISCUSSION

The results of this experiment clearly indicate that manipulated infant
rats exhibit a physiological response to stress at an earlier age than do
nonmanipulated infants. It should be further noted that at 16 days, when
both groups exhibit significant depletion, the manipulated Ss show significantly greater depletion (9) than the nonmanipulated Ss. The 16-day nonmanipulated Ss showed 20% depletion, corresponding to the 19% depletion
obtained by Jailer for this age group, whereas the manipulated group had
a depletion of 30%. The 30% depletion exhibited by the manipulated animals
closely resembles the adult response to cold stress, which has been reported
to be between 30 and 60% depletion. It appears that manipulation during
infancy results in accelerated maturation in the systems involved in
response to cold stress, as evaluated by ascorbic-acid depletion.

It has been suggested that there exists a dual mechanism which is responsible for activation of the pituitary-adrenal system under stress. One
of these mechanisms involves blood concentration of ACTH and adrenal-
cortical hormones and is considered as a self-regulating hormonal system
(13). The other involves the response of the central and autonomic nervous
systems. For certain types of stress, such as histamine and epinephrine
injection, and laparatomy, there is evidence (2, 11) that the self-regulatory
hormonal system can operate in the absence of an intact hypothalamo-
hypophysial system. However, neurotropic stress such as restraint, intense
sound, and cold apparently do not occur unless the hypothalamo-hypophysial system is functioning. It would appear, therefore, that one of the effects
of manipulation in infancy is accelerated maturation of the systems
involved in the response to neurotropic stress. Since the exact mechanisms
involved in the response under investigation are not known, it is difficult
to implicate the exact site of action. Furthermore, this study investigated
only one response mechanism, and it is possible that many other developmental processes are affected by the manipulation procedures employed,
including that of the central nervous system. In general, the results of the

study demonstrate an interaction between experience and maturation. The extent of this interaction remains to be determined.

There are two additional points which warrant consideration. First, it should be noted that throughout this paper the term "manipulation" has been used to describe a procedure which has previously been called "handling." Since handling has been used (1, 14, 16) to describe a procedure which involves fondling, stroking, and gentling, it is necessary to distinguish between the handling procedure which involves gentling and the handling procedure which consists merely of transporting the S from one place to another. It is apparent that these different procedures differ markedly in the manner in which the S is manipulated, and there is no reason to assume at this time that the effects produced by these different procedures are the same. It is possible that subsequent research will show that the critical aspects of these procedures which result in the changes observed in adulthood and infancy might be the same, but for the present it is important, in order to avoid confusion and erroneous comparisons, to make a clear distinction between what is involved in so-called handling or gentling and what is done in what we are now calling manipulation.

Second, there has been a noticeable tendency among many investigators in this area to use the terms "early" and "infantile" experience interchangeably (14, 16). In the majority of studies in which infantile and early experience are considered as one and the same thing, the experimental treatment is not initiated until the S is weaned, approximately 21 days of age. Unlike the extremely dependent and undeveloped infant, 21-day-old rats are fully able to maintain themselves under normal laboratory conditions and are far advanced physiologically. In view of the evidence concerning critical periods in development (15), it is erroneous to assume that experimental treatments initiated during the preweaning period give rise to the same effects produced by experimental treatments given during the postweaning period. It is critical, therefore, that in the future a clear distinction be made between preweaning (infantile), postweaning (early), and other prior experiences.

SUMMARY

The present study was performed to investigate the effects of infantile manipulation upon the development of a stress response to cold as measured by adrenal ascorbic-acid depletion.

Groups of manipulated and nonmanipulated infant rats were run at 10, 12, 14, and 16 days of age. Approximately half the animals were stressed by placing them in a small compartment at a temperature of 5°C. for 90 min. The remaining nonstressed Ss were killed and their adrenals immediately assayed to determine initial adrenal ascorbic-acid levels. The adrenal ascorbic-acid content of the stressed Ss was then assayed and depletion determined.

The manipulated Ss showed significant depletion at 12, 14, and 16 days of age, whereas the nonmanipulated rats failed to show significant depletion until 16 days, a finding in line with that previously reported. In addition, at 16 days, the manipulated Ss evidenced a depletion of 110 mg.% which approximates the level normally seen in adult rats to the same stress, whereas the nonmanipulated Ss showed a depletion of 68 mg.%, a level approximating that previously reported for the 16- to 25-day-old rat. The implication of the results was discussed in terms of the effects of infantile experience on the maturation of the organism, and the possibility of a permanent alteration in stress-response reactivity was presented. In addition, the need for clarification of the term "handling" and the clear differentiation of infantile from early experience was emphasized.

REFERENCES

1 Bernstein, L. The effects of variations in handling upon learning and retention. *J. comp. physiol. Psychol.*, 1957, **50**, 162–167.

2 Fortier, C. Dual control of adrenocorticotrophin release. *Endocrinology*, 951, **49**, 782.

3 Glick, D., Alpert, M., & Stecklein, H. C. Studies in histochemistry: XXVII. The determination of L-ascorbic acid, and dehydro-L-ascorbic acid plus diketo-L-gulonic acid in microgram quantities of tissue. *J. histochem. cytochem.*, 1953, **1**, 326–335.

4 Hunt, H. F., & Otis, L. S. Restricted experience and "timidity" in the rat. *Amer. Psychologist*, 1955, **10**, 432. (Abstract)

5 Jailer, J. W. The maturation of the pituitary-adrenal axis in the new-born rat. *Endocrinology*, 1950, **46**, 420–425.

6 Levine, S. A further study of infantile handling and adult avoidance learning. *J. Pers.*, 1956, **25**, 70–80.

7 Levine, S. Infantile experience and consummatory behavior in adulthood. *J. comp. physiol. Psychol.*, 1957, **50**, 609–612.

8 Levine, S. Infantile experience and resistance to physiological stress. *Science*, 1957, **126**, 405.

9 Levine, S., Alpert, M., & Lewis, G. W. Infantile experience and maturation of the pituitary-adrenal axis. *Science*, 1957, **126**, 1347.

10 Levine, S., Chevalier, J. A., & Korchin, S. J. The effects of shock and handling in infancy on later avoidance learning. *J. Pers.*, 1956, **24**, 475–493.

11 Long, C. N. H. The role of epinephrine in the secretion of the adrenal cortex. In *Ciba colloquia on endocrinology*, Vol. IV. Boston: Little, Brown, 1952. P. 139.

12 Rinfret, A. P., and & Hane, S. Depletion of adrenal ascorbic acid following stress in the infant rat. *Endocrinology*, 1955, **56**, 341–344.

13 Sayers, G. The adrenal cortex and homeostasis. *Physiol. Rev.*, 1950, **30**, 241–320.

14 Scott, J. H. Some effects at maturity of gentling, ignoring, or shocking rats during infancy. *J. abnorm. soc. Psychol.*, 1955, **51**, 412–414.

15 Scott, J. P., & Marston, M. V. Critical periods affecting the development of normal and maladjustive social behavior of puppies. *J. genet. Psychol.*, 1950, **77**, 25–60.

16 Weininger, O. The effects of early experience on behavior and growth characteristics. *J. comp. physiol. Psychol.*, 1956, **49**, 1–9.

Psychosomatics
and Psychopathology

AVOIDANCE BEHAVIOR
AND THE DEVELOPMENT OF
GASTRODUODENAL ULCERS

Joseph V. Brady, Robert W. Porter,
Donald G. Conrad, and John W. Mason
WALTER REED ARMY INSTITUTE OF RESEARCH

Source   *Reprinted from the* **Journal of the Experimental**
Analysis of Behavior, *1958,* **1,** *(1), 69–73, with permis-*
sion of the authors and the Society for the Experimental
Analysis of Behavior, Inc.

Observations in our laboratory over the past year or more have revealed the development of extensive gastrointestinal lesions in a series of some 15 monkeys restrained in chairs and subjected to a variety of prolonged behavioral conditioning and/or intracerebral self-stimulation experiments (1). The behavioral studies focused upon emotional conditioning procedures of the "fear" or "anxiety" type, and upon avoidance of noxious electric shocks to the feet. Intracerebral self-stimulation through chronically implanted electrodes involved various limbic-system structures. While the program for each animal in this initial series varied considerably, all were subjected to intensive experimental study for at least 2 to 8 weeks. Five control monkeys, subjected only to restraint in the chair for similar periods, however, showed no gastrointestinal complications.

The present report describes the results of an experiment designed to define some of the more specific behavioral factors contributing to the etiology of this lethal pathological picture. Eight rhesus monkeys, restrained in chairs, as illustrated in Fig. 1 [omitted in reprinting] were divided into pairs and conditioned according to a "yoked-chair" avoidance procedure. Each pair of monkeys received brief electric shocks (5 milliamperes, 60-cycle AC, for 0.5 second) to the feet from a common source every 20 seconds unless the experimental animal of the pair pressed a lever which delayed the shock another 20 seconds for both animals (2). Inactivation of the lever available to the control animal insured an equal number and temporal distribution of shocks to both monkeys ("physical trauma"), while providing the avoidance contingency for only the experimental animal. Each pair of monkeys received 6-hour sessions on this procedure, alternating with 6-hour "off-periods" (no shocks) 24 hours each day for periods up to 6 or 7 weeks. A red light was illuminated in plain view of both animals during the 6-hour "avoidance" periods, and was turned out during the 6-hour off-periods. The experimental procedure was programmed and the animals' behavior recorded automatically by timers, magnetic counters, cumulative-work recorders, and associated relay circuits. Lever responses and shocks were recorded continuously for all animals, and separate counts were maintained for the avoidance periods and for the off-periods. Throughout the entire experiment, urine was collected continuously from all animals in 24- or 48-hour samples for 17-hydroxycorticosteroid determinations.

The avoidance behavior was trained initially during two preliminary daily sessions of 2 to 4 hours. The training procedure involved the use of a short 5-second interval between shocks in the absence of a lever response (the "shock-shock" or "S-S" interval) and a 20-second interval between lever responses and shocks (the "response-shock" or "R-S" interval). At the outset, a lever response by either animal of a given pair delayed the shock for both animals and no further "shaping" of the behavior was attempted. Within the first preliminary session, however, one monkey of each pair was observed to develop avoidance lever-pressing before its partner and was selected as the experimental animal. At this point in the preliminary training procedure, both the "shock-shock" and the "response-shock" intervals were set at 20 seconds and the control monkey's lever was made ineffective with respect to avoiding shocks for the remainder of the experiment.

Within a few hours after the initiation of the alternating 6-hour sessions, the experimental animals of each pair had developed stable avoidance lever-pressing rates (Fig. 2) which showed little change throughout the experiment. Responses during the 6-hour off-periods in the absence of the red light rapidly dropped to a low level, as shown in Fig. 2, and also remained there throughout the experiment. Since the lever-pressing rates for the experimental animals during the 6-hour avoidance periods approximated 15 to 20 responses per minute, the behavior effectively prevented all

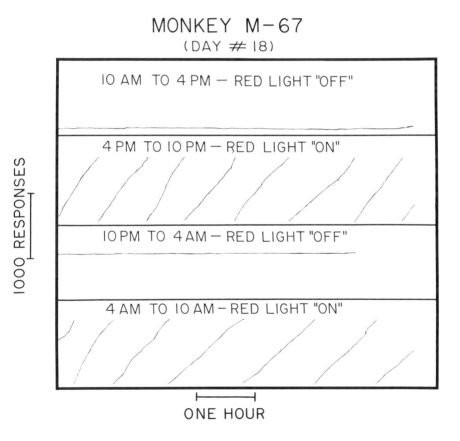

FIGURE 2 *A sample cumulative-response curve showing one 24-hour session (alternating 6-hour "on-off" cycles) for experimental "avoidance" monkey M-67 on day No. 18. The oblique "pips" on the record indicate shocks.*

but an occasional shock for both animals throughout the alternating 6-hour "on-off" cycles of any given 24-hour period. The shock rates never exceeded 2 per hour during the 6-hour avoidance periods, and typically averaged less than 1 per hour. For the most part, only somewhat variable "operant levels" of lever-pressing were maintained by the control animals of each pair, although one of these animals did appear to develop what might be termed a "superstitious avoidance" rate during the 3-week alternating procedure. From an initial rate not exceeding 1 response per hour during the first few days on the procedure, this control monkey gradually increased his output to 2 responses per minute by the 10th day, and ultimately reached a peak of 5 responses per minute on the 20th day. During the succeeding 5-day period, however, his rate again gradually declined to relatively high levels of considerably less than 1 response per minute. Throughout this entire period, the experimental animal of this pair maintained a lever-pressing response rate of almost 20 responses per minute.

Measurement of the urinary excretion of total 17-hydroxycorticosteroids (17-OH-CS) at selected stages during the experiment revealed slight increases in the 24-hour 17-OH-CS output in both monkeys of each pair during the initial phases of avoidance conditioning. Otherwise, the samples tested in subsequent phases of the experiments showed no evidence of increased adrenal cortical activity, as judged by the 24-hour 17-OH-CS excretion. Fluctuations outside the normal range which may have occurred within individual 6-hour avoidance or rest periods cannot, however, be excluded by the data on 24-hour urine portions.

With the first pair of monkeys, the death of the avoidance animal after 23 days terminated the experiment during one of the 6-hour avoidance periods. With the second pair, the avoidance monkey again expired during one of the 6-hour "on-periods," this time 25 days after the start of the experiment. With the third pair in this series, the death of the experimental animal again terminated the experiment during one of the avoidance cycles, this time only 9 days after initiation of the alternating 6-hour on-off procedure. And the experimental animal of the fourth pair of monkeys was sacrificed in a moribund condition after 48 days on the avoidance procedure. In all instances, gross and microscopic analysis revealed the presence of extensive gastrointestinal lesions with ulceration as a prominent feature of the pathological picture in the experimental animals. However, none of the control animals sacrificed for comparison with their experimental partners and subjected to complete postmortem examination, showed any indications of such gastrointestinal complications.

The results obtained with this technique, while consistent with previous reports of experimentally produced "psychosomatic" conditions (3), must be considered only as the initial findings of a programmatic effort to systematically define the variables of which this phenomenon may be a function. Follow-up studies, presently in progress, strongly suggest that selection criteria for experimental and control animals, relative degrees of "social contact" or isolation during the experiment, and possibly even constitutional factors may play a critical role in the development of gastro-intestinal pathology as a consequence of such "behavioral stress."

REFERENCES

1 Porter, R. W., Brady, J. V., Conrad, D. G., and Mason, J. W. Occurrence of gastro-intestinal lesions in behaviorally conditioned and intracerebral self-stimulated monkeys. Federation Proc., 1957, **16**, 101–102.

2 Sidman, M. Avoidance conditioning with brief shock and no exteroceptive warning signal. Science. 1953, **118**, 157–158.

3 Sawrey, W. L., Conger, J. J., and Turrell, E. S. An experimental investigation of the role of psychological factors in the production of gastric ulcers in rats. J. comp. physiol. Psychol. 1956, **49**, 457–461.

BIOCHEMICAL THEORIES
OF SCHIZOPHRENIA

Seymour S. Kety

NATIONAL INSTITUTE OF MENTAL HEALTH

Editor's Note   This article requires considerable bio-chemical background. It also departs from the general type of reading in this collection in that it is a critical review of a large number of studies rather than a report of original work. The reason for this should become obvious as the article is read. Although there has been a great deal of exciting and suggestive work done on possible biochemical bases of schizophrenia, the evidence is largely contradictory and inconclusive and it would have been impractical to reprint a sufficient number of articles to present anything approaching a balanced view of the current status of the field. Nonetheless, the questions involved are of such great interest that it would be a shame not to provide a closer look at the data than current textbooks give.

Source   Reprinted from **Science,** *June 5 and June 12, 1959,* **129,** *1528–1532 and 1590–1596, with permission of the author and the American Association for the Advancement of Science.*

PART I

The concept of a chemical etiology in schizophrenia is not new. The Hippocratic school attributed certain mental aberrations to changes in the composition of the blood and disturbances in the humors of the brain, but it was Thudichum (*1*), the founder of modern neurochemistry, who in 1884 expressed the concept most cogently: "Many forms of insanity are unquestionably the external manifestations of the effects upon the brain substance of poisons fermented within the body, just as mental aberrations accompanying chronic alcoholic intoxication are the accumulated effects of a relatively simple poison fermented out of the body. These poisons we shall, I have no doubt, be able to isolate after we know the normal chemistry to its uttermost detail. And then will come in their turn the crowning discoveries to which our efforts must ultimately be directed, namely, the discoveries of the antidotes to the poisons and to the fermenting causes and processes which produce them." In these few words were anticipated and encompassed most of the current chemical formulations regarding schizophrenia.

It may be of value to pause in the midst of the present era of psychochemical activity to ask how far we have advanced along the course plotted by Thudichum. Have we merely substituted "enzymes" for "ferments" and the names of specific agents for "poisons" without altering the completely theoretical nature of the concept? Or, on the other hand, are there some well-substantiated findings to support the prevalent belief that this old and stubborn disorder which has resisted all previous attempts to expose its etiology is about to yield its secrets to the biochemist?

An examination of the experience of another and older discipline may be of help in the design, interpretation, and evaluation of biochemical studies. The concepts of the pathology of schizophrenia have been well reviewed recently (*2*). As a result of findings of definite histological changes in the cerebral cortex of patients with schizophrenia which were described by Alzheimer at the beginning of the present century and confirmed by a number of others, an uncritical enthusiasm for the theory of a pathological lesion in this disease developed, and this enthusiasm penetrated the thinking of Kraepelin and Bleuler and persisted for 25 years. This was followed by a period of questioning which led to the design and execution of more critically controlled studies and, eventually, to the present consensus that a pathological lesion characteristic of schizophrenia or any of its subgroups remains to be demonstrated.

Earlier biochemical theories and findings related to schizophrenia have been reviewed by a number of authors, of whom McFarland and Goldstein (*3*), Keup (*4*), and Richter (*5*) may be mentioned (*6*). Horwitt and others (7–9) have pointed out some of the difficulties of crucial research in this area. It is the purpose of this review to describe the biochemical trends in schizophrenia research of the past few years, to discuss current theories, and to examine the evidence which has been used to support them.

SOURCES OF ERROR

Because of the chronicity of the disease, the prolonged periods of institutionalization associated with its management, and the comparatively few objective criteria available for its diagnosis and the evaluation of its progress, schizophrenia presents to the investigator a large number of variables and sources of error which he must recognize and attempt to control before he may attribute to any of his findings a primary or characteristic significance.

Despite the phenomenological similarities which permitted the concept of schizophrenia as a fairly well defined symptom complex to emerge, there is little evidence that all of its forms have a common etiology or pathogenesis. The likelihood that one is dealing with a number of different disorders with a common symptomatology must be recognized and included in one's experimental design (8, 10, 11). Errors involved in sampling from heterogeneous populations may help to explain the high frequency with which findings of one group fail to be confirmed by those of another. Recognition that any sample of schizophrenics is probably a heterogeneous one would seem to indicate the importance of analyzing data not only for mean values but also for significant deviations of individual values from group values. The biochemical characteristics of phenylketonuria would hardly have been detected in an average value for phenylalanine levels in blood in a large group of mentally retarded patients.

Most biochemical research in schizophrenia has been carried out in patients with a long history of hospitalization in institutions where overcrowding is difficult to avoid and where hygienic standards cannot always be maintained. It is easy to imagine how chronic infections, especially of the digestive tract, might spread among such patients. The presence of amebiasis in a majority of the patients at one large institution has been reported (12), and one wonders how often this condition or a former infectious hepatitis has caused the various disturbances in hepatic function found in schizophrenia. Even in the absence of previous or current infection, the development of a characteristic pattern of intestinal flora in a population of schizophrenic patients living together for long periods and fed from the same kitchen is a possibility which cannot be dismissed in interpreting what appear to be deviant metabolic pathways.

In variety and quality the diet of the institutionalized schizophrenic is rarely comparable to that of the nonhospitalized normal control. Whatever homeostatic function the process of free dietary selection may serve is often lost between the rigors of the kitchen or the budget and the over-riding emotional or obsessive features of the disease. In the case of the "acute" schizophrenic, the weeks and months of emotional turmoil which precede recognition and diagnosis of the disease are hardly conducive to a normal dietary intake. Kelsey, Gullock, and Kelsey (13) confirmed findings of certain abnormalities in thyroid function previously reported in schizophrenia and showed that in their patients these abnormalities resulted from a dietary deficiency of iodine, correctable by the introduction of iodized salt into the hospital diet. It is not surprising that a dietary vitamin deficiency has been found to explain at least two of the biochemical abnormalities recently attributed to schizophrenia (9, 14–16). It is more surprising that the vitamins and other dietary constituents, whose role in metabolism has become so clearly established, should so often be relegated to a position of unimportance in consideration of the intermediary metabolism of schizophrenics. Horwitt (17) has found signs of liver dysfunction during ingestion of a diet containing borderline levels of protein, while nonspecific vitamin therapy accompanied by a high protein and carbohydrate diet has been reported to reverse the impairment of hepatic function in schizophrenic patients (18).

Another incidental factor which sets the schizophrenic apart from the normal control is the long list of therapies to which he may have been exposed. Hypnotic and ataractic drugs and their metabolic products or effects produce changes which have sometimes been attributed to the disease. Less obvious is the possibility of residual electrophysiological or biochemical changes resulting from repeated electroshock or insulin coma.

Emotional stress is known to cause profound changes in man—in adrenocortical and thyroid function (19), in the excretion of epinephrine and norepinephrine (20), and in the excretion of water, electrolytes, or creatinine (21), to mention only a few recently reported findings. Schizophrenic illness is often characterized by marked emotional disturbance even in what is called the basal state and by frequently exaggerated anxiety in response to routine and research procedures. The disturbances in behavior and activity which mark the schizophrenic process would also be expected to cause deviations from the normal in many biochemical and metabolic measures—in volume and concentration of urine, in energy and nitrogen metabolism, in the size and function of numerous organic systems. The physiological and biochemical changes which are secondary to the psychological and behavioral state of the patient are of interest in themselves, and understanding of them contributes to total understanding of the schizophrenic process; it is important, however, not to attribute to them a primary or etiological role.

An additional source of error which must be recognized is one which is common to all of science and which it is the very purpose of scientific method, tradition, and training to minimize—the subjective bias. There are reasons why this bias should operate to a greater extent in this field than in many others. Not only is the motivation heightened by the tragedy of this problem and the social implications of findings which may contribute to its solution, but the measurements themselves, especially of the changes in mental state or behavior, are so highly subjective, and the symptoms are so variable and so responsive to nonspecific factors in the milieu, that only the most scrupulous attention to controlled design will permit the conclusion that a drug, or a diet, or a protein fraction of the blood, or an extract of the brain is capable of causing or ameliorating some of the manifestations of the disease. This is not to suggest that the results of purely chemical determinations are immune to subjective bias; the same vigilance is required there to prevent the hypothesis from contaminating the data. In a field with as many variables as this one, it is difficult to avoid the subconscious tendency to reject for good reason data which weaken a hypothesis while uncritically accepting those data which strengthen it. Carefully controlled and "double blind" experimental designs which are becoming more widely utilized in this area can help to minimize this bias.

Obvious as many of these sources of error are, it is expensive and difficult, if not impossible, to prevent some of them from affecting results obtained in this field, especially in the preliminary testing of interesting hypotheses. It is in the interpretation of these results, however, and in the formulating of conclusions, that the investigator has the opportunity, and indeed the responsibility, to recognize and evaluate his uncontrolled variables rather than to ignore them, for no one knows better than the investigator himself the possible sources of error in his particular experiment. There are enough unknowns in our guessing game with nature to make it unnecessary for us to indulge in such a sport with one another.

SCHIZOPHRENIA PROGRAM OF THE LABORATORY OF CLINICAL SCIENCE

Since 1956, the Laboratory of Clinical Science of the National Institute of Mental Health has been developing and pursuing a program of biological research in schizophrenia designed to minimize many of the sources of error discussed above while increasing the opportunity to detect, and to correlate with psychiatric and behavioral information, true biological characteristics if they exist. One of the wards houses a group of approximately 14 clearly diagnosed schizophrenic patients, representative of as many clinical subgroups as possible, chosen from a patient population of 14,000. In selecting these patients an attempt was made to minimize the variables of age, sex, race, and physical illness and, on the basis of careful family surveys, to maximize the likelihood of including within the group individuals representative of whatever genetic subgroups of the disease may exist (10). These patients are maintained for an indefinite period of time on a good diet, receiving excellent hygienic, nursing, medical, and psychiatric care. Each patient receives a careful and sophisticated psychiatric and genealogical characterization, and detailed daily records are kept on his psychiatric and behavioral status; these, it is hoped, will be of value in a more complete interpretation of biological findings. No specific therapy is employed or even found to be necessary, and drugs or dietary changes are introduced only for research purposes and for short periods of time. The other ward houses a comparable number of normal controls, who volunteer to remain for protracted periods of time on the same diet and in a reasonably similar milieu. We recognize, of course, that only a few of the variables are thus controlled and that any positive difference which emerges in this preliminary experiment between some or all of the schizophrenics and the normal population will have to be subjected to much more rigorous examination before its significance can be evaluated. Such reexamination has rarely been necessary, since our schizophrenic patients, individually or as a group, have shown little abnormality in the biological studies which have thus far been completed (9, 14, 22–24).

OXYGEN, CARBOHYDRATE, AND ENERGETICS

A decrease in basal metabolism was found in schizophrenia by earlier workers, although more recent work has not confirmed this (5), and theories attributing the disease to disturbances in the fundamental mechanisms of energy supply or conversion in the brain have enjoyed some popularity, but on the basis of extremely inadequate evidence, such as spectroscopic oximetry of the ear lobe or nail bed (25). Our finding of a normal rate of cerebral circulation and oxygen consumption in schizophrenic patients (26) was confirmed by Wilson, Schieve, and Scheinberg (27) and, more recently, in our laboratory by Sokoloff and his associates (28), who also found a normal rate of cerebral glucose consumption in this condition. These studies make it appear unlikely that the moderate decrease in these functions reported by Gordan and his associates (29), but only in patients with long-standing disease, is fundamental to the disease process. These studies do not, of course, rule out a highly localized change in energy metabolism somewhere in the brain, but cogent evidence for such a hypothesis has yet to be presented.

Richter (5) has pointed out the uncontrolled factors in earlier work which indicated that a defect in carbohydrate metabolism was characteristic of the schizophrenic disease process. The finding in schizophrenia of an abnormal glucose tolerance in conjunction with considerable other evidence of hepatic dysfunction (30), or evidence of an abnormally slow metabolism of lactate in the schizophrenic (31), do not completely exclude incidental hepatic disease or nutritional deficiencies as possible sources of error. Horwitt and his associates (32) were able to demonstrate and correct similar abnormalities by altering the dietary intake of the B group of vitamins.

Evidence for greater than normal anti-insulin or hyperglycemic activity in the blood or urine of a significant segment of schizophrenic patients was reported in 1942 by Meduna, Gerty, and Urse (33) and as recently as 1958 by Moya and his associates (34). Some progress has been made in concentrating or characterizing such factors in normal (35) urine as well as in urine from schizophrenics (36). Harris (37) has thrown some doubt on the importance of such anti-insulin mechanisms in the pathogenesis of schizophrenia, and it is hoped that further investigation may clarify the nature of the substance or substances involved and their relevance to schizophrenia.

Defects in oxidative phosphorylation have been thought to occur in this disease. Reports of alterations in the phosphorus metabolism of the erythrocyte (38) await further definition and independent confirmation.

Two recent reports of a more normal pattern of carbohydrate metabolism and of clinical improvement following the infusion of glutathione (39) in psychotic patients, some of whom were schizophrenic, are perhaps of interest. There is little verifiable evidence for a reduction in the blood glutathione index in schizophrenia (9); one group which has repeatedly postulated this reduction has done so on the basis of decreasingly convincing data (16, 40), while our laboratory has failed to find it at all (14), and a very recent report publishes identical figures for the schizophrenic and normal groups (41). Clinical and biochemical improvement in a variety of psychoses following glutathione infusion, even if it is accepted without the necessary controls, suggests at best that glutathione is of secondary and nonspecific import.

It is difficult for some to believe that a generalized defect in energy metabolism—a process so fundamental to every cell in the body—could be responsible for the highly specialized features of schizophrenia. On the other hand, a moderate lack of oxygen, an essential requirement of practically every tissue, produces highly selective manifestations involving especially the higher mental functions and as suggestive of schizophrenia as manifestations produced by many of the more popular hallucinogens. It may not, therefore, be completely appropriate that, in a search for biochemical factors etiologically related to schizophrenic psychoses, the center of interest today appears to have shifted to other, more specialized aspects of metabolism.

AMINO ACIDS AND AMINES

The well-controlled studies of the Gjessings (42) on nitrogen metabolism in periodic catatonia arouse considerable interest in that they suggest the possibility of a relationship between intermediary protein metabolism and schizophrenia, although earlier workers had postulated defects in amino acid metabolism in this disease (43). The hallucinogenic properties of some compounds related directly or indirectly to biological amines reawakened this interest, and the techniques of paper chromatography offered new and almost unlimited opportunity for studying the subject.

The first group to report chromatographic studies of the urine of schizophrenic and control groups found certain differences in the amino acid pattern and, in addition, the presence of certain unidentified imidazoles in the urine of schizophrenics (44). Although a normal group of comparable age was used for comparison, there is no indication of the extent to which dietary and other variables were controlled, and the authors were properly cautious in their conclusions. In a more extensive series of studies, another group has reported a significantly higher than normal concentration of aromatic compounds in the urine of schizophrenic patients (45) and has suggested that there are certain qualitative differences in the excretion of such compounds (46). Others have reported the abnormal presence of unidentified amines (47) or indoles (48), and one group has reported the absence of a normally occurring indole (49) in the urine of schizophrenic patients. In some of these studies there appears to have been no control relative to possible drug therapy or to volume or concentration of urine, and in few of them was there control of diet. There are numerous mechanisms whereby vitamin deficiencies may cause substantial changes in the complex patterns of the intermediary metabolism of amino acids. In addition, the fact that a large number of aromatic compounds in the urine have recently been shown to be of dietary origin (50) suggests the need for considerably more caution than has usually been employed in drawing conclusions with regard to this variable. Another point which has not been emphasized sufficiently is that chromatographic procedures which make possible the simultaneous determination of scores of substances, many of them unknown, require statistical analyses somewhat different from those which were developed for the testing of single, well-defined hypotheses. It is merely a restatement of statistical theory to point out that in a determination of 100 different compounds carried out simultaneously in two samples of the *same* population, five would be expected to show a difference significant at the 0.05 level! It is interesting to note that a more recent study was able to demonstrate considerably fewer differences between the urines of normal and schizophrenic populations and drew very limited and guarded conclusions (51). In our own laboratory, Mann and LaBrosse (24) undertook a search for urinary phenolic acids, in terms of quantity excreted in a standard time interval rather than in terms of concentration, which disclosed significantly higher levels of four compounds in the urine of schizophrenics than in that of the normal test subjects. These compounds were found to be known metabolites of substances in coffee, and their presence in the urine was, in fact, better correlated with the ingestion of this beverage than with schizophrenia.

The hypothesis that a disordered amino acid metabolism is a fundamental component of some forms of schizophrenia remains an attractive though fairly general one, chromatography as a means of searching for supporting evidence is convenient and valuable, and preliminary indications of differences are certainly provocative. Proof that any of these differences are characteristic of even a segment of the disease rather than artifactual or incidental has not yet been obtained.

THE EPINEPHRINE HYPOTHESIS

The theory which relates the pathogenesis of schizophrenia to faulty metabolism of epinephrine (52–54) is imaginative, ingenious, and plausible. It postulates that the symptoms of this disease are caused by the action of abnormal, hallucinogenic derivatives of epinephrine, presumably adrenochrome or adrenolutin. By including the concept of an enzymatic, possibly genetic, defect with another factor, epinephrine release, which may be activated by stressful life situations (22), it encompasses the evidence for sociological as well as constitutional factors in the etiology of the schizophrenias.

The possibility that some of the oxidation products of epinephrine are psychotomimetic received support from anecdotal reports of psychological disturbances associated with the therapeutic use of the compound, especially when it was discolored (52), and from some early experiments in which the administration of adrenochrome or adrenolutin in appreciable dosage was followed by certain unusual mental manifestations (54). A number of investigators failed to demonstrate any hallucinogenic properties in adrenochrome (55), and the original authors were not always able to confirm their earlier results.

Meanwhile, reports were emerging from the group at Tulane University, suggesting a gross disturbance in epinephrine metabolism in schizophrenic patients. Five years previously, Holmberg and Laurell (56) had demonstrated a more rapid oxidation of epinephrine in vitro in the presence of pregnancy serum than with serum from the umbilical cord and had suggested that this was due to higher concentrations of ceruloplasmin in the former. There had also been a few reports of an increase in levels of this protein in the blood of schizophrenics. Leach and Heath (57) reported a striking acceleration in the in vitro oxidation of epinephrine in the presence of plasma from schizophrenic patients as compared with that from normal subjects and shortly thereafter implicated ceruloplasmin or some variant of ceruloplasmin as the oxidizing substance (58). Hoffer and Kenyon (59) promptly reported evidence that the substance formed from epinephrine by blood serum in vitro was adrenolutin and pointed out how this strengthened the epinephrine hypothesis.

All of the evidence does not, however, support the epinephrine theory. In the past few years the major metabolites of epinephrine have been identified: 3-methoxy-4-hydroxymandelic acid, by Armstrong and his associates (60), and its precursor, metanephrine, by Axelrod and his coworkers of this laboratory (61), where, in addition, the principal pathways of epinephrine metabolism in animals (62) and man (63) have been demonstrated. The metabolites of C^{14}-labeled epinephrine in the urine of schizo-phrenic patients (64) and in normal man (65) have been studied inde-pendently by others. No evidence has been found for the oxidation of epinephrine via adrenochrome and adrenolutin in any of these populations. Although it has been reported that there are appreciable amounts of adrenochrome in the blood of normal subjects and that these amounts increase considerably following administration of lysergic acid diethylamide (66), Szara, Axelrod, and Perlin, using techniques of high sensitivity, have been unable to detect adrenochrome in the blood of normal test subjects or in that of acute or chronic schizophrenic patients (22). In a recent ingenious study of the rate of destruction of epinephrine in vivo, no differ-ence between normal subjects and schizophrenic patients was found in this regard (67). Finally, it has been shown, by McDonald (9) in our laboratory and by members of the Tulane group themselves (16), that the low level of ascorbic acid in the blood is an important and uncontrolled variable in the rapid in vitro oxidation of epinephrine by plasma from schizophrenic patients. The fact that McDonald has been able to produce wide fluctuations in the epinephrine oxidation phenomenon, from normal to highly abnormal rates, in both normal subjects and schizophrenics merely by altering the level of ascorbic acid in the blood by dietary means, and that this has had no effect on the mental processes of either group, is quite convincing evidence of the dietary and secondary nature of the phenomenon.

It should be pointed out that none of this negative evidence invalidates the theory that some abnormal product of epinephrine metabolism, existing somewhere in the body, produces the major symptoms of schizophrenia; it does, however, considerably weaken the evidence which has been used to support the theory. In addition, there is the bothersome observation of numerous workers (68) that the administration of epinephrine to schizo-phrenics, which, according to the theory, should aggravate the psychotic symptoms, is not accompanied by appreciably greater mental disturbance than occurs in normal subjects.

Quite recently a new report on inconstant psychotomimetic effects of epinephrine oxidation products in a small number of subjects has appeared (69), with evidence suggesting that the psychotoxic substance is neither adrenochrome nor adrenolutin, that it is active in microgram quantities, and that it is highly labile. This report, like the previous ones which de-scribed the psychotomimetic effects of epinephrine products, is highly sub-jective and incompletely controlled. Even if these conclusions are accepted, the relevance of such hallucinogens to, or their presence in, schizophrenia remains to be demonstrated.

REFERENCES AND NOTES

1 J. W. L. Thudichum, *A Treatise on the Chemical Constitution of the Brain* (Balliere, Tindall, and Cox, London, 1884).

2   G. Peters, "Dementia praecox," in *Handbuch der Speziellen Pathologischen Anatomie und Histologie*, Lubarsch, Henke, and Rössle, Eds. (Springer, Berlin, 1956), vol. 13, pt. 4, pp. 1–52; G. B. David, "The pathological anatomy of the schizophrenias," in *Schizophrenia: Somatic Aspects* (Pergamon, London, 1957), pp. 93–130; D. K. Dastur, *A.M.A. Arch. Neurol. Psychiat.* **81**, 601 (1959).

3   R. A. McFarland and H. Goldstein, *Am. J. Psychiat.* **95**, 509 (1938).

4   W. Keup, *Monatsschr. Psychiat. Neurol.* **128**, 56 (1954).

5   D. Richter, "Biochemical aspects of schizophrenia," in *Schizophrenia: Somatic Aspects* (Pergamon, London, 1957), pp. 53–75.

6   For the most recent review see J. D. Benjamin, *Psychosom. Med.* **20**, 427 (1958).

7   M. K. Horwitt, *Science* **124**, 429 (1956).

8   E. V. Evarts, *Psychiat. Research Repts.* **9**, 52 (1958).

9   R. K. McDonald, *J. Chronic Diseases* **8**, 366 (1958).

10 S. Perlin and A. R. Lee, *Am. J. Psychiat.*, in press.

11 D. A. Freedman, *Diseases of Nervous System* **19**, 108 (1958).

12 P. Vestergaard, M. T. Abbott, N. S. Kline, A. M. Stanley, *J. Clin. Exptl. Psychopathol.* **19**, 44 (1958).

13 F. O. Kelsey, A. H. Gullock, F. E. Kelsey, *A.M.A. Arch. Neurol. Psychiat.* **77**, 543 (1957).

14 R. K. McDonald, "Plasma ceruloplasmin and ascorbic acid levels in schizophrenia," paper presented at the annual meeting of the American Psychiatric Association, Chicago, Ill., 1957.

15 M. H. Aprison and H. J. Grosz, *A.M.A. Arch. Neurol. Psychiat.* **79**, 575 (1958).

16 C. Angel, B. E. Leach, S. Martens, M. Cohen, R. G. Heath, *ibid.* **78**, 500 (1957).

17 M. K. Horwitt, "Report of Elgin Project No. 3 with Emphasis on Liver Dysfunction," *Nutrition Symposium Ser. No. 7* (National Vitamin Foundation, New York, 1953), pp. 67–83.

18 R. Fischer, F. Georgi, R. Weber, R. M. Piaget, *Schweiz. med. Wochschr.* **80**, 129 (1950).

19 F. Board, H. Persky, D. A. Hamburg, *Psychosom. Med.* **18**, 324 (1956).

20 R. Elmadjian, J. M. Hope, E. T. Lamson, *J. Clin. Endocrinol. and Metabolism* **17**, 608 (1957).

21 W. W. Schottstaedt, W. J. Grace, H. G. Wolff, *J. Psychosom. Research* **1**, 147 (1956); *ibid.* **1**, 292 (1956).

22 S. Szara, J. Axelrod, S. Perlin, *Am. J. Psychiat.* **115**, 162 (1958).

23 I. J. Kopin, *Science* **129**, 835 (1959); C. Kornetsky, personal communication.

24 J. D. Mann and E. H. Labrosse, *A.M.A. Arch. Genl. Psychiat.*, in press.

25 J. W. Lovett Doust, *J. Mental Sci.* **98**, 143 (1952).

26 S. S. Kety, R. B. Woodford, M. H. Harmel, F. A. Freyhan, K. E. Appel, C. F. Schmidt, *Am. J. Psychiat.* **104**, 765 (1948).

27 W. P. Wilson, J. F. Schieve, P. Scheinberg, *A.M.A. Arch. Neurol. Psychiat.* **68**, 651 (1952).

28 L. Sokoloff, S. Perlin, C. Kornetsky, S. S. Kety, *Ann. N.Y. Acad. Sci.* **66**, 468 (1957).

29 G S. Gordan, F. M. Estess, J. E. Adams, K. M. Bowman, A. Simon, *A.M.A. Arch. Neurol. Psychiat.* **73**, 544 (1955).

30 V. Longo, G. A. Buscaino, F. D'Andrea, A. Uras, E. Ferrari, F. Rinaldi, F. Pasolini, *Acta Neurol.* (*Naples*) Quad. III, **21** (1953).

31 M. D. Altschule, D. H. Henneman, P. Holliday, R. M. Goncz, *A.M.A. Arch. Internal Med.* **98**, 35 (1956).

32 M. K. Horwitt, E. Liebert, O. Kreisler, P. Wittman, *Bull. Natl. Research Council* (*U.S.*) *No. 116* (1948).

33 L. J. Meduna, F. J. Gerty, V. G. Urse, *A.M.A. Arch. Neurol. Psychiat.* **47**, 38 (1942).

34 F. Moya, J. Dewar, M. MacIntosh, S. Hirsch, R. Townsend, *Can. J. Biochem. and Physiol.* 36, 505 (1958).

35 F. Moya, J. C. Szerb, M. MacIntosh, *ibid.* 34, 563 (1956).

36 M. S. Morgan and F. J. Pilgrim, *Proc. Soc. Exptl. Biol. Med.* 79, 106 (1952).

37 M. M. Harris, *A.M.A. Arch. Neurol. Psychiat.* 48, 761 (1942).

38 I. Boszormenyi-Nagy, F. J. Gerty, J. Kueber, *J. Nervous Mental Disease* 124, 413 (1956); I. Boszormenyi-Nagy and F. J. Gerty, *ibid.* 121, 53 (1955).

39 M. D. Altschule, D. H. Henneman, P. D. Holliday, R. M. Goncz, *A.M.A. Arch. Internal Med.* 99, 22 (1957); M. P. Surikov, G. K. Ushakov, B. N. Il'ina, A. A. Verbliunskaia, L. K. Khokhlov, *Zhur. Nevropatol.* 57, 237 (1957).

40 S. Martens, B. E. Leach, R. G. Heath, M. Cohen, *A.M.A. Arch. Neurol. Psychiat.* 76, 630 (1956).

41 A. J. Barak, F. L. Humoller, J. D. Stevens, *ibid.* 80, 237 (1958).

42 R. Gjessing, *J. Mental Sci.* 84, 608 (1938). ———, *Arch. Psychiat. Nervenkrankh.* 108, 525 (1939); L. Gjessing, A. Bernhardsen, H. Frøshaug, *J. Mental Sci.* 104, 188 (1958).

43 V. M. Buscaino, *Acta Neurol. (Naples)* 13, 1 (1958).

44 H. K. Young, H. K. Berry, E. Beerstecher, *Univ. Texas Publ. No. 5109* (1951), pp. 189–197.

45 P. L. McGeer, F. E. McNair, E. G. McGeer, W. C. Gibson, *J. Nervous Mental Disease* 125, 166 (1957).

46 E. G. McGeer, W. T. Brown, P. L. McGeer, *ibid.* 125, 176 (1957).

47 F. Georgi, C. G. Honegger, D. Jordan, H. P. Rieder, M. Rottenberg, *Klin. Wochschr.* 34, 799 (1956).

48 L. M. Riegelhaupt, *J. Nervous Mental Disease* 123, 383 (1956).

49 E. J. Cafruny and E. F. Domino, *A.M.A. Arch. Neurol. Psychiat.* 79, 336 (1958).

50 M. D. Armstrong and K. N. F. Shaw, *J. Biol. Chem.* 225, 269 (1956); ———, M. J. Gortatowski, H. Singer, *ibid.* 232, 17 (1958); M. D. Armstrong, P. E. Wall, V. J. Parker, *ibid.* 218, 921 (1956); A. N. Booth, O. H. Emerson, F. T. Jones, F. Deeds, *ibid.* 229, 51 (1957); T. P. Waalkes, A. Sjoerdsma, C. R. Creveling, H. Weissbach, S. Udenfriend, *Science* 127, 648 (1958).

51 R. M. Acheson, R. M. Paul, R. V. Tomlinson, *Can. J. Biochem. Physiol.* 36, 295 (1958).

52 H. Osmond, *Diseases of Nervous System* 16, 101 (1955).

53 ——— and J. Smythies, *J. Mental Sci.* 98, 309 (1952); A. Hoffer, *J. Clin. Exptl. Psychopathol.* 18, 27 (1957).

54 A. Hoffer, H. Osmond, J. Smythies, *J. Mental Sci.* 100, 29 (1954).

55 M. Rinkel and H. C. Solomon, *J. Clin. Exptl. Psychopathol.* 18, 323 (1957).

56 C. G. Holmberg and C. B. Laurell, *Scand. J. Clin. & Lab. Invest.* 3, 103 (1951).

57 B. E. Leach and R. G. Heath, *A.M.A. Arch. Neurol. Psychiat.* 76, 444 (1956).

58 B. E. Leach, M. Cohen, R. G. Heath, S. Martens, *ibid.* 76, 635 (1956).

59 A. Hoffer and M. Kenyon, *ibid.* 77, 437 (1957).

60 M. D. Armstrong, A. McMillan, K. N. F. Shaw, *Biochim. et Biophys. Acta* 25, 422 (1957).

61 J. Axelrod and R. Tomchick, *J. Biol. Chem.* 233, 702 (1958).

62 J. Axelrod, S. Senoh, B. Witkop, *ibid.* 233, 697 (1958).

63 E. H. Labrosse, J. Axelrod, S. S. Kety, *Science* 128, 593 (1958).

64 O. Resnick, J. M. Wolfe, H. Freeman, F. Elmadjian, *ibid.* 127, 1116 (1958).

65 N. Kirshner, McC. Goodall, L. Rosen, *Proc. Soc. Exptl. Biol. Med.* 98, 627 (1958).

66 A. Hoffer, *Am. J. Psychiat.* 114, 752 (1958).

67 B. Holland, G. Cohen, M. Goldenberg, J. Sha, L. Leifer, *Federation Proc.* 17, 378 (1958).

68 E. Lindemann, *Am. J. Psychiat.* 91, 983 (1935); R. G. Heath, B. E. Leach, L.

W. Byers, S. Martens, C. A. Feigley, *ibid*. **114**, 683 (1958); J. B. Dynes and
H. Tod, *J. Neurol. Psychiat.* **3**, 1 (1940); and workers in this laboratory.
69 G. Taubmann and H. Jantz, *Nervenarzt* **28**, 485 (1957).

PART II

In part I of this article [*Science*, **129**, 1528 (1959)], an attempt was
made to discuss the possible sources of error peculiar to biological research
in schizophrenia, including the possible heterogeneity of that symptom
complex and the presence of certain biological features—such as adventi-
tious disease, nutritional deficiencies, disturbances associated with abnormal
motor or emotional states, and changes brought about by treatment, all
of which may be said to result from the disease or from its current management rather than to be factors in its genesis. The difficulty of avoiding
subjective bias was emphasized. Some of the hypotheses relating to oxygen,
carbohydrate, and energy metabolism, to amino acid metabolism, and to
epinephrine were presented, and the existing evidence relevant to them
was discussed. Among the recent or current concepts there remain to be
discussed those concerned with ceruloplasmin, with serotonin, and with
the general genetic aspects of schizophrenic disorders.

CERULOPLASMIN AND TARAXEIN

The rise and fall of interest in ceruloplasmin as a biochemical factor
significantly related to schizophrenia is one of the briefest, if not one of
the most enlightening, chapters in the history of biological psychiatry. The
upsurge of interest can be ascribed to a report that a young Swedish
biochemist had discovered a new test for schizophrenia. The test depended
upon the oxidation of N,N-dimethyl-*p*-phenylenediamine by ceruloplasmin
(*1, 2*). It is difficult to understand the exaggerated interest which this
report aroused, since Holmberg and Laurell (*3*) had demonstrated previously that ceruloplasmin was capable of oxidizing a number of substances,
including phenylenediamine and epinephrine, and Leach and Heath (*4*)
had already published a procedure based on epinephrine oxidation which
was equally valid as a means of distinguishing schizophrenics from normal
subjects and had identified the oxidizing substance as ceruloplasmin (*5*).
All of these observations were compatible with earlier reports in the German literature (*6*) of an increase in serum copper in schizophrenia and
with the demonstration that practically all of the serum copper was in
the form of ceruloplasmin and that the levels of this compound in blood
were elevated during pregnancy and in large number of diseases (*7,
8*). There had even been preliminary observations of an increase in blood
ceruloplasmin in schizophrenia (*8*). Following the announcement of the
Akerfeldt test, however, interest in copper and ceruloplasmin rose, and
very soon a number of investigators reported this reaction, or some modi-

fication of it, to be positive in a high percentage of schizophrenics (2, 9), although as a diagnostic test the Akerfeldt procedure was discredited because of the large number of diseases, besides schizophrenia, in which the results were positive. Both Akerfeldt and Heath recognized that ascorbic acid could inhibit the oxidation of phenylenediamine and of epinephrine, respectively, but neither felt that this was crucial to his findings, since each had satisfied himself that the feeding of large doses of ascorbic acid to the patients had not influenced the respective reactions (2). In addition, Abood (9), who used a modification of the Akerfeldt procedure which was not affected by ascorbic acid, was able to obtain a positive reaction indicating abnormally high ceruloplasmin levels in two-thirds of the more than 250 schizophrenics he had examined.

In the past 18 months there has been a remarkable decline in the interest in, and the reported levels of, ceruloplasmin in schizophrenia. In May of 1957, McDonald (10) reported his findings on three groups of schizophrenics, one group from the wards of the National Institute of Mental Health, where the patients had been maintained on a more than adequate diet, and two groups from state hospitals. He performed the Akerfeldt test and the Abood modification of it, as well as independent tests to measure ascorbic acid and copper, on these groups and on three groups of controls. In none of the schizophrenic groups was there an increase in serum copper or other evidence of increase in ceruloplasmin. In the state-hospital patients and one group of controls, however, ascorbic acid levels were low and the results of Akerfeldt tests were positive, whereas in schizophrenic patients from the National Institute of Mental Health, levels of ascorbic acid were normal and the results of Akerfeldt tests were negative. It was clear that a high ceruloplasmin level was not characteristic of schizophrenia and that a positive response to the Akerfeldt test, where it occurred, could be completely explained by a dietary insufficiency of ascorbic acid.

In findings of the Tulane group, the mean values for serum copper in schizophrenia have decreased from a high of 216 micrograms per 100 milliliters in 1956 (5) to 145 micrograms per 100 milliliters at the end of 1957 (4), mean normal values having remained at 122 and 124 micrograms per 100 milliliters during the same period. Other groups have found slight differences or no differences at all with respect to blood levels of ceruloplasmin or copper between schizophrenic and normal subjects (11) and no support for the theory that the Akerfeldt test is a means of distinguishing between schizophrenic and nonschizophrenic patients (12). It is not clear why some schizophrenics apparently show an elevated level of ceruloplasmin in the blood; among suggested explanations are dietary factors, hepatic damage, chronic infection, or the possibility that excitement tends to raise the level of ceruloplasmin in the blood, as preliminary experiments appear to indicate (13).

Quite early in their studies, members of the Tulane group recognized that the potent oxidant effects of the serum of schizophrenics on epinephrine in vitro could not be satisfactorily explained by the ceruloplasmin levels alone (5). Before they recognized the importance to this reaction of ascorbic acid deficiency (14), they had postulated the presence in the blood of schizophrenics of a qualitatively different form of ceruloplasmin (5), which they proceeded to isolate and to test in monkey and man, and to which they have given the name taraxein (from the Greek root tarassein, meaning "to disturb"). They have reported that when certain batches of this material were tested in monkeys, marked behavioral and electroencephalographic changes occurred. When samples of these active batches were injected intravenously at a rapid rate into carefully selected prisoner volunteers, all of the subjects developed symptoms which have been described as characteristic of schizophrenia—disorganization and fragmentation of thought, autism, feelings of depersonalization, paranoid ideas, auditory hallucinations, and catatonic behavior (15–17).

Demonstration of toxic materials in the blood and in the body fluids of schizophrenic patients is not new. The voluminous and inconclusive work of earlier investigators was well reviewed by Keup in 1954 (6). Since that time, many new reports have appeared, although there has been no extensive substantiation of any of them. The results of one, on the toxicity of serum and urine of schizophrenic patients for the larvae of Xenopus laevis (18), were disputed by the laboratory in which the work was done (19). Edisen (20) was unable to demonstrate toxicity of such serum for the species of tadpole previously used, or for other species and other genera. A report that serum from schizophrenic patients is toxic to cells in tissue culture (21) lost some of its significance when 1 year later the same laboratory reported that the sera of surgical patients (22) was of comparable toxicity. Reports that injection of certain extracts of the urine of schizophrenic patients induces electroencephalographic and behavioral changes in rats (23) or disturbances in web construction in spiders (24) have not yet received confirmation in the scientific literature. Such urine, however, has been reported to have no effect on the Siamese fighting fish, which is remarkably sensitive to certain hallucinogens (25). Contrary to earlier findings, a recent attempt to demonstrate behavioral changes in rats following the injection of cerebrospinal fluid from catatonic patients was unsuccessful (26). A highly significant decrease in rope-climbing speed in rats injected with sera from psychotic patients as opposed to sera from nonpsychotic controls has been reported by Winter and Flataker (27). Their later finding (28) that the phenomenon occurs with sera of patients with a wide variety of mental disorders, including mental retardation and alcoholism, and that there is a considerable variation in this index between similar groups at different hospitals, coupled with the inability of at least one other investigator (29) to demonstrate this phenomenon in the small group of schizophrenic patients under investigation in this laboratory, suggests that the quite real and statistically significant phenomenon originally observed may be related to variables other than those specific for, or fundamental to, schizophrenia. More recently, Ghent and Freedman (29) have reported their inability to confirm the observations of Winter and Flataker.

It has been reported that rabbits pretreated with serum from schizophrenics do not exhibit a pressor response following the local application of an epinephrine solution to the cerebral cortex (30). No difference between the action of sera from normal subjects and that from schizophrenics was demonstrated by means of this procedure in tests of sera from a small number of individuals on our wards.

The significance of all of these studies in animals, whether the studies are successful or unsuccessful in demonstrating a toxic factor in schizophrenia, is quite irrelevant to, and considerably dwarfed by, the implications of the taraxein studies. It is because of the tremendous implications which these results could have in the etiology and rational therapy of this important disorder that a reviewer must evaluate them with even more than the usual care.

In the first place, the important biochemical phenomena originally reported in schizophrenia—lowered blood levels of glutathione and rapid oxidation of epinephrine in vitro—which prompted the search for taraxein and directed work on its isolation toward the ceruloplasmin fraction of serum (15, 16, 17,), have since been controverted by data reported by the same group, as well as by others and have been regarded by most workers as spurious or at least unrelated in any direct way to the schizophrenic process (14, 31). This, in itself, does not preclude the possible validity of the taraxein phenomenon, since bona fide discoveries have occasionally been made on the basis of erroneous leads; it does, however, reduce the probability of its occurrence from that involved in a logical interrelationship of sequential proven steps to the extremely small chance of selecting this particular and heretofore unknown substance from the thousands of substances which occur in blood and which might have been chosen.

One attempt by Robins, Smith, and Lowe (32) to confirm the Tulane findings, in tests in which they used comparable numbers and types of subjects and at least equally rigorous controls, was quite unsuccessful. In 20 subjects who at different times received saline or extracts of blood from normal or schizophrenic donors, prepared according to the method for preparing taraxein, there were only five instances of mental or behavioral disturbance resembling those cited in the original report on taraxein, and these occurred with equal frequency following the administration of saline, extracts of normal plasma, or taraxein. It is easy to dismiss the negative findings with taraxein on the basis of the difficulty of reproducing exacty the 29 steps described in its preparation; it is considerably more difficult to dismiss the observation that a few subjects who received only saline or normal blood extract developed psychotic manifestations similar to those reported with taraxein.

During the preliminary investigations it was stated, on the basis of unpublished studies (5), that taraxein was qualitatively different from cerulo-plasmin. A physicochemical or other objective characterization of taraxein would do much to dispel some of the confusion regarding its nature. Is it possible, for example, that taraxein is, in fact, ceruloplasmin but ceruloplasmin that derives its special properties from the psychosocial characteristics of the situation in which it has been tested? This question was raised more than a year ago (33), and since then additional evidence has become available which tends to support it. This is a detailed report from a psychoanalyst at Tulane of the experience of one of his patients who received taraxein (34). Even though a "double blind" procedure was said to have been used, there are enough possibilities for the operation of unconscious bias in this one case, if it is at all typical of the means used to demonstrate the psychotomimetic properties of taraxein, to raise some doubts concerning the validity of these properties. The subject, a psychiatric resident, knew before the injection that he was to get either saline or a potent sample of taraxein which had made a monkey catatonic for several hours. Immediately following the injection he noted venous distension, tachycardia, a swollen feeling of the head, and flushing of the head and face, which, a footnote explains, was probably a reaction to the ammonium sulfate in the taraxein solution. Following these symptoms, which the subject could hardly have attributed to saline, there ensued a period of introspective cogitation, with occasional mild mental disturbances quite compatible with the anxiety-producing nature of the situation, with the preparation and cues which the subject had received, and with his anticipation of marked psychotic reactions and not necessarily symptomatic of a chemical toxin at all. The changes were not qualitatively dissimilar to those which Robins and his associates had on a few occasions obtained with their control solutions (32). The report of the observer who injected the material was longer and mentioned more numerous and more bizarre subjective feelings than the subject himself reported. The observer's summary of the subject's reactions as blocking of thought processes, autism, bodily estrangement, and suspiciousness seems incompletely supported by the subject's retrospective report.

The possibility, remote as it may be, that the reported effects of taraxein are the result of a combination of suggestion, nonspecific toxic reactions from ammonium sulfate or other contaminants, and reinforcement of these cues by the unconscious biases of subject and observer through the device of an unstructured interview, is one which has not been ruled out. Hypotheses related to the mechanism of action of this material have moved from concern with abnormalities in the blood to concern with abnormalities in the blood-brain barrier; but the question of whether taraxein acts as a biological cause or as a mediator of some of the symptoms of schizophrenia is by no means resolved. I have already mentioned the only attempt of which I am aware on the part of an independent group to confirm the original results in a controlled series of significant size, and that attempt was unsuccessful.

SEROTONIN

Serotonin, an important derivative of tryptophan, was first shown to exist in the brain in high concentration by Amin, Crawford, and Gaddum (35). Interest in its possible function in the central nervous system and speculation that it might even be related to schizophrenia were inspired by the finding that certain hallucinogens, notably lysergic acid diethylamide, could, in extremely low concentration, block the effects of serotonin on smooth muscle. Thus, Woolley and Shaw in 1954 (36) wrote: "The demonstrated ability of such agents to antagonize the action of serotonin in smooth muscle and the finding of serotonin in the brain suggest that the mental changes caused by the drugs are the result of a serotonin-deficiency which they induce in the brain. If this be true, then the naturally occurring mental disorders—for example, schizophrenia—which are mimicked by these drugs, may be pictured as being the result of a cerebral serotonin deficiency arising from a metabolic failure. . . ." Simultaneously, in England, Gaddum (37) was speculating, "it is possible that the HT in our brains plays an essential part in keeping us sane and that the effect of LSD is due to its inhibitory action on the HT in the brain." Since that time additional evidence has appeared to strengthen these hypotheses.

Levels of serotonin have been found to be considerably higher in the limbic system and other areas of the brain which appear to be associated with emotional states (38) than elsewhere. Bufotenin, or dimethyl serotonin, extracted from a hallucinogenic snuff of West Indian tribes, was found to have some properties similar to those of lysergic acid diethylamide (39). A major discovery was the finding that the ataractic agent, reserpine, causes a profound and persistent fall in the level of serotonin in the brain (40), a process which more closely parallels the mental effects of reserpine than does its own concentration in the brain. By administration of the precursor, 5-hydroxytroptophan, the levels of serotonin can be markedly elevated in the brain, with behavioral effects described as resembling those of lysergic acid diethylamide (41)—a finding quite at odds with the original hypotheses. On the other hand, administration of this precursor to mental patients, along with a benzyl analog of serotonin to block the peripheral effects of the amine, has been reported, in preliminary trials, to suppress the disease (42), while confusion is compounded by the report that the benzyl analog alone is an effective tranquilizing drug in chronically psychotic patients (43).

Still another bit of evidence supporting the hypotheses of a central function for serotonin was the accidental discovery of toxic psychoses in a certain fraction of tuberculous patients treated with iproniazid (44, 45), which has led to the therapeutic use of this drug in psychic depression. It is known that iproniazid inhibits the action of monoamine oxidase, an enzyme which destroys serotonin, and it has been shown that iproniazid increases the levels of this amine in the brain (41).

There are certain inconsistencies in the data cited above to support the serotonin hypotheses, and no single theory has been found to explain all of the findings, even though full use is made of the concept of "free" and "bound" forms and of the common pharmacological principle of stimulant and depressant effects from the same drug under different circumstances. Moreover, certain weaknesses have appeared in each of the main supporting hypotheses, and these should be noted.

Although the ability of the hallucinogen lysergic acid diethylamide to block effects of serotonin on smooth muscle prompted the development of the hypotheses relating serotonin to mental function or disease, a number of lysergic acid derivatives have since been studied, and the correlation between mental effects and antiserotonin activity in the series as a whole is quite poor (46). One of these compounds is 2-bromo-lysergic acid diethylamide; this has 1.5 times the antiserotonin activity of lysergic acid diethylamide, and through this property, its presence in the brain, after systemic administration, can be demonstrated, but in doses more than 15 times as great it produces none of the mental effects of lysergic acid diethylamide (46). A recent report that, at least in one preparation, lysergic acid diethylamide in low concentration behaves like serotonin and does not antagonize it (47) seems to reconcile some of the empirical inconsistencies in the field, although it is quite at odds with the original hypotheses based on the antagonistic action of lysergic acid diethylamide.

Levels of norepinephrine as well as serotonin are markedly lowered in the brain following administration of reserpine (48). In fact, the brain concentrations of these two amines follow each other so closely in their response to reserpine as to suggest some mechanism common to both and perhaps obtaining as well for other active amines in the brain. In one study, 3,4-dihydroxyphenylalanine, a precursor of norepinephrine, was capable of counteracting the behavioral effects of reserpine, whereas the precursor of serotonin was ineffective (49). Moreover, the effects of iproniazid are not limited to brain serotonin; a comparable effect on norepinephrine has been reported (50), and it is possible that other amines or substances still to be discovered in the brain may be affected by what may be a nonspecific inhibitor of a relatively nonspecific enzyme. Of great interest in this connection are recent studies of Olds and Olds (51) indicating a positive behavioral response for iproniazid injected into the hypothalamus but not for serotonin or norepinephrine.

Chlorpromazine, which has the same therapeutic efficacy as reserpine in disturbed behavior, is apparently able to achieve this action without any known effect on serotonin. In addition, the provocative observation that iproniazid, which elevates serotonin levels in the brain, can cause a toxic psychosis loses some of its impact when one realizes that isoniazid, which does not inhibit monoamine oxidase and can hardly raise the brain serotonin concentration, produces a similar psychosis (45, 52).

It seems reasonable to conclude that the serotonin as well as the norepinephrine in the brain have some important functions there, and the evidence in general supports this thesis, even though it also suggests that their roles still remain to be defined.

If the picture of the role which serotonin plays in central nervous function is blurred, the direct evidence to support the early speculations that it is involved in mental illness is meager and contradictory. From all of the evidence cited above, one could find a basis for predicting that in schizophrenia the serotonin levels in the brain, if they are altered at all, should be quite low or quite high. Results confirming both predictions have been reported.

The urinary excretion of 5-hydroxyindoleacetic acid has been used as an indicator of the portion of ingested tryptophan which is metabolized through serotonin to form that end product. Although excretion of 5-hydroxyindoleacetic acid is normal in schizophrenic patients under ordinary circumstances (53), it may be altered by challenging the metabolic systems with large doses of tryptophan. Zeller and his associates have reported a failure on the part of schizophrenics, under these circumstances, to increase their output of 5-hydroxyindoleacetic acid, while nonpsychotic controls double theirs (54). Banerjee and Agarwal, on the other hand, have reported exactly the opposite results; in their study it was the schizophrenics who doubled their output of the serotonin end product, while the output of the controls remained unchanged (55).

Kopin, of our laboratory, has had the opportunity to perform a similar study on schizophrenics and normal controls maintained on a good and reasonably controlled diet and given no drugs. In each group there was a slightly greater than twofold increase in output of 5-hydroxyindoleacetic acid following a tryptophan load, and there was no significant deviation from this pattern in any single case (56).

That the heuristic speculations of Woolley and Shaw, and of Gaddum, have not yet been established does not mean that they are invalid. The widespread experimental activity which they stimulated has broadened and deepened our knowledge of the metabolism and pharmacology of serotonin and of its effects on behavior and may lead the way to definitive evaluation of its possible role in normal and pathological states.

GENETICS AND SCHIZOPHRENIC DISORDERS

Many of the current hypotheses concerning the schizophrenia complex are original and attractive even though, up to this time, evidence directly implicating any one of them in the disease itself is hardly compelling. There is, nevertheless, cogent evidence that is responsible to a large extent for the present reawakening of the long dormant biochemical thinking in this area and sufficiently convincing to promote its continued development. Genetic sudies have recently assumed such a role, and it appears worth while briefly to review them in the present context.

In earlier studies on large populations, a remarkable correlation was

Table 1. Concordance rates for schizophrenia found in studies of twins

	Number of pairs		Concordance rate* (%)	
Investigator	*Dizygotic*	*Monozygotic*	*Dizygotic*	*Monozygotic*
Luxenburger (1928)	48	17	2	59 (67)
Rosanoff *et al.* (1934)	101	41	10	61
Kallmann (1946)	517	174	10 (15)	69 (86)
Slater (1953)	115	41	11 (14)	68 (76)

* Figures in parentheses indicate rate after correction for the chance that a co-twin, normal at the time of observation, may develop the disease later.

reported between the incidence of schizophrenia and the degree of consanguinity in relatives of known schizophrenics (57). These findings were not conclusive, however, since the influence of socioenvironmental factors was not controlled. Better evidence is obtained from the examination of the co-twins and siblings of schizophrenics; a number of such studies have been completed and are summarized in Table 1 (57–59). The concordance rate for schizophrenia is extremely high for monozygotic twins in all the studies, while that for dizygotic twins is low and not significantly different from that in siblings, to which, of course, dizygotic twins are quite comparable genetically. Even these studies, however, are not completely free from possible sources of error, and this makes it difficult to arrive at a definitive conclusion regarding the role of genetic factors in this disease. One cannot assume that environmental similarities and mutual interactions in identical twins, who are always of the same sex and whose striking physical congruence is often accentuated by parental attitudes, play an insignificant role in the high concordance rate of schizophrenia in this group. This factor could be controlled by a study of twins separated at birth (of such twins no statistically valid series has yet been compiled) or by a comparison of the concordance rates in monozygotic twins and in dizygotic twins whose zygosity had been mistakenly evaluated by the twins themselves and by their parents and associates. Another possible means of better controlling the environmental variables would be to make a careful study of schizophrenia in adopted children, with comparison of the incidence in blood relatives and in foster relatives. Perhaps only a survey on a national scale would provide the requisite numbers of cases for any of these studies.

A less satisfactory resolution of this problem can be obtained by an appraisal of environmental similarities in normal fraternal and identical twins. Such a study, on over 100 specific aspects of the environment, has been made (60), and I have assembled the results into a rough index of environmental similarity (Table 2). Although a difference is apparent, in the crude measurement of environmental congruence, between identical

Table 2. Environmental factors in studies of schizophrenia in twins

Sex	Environmental similarity in normal twins* (%)	Number of pairs	Concordance with respect to schizophrenia† (%)	Number of pairs
	Identical twins			
Same	61	70	86	174
	Fraternal twins			
Same	53	69	18	296
Different	26	55	10	221
	Siblings			
Same			16	
Different			12	

* Estimated from data of P. T. Wilson (1934).
† From data of F. J. Kallmann (1946).

and fraternal twins of like sex, it is not statistically significant and can account for only a small fraction of the large difference in concordance with respect to schizophrenia between these types of twins. On the other hand, there is a highly significant difference in environmental similarity between fraternal twins of like and unlike sex which is sufficient to account for the difference in concordance with respect to schizophrenic psychosis between them, for which, of course, there is no tenable genetic explanation.

Two recent reports have been used, but by no means conclusively, in support of the position that too much significance has been attached to environmental factors as determining causes in this disease group. Chapman (61), reporting a case of concordant early infantile autism in identical twins, points out that this disorder has never been reported as concordant in fraternal twins, whereas it has been described in three sets of identical twins. Since fraternal twins occur nearly three times as frequently as identical twins, the evidence cited is suggestive, in spite of the small numbers involved; furthermore, the disease may develop before the personal identifications and interactions peculiar to monozygotic twins have had much chance to operate. Another interesting finding in over 150 families with a single schizophrenic member is that no ordinal position in the family appears to carry specific vulnerability to schizophrenia (62)—a finding completely compatible with genetic theory but more difficult to reconcile with theories of environmental etiology if the assumption is correct that different positions within the family are subject to varying degrees of stress. Of course one may argue quite properly that schizophrenogenic stress exists and can be evaluated only in terms of the reaction between each individual and his own environment, so that any position on a social, economic, occupational, or birth-order scale may be associated with greatly different degrees of stress for different individuals.

Another possible source of error in the twin studies which have been reported is the personal bias of the investigators who made the judgment of zygosity and the diagnosis of schizophrenia in the co-twins. Until a more definitive study is carried out in which these judgments are made independently, a rough evaluation is possible, at least for the diagnosis of schizophrenia, if not for zygosity, on the basis of diagnoses arrived at in the various hospitals to which the co-twins may have been admitted before or irrespective of their involvement in the study—diagnoses which are not likely to have been contaminated by knowledge about their zygosity. Kallmann has been kind enough to review the material collected in his 1946–49 survey from that point of view. Of 174 monozygotic co-twins of schizophrenic index cases, 103, or 59 percent, had been diagnosed schizophrenic by Kallmann, while 87, or 50 percent, had received a psychiatric hospital diagnosis of schizophrenia prior to any examination made by him. On the other hand, he had made the diagnosis of schizophrenia in 47, or 9.1 percent, of 517 dizygotic co-twins as compared to a hospital diagnosis in 31, or 6 percent. Although the concordance rates based only on hospital diagnoses are lower in both types of twins, for obvious reasons, the striking difference between the two concordance rates remains. Slater (59) has published individual protocols of his cases from which I have made judgments of zygosity and schizophrenia. Of 21 pairs of twins who could be considered definitely uniovular, 15, or 75 percent, were concordant with respect to the simple criterion of admission to a mental hospital, whereas in only 12, or 10.3 percent, of 116 binovular or questionably binovular pairs was there a history of the co-twin's having been admitted to a mental hospital for any psychosis. On the basis of this analysis of the two most recent series, it seems that only a small component of the great difference in concordance rates reported for schizophrenia between uniovular and binovular twins can be attributed to the operation of personal bias in the diagnosis of the disease in the co-twin.

Even the most uncritical acceptance of all the genetic data, however, cannot lead to the conclusion that the schizophrenic illnesses are the result of genetic factors alone. In 14 to 30 percent of the cases in which schizophrenia occurs in one of a pair of monozygotic twins, the genetically identical partner is found to be free of the disorder (Table 1). Attention has already been called (Table 2) to the higher concordance with respect to schizophrenia and the greater environmental similarities in like-sexed fraternal twins or siblings than in those of unlike sex, and from the same source (57) a difference in concordance is reported between monozygotic twins separated some years before the study (77.6 percent) as opposed to those not separated (91.5 percent). Neither of these observations is compatible with a purely genetic etiology of the disease, and both suggest the operation of environmental factors. Rosenthal (63) and Jackson (64) have pointed out the striking preponderance of female over male pairs concordant for schizophrenia in all of the reported series, whether they be monozygotic or dizygotic twins, siblings, or parent-child pairs. If sampling errors resulting from the greater mobility of males are excluded and the observations are taken as a reflection of the true incidence of this phenomenon, several explanations for it on the basis of social interaction can be given, but none based on purely genetic grounds, unless sex linkage is invoked, for which there is no other evidence.

Clausen has critically reviewed the extensive literature supporting the importance of environmental factors in the etiology of schizophrenic disorders (65). The evidence there seems quite as suggestive as the genetic evidence but by no means more conclusive, since few studies in either field have been completely objective or adequately controlled.

It is both interesting and important to note that even if the conclusions of both the genetic and the environmental approaches to the etiology of schizophrenic psychoses are accepted uncritically, they are not mutually exclusive. Both are compatible with the hypothesis that this group of diseases results from the operation of socioenvironmental factors on some hereditary predisposition, or from an interaction of the two, each being necessary but neither alone sufficient. An excellent example of such a relationship is seen in tuberculosis, where the importance of the environmental microbial factor is undisputed and where, as Lurie (66) has shown, genetic susceptibility is likewise important; a population sufficiently heterogeneous with respect to susceptibility and exposure to tuberculosis yields results in contingency and twin studies (67) which, before the discovery of the tubercle bacillus, could easily have been used to prove a primary genetic cause—almost as convincingly as the results of similar studies have been used to prove such a cause in schizophrenia. Interestingly enough, studies of tuberculosis made from the socioenvironmental point of view would obviously provide data offering equally convincing proof that exogenous, social, and economic factors play a part. One hypothesis with respect to the schizophrenic psychoses which remains compatible with all the evidence from the genetic as well as the psychosocial disciplines is that these disorders, like tuberculosis, require the operation of environmental factors upon a genetically determined predisposition.

RÉSUMÉ

Although the evidence for genetic and therefore biological factors as important and necessary components in the etiology of many or all of the schizophrenias is quite compelling, the sign-posts pointing the way to their discovery are at present quite blurred and, to me at least, illegible.

Genetic factors may operate through some unbiquitous enzyme system to effect general changes in one or another metabolic pathway—changes detectable through studies of blood or urine—and it is to be hoped that the currently active search in these areas will continue.

It is at least equally possible, however, that these genetic factors may operate only through enzymes or metabolic processes peculiar to or confined within the brain, or even within extremely localized areas of the brain. We are in need of new hypotheses such as those of Elkes (68) and many already discussed. In this connection, gamma-amino-butyric acid appears to be just as interesting a substance about which to construct working hypotheses as are the catechols or the indoles. It has been isolated only from nervous tissue, and its metabolism in such tissue has been investigated in some detail(69), while its neurophysiological properties appear to be better defined than are those of the other two groups (70); in addition, its inhibitory properties may have special relevance to diseases where a failure in central inhibition seems to be involved.

Amphetamine possesses remarkable psychotomimetic properties which should not be overlooked. Its ability to produce a clinical syndrome often indistinguishable from schizophrenia (71) and the possible relation of amphetamine to the naturally occurring catechol amines make it at least as interesting as lysergic acid diethylamide.

In addition to techniques at present available in neurochemistry, neurophysiology, and behavioral pharmacology, the development of new methods designed to yield information on processes occurring within the psychotic brain will be needed before our explorations in this field have been exhausted.

But the biochemist must not lose sight of the possibility, which is certainly as great as any of the others, that the genetic factors in schizophrenia operate to determine inappropriate interconnections or interaction between chemically normal components of the brain; if that should prove to be the case, the physiological psychologist, the neurophysiologist, or the anatomist is likely to find meaningful information long before the biochemist does. It would take many biochemists a long time to find a noisy circuit in a radio receiver if they restricted themselves to chemical techniques.

These possibilities are mentioned only to indicate how large is the haystack in which we are searching for the needle; one cannot avoid a feeling of humility when one realizes how slight the chance is that any one of us has already found it, or will find it in a relatively short time.

That is no cause for discouragement, however. It is not necessary that one be convinced of the truth of a particular hypothesis to justify devoting one's energies to testing it. It is enough that one regard it as worth testing, and that the tools be adequate. Modern biochemistry, with its wealth of new knowledge of intermediary metabolism and its array of new techniques for the separation and identification of compounds and the tracing of their metabolic pathways, has provided the biologist interested in mental illness with an armamentarium which his predecessor of only a generation ago could hardly have envisioned. If he chooses from among the approaches which may lead to a definition of the biological factors in schizophrenia those which will in any case lead to a better understanding of the nervous system and of thought processes and behavior, the present surge of enthusiasm will not have been misdirected.

REFERENCES AND NOTES

1 S. Akerfeldt, *Science* **125**, 117 (1957).
2 F. A. Gibbs, Ed., *Blood Tests in Mental Illness* (Brain Research Foundation, Chicago, 1957).
3 C. G. Holmberg and C. B. Laurell, *Scand. J. Clin. & Lab. Invest.* **3**, 103 (1951).
4 B. E. Leach and R. G. Heath, *A.M.A. Arch. Neurol. Psychiat.* **76**, 444 (1956).
5 B. E. Leach, M. Cohen, R. C. Heath, S. Martens, *ibid.* **76**, 635 (1956).
6 W. Keup, *Monatsschr. Psychiat. Neurol.* **128**, 56 (1954).
7 C. G. Holmberg and C. B. Laurell, *Acta Chem. Scand.* **2**, 550 (1948).
8 H. Markowitz, C. J. Gubler, J. P. Mahoney, G. E. Cartwright, M. M. Wintrobe, *J. Clin. Invest.* **34**, 1498 (1955).
9 L. G. Abood, F. A. Gibbs, E. Gibbs, *A.M.A. Arch. Neurol. Psychiat.* **17**, 643 (1957).
10 R. K. McDonald, "Plasma ceruloplasmin and ascorbic acid levels in schizophrenia," paper presented at the annual meeting of the American Psychiatric Association, Chicago, Ill., 1957.
11 I. H. Scheinberg, A. G. Morell, R. S. Harris, A. Berger, *Science* **126**, 925 (1957); M. K. Horwitt, B. J. Meyer, A. C. Meyer, C. C. Harvey, D. Haffron, *A.M.A. Arch. Neurol. Psychiat.* **78**, 275 (1957); C. E. Frohman, M. Goodman, E. D. Luby, P. G. S. Beckett, R. Senf, *ibid.* **79**, 730 (1958); M. H. Aprison and H. J. Grosz, *ibid.* **79**, 575 (1958).
12 M. H. Aprison and A. L. Drew, *Science* **127**, 758 (1958).
13 A. M. Ostfeld, L. G. Abood, D. A. Marcus, *A.M.A. Arch. Neurol. Psychiat.* **79**, 317 (1958).
14 C. Angel, B. E. Leach, S. Martens, M. Cohen, R. G. Heath, *ibid.* **79**, 500 (1957).
15 R. G. Heath, S. Martens, B. E. Leach, M. Cohen, C. A. Feigley, *Am. J. Psychiat.* **114**, 917 (1958).
16 R. G. Heath, B. E. Leach, L. W. Byers, S. Martens, C. A. Feigley, *ibid.* **114**, 683 (1958).
17 R. G. Heath, S. Martens, B. E. Leach, M. Cohen, C. Angel, *ibid.* **114**, 14 (1957).
18 R. Fischer, *Proc. Intern. Physiol. Congr., 19th Congr.* (1953), pp. 350–351.
19 F. Georgi, H. P. Rieder, R. Weber, *Science* **120**, 504 (1954).
20 C. B. Edisen, *Diseases of Nervous System* **17**, 77 (1956).
21 S. Fedoroff, *Anat. Record* **121**, 394 (1955).
22 ———— and A. Hoffer, *J. Nervous Mental Disease* **124**, 396 (1956).
23 J. Wada, *Proc. Soc. Biol. Psychiatrists, 12th Ann. Conv.* (1957).
24 H. P. Rieder, *Psychiat. et Neurol.* **134**, 378 (1957).
25 K. Smith and A. C. Moody, *Diseases of Nervous System* **17**, 327 (1956).
26 A. K. Shapiro, *J. Nervous Mental Disease* **123**, 65 (1956).
27 C. A. Winter and L. Flataker, *Proc. Soc. Biol. Psychiatrists, 12th Ann. Conv.* (1957).
28 ————, *A.M.A. Arch. Neurol. Psychiat.* **80**, 441 (1958).
29 C. Kornetsky, personal communication; L. Ghent and A. M. Freedman, *Am. J. Psychiat.* **115**, 465 (1958).
30 B. Minz and E. J. Walaszek, *Compt. rend.* **244**, 1974 (1957).
31 R. K. McDonald, *J. Chronic Diseases* **8**, 366 (1958); A. J. Barak, F. L. Humoller, J. D. Stevens, *A.M.A. Arch. Neurol. Psychiat.* **80**, 237 (1958).
32 E. Robins, K. Smith, I. P. Lowe, in "Neuropharmacology," *Trans. Josiah Macy, Jr. Foundation, 4th Conf.* (1957).
33 S. S. Kety, in *ibid.* (1957).
34 H. I. Lief, *A.M.A. Arch. Neurol. Psychiat.* **78**, 624 (1957).

35 A. H. Amin, T. B. B. Crawford, J. H. Gaddum, *J. Physiol.* (*London*) **126**, 596 (1954).

36 D. W. Woolley and E. Shaw, *Science* **119**, 587 (1954).

37 J. H. Gaddum, in *Ciba Foundation Symposium on Hypertension* (Little, Brown, Boston, 1954).

38 D. F. Bogdanski, H. Weissbach, S. Udenfriend, *J. Neurochem.* **1**, 272 (1957); M. K. Paasonen, P. D. MacLean, N. J. Giarman, *ibid.* **1**, 326 (1957).

39 E. V. Evarts, *A.M.A. Arch. Neurol. Psychiat.* **75**, 49 (1956); H. D. Fabing and J. R. Hawkins, *Science* **123**, 886 (1956).

40 P. A. Shore, A. Pletscher, E. G. Tomich, A. Carlsson, R. Kuntzman, B. B. Brodie *Ann. N.Y. Acad. Sci.* **66**, 609 (1957).

41 S. Udenfriend, H. Weissbach, D. F. Bogdanski, *ibid.* **66**, 602 (1957).

42 D. W. Woolley, *Science* **125**, 752 (1957).

43 L. H. Rudy, E. Costa, F. Rinaldi, H. E. Himwich, *J. Nervous Mental Disease* **126**, 284 (1958).

44 G. E. Crane, *ibid.* **124**, 322 (1956).

45 H. Pleasure, *A.M.A. Arch. Neurol. Psychiat.* **72**, 313 (1954).

46 E. Rothlin, *Ann. N.Y. Acad. Sci.* **66**, 668 (1957).

47 J. H. Welsh and A. C. McCoy, *Science* **125**, 348 (1957).

48 M. Holzbauer and M. Vogt, *J. Neurochem.* **1**, 8 (1956); M. Vogt, in *Metabolism of the Nervous System*, D. Richter, Ed. (Pergamon, London, 1957), pp. 553–565.

49 A. Carlsson, M. Lindqvist, T. Magnusson, *Nature* **180**, 1200 (1957).

50 S. Spector, D. Prockop, P. A. Shore, B. B. Brodie, *Science* **127**, 704 (1958).

51 J. Olds and M. E. Olds, *ibid.* **127**, 1175 (1958).

52 S. L. O. Jackson, *Brit. Med. J.* **2**, 743 (1957).

53 G. A. Buscaino and L. Stefanachi, *A.M.A. Neurol. Psychiat.* **80**, 78 (1958); A. Feldstein, H. Hoagland, H. Freeman, *Science* **128**, 358 (1958).

54 E. A. Zeller, J. Bernsohn, W. M. Inskip, J. W. Lauer, *Naturwissenschaften* **44**, 427 (1957); J. W. Lauer, W. M. Inskip, J. Bernsohn, E. A. Zeller, *A.M.A. Arch. Neurol. Psychiat.* **80**, 122 (1958).

55 S. Banerjee and P. S. Agarwal, *Proc. Soc. Exptl. Biol. Med.* **97**, 657 (1958).

56 I. J. Kopin, *Science* **129**, 835 (1959).

57 F. J. Kallmann, *Am. J. Psychiat.* **103**, 309 (1946).

58 H. Luxenburger, *Z. ges. Neurol. Psychiat.* **116**, 297 (1928); A. J. Rosanoff, L. M. Handy, I. R. Plesset, S. Brush, *Am. J. Psychiat.* **91**, 247 (1934).

59 E. Slater, "Psychotic and Neurotic Illnesses in Twins," *Medical Research Council Special Report No. 278* (H. M. Stationery Office, London, 1953).

60 P. T. Wilson, *Human Biology* **6**, 324 (1934).

61 A. H. Chapman, *A.M.A. Arch. Neurol. Psychiat.* **78**, 621 (1957).

62 H. J. Grosz and I. Miller, *Science* **128**, 30 (1958).

63 D. Rosenthal, *J. Nervous Mental Disease*, in press.

64 D. D. Jackson, in "The Study of Schizophrenia," D. D. Jackson, Ed. (Basic Books, New York, in press).

65 J. A. Clausen, *Sociology Today*, Merton, Broom, and Cottrell, Eds. (Basic Books, New York, 1959).

66 M. B. Lurie, S. Abramson, A. Heppelston, *J. Exptl. Med.* **95**, 119 (1952).

67 K. Planansky and G. Allen, *Am. J. Human Genet.* **5**, 322 (1953).

68 J. Elkes, in "Neuropharmacology," *Trans. Josiah Macy, Jr. Foundation, 3rd Conf.* (1956).

69 E. Roberts and S. Frankel, *J. Biol. Chem.* **187**, 55 (1950); E. Roberts, M. Rothstein, C. F. Baxter, *Proc. Soc. Exptl. Biol. Med.* **97**, 796 (1958).

70 D. P. Purpura, M. Girardo, H. Grundfest, *Science* **125**, 1200 (1957); K. Iwama and H. H. Jasper, *J. Physiol.* (*London*) **138**, 365 (1957).

71 P. H. Connell, *Biochem. J.* **65**, 7p (1957).

Index

Index